REVIEW TEXT IN
CHEMISTRY

By MAXWELL GELENDER

Chairman, Department of Physical Sciences
Benjamin Franklin High School, New York City

Edited by SAUL L. GEFFNER

Chairman, Department of Physical Sciences
Forest Hills High School, New York City

Science Editor, Amsco School Publications, Inc.

Dedicated to Serving Our Nation's Youth

AMSCO SCHOOL PUBLICATIONS, Inc.
315 Hudson Street　　New York, N.Y. 10013

PREFACE

Review Text in Chemistry provides the teacher and pupil with a modern approach to chemistry based upon an understanding of fundamental concepts. The organization of this book is sufficiently broad to permit its use as a supplement to any textbook. The essential features are as follows:

1. *Presentation:* The organization of content enables the student to grasp fundamental principles and broad generalizations with a minimum of memorization. The concepts developed in the chapter on atomic structure and the periodic table are utilized throughout the book and serve as a unifying theme. In an elementary manner, the principles of oxidation-reduction have been utilized to further the understanding of chemical change.

2. *Visualization:* The book is replete with clear, simple illustrations. Expertly drawn, they contribute to a better understanding of the text. Color has been utilized to highlight important ideas.

3. *Recent Developments:* A completely thorough and accurate treatment of nuclear chemistry appears in this book. Reference is also made to chemical bonding, ion-exchange, and newer synthetics.

4. *Questions for Practice and Review:* Each chapter terminates with a Study Guide containing considerable review material in the form of both short answer and essay questions. The questions are arranged in a logical sequence following the presentation of subject matter. Upon completion of the questions in a unit, the student has an organized outline of the essentials necessary for understanding the text. To challenge the more enthusiastic students, there are more difficult questions indicated by asterisks. Finally, in the appendix, there are a large number of additional short answer questions and several specimen New York State examinations to serve as a review of the year's work.

5. *Calculations and Problems:* An entire chapter has been devoted to chemical calculations. To provide adequate practice and review, a large number of varied problems appears not only at the end of this chapter, but also at the end of other chapters.

6. *Appendix:* The appendix contains several additional features useful for both review and enrichment. Included are:

   a. A comprehensive discussion of the uses of chemical reference tables.
   b. A review of fundamental chemical principles.
   c. A complete summary of equations.
   d. Additional chemical calculations.
   e. A sample of College Board type questions in chemistry, with answers. This section, devoted to a series of different types of practice questions with detailed answers, can be used as a diagnostic test in preparation for the College Board Examinations in Chemistry.

—M. G.

CONTENTS

CONTENTS

1 INTRODUCTION

1. WHAT IS CHEMISTRY?

Chemistry is that branch of science dealing with the study of matter: its properties and uses, and the changes that different kinds of matter undergo. Chemistry is a body of knowledge organized into "big ideas" or principles, a thorough understanding of which is necessary for mastery of the subject.

2. THE SCIENTIFIC METHOD

The scientist is constantly asking questions of nature. He is interested in finding out how things work. Infrequently, an intelligent guess or even a bit of luck may help him to find the answers to these questions. More often, however, he follows a systematic procedure called the scientific method.

The scientific method is a logical and orderly procedure which invariably involves experimentation.

The scientific method can be described briefly in the following steps:

a. A clear statement of the problem to be solved.

b. The collection of all available facts related to the problem.

c. The formulation of a working hypothesis, or theory, based upon these facts.

d. The testing of this hypothesis through a series of carefully planned and controlled experiments.

e. The formulation, if possible, of a law or generalization based upon the results of these experiments.

f. The application and confirmation of the law in the solution of related problems or in the prediction of hitherto unknown phenomena.

3. THEORIES AND LAWS

a. *A theory is a scientific guess or explanation of observed or known facts based upon all available evidence.* In the light of new findings, some theories are often modified or even discarded. The Atomic

1

Theory, the Electron Theory, and the Theory of Ionization are examples of theories which have been modified from time to time.

b. A law is an accurate and acceptable statement or generalization which satisfactorily explains the uniform behavior of matter and energy. When theories are proven beyond a doubt, they become scientific laws. Some important chemical laws are the Law of Definite Proportions, the Law of Multiple Proportions, the Law of Conservation of Matter, and the Law of Conservation of Energy.

4. MATTER

Matter is anything that has weight and occupies space (volume). Examples are wood, water, air, iron, coal, and sulfur.

We can measure length, volume, and weight of matter in either the English or metric system. The metric system, because of its greater ease in handling, is more frequently used in scientific work.

The following table lists some of the units of measurement in the English and metric systems.

UNIT	ENGLISH SYSTEM	METRIC SYSTEM
length volume weight	inch, foot, yard cubic inch, cubic foot ounce, pound, ton	millimeter, centimeter, meter cubic centimeter, liter gram, kilogram

From the above units, other units, such as density, may be derived.

$$\text{density} = \frac{\text{weight}}{\text{volume}} \text{ or } \frac{\text{pounds}}{\text{cubic feet}} \text{ or } \frac{\text{grams}}{\text{cubic centimeters}}$$

A table of important equivalents follows.

2.54 centimeters = 1 inch
1,000 cubic centimeters = 1 liter (approx.)
1,000 milliliters = 1 liter
1 liter = 1.06 quarts
453.6 grams = 1 pound
1 kilogram = 2.2 pounds

In the laboratory, the graduated cylinder is used to measure volume, and the platform balance to measure weight.

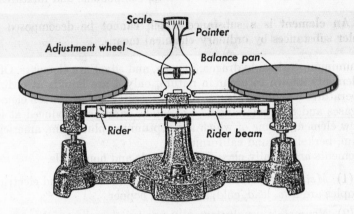

Fig. 4. Platform Balance

5. STATES OF MATTER

Matter may exist in three different physical states or forms:

a. **Solids** have a definite shape and a definite volume.

b. **Liquids** occupy a definite volume, but take the shape of their containers.

c. **Gases** have neither a definite shape nor a definite volume.

A gas takes the shape of its container. The volume of a confined gas depends upon the temperature and the pressure.

The physical state of a substance depends upon temperature; if the substance is a gas, pressure is also a factor. For example, water, a liquid at ordinary temperatures, changes to a gas (steam) when it is boiled and to a solid (ice) when it is frozen. Oxygen, on the other hand, can be changed into a liquid or a solid by cooling and compressing it sufficiently. Other gases can be similarly changed.

The physical states of matter may be explained by assuming that matter is composed of very small particles called molecules, which are in constant motion. In solids, these molecules are packed very close together. In liquids, they are not so close together and can roll easily over one another. In gases, the molecules are widely separated and uniformly distributed throughout the container.

6. KINDS OF MATTER

Matter may be classified as elements, compounds, and mixtures.

a. An **element** is a substance which cannot be decomposed into simpler substances by ordinary chemical means.

Aluminum, carbon, hydrogen, oxygen, and silver are elements. Of the 92 elements known to occur in nature, only 4 are liquids at ordinary temperatures—gallium, cesium, mercury, and bromine. Eleven elements are gases and the remaining 77 are solids. Man has produced at least 10 new elements, some of which are neptunium, plutonium, americium, curium, berkelium, and californium.

Elements are usually classified as metals and nonmetals.

(1) *Metals* usually have a luster and conduct heat and electricity. Examples are iron, lead, gold, silver, and copper.

(2) *Nonmetals* usually are gases or brittle solids without luster; most are poor conductors. Examples are oxygen, chlorine, nitrogen, sulfur, and iodine.

b. A **compound** is a substance composed of two or more elements chemically combined in definite proportions by weight.

The proportions in a compound never vary. In forming a compound, elements lose their individual properties, adopting the new characteristics of the compound. Water, which is composed of hydrogen and oxygen, has properties altogether different from those of either hydrogen or oxygen. Water, sodium chloride, and carbon dioxide are examples of compounds. The composition of a compound may be altered only by chemical means.

Since elements and compounds have an unchanging composition, they are called *pure substances.* Mixtures, on the other hand, have a variable composition and are called *impure substances.*

c. A **mixture** is a substance composed of two or more elements or compounds which are not chemically combined.

In a mixture, each of the components retains its original properties, and may be separated from the mixture by physical or mechanical means. Thus, in a mixture of salt and sand, each ingredient can be easily seen. The salt can be separated from the sand by dissolving it out with water.

The proportions in a mixture may vary, as in the case of air, which is a mixture of several substances. The proportion of each of the substances in air varies with climate and altitude.

The table below summarizes the essential differences between compounds and mixtures.

COMPOUND	MIXTURE
1. Component elements are chemically combined.	1. Component parts are not chemically combined.
2. Composition is fixed.	2. Composition varies.
3. Has properties different from original elements.	3. Retains properties of components.
4. Can be separated into its component elements by chemical means only.	4. Can be separated into its component parts by physical means.

7. PROPERTIES OF MATTER

A **property** is a characteristic of a substance which enables us to recognize it.

The properties of a substance also suggest its possible uses. Properties may be classified as physical and chemical.

a. **Physical properties** *include state, color, odor, taste, density, and solubility.*

b. **Chemical properties** *concern the manner in which a substance reacts with other substances.* Two common chemical properties are combustibility (burning) and the ability to support combustion. Hydrogen is combustible; oxygen supports combustion.

8. CHANGES OF MATTER

Matter may undergo two kinds of change, physical and chemical.

a. **A physical change** is a change in form or state without a change in composition.

The chopping of wood, breaking of glass, and dissolving of salt in water are physical changes.

b. **A chemical change** is one in which a substance loses the properties by which we recognize it and produces a new substance.

A chemical change is therefore a change in composition. The rusting of iron, burning of fuels, and decaying of food are chemical changes.

Chemical changes are accompanied by the absorption or liberation of energy, usually in the form of heat. Thus, when substances burn, heat is liberated. If sufficient heat is liberated, light may also be emitted.

Two common types of chemical change are synthesis and analysis. *Synthesis* is the combining of two or more substances, usually elements, to form a single compound. *Analysis* is the decomposition of a compound into two or more substances, usually elements.

SYNTHESIS: mercury + oxygen → mercuric oxide
ANALYSIS: water → hydrogen + oxygen

9. CONSERVATION OF MATTER

The *Law of Conservation of Matter* was established by Lavoisier, an 18th-century French chemist. The law states:

In ordinary chemical reactions, matter can be neither created nor destroyed.

Thus, in a chemical change, the total weight of all the reacting substances is equal to the total weight of all the products. Note in Fig. 9 below that the reaction between 56 grams of iron and 32 grams of sulfur produces 88 grams of iron sulfide.

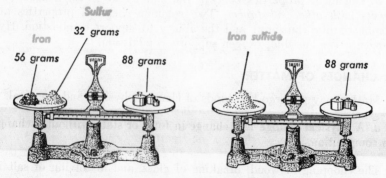

Fig. 9. Conservation of Matter

10. THE WORK OF THE CHEMIST

The chemist is constantly seeking to learn nature's secrets. Through experimentation, he is always testing hypotheses and formulating new theories and laws. At the same time, he is seeking ways and means of meeting the increasing demand for more and better goods.

Modern chemical industry utilizes many important basic raw materials, such as petroleum, coal, natural gas, wood, air, water, sulfur, salt, and limestone. From these raw materials, rubber, nylon, dyes, and drugs are manufactured. To maintain and improve our standard of living, the raw materials needed by the industrial chemist must be relatively cheap and abundant. Such is not always the case. Sometimes important raw materials are so scarce or difficult to obtain as to be classified as *critical*, or so necessary for defense production as to be called *strategic*.

To assure an adequate supply of raw materials, it is necessary to do the following:

a. **Locate New Sources and Use Existing Sources Now Considered Impractical.** Sea water is being utilized as a source of magnesium and bromine. Oil companies are successfully drilling for oil deposited in the ground underneath the sea. Taconite, a low-grade iron ore, is at present supplementing the decreasing supply of our major iron ore, hematite. Synthetic fibers (like nylon and dacron), when blended with natural fibers (like wool or cotton), provide textiles with many desirable properties. Paper made from synthetic fibers has been prepared in the laboratory and found to have properties superior to paper presently in use.

b. **Conserve Existing Materials.** The chemist is always trying to find ways to convert waste products into useful by-products. Coal tar, a very valuable source of industrial chemicals, was at one time a waste product. Much of our future gasoline may be synthesized from coal and natural gas, if our present supplies diminish.

c. **Develop Substitutes.** During recent years, scientists have developed atomic energy. This new form of energy is becoming a vital source of power for industry and transportation; a valuable tool in the research laboratory; a boon in the treatment of certain diseases; but, unfortunately, the destructive force in atomic and hydrogen bombs.

The questions preceded by an asterisk (*) generally require more thought and further study.

1. *a.* Chemistry is concerned with the study of (1) forces (2) heat (3) energy (4) matter.

   b. Mastery of the subject requires a thorough understanding of "big ideas," sometimes called _____.

2. *a.* The scientific method is based essentially on (1) chance (2) reasoning (3) superstition (4) clever guesswork.

   b. List the important steps in the scientific method.

   c. Using the scientific method, how would you proceed to determine whether a substance is a compound or a mixture?

3. *a.* Give a definition and an illustration of a scientific theory.

   b. Scientific theories (1) always change (2) never change (3) change when new evidence is found (4) always become laws.

   c. Theories which have been proven beyond a doubt are called _____.

4. *a.* Matter is anything which has _____ and occupies _____.

   b. Air, water, and rock are examples of (1) liquids (2) solids (3) gases (4) matter.

5. *a.* Three units for measuring matter are length, _____, and _____.

   b. The system of measurement more frequently used in scientific measurement is the _____ system.

   c. The liter is a unit of (1) weight (2) volume (3) density (4) length.

   d. One liter equals approximately one (1) gill (2) pint (3) quart (4) gallon.

   e. A milliliter is equal to approximately (1) 1 cubic centimeter (2) 1 milligram (3) 1 kilogram (4) 1,000 liters.

   f. Nine pounds are equivalent to approximately *four kilograms.* [True or false? If false, correct the italicized term.]

6. *a.* Explain how a platform balance may be used to measure weight.

  *b. What precautions should be followed in using such a balance?

7. Volume is commonly measured in the laboratory by using a (1) graduated cylinder (2) quart bottle (3) balance calibrated in liters (4) beaker.

8. *a.* The three states of matter are _____, _____, and _____.

   b. Explain the important differences between the states of matter.

  *c. Explain how it may be possible to liquefy air.

  *d. Why does the physical state of a substance depend on temperature and pressure?

9. *a.* Matter consists of very small particles called _____.

   b. They are very close together in (1) gases (2) liquids (3) solids (4) gases and liquids.

10. *a.* Matter may be classified as _____, _____, or _____.
    b. When is a substance called an element?
    c. Approximately how many elements are known?
11. *a.* Elements are usually classified as _____ or _____.
    b. Most nonmetals (1) have a luster (2) conduct heat and electricity (3) are liquids (4) are gases or solids.
    c. In the following group, the substance that is not a metal is (1) tin (2) brass (3) oxygen (4) copper.
    d. In the following group, the substance that is not a nonmetal is (1) chlorine (2) uranium (3) sulfur (4) carbon.
12. *a.* A substance composed of two or more elements chemically united is called (1) an allotrope (2) a compound (3) an isotope (4) a mixture.
    b. The proportions in a compound _____ vary.
    c. The composition of a compound can be altered only by _____ means.
    d. When are substances classified as compounds?
    e. Name three common compounds and tell why they are classified as such.
    f. How would you determine whether a substance is an element or a compound?
13. *a.* A mixture has a (an) _____ composition.
    b. The component parts of a mixture (1) must be separated by chemical means (2) never vary (3) are chemically combined (4) may vary.
    c. Are solutions mixtures or compounds? Explain.
    d. In tabular form, summarize the essential differences between compounds and mixtures.
14. *a.* The properties of substances enable us to _____ (weigh, identify) these substances.
    b. Physical properties include state, color, odor, taste, solubility, and _____.
    c. Two common chemical properties are _____ and _____.
15. *a.* How does a chemical change differ from a physical change?
    b. Name three chemical changes and three physical changes.
    c. Give reasons for your classification of the changes selected.
16. The decomposition of a compound into its elements is called _____, while the building up of a compound from its elements is called _____.
17. *a.* In a chemical reaction, the starting substances and the resulting products have the same _____.
    b. How did Lavoisier prove the Law of Conservation of Matter?
    c. Could the science of chemistry have developed as much as it has without such a law? Explain.
18. *a.* A basic raw material used by the chemist is (1) steel (2) nylon (3) petroleum (4) penicillin.
    b. A useful substance formerly discarded as a waste product is _____.
    c. A new source of energy developed by scientists in recent years is called _____ energy.

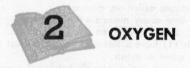

2 OXYGEN

1. OCCURRENCE

Oxygen is the most abundant of all the elements. It is found in nature both free and combined. It is free in the air to the extent of about 21% by volume, combined with hydrogen in water to the extent of about 89%, and combined with many other elements in the earth's crust to the extent of about 50% by weight.

2. LABORATORY PREPARATION

Oxygen may be prepared from substances containing oxygen, such as chlorates, oxides, and peroxides.

a. **Decomposition of Potassium Chlorate.** A mixture of potassium chlorate and manganese dioxide is placed in a test tube. The test tube is connected by means of a delivery tube to the collecting bottle, as shown in the figure below. The mixture is then heated gently and the oxygen collected by the displacement of water.

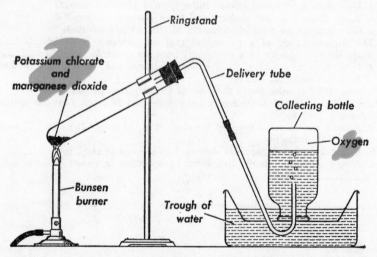

Fig. 2a. Laboratory Preparation and Collection of Oxygen

10

The manganese dioxide in this reaction acts as a catalyst, or catalytic agent. *A catalytic agent is a substance which changes the speed of a chemical reaction without being permanently changed itself.* In this reaction, manganese dioxide speeds up the production of oxygen. When potassium chlorate is heated alone, oxygen is liberated slowly. The complete reaction may be represented by a chemical equation as follows:

$$2 \text{ KClO}_3 \xrightarrow[\text{[catalyst]}]{\text{manganese dioxide}} 2 \text{ KCl} + 3 \text{ O}_2 \uparrow$$

potassium chlorate   potassium chloride   oxygen

A chemical equation is the chemist's shorthand statement describing what occurs in a reaction.

An equation expresses a quantitative (exact) weight relationship between the starting substance (or substances) and the product (or products). (See 9, page 6, "Law of Conservation of Matter.")

The composition of each compound in the chemical equation is indicated by the formula of the compound. Where the product of a reaction is a gas, an upward arrow ($\uparrow$) is used after the formula. The catalytic agent is not placed in the equation proper because it undergoes no permanent change. Instead, it is usually placed under or over the horizontal arrow ($\rightarrow$). (Chemical formulas and equations will be studied in detail in later chapters.)

b. **Decomposition of Mercuric Oxide.** Mercuric oxide, a red powder, when heated strongly in a test tube, decomposes into mercury and oxygen. The mercury (also called quicksilver) collects on the cooler walls of the test tube in the form of droplets. A glowing splint inserted into the test tube during the heating bursts into flame, showing that oxygen is being liberated.

$$2 \text{ HgO} \rightarrow 2 \text{ Hg} + \text{O}_2 \uparrow$$

mercuric oxide   mercury   oxygen

This experiment was first performed in 1774 by Joseph Priestley, an English chemist, who thus discovered oxygen. Later, the experiment was repeated by Lavoisier, who gave oxygen its name and explained its part in burning.

c. **Electrolysis of Water.** Both oxygen and hydrogen are obtained by the electrolysis of water. [See (4), page 24.]

d. From Peroxides

(1) *Decomposition of Hydrogen Peroxide*

$$2 H_2O_2 \rightarrow 2 H_2O + O_2 \uparrow$$
hydrogen   water   oxygen
peroxide

Manganese dioxide may be used as a catalyst in the above reaction.

(2) *Action of Sodium Peroxide on Water*

$$2 Na_2O_2 + 2 H_2O \rightarrow 4 NaOH + O_2 \uparrow$$
sodium   water   sodium   oxygen
peroxide   hydroxide

3. COMMERCIAL PREPARATION

a. Electrolysis of Water. [See (4), page 24.]

b. Fractional Distillation of Liquid Air.
Since air is a mixture, its components—largely nitrogen and oxygen—may be separated by physical means. By cooling and compressing, the air is changed to a liquid and then allowed to evaporate. Because liquid nitrogen has a lower boiling point, it evaporates first, leaving almost pure oxygen behind. Most of the oxygen used commercially is obtained from air by this process.

4. PHYSICAL PROPERTIES

State: gas
Color: colorless
Odor: odorless
Density: slightly denser than air
Solubility: slightly soluble in water

Oxygen is a colorless, odorless, and tasteless gas. It is slightly denser than air and slightly soluble in water. Fish use oxygen dissolved in water, not oxygen combined with the hydrogen. Under normal atmospheric pressure (sea level), oxygen becomes a liquid at $-183°C$.

5. CHEMICAL PROPERTIES

Oxygen is extremely active, combining readily with most elements to form new substances called oxides. *When the union of oxygen and another element is accompanied by noticeable heat and light, the process is called combustion, or burning.* Oxygen itself does not burn but supports combustion. A glowing splint, for example, when thrust into a bottle of oxygen, bursts into flame. This is the test for oxygen.

Oxygen:
1. Does not burn.
2. Supports combustion.

Substances burn more readily in oxygen than in air because air contains only about 21% oxygen. Charcoal (carbon) and steel wool (iron), which only glow in air when heated, burn brightly in oxygen. Sulfur and phosphorus burn very brilliantly in oxygen. Sulfur burns with a bright-blue flame, producing a gas with a choking odor. Phosphorus burns with a dazzling white light, producing a white powdery substance. The combination of these elements with oxygen to form oxides is shown in the following equations:

$$\underset{\text{carbon}}{C} \;+\; \underset{\text{oxygen}}{O_2} \;\rightarrow\; \underset{\substack{\text{carbon}\\\text{dioxide}}}{CO_2 \uparrow}$$

$$\underset{\text{sulfur}}{S} \;+\; \underset{\text{oxygen}}{O_2} \;\rightarrow\; \underset{\substack{\text{sulfur}\\\text{dioxide}}}{SO_2 \uparrow}$$

$$\underset{\text{phosphorus}}{4\,P} \;+\; \underset{\text{oxygen}}{5\,O_2} \;\rightarrow\; \underset{\substack{\text{phosphorus}\\\text{pentoxide}}}{2\,P_2O_5}$$

$$\underset{\text{magnesium}}{2\,Mg} \;+\; \underset{\text{oxygen}}{O_2} \;\rightarrow\; \underset{\substack{\text{magnesium}\\\text{oxide}}}{2\,MgO}$$

6. OXIDATION

The combining of a substance with oxygen is called oxidation. In later chapters, we shall see that the term oxidation has been broadened to include many reactions not involving oxygen.

There are two kinds of oxidation: rapid oxidation and slow oxidation.

a. **Rapid oxidation** *is oxidation accompanied by noticeable light and heat.* Ordinary burning is an example of rapid oxidation in air. The conditions for burning are oxygen and a combustible substance (fuel) raised to its kindling temperature.

At the end of the 18th century, Lavoisier discovered the true nature of burning. Lavoisier's experiment can be summarized as follows: When mercury was heated in a vessel containing air, a red powder was formed and a volume of oxygen was consumed. Upon further heating, the red powder re-formed the original quantity of mercury and the same volume of oxygen.

Lavoisier's experiment had two important consequences. The use of careful weighing techniques enabled him to establish the Law of Conservation of Matter. The removal of oxygen during combustion explained the true nature of burning.

Lavoisier thus overthrew the *phlogiston theory*. This theory assumed that when substances burn, phlogiston was removed in the form of flame.

b. Slow oxidation *is oxidation not accompanied by noticeable light and heat.* The rusting of iron and the decaying of plant and animal matter are examples of slow oxidation. Vegetable oils are used in paints because the oils harden on undergoing slow oxidation. The heat liberated during slow oxidation is not easily detected because it does not have a chance to accumulate.

7. KINDLING TEMPERATURE

The kindling temperature is the lowest temperature at which a substance begins to burn in air. Substances differ in their kindling temperatures. Four substances arranged in the order of their increasing kindling temperatures are phosphorus, sulfur, charcoal, and coal. Because of its low kindling temperature, white phosphorus is stored under water.

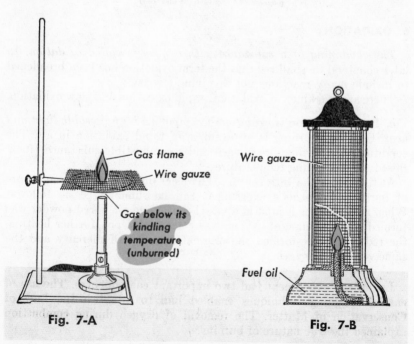

Fig. 7-A   Fig. 7-B

If the temperature of a substance is kept below its kindling point, the substance cannot burn. Thus, gas rising from an open, unlighted Bunsen burner can be made to burn *above*, not below, a wire gauze held over the burner. Note in Fig. 7-*A* that the wire gauze conducts heat away from the flame so rapidly that the gas cannot reach its kindling temperature below the gauze. This principle was utilized by Davy in the construction of the miner's safety lamp (Fig. 7-*B*).

8. EFFECT OF SURFACE ON RATE OF BURNING

Increasing the surface of the fuel exposed to the air will speed up burning. This is so because burning takes place only at the surface, where the fuel particles and the oxygen are in contact. Thus, the "gun" in the home oil burner sprays the fuel as fine droplets to speed up burning.

Kindling wood is more easily set on fire than the same amount of wood in the form of a log. Furthermore, if the log were converted to fine sawdust and exposed to air and ignited, an explosion would result. *An explosion is the instantaneous burning of a finely divided combustible substance, liberating large volumes of hot gases.* When finely divided matter in coal mines and flour mills is accidentally ignited, a dust explosion occurs.

9. SPONTANEOUS COMBUSTION

Spontaneous combustion is burning started by the accumulation of the heat of slow oxidation. The conditions for spontaneous combustion are the presence of a substance of low kindling temperature, a supporter of combustion, and heat accumulated by slow oxidation.

Oily cotton waste or painters' rags, in the absence of proper ventilation (as when stored in a wooden closet), frequently ignite spontaneously. This happens when heat, accumulated from slow oxidation, brings the oil to its kindling temperature. Such materials must be stored in closed metal containers.

10. COMBUSTION WITHOUT OXYGEN

To describe a chemical reaction accompanied by noticeable light and heat, we use the term *combustion*. However, combustion reactions do not necessarily involve oxygen. For example, chlorine gas and sulfur vapor also support the burning or combustion of metals. Combustion reactions with or without oxygen are similar, according to modern chemical theory. Both processes involve transfer of electrons, a concept which will be treated later.

11. USES

a. **Respiration.** Oxygen is necessary for all life. All plants and animals continually take in oxygen and give off carbon dioxide. Oxygen is used in hospitals in the treatment of respiratory diseases such as pneumonia. In cases of drowning, electrical shock, and asphyxiation, oxygen is administered to help restore normal respiration. Because of the lack of sufficient oxygen at high altitudes, aviators and mountain climbers are equipped with tanks of oxygen and breathing helmets.

b. **Burning.** The burning of fuels requires oxygen. In the oxyhydrogen blowtorch (see figure, page 27), and in the oxyacetylene blowtorch, pure oxygen is used to support the combustion of the hydrogen and acetylene, which are used as fuels. Because they produce very high temperatures, these blowtorches are used for cutting and welding steel. Airplanes at high altitudes and submarines below the surface of the water use oxygen not only to maintain respiration, but also to improve the combustion of fuel.

12. THE BUNSEN BURNER

The Bunsen burner is a device for the production of a hot, clean flame by burning a fuel gas in air.

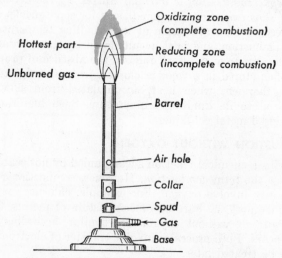

Fig. 12. The Bunsen Burner and Flame

The four main parts of the Bunsen burner, illustrated in Fig. 12, are as follows:

a. The **base** supports the device.

b. The **spud** is a nozzle through which the fuel gas enters the barrel at high speed. The rapid passage of gas through the spud draws air through the air holes into the barrel.

c. The **collar** regulates the amount of air entering the barrel. This is done by changing the size of the air holes.

d. The **barrel** acts as a mixing chamber for air and gas. Rising to the top of the barrel, the mixture burns and produces the flame.

Figure 12 also shows that the Bunsen flame consists of three distinct *zones*, sometimes called *cones*. The innermost zone directly above the barrel consists of gas that has not reached its kindling point and hence is unburned. The middle zone is the region of incomplete combustion. Since the gas in this zone requires more oxygen, it is called the *reducing zone*. The outermost zone, which is light-purple in color, is the region of complete combustion and is called the *oxidizing zone*. The hottest part of the flame is directly above the tip of the reducing zone.

When the air holes are closed, incomplete combustion takes place. The flame is luminous (yellow) due to the presence of incandescent (glowing) particles of carbon. On the other hand, when the air holes are opened, more complete combustion occurs. As a result, the flame is smaller and nonluminous (bluish), but cleaner and hotter.

If a Bunsen burner is ignited while the gas pressure is low, the flame may travel down the barrel and burn at the spud, causing what is called "striking back." To prevent this, the air holes should be almost completely closed before lighting the burner.

CAUTION If the flame has "struck back," allow the hot barrel to cool before adjusting the air supply.

When natural gas is used in place of manufactured gases, such as water gas or coal gas, it is necessary to modify existing devices. Bunsen burners, gas stoves, and gas refrigerators now have special gas burners which permit them to burn natural gas. Natural gas provides more heat than an equal weight of any manufactured gas.

OZONE

13. OCCURRENCE

Ozone is produced in the air during lightning storms, and is found in the air around high-voltage electrical machines. Ozone also occurs in the upper atmosphere in small concentrations.

14. PREPARATION

Ozone is prepared by passing high-voltage electricity through oxygen or air. Ozone is formed from a rearrangement of oxygen atoms, *three* volumes of oxygen producing *two* volumes of ozone, as shown below.

$$3 \ \underset{\text{oxygen}}{O_2} + \text{energy} \rightarrow 2 \ \underset{\text{ozone}}{O_3} \uparrow$$

This reaction requires considerable energy, which accounts for the fact that ozone has greater chemical activity than oxygen.

15. PHYSICAL PROPERTIES

Ozone is a bluish gas with a pungent, irritating odor, slightly more soluble in water than is oxygen, and one and one-half times as dense. Ozone is an allotropic form of oxygen.

Allotropic forms of an element are different forms of the same element having different properties.

The allotropic forms of an element all exist in the same state. Sulfur, phosphorus, and carbon also have allotropic forms.

16. CHEMICAL PROPERTIES

Ozone is more active than oxygen. Ozone readily oxidizes substances like silver and rubber, which are unaffected by oxygen.

$$2 \ \underset{\text{silver}}{Ag} + \underset{\text{ozone}}{O_3} \rightarrow \underset{\substack{\text{silver}\\\text{oxide}}}{Ag_2O} + \underset{\text{oxygen}}{O_2} \uparrow$$

Ozone is very unstable, changing readily into oxygen.

17. USES

a. **Bleaching Agent:** bleaches oils and waxes.

b. **Deodorizing:** removes undesirable odors from kitchens, slaughter-houses, cold-storage rooms, theaters, and office buildings.

c. **Water Purification:** used in some water supplies to kill bacteria.

1. *a.* The most abundant element is _____.
   b. This element is present in the atmosphere to the extent of about _____ per cent by volume.
2. *a.* The compound decomposed when oxygen is prepared by heating potassium chlorate and manganese dioxide is _____.
   b. The manganese dioxide acts as a (an) _____ agent.
   c. The substances left in the generating test tube are _____ and _____.
   d. Make a labeled diagram to illustrate the laboratory preparation and collection of oxygen.
   e. Write the word equation for the reaction.
3. *a.* Priestley prepared oxygen by decomposing _____.
   b. Write the word equation for the reaction.
4. Lavoisier first demonstrated the true nature of _____.
5. *a.* The electrolysis of water yields _____ and _____.
   b. Write the word equation.
6. *a.* Oxygen may also be prepared in the laboratory by the decomposition of _____ or the decomposition of _____.
   b. Complete the following word equations:
      (1) _____ → water + oxygen
      (2) _____ + water → sodium hydroxide + _____
7. *a.* The principal commercial sources of oxygen are air and _____.
   b. Explain how oxygen is obtained from air.
   c. The production of oxygen from liquid air is a _____ change.
8. Oxygen is _____ (color) and _____ (odor). It is _____ (less dense, denser) than air and _____ (slightly, moderately, very) soluble in water. It is _____ (difficult, easy) to liquefy.
9. *a.* Oxygen does not _____ but does support _____.
   b. Describe a test to prove that an unknown gas is oxygen.
   c. A splinter burning in a bottle of air goes out after a time because it (1) burns up the air (2) consumes most of the oxygen (3) forms a poisonous gas (4) consumes most of the nitrogen.
10. *a.* Substances which glow in air when heated burn more _____ in oxygen.
    b. When elements combine with oxygen, compounds called _____ are formed.
11. Complete the following word equations:
    a. carbon + oxygen →
    b. sulfur + oxygen →
    c. phosphorus + oxygen →
    d. magnesium + oxygen →
12. Under what conditions may oxygen compounds ending in -ate be formed?
13. Distinguish between rapid and slow oxidation, giving an example of each.

*14. Describe the experiment which Lavoisier performed to prove the true nature of burning.

15. *a.* Define (1) combustion (2) kindling temperature.
    b. Describe an experiment to determine the order of the kindling temperatures of the following substances: sulfur, charcoal, phosphorus, and coal.
    c. As a safety precaution, phosphorus should be stored under _____.

16. *a.* If the temperature of a substance is kept below its kindling point, the substance cannot _____.
    b. Describe a laboratory experiment to illustrate the principle of the Davy safety lamp.

17. *a.* Ordinary burning and an explosion are alike in that neither occurs until the combustible matter reaches (1) its boiling point (2) its kindling point (3) red heat (4) room temperature.
    b. Explain how the "gun" in the oil burner speeds up the burning of the oil.
    c. How do dust explosions occur? What steps can be taken to prevent such explosions?

18. *a.* What is meant by spontaneous combustion?
    b. Many fires are caused by spontaneous combustion.
        (1) What precautions should be taken in the home or elsewhere to prevent spontaneous combustion?
        (2) Give two examples of conditions that may cause spontaneous combustion.

19. Combustion reactions always involve (1) oxygen (2) sulfur (3) chlorine (4) the liberation of noticeable light and heat.

20. *a.* All living things take in the gas _____ and give off _____.
    b. Why does the oxyhydrogen torch produce such high temperatures?

21. *a.* Make a labeled diagram of the Bunsen burner, showing all the important parts.
    b. The mixing of air with gas in the Bunsen burner makes the flame hotter because (1) the flame is luminous (2) the flame is nonluminous (3) combustion is more complete (4) the flame is larger.
    c. The hottest part of the Bunsen flame is (1) just above the outer cone (2) at the top of the outer cone (3) in the innermost cone (4) just above the middle cone.

22. *a.* Explain what is meant by a flame "striking back."
    b. How may "striking back" be prevented?
    c. What should be done if a flame has "struck back"?

23. *a.* Ozone is prepared from _____ by the use of _____.
    b. Write the word equation for the reaction.
    c. Explain why ozone is more active than oxygen.

24. Ozone is an *amphoteric* form of oxygen. [True or false? If false, correct the italicized term.]

25. *a.* The reaction between ozone and magnesium yields the compound magnesium (1) carbide (2) carbonate (3) ozonide (4) oxide.
    b. Being unstable, ozone changes readily into _____.

26. *a.* State two uses of ozone.
    b. What property of ozone makes these uses possible?

3 HYDROGEN

1. OCCURRENCE

Unlike oxygen, hydrogen occurs in nature in the free state in minute quantities only. Hydrogen is found abundantly in combined form with oxygen, carbon, sulfur, and nitrogen. The most common hydrogen compound is water, which contains 11% hydrogen by weight. Hydrogen is also found in almost all animal and plant tissues, and in most fuels.

2. PREPARATION

Just as oxygen is prepared from compounds containing oxygen, hydrogen is prepared from its compounds, usually an acid or water.

a. **Obtaining Hydrogen from Certain Acids.** This is the standard laboratory method for preparing hydrogen. All acids contain hydrogen. A metal more active than hydrogen will react with certain acids to replace the hydrogen.

Zinc is placed in a generator bottle and hydrochloric acid (or *dilute* sulfuric acid) is poured through the thistle tube. (See Fig. 2a below.) The bottom of the thistle tube extends into the liquid, so that the gas will escape through the delivery tube, *not* through the thistle tube.

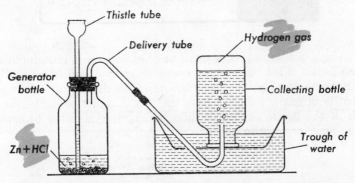

Fig. 2a. Laboratory Preparation and Collection of Hydrogen

The zinc reacts with the acid, replacing the hydrogen and liberating it as a gas. A zinc compound, called a *salt*, is also formed and remains in the generator. Because of its limited solubility, hydrogen is collected by the displacement of water.

$$Zn + 2 HCl \rightarrow ZnCl_2 + H_2 \uparrow$$

zinc   hydrochloric   zinc   hydrogen
acid   chloride

$$Zn + H_2SO_4 \rightarrow ZnSO_4 + H_2 \uparrow$$

zinc   dilute   zinc   hydrogen
sulfuric   sulfate
acid

To replace the hydrogen in acids, only those metals more active than hydrogen may be used. Two such metals, in addition to zinc, are magnesium and iron. On the other hand, copper, silver, and gold are too inactive to liberate hydrogen from acids.

Nitric acid or *concentrated* sulfuric acid will generally not react with metals to produce hydrogen. These acids are strong oxidizing agents and may oxidize any hydrogen that is liberated to form water.

b. Obtaining Hydrogen from Water

(1) *Action of a Metal on Cold Water.* Since this method of producing hydrogen is difficult to control, it is generally used for demonstration only. Very active metals such as potassium, sodium, and calcium decompose water, liberating hydrogen and forming a compound called a *base*.

CAUTION	Use only a very small quantity of the above metals because the reaction is usually violent.

Hydrogen may be prepared from the reaction between sodium and water. Using a wire holder, a *small* piece of sodium is introduced into a small bottle filled with water and resting in a pan of water. The sodium reacts quickly, liberating hydrogen which displaces the water. The bottle of gas is removed from the pan. A flame brought near the mouth of the bottle causes the liberated hydrogen either to explode with a "pop" or to burn quietly.

$$2 Na + 2 H_2O \rightarrow 2 NaOH + H_2 \uparrow$$

sodium   water   sodium   hydrogen
hydroxide

In place of sodium, potassium may be used. In this case, however, the reaction is even more vigorous. The considerable heat produced is usually sufficient to ignite the hydrogen formed.

$$2 \text{ K } + 2 \text{ H}_2\text{O} \rightarrow 2 \text{ KOH} + \text{ H}_2 \uparrow$$
$$\text{\small potassium} \quad \text{\small water} \quad \text{\small potassium} \quad \text{\small hydrogen}$$
$$\text{\small hydroxide}$$

Calcium reacts less violently with water than does either sodium or potassium.

(2) *Action of a Metal on Steam.* This is a commercial method of preparing hydrogen. Metals less active than potassium, sodium, or calcium, but more active than hydrogen, require heat to react with water. Thus, as shown in the figure below, when steam is passed over red-hot iron (steel wool), the iron combines with the oxygen of the steam, forming an oxide of iron and liberating hydrogen.

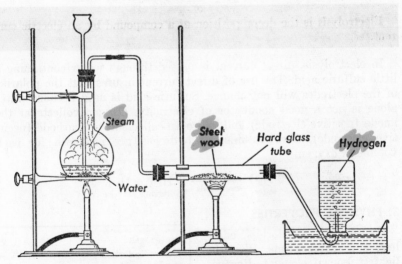

Fig. 2b(2). Reduction of Steam by Iron

$$4 \text{ H}_2\text{O} + 3 \text{ Fe} \rightarrow \text{Fe}_3\text{O}_4 + 4 \text{ H}_2 \uparrow$$
$$\text{\small steam} \quad \text{\small iron} \quad \text{\small iron} \quad \text{\small hydrogen}$$
$$\text{\small oxide}$$

A chemical reaction in which a substance (such as iron) removes oxygen from a compound (such as water) is called reduction. As in the case of oxidation, we shall see later that the term reduction has also been broadened to include reactions that do not involve oxygen. In the reaction between iron and steam, the iron acts as a *reducing agent.*

(3) *Action of Hot Coke (Carbon) on Steam.* Most hydrogen is obtained commercially by this method. Steam is passed over hot coke, which, like iron, acts as a reducing agent. A mixture of hydrogen and carbon monoxide, called *water gas,* is formed.

$$H_2O + \quad C \quad \rightarrow \underbrace{CO + H_2}_{\text{water gas}}$$
$$\text{steam} \quad\quad \text{carbon}$$

There are several methods of separating the hydrogen from the carbon monoxide. One method commonly used is to cool and compress the mixture of gases sufficiently to liquefy the carbon monoxide only, thus releasing hydrogen which is still gaseous.

(4) *Electrolysis of Water.* Hydrogen is also prepared both in the laboratory and commercially by the electrolysis of water.

Electrolysis is the decomposition of a compound by an electric current.

In electrolysis, direct current is passed through water containing a little sulfuric acid. The use of direct current insures that the polarity of the electrodes will not change. Sulfuric acid is used because water alone is not a good conductor of electricity. Oxygen collects at the anode (positive electrode) and hydrogen collects at the cathode (negative electrode). Two volumes of hydrogen are produced for each volume of oxygen.

$$2\,H_2O \xrightarrow{\text{electrolysis}} 2\,H_2 \uparrow + O_2 \uparrow$$
$$\text{water} \quad\quad\quad\quad \text{hydrogen} \quad \text{oxygen}$$

3. PHYSICAL PROPERTIES

Hydrogen is a colorless, odorless, and tasteless gas. It is the lightest known element. Because of its extremely low density, hydrogen will diffuse (spread) very rapidly through the walls of most

State: gas
Color: colorless
Odor: odorless
Density: least dense element
Solubility: slightly soluble in water

containers. It is only very slightly soluble in water, and hence can be collected by displacement of water. Hydrogen can be *adsorbed* (stored on the surface) by certain metals, such as platinum and palladium. Heat is liberated during the adsorption of the hydrogen by the metal, causing the hydrogen to reach its kindling point and therefore burn. This principle is used in some gas lighters.

In recent years, two new forms of hydrogen, called *isotopes*, have been isolated. These forms, called *deuterium* and *tritium*, are heavier than ordinary hydrogen, while exhibiting the same chemical properties.

4. CHEMICAL PROPERTIES

a. **Combustibility.** Hydrogen is not a very active element. It is combustible but does not support combustion. A burning splint, for example, when inserted in a bottle of hydrogen causes the hydrogen to

> Hydrogen:
>
> 1. Is combustible (burns to form water).
> 2. Is generally a reducing agent.

burn at the mouth of the bottle. Inside the bottle, however, the burning splint is extinguished, showing that hydrogen does not support combustion. Cavendish, an English scientist, is credited with the discovery of hydrogen and its combustibility.

The pure gas burns quietly in oxygen or air with a pale-blue flame to form water, as shown in Fig. 4a. This is the test for hydrogen. Hydrogen gets its name from the Greek, meaning "water former."

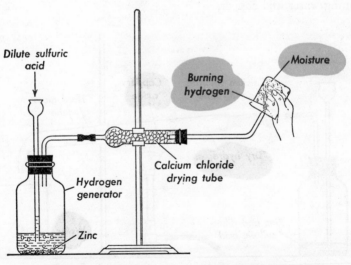

Fig. 4a. Burning Hydrogen to Form Water

$$2 H_2 + O_2 \rightarrow 2 H_2O$$
hydrogen   oxygen   water

If hydrogen is mixed with oxygen or air and the mixture is ignited or heated, an explosion results and water is formed. In order to determine whether a sample of hydrogen is pure, ignite a small portion of the gas in a test tube. If it burns quietly, it is pure hydrogen; if it explodes ("pops"), it is impure.

CAUTION   Observe the above procedure in all experimentation involving large quantities of hydrogen.

b. **Reaction with Metals.** Under certain conditions, hydrogen may behave as a nonmetal, reacting with metals to form *hydrides*.

$$2 \text{ Na} + \text{H}_2 \rightarrow 2 \text{ NaH}$$
sodium hydride

Hydrides are used as drying agents.

c. **Reducing Agent.** When dry hydrogen is passed over heated copper oxide, the hydrogen removes the oxygen from the copper oxide, forming water and copper.

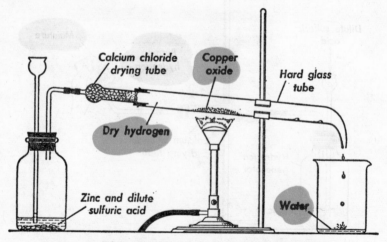

Fig. 4c. Reduction of Copper Oxide by Hydrogen

$$\text{CuO} + \text{H}_2 \rightarrow \text{H}_2\text{O} + \text{Cu}$$
copper oxide   hydrogen   water   copper

Hydrogen is the *reducing agent*, that is, a substance which removes oxygen from a compound. The process is called *reduction*. Copper oxide is the *oxidizing agent*, a substance which supplies oxygen. The process is called *oxidation*. Reduction and oxidation are, therefore, opposite processes and take place at the same time. In the previous reaction, for example, copper oxide is reduced and hydrogen is oxidized.

According to modern concepts, oxidation-reduction involves a loss and gain of electrons. This idea will be discussed in later chapters.

5. USES

a. Fuel

(1) The *oxyhydrogen blowtorch* uses hydrogen as a fuel gas. This torch consists of two concentric tubes not connected to each other. Hydrogen under pressure is forced through the outer tube and oxygen through the inner tube. To operate, the hydrogen is turned on and ignited; then the oxygen is turned on until a flame with a very high temperature is produced. The oxyhydrogen blowtorch is used in the melting of platinum and in welding.

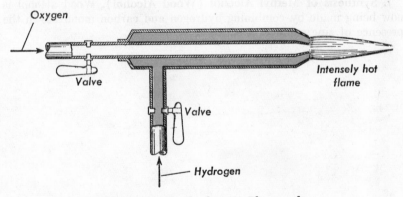

Fig. 5a(1). Oxyhydrogen Blowtorch

(2) The *atomic hydrogen torch* is another type of torch utilizing hydrogen for welding. Hydrogen gas is passed through an electric arc. The temperature of the arc breaks down the hydrogen molecules into atoms. The burning of the atomic hydrogen thus produced develops temperatures as high as 5,000°C. It is thought that the heat developed is the result of hydrogen atoms combining to form molecules which subsequently burn.

b. **Airships.** Hydrogen has been used to fill dirigibles and balloons because it is less dense (lighter) than air and consequently has great lifting power. Because hydrogen forms explosive mixtures with air, hydrogen is being replaced by helium. Although helium is twice as dense as hydrogen, it is not flammable and has about 92% the lifting power of hydrogen.

c. **Hydrogenation.** When hydrogen is passed through vegetable oils in the presence of a catalytic agent like nickel, solid fats are produced. This process is called *hydrogenation.* Vegetable shortening is prepared in this manner. Some fuels are also produced by hydrogenation processes.

d. **Reducing Agent.** Because hydrogen removes oxygen from many compounds, it is used as a reducing agent. Metals like tungsten and molybdenum are extracted from their oxide ores by reduction with hydrogen.

e. **Synthesis of Ammonia.** Under certain conditions, hydrogen combines directly with nitrogen to form ammonia. This process is known commercially as the Haber process.

f. **Synthesis of Methyl Alcohol (Wood Alcohol).** Wood alcohol is now being made by combining hydrogen and carbon monoxide in the presence of zinc oxide as a catalyst.

1. *a.* Hydrogen occurs on earth largely in the _____ state.
   b. The most common hydrogen compound is _____.
   c. Hydrogen occurs (1) combined in acids (2) combined with zinc (3) free in acids (4) free in water.

2. *a.* The reaction between zinc and certain acids produces the element _____ and a compound called a (an) _____.
   b. Hydrogen cannot be prepared by the action of acids on (1) zinc (2) magnesium (3) iron (4) copper.

3. Complete the following word equations:
   a. magnesium + hydrochloric acid →
   b. iron + sulfuric acid →
   c. zinc + hydrochloric acid →

4. *a.* Make a labeled diagram to illustrate the laboratory preparation and collection of hydrogen.
   b. Why is a thistle tube used in this experiment?
   c. Why must the lower end of the thistle tube dip below the surface of the liquid?

5. *a.* Active metals decompose water, forming hydrogen and a (an) _____.
   b. Hydrogen may be prepared by reacting steam with hot (1) copper (2) iron (3) mercury (4) platinum.
   c. Complete the following word equations:
   (1) calcium + water →
   *(2) magnesium + hot water →

6. *a.* Make a labeled diagram of the apparatus used in the electrolysis of water.
   b. In this process, hydrogen is liberated at the _____ electrode and oxygen at the _____ electrode.
   c. In forming water, 40 cc of hydrogen will unite with (1) 5 cc (2) 10 cc (3) 20 cc (4) 40 cc of oxygen.

7. A commercial fuel which may be used as a source of hydrogen is _____.

8. *a.* Hydrogen is (1) less dense than air and inert (2) very soluble in water and combustible (3) odorless and a reducing agent (4) denser than air and tasteless.
   b. It is collected in the laboratory by water displacement because it is
   _____.
   c. Explain how hydrogen may be used in gas lighters.
   d. The names of the two hydrogen isotopes are _____ and _____.

9. *a.* A gas that produces only water when it burns is (1) a compound containing hydrogen (2) hydrogen (3) a mixture containing hydrogen (4) water gas.

    b. _____ discovered hydrogen.

    c. Two hydrogen generators are set up in the laboratory. The gas coming from one of these generators may be lighted with safety. It would be dangerous to light the product issuing from the second generator.

    (1) Name the gas or gases coming from each generator.

    (2) Tell how it can be proved that the gas from a hydrogen generator is safe to ignite.

    (3) Write the equation to show what happens when hydrogen burns.

    (4) Compare the products and the speeds of the burning of hydrogen from the two generators. Give reasons.

10. *a.* Make a labeled diagram to show what happens when hydrogen is passed over heated copper oxide.

    b. Write a word equation for the reaction.

    *c. State an important precaution that should be followed in performing this experiment.

    *d. Explain why reduction in a given reaction is always accompanied by oxidation.

11. *a.* Using a labeled diagram, explain the operation of the oxyhydrogen blowtorch.

    b. The hottest flame is produced by the (1) oxyacetylene torch (2) oxyhydrogen torch (3) atomic hydrogen torch (4) miner's safety lamp.

    c. Helium is preferred to hydrogen in airships because helium (1) has greater lifting power (2) is less dense (3) is cheaper (4) does not form explosive mixtures with air.

    d. The process by which cottonseed oil is converted into solid fats is called *hydrolysis*. [True or false? If false, correct the italicized term.]

    e. Complete the following word equations:

    (1) tungsten oxide + hydrogen →

    (2) molybdenum oxide + hydrogen →

    f. Synthetic wood alcohol can be made from the catalytic reaction between hydrogen and _____.

4 WATER AND SOLUTION

WATER

1. OCCURRENCE

Water is the most abundant and universally distributed compound. Three-fourths of the earth's surface is covered with water in the form of rivers, lakes, and oceans. Considerable water is also found underground and in the atmosphere. All living matter, rocks, minerals, and foods contain varying quantities of water.

2. COMPOSITION OF WATER BY VOLUME

Water is composed of two parts of hydrogen to one part of oxygen by volume. This ratio may be determined experimentally by analysis and synthesis.

a. Analysis is the decomposition of a compound into its elements. Note in Fig. 2a that the liberation of 20 cc of hydrogen by the passage of a direct current through water is accompanied by the liberation of 10 cc of oxygen. This proves that water is composed of 2 parts of hydrogen to 1 part of oxygen by volume.

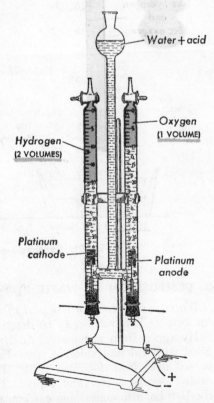

Water + acid

Oxygen
(1 VOLUME)

Hydrogen
(2 VOLUMES)

Platinum
cathode

Platinum
anode

Fig. 2a. Analysis of Water by Volume

b. **Synthesis** is the combining of two or more elements to form a compound. The eudiometer (gas-measuring) tube, shown in Fig. 2*b*, contains a mixture of 30 cc of hydrogen and 10 cc of oxygen, before explosion. After explosion, only 20 cc of hydrogen unite with 10 cc of oxygen to form water, leaving 10 cc of hydrogen uncombined. This again proves the volume ratio—hydrogen : oxygen = 2:1.

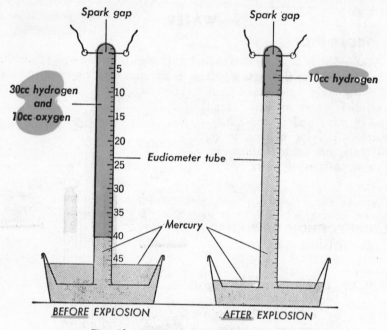

Fig. 2b. Synthesis of Water by Volume

3. COMPOSITION OF WATER BY WEIGHT

Water is composed of one part of hydrogen to eight parts of oxygen by weight. This ratio may be determined experimentally, as follows:

Hydrogen from a generator is dried by passing it through a tube filled with calcium chloride. (See Fig. 3.) The dry hydrogen is then passed over heated copper oxide. The hydrogen reduces the copper oxide, forming water and copper. The water formed is absorbed in the U-tube, also containing calcium chloride. Before heating, the copper oxide is weighed; the U-tube of calcium chloride is also previously weighed.

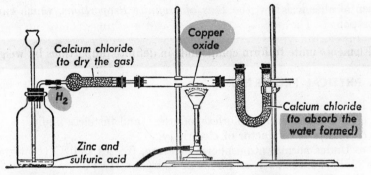

Fig. 3. Synthesis of Water by Weight

To determine the weight ratio of the elements in water, it is necessary to determine the weights of hydrogen and oxygen that combine. This may be done in three steps:

a. Find the *weight of water* formed. We do this by determining the increase in weight of the U-tube. Let us suppose that this increase is 18 grams.

b. Find the *weight of oxygen* required to form 18 grams of water. This weight, which is the loss in weight of the copper oxide tube, is equal to 16 grams.

c. Find the *weight of hydrogen* required. Since 18 grams of water were formed from 16 grams of oxygen, 2 grams of hydrogen were required.

Therefore, the weight ratio of the elements in water is 2 grams of hydrogen to 16 grams of oxygen, or hydrogen:oxygen as 1:8.

COMPOSITION OF WATER

	HYDROGEN	OXYGEN
By volume	2	1
By weight	1	8

4. LAW OF DEFINITE PROPORTIONS

The study of water has shown that it always contains one part of hydrogen to eight parts of oxygen by weight. All compounds have a fixed or definite composition. This relationship is expressed by a fundamental chemical law, the *Law of Definite Proportions,* which can be stated:

Elements unite to form compounds in definite proportions by weight.

5. PHYSICAL PROPERTIES

Pure water:

a. Is a transparent, colorless, odorless, and tasteless liquid.

b. Is a poor conductor of electricity.

c. Under normal atmospheric pressure, freezes at 0°C (centigrade) or 32°F (Fahrenheit), and boils at 100°C or 212°F.

d. Is frequently called the *universal solvent* because it dissolves so many different substances.

Although most liquids contract on freezing, water *expands* on freezing. With expansion, ice becomes less dense than water, and will therefore float in water.

6. WATER AS A STANDARD

a. **For Weight.** Water is the standard on which the metric unit of weight is based. *One gram is defined as the weight of one cubic centimeter of water at 4°C.*

b. **For Specific Gravity.** Water is the standard for measuring the specific gravity of liquids and solids. *Specific gravity is defined as the ratio of the density of a given liquid or solid to the density of water.* Thus, iron, which has a specific gravity of 7.6, is 7.6 times as dense as water.

c. **For Heat Units.** Water is the standard for expressing amount of heat. *The calorie is defined as the amount of heat required to raise the temperature of 1 gram of water 1°C.* A *British thermal unit (BTU)* may be similarly defined in English units.

7. CHEMICAL PROPERTIES

a. **Stability.** Water is an exceedingly stable compound. Except for the relative ease with which it can be decomposed by electrolysis, extremely high temperatures (above 3,000°C) are needed to decompose it.

b. **Action on Metals.** Active metals such as sodium, potassium, lithium, and calcium react with water to form bases and hydrogen.

$$2 \text{ M} + 2 \text{ H}_2\text{O} \rightarrow 2 \text{ MOH} + \text{H}_2 \uparrow$$

active   water   [base]   hydrogen
metal

c. Action on Oxides

(1) Metallic oxides which react with water to form bases are called *basic anhydrides*.

$$CaO + H_2O \rightarrow Ca(OH)_2$$

calcium   water   calcium
oxide   hydroxide

(2) Nonmetallic oxides which react with water to form acids are called *acid anhydrides*.

$$CO_2 + H_2O \rightarrow H_2CO_3$$

carbon   water   carbonic
dioxide   acid

d. Action as a Catalyst.

The presence of water seems to promote certain reactions. For example, a spark will not ignite a mixture of dry hydrogen and dry oxygen, whereas reaction takes place readily in the presence of moisture. In reactions of this sort, water is apparently a catalytic agent.

e. Water and Ionic Reactions.

Water also enters into a variety of reactions related to ionization.

8. MAKING WATER FIT FOR USE

Water in nature contains impurities. Small quantities of impurities usually are not objectionable, but large quantities may render water distasteful or unsafe. In certain ways, nature removes some foreign matter. But, for the most part, it is the task of man to make water drinkable (*potable*). Communities employ several of the following methods to remove from water those impurities that cause disease and undesirable taste, color, and odor.

a. Sedimentation.

Water is allowed to flow into reservoirs or settling tanks where most of the large, suspended solids settle to the bottom. The partly clear water then undergoes further purification.

b. Coagulation.

When added to water, alum produces a sticky, jelly-like precipitate of aluminum hydroxide. The precipitate settles to the bottom, dragging down with it fine, suspended particles which sometimes cause water to be cloudy, or turbid. Bacteria also cling to the precipitate as it settles.

c. Filtration.

Water is filtered through beds of gravel and sand to remove suspended solids. In the laboratory, water containing undissolved particles is passed through filter paper supported in a funnel.

d. **Aeration.** Water is sprayed into the air to oxidize organic matter that gives water an unpleasant odor or taste. This treatment, usually in the presence of sunlight, also helps destroy some bacteria, and adds to the pleasant taste of water.

e. **Chlorination.** To kill bacteria, chlorine is often added to the water in the proportion of about four pounds of chlorine to one million pounds of water. Ozone is sometimes used instead of chlorine. Water in swimming pools is treated with chlorine to kill bacteria.

f. **Boiling.** Active boiling of water for fifteen or twenty minutes kills disease-producing germs. This method is used in the home and by campers and hikers when the purity of a water supply is unknown or suspect.

g. **Other Methods.** Copper sulfate (blue vitriol) added to reservoir water kills algae and other small plants. Ultraviolet rays produced by mercury vapor lamps destroy bacteria in swimming pools.

9. MAKING CHEMICALLY PURE WATER

Potable water still contains dissolved impurities. The removal of these impurities by distillation and ion exchange forms chemically pure water.

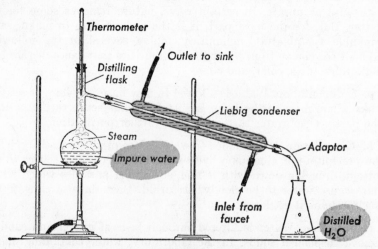

Fig. 9a. Distillation of Water

a. **Distillation.** This process (Fig. 9*a*) consists of boiling the impure water and then cooling the resulting steam so that it condenses to form distilled water. Dissolved solids remain behind in the distilling flask.

Drinking water can be made from sea water by distillation. Distilled water is used in storage batteries, in the preparation of medicines, and in chemical research.

b. **Ion Exchange.** A number of synthetic resins are used to remove dissolved solids or mineral matter from water. This process, involving ion exchange, produces chemically pure water. It is especially suited for large-scale water purification.

SOLUTIONS AND SUSPENSIONS

10. WHAT IS A SOLUTION?

A solution is a uniform mixture of varying proportions.

The dissolved substance does not settle upon standing. Solutions are clear and transparent.

The dissolved substance is called the *solute*, while the substance which does the dissolving is called the *solvent*. Thus, in a salt solution, salt is the solute and water is the solvent.

Solutes may be solids, liquids, or gases, while most of the common solvents are usually liquids. Thus, a liquid such as glycerine or a gas such as carbon dioxide will dissolve in water. When alcohol is the solvent, the solution is called a *tincture,* such as tincture of iodine.

11. THE NATURE OF SOLUTION

When a solute dissolves in a solvent, the change is usually considered to be physical. In some cases, however, especially where there are unusual volume changes, the act of solution is probably a chemical change. Thus, when a liter of alcohol and a liter of water are mixed, the resulting total volume is less than two liters. This contraction in volume suggests a chemical change.

The evolution or absorption of heat during solution may also indicate a chemical change. When sulfuric acid is added to water, considerable heat is evolved. New substances have been isolated from this mixture, indicating that a chemical change has occurred. This process is sometimes referred to as *hydration* or *solvation.*

12. TYPES OF SOLUTION

Solutions are classified on the basis of the relative amount of solute to solvent.

a. A **dilute solution** *is one which contains a relatively small amount of solute dissolved in a large amount of solvent.*

b. A **concentrated solution** *is one which contains a relatively large amount of solute dissolved in a small amount of solvent.*

c. An **unsaturated solution** *is one that can dissolve more solute at a given temperature and pressure.*

d. A **saturated solution** *is one in which a given volume of solvent has dissolved all the solute that it can under given conditions of temperature and pressure.*

Saturated solutions may be either dilute or concentrated, depending on the solubility of the solute. A saturated solution of calcium hydroxide, which is only slightly soluble, contains a smaller proportion of solute to solvent and is therefore dilute. A saturated salt solution contains a larger proportion of solute to solvent and is therefore concentrated.

e. A **supersaturated solution** *is one that holds more solute than it normally can at a given temperature.* If we make a hot, saturated solution of a very soluble substance such as hypo and let it cool slowly without being disturbed, the excess solute will remain in solution instead of crystallizing out. Shaking, stirring, or adding a crystal of hypo to this supersaturated solution will cause the excess solute to crystallize out, leaving a saturated solution of hypo.

The concentration of a solution may also be expressed in a more quantitative manner. *Molar, molal,* and *normal* solutions are discussed on page 437.

13. DETERMINING THE TYPE OF SOLUTION

Add a pinch of solute to the solution. If the solute dissolves, the solution is unsaturated. If the solute falls to the bottom and remains undissolved, the solution is saturated. If *seeding,* that is, adding more solute, causes the solution to crystallize, the solution was originally supersaturated.

14. CONDITIONS AFFECTING SOLUBILITY

a. Temperature

(1) *Solids*

In general, the solubility of solids increases with an increase in the temperature of the solvent.

The relationship between the effect of temperature and the solubility of certain solids is summarized in the solubility curves below:

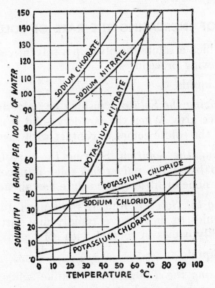

Fig. 14. Solubility Curves

Where the curve is *horizontal,* as in the case of sodium chloride (NaCl), a change in temperature does not affect the solubility to any extent. Where the curve *rises sharply,* as in the case of potassium nitrate (KNO_3), solubility increases with a rise in temperature.

(2) *Gases*

The solubility of gases decreases with an increase in temperature of the solvent.

Gases are more soluble in cold water than in warm water. When a glass of cold water is allowed to stand, bubbles of air appear on the inside walls of the glass.

b. **Pressure.** Solids and liquids are extremely difficult to compress. Gases, on the other hand, are easily compressed.

The solubility of gases increases with an increase in pressure of the gas.

Carbonated water is made by dissolving carbon dioxide in water under increased pressure.

15. METHODS OF INCREASING THE RATE OF SOLUTION

The rate at which a solute dissolves in a solvent can be increased by each of the following procedures:

a. **Solids in Liquids**

(1) *Pulverizing the Solute.* Crushing or pulverizing the solid increases its surface area. When the powdery solid is now placed in the solvent, more of the solute comes in contact with the solvent.

(2) *Agitating the Solution.* Stirring the mixture of solute and solvent tends to bring the pulverized solid into contact with fresh solvent in which none or little of the solute has already dissolved.

(3) *Heating the Solvent.* Raising the temperature of the solvent causes its molecules to move more rapidly and farther apart. Thus, solute more readily comes in contact with solvent molecules.

b. **Gases in Liquids**

(1) *Decreasing the Temperature.* Unlike solids, gases are more soluble in cold water than in hot water. Bottles of seltzer or soda pop are kept refrigerated in order to keep the carbon dioxide gas in solution.

(2) *Increasing the Pressure.* The rate at which gases dissolve in liquids is directly proportional to the pressure applied. Thus, as pressure is increased, more gas dissolves. Increased pressure is used to dissolve large volumes of carbon dioxide in effervescent beverages.

16. WHAT IS A SUSPENSION?

A suspension is a nonuniform mixture of insoluble particles which slowly settle on standing.

Suspensions are usually opaque and cloudy. Examples of suspensions are powdered clay or mud in water, and dust in air.

The characteristics of solutions and suspensions are compared in the following table:

FACTOR	SOLUTION	SUSPENSION
Clarity	Clear, transparent	Cloudy, muddy
Precipitation	Solute does not settle	Particles eventually settle to bottom
Separation	Evaporation, distillation	Sedimentation, filtration, coagulation
Particle size	Invisible (molecular)	Large, easily seen
Distribution of particles	Uniform	Nonuniform

COLLOIDS

17. WHAT IS A COLLOIDAL DISPERSION?

A colloidal dispersion is a suspension in which the suspended particles readily pass through ordinary filters and do not settle out on standing.

Particles which behave in this manner are called colloidal and are said to be in the colloidal state. Colloidal particles are larger than the particles in a solution, but smaller than the particles in a suspension. In reality, therefore, a colloid represents a particle the size of which falls within a certain range.

18. PROPERTIES OF COLLOIDAL DISPERSIONS

a. **Brownian Movement.** Brownian movement is the erratic motion of colloidal particles resulting from the bombardment of these particles by the constantly moving, but considerably smaller, molecules of the suspending medium.

b. **Tyndall Effect.** Making colloidal particles visible by illuminating them with a powerful beam of light is known as the Tyndall effect. The particles in a solution are too small, and the particles in a suspension are too large, to display this same effect. (See Fig. 18*b*.)

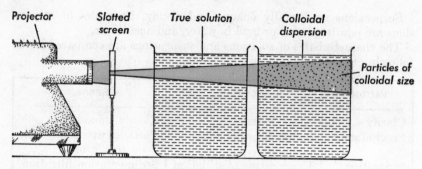

Fig. 18b. Tyndall Effect

c. **Surface Area.** As a particle is subdivided, its surface area increases. Colloidal particles, because of their state of subdivision, have a tremendous surface area. Since adsorption takes place on the surface only, such particles are excellent adsorbents.

d. **Electric Charge.** Because they have a considerable surface area, colloidal particles may adsorb ions from the dispersing medium and thus acquire an electric charge. Generally, colloidal metals are positively charged, while colloidal oxides and hydroxides are negatively charged.

19. WHAT IS AN EMULSION?

An emulsion is a permanent suspension of two immiscible liquids in the presence of an emulsifying agent. The particles in the emulsion are of colloidal size. In order to make an emulsion, it is necessary to select two liquids which are not completely soluble in each other. Such liquids are called *nonmiscible,* or *immiscible.*

Liquids such as oil and water, or kerosene and water, are examples of immiscible liquids. When shaken together, oil and water form a temporary suspension which quickly separates into two distinct layers. By shaking a little soap solution with oil and water, an emulsion is obtained. The soap, which prevents the oil droplets from coalescing (joining), is called an *emulsifying agent,* or a *protective colloid.* Mayonnaise is an emulsion of vinegar and oil, with egg yolk added as the protective colloid. The egg yolk forms a protective coating around the oil droplets, preventing their coalescence.

20. TESTS FOR COLLOIDAL DISPERSIONS

Since colloidal dispersions resemble true solutions in appearance, it is often necessary to distinguish one from the other. The microscope may be used to detect Brownian movement, or a strong beam of light may be used to study the Tyndall effect. The presence of colloidal particles may thus be established.

21. APPLICATIONS OF COLLOIDS

a. **Precipitation of Dust and Smoke.** Dust and smoke contain particles of colloidal size. Since they are electrically charged, they may be precipitated by electrostatic attraction. This is the principle of the *Cottrell precipitator,* which precipitates colloidal dust electrically.

b. **"Salting-out" Processes.** The addition of table salt causes certain colloids to precipitate. Soap is separated from glycerine, commercially, in this manner. Proteins may also be precipitated by "salting-out" procedures.

c. **Metallurgical Processes.** Many metallic ores occur in nature in low concentrations. It is therefore necessary to concentrate the ore by removing the undesirable material, called *gangue.* The ore is ground to colloidal size and the properties of colloids are utilized to separate the metal from the gangue. Similar techniques are now being utilized in other industries.

CRYSTALLIZATION

22. WHAT IS A CRYSTAL?

A crystal is a solid that has a definite geometric shape. The structure of a crystal depends upon the regular, internal arrangement of its component particles.

23. PREPARATION OF CRYSTALS

Crystals may occur in nature, or they can be prepared in the laboratory either by cooling a hot saturated solution or evaporating a dilute solution. Crystals may also be obtained by the slow cooling of a fused (melted) substance, as in the preparation of prismatic sulfur; or by sublimation, as in the preparation of iodine.

24. WATER OF HYDRATION

Water of hydration, sometimes called water of crystallization, is the definite amount of water that some substances combine with chemically in forming crystals. Crystalline copper sulfate, washing soda, and alum are examples of substances whose crystals contain water of crystallization. Sodium nitrate and potassium chlorate are crystalline substances which do not contain water of crystallization.

The presence of water of crystallization can be shown by heating a crystal in a test tube held in a horizontal position. Water is driven out and an *anhydrous* (without water) substance, usually a powder, remains. Although a substance may not contain water of crystallization, it may have mechanically contained water. Substances such as potassium chlorate will decrepitate (crackle) when heated. The water that is mechanically held vaporizes and expands, bursting the crystal.

Substances containing water of hydration are known as *hydrates*. Some typical hydrates are:

COMMON NAME	FORMULA	CHEMICAL NAME
Alum	$K_2SO_4 \cdot Al_2(SO_4)_3 \cdot 24\,H_2O$	Potassium aluminum sulfate
Blue vitriol	$CuSO_4 \cdot 5\,H_2O$	Copper sulfate
Borax	$Na_2B_4O_7 \cdot 10\,H_2O$	Sodium tetraborate
Washing soda	$Na_2CO_3 \cdot 10\,H_2O$	Sodium carbonate

25. EFFLORESCENT SUBSTANCES

An efflorescent substance is one which loses water of crystallization when exposed to the air. Crystallized sodium carbonate (washing soda) is an efflorescent substance and changes to a white powder (anhydrous sodium carbonate) on exposure to air.

26. DELIQUESCENT SUBSTANCES

A deliquescent substance is one which, when exposed to the air, absorbs enough moisture to become wet. Under proper conditions, a solution can be formed. Sodium hydroxide (caustic soda), calcium chloride, and magnesium chloride are examples of deliquescent substances. Calcium chloride keeps down the dust on roads and subway stations. It is also used to dry moist gases and reduce dampness in cellars. Magnesium chloride is the deliquescent impurity in table salt which causes the latter to cake.

27. HYGROSCOPIC SUBSTANCES

Substances that can absorb moisture from the air without becoming wet are known as hygroscopic substances. Hair, fur, wool, rice, and starch are examples of hygroscopic substances. Rice is placed in a salt shaker to help keep the salt dry, while starch is added to baking powder to prevent moisture from decomposing the baking powder.

HYDROGEN PEROXIDE

Like water, hydrogen peroxide is also composed of hydrogen and oxygen.

28. PREPARATION

Hydrogen peroxide is prepared by treating barium peroxide with dilute sulfuric acid.

$$\underset{\substack{\text{barium} \\ \text{peroxide}}}{BaO_2} + \underset{\substack{\text{sulfuric} \\ \text{acid}}}{H_2SO_4} \rightarrow \underset{\substack{\text{hydrogen} \\ \text{peroxide}}}{H_2O_2} + \underset{\substack{\text{barium} \\ \text{sulfate}}}{BaSO_4} \downarrow$$

29. PHYSICAL PROPERTIES

Pure hydrogen peroxide is a colorless, syrupy liquid, one and one-half times as dense as water. It is extremely soluble in water.

30. CHEMICAL PROPERTIES

Pure hydrogen peroxide is very unstable. It decomposes readily into water and oxygen.

$$\underset{\substack{\text{hydrogen} \\ \text{peroxide}}}{2\,H_2O_2} \rightarrow \underset{\text{water}}{2\,H_2O} + \underset{\text{oxygen}}{O_2} \uparrow$$

Ordinary peroxide is a 3% solution of hydrogen peroxide in water. Brown bottles are used to retard its decomposition by light.

31. USES

Hydrogen peroxide is frequently used as an oxidizing agent, decomposing to form water and oxygen. Hair, silk, and wool can be bleached by a 3% solution of hydrogen peroxide. Such a solution can also be used as a mild antiseptic. Pure (100%) hydrogen peroxide, because of its high oxygen content, is an extremely dangerous substance to handle. Because of this high oxygen content, it is used in rocket engines.

32. LAW OF MULTIPLE PROPORTIONS

Water is composed of eight parts of oxygen to one part of hydrogen by weight. Hydrogen peroxide contains sixteen parts of oxygen to one part of hydrogen by weight. The weight of hydrogen in both compounds is the same, or fixed. If we now compare the weight of oxygen in water (16) with the weight of oxygen in hydrogen peroxide (32), we find a simple ratio of 1:2. This relationship illustrates the *Law of Multiple Proportions*, first discovered by the English scientist, John Dalton. This law states:

> When two elements form more than one compound, with the weight of one element remaining fixed, the different weights of the other element always relate to each other in a simple ratio.

Any pair or group of compounds can be used to illustrate the Law of Multiple Proportions if it is composed of the same elements. Examples of such compounds are:

H_2O and H_2O_2	$SnCl_2$ and $SnCl_4$
water hydrogen peroxide	stannous chloride stannic chloride
$FeCl_2$ and $FeCl_3$	N_2O_3 and N_2O_5
ferrous chloride ferric chloride	nitrogen peroxide nitrogen pentoxide

1. Why is water considered the most abundant and universally distributed compound?

2. *a.* The composition of water by volume is _____ part(s) of oxygen to _____ part(s) of hydrogen.

   b. A mixture of 32 cc of oxygen and 20 cc of hydrogen is exploded. _____ cc of _____ (oxygen, hydrogen) remain uncombined.

   c. Describe an experiment to prove the volume composition of water by synthesis.

3. *a.* The composition of water by weight is one _____ part(s) of hydrogen to _____ part(s) of oxygen.

   b. A mixture of 32 grams of oxygen and 20 grams of hydrogen is exploded. _____ grams of _____ (oxygen, hydrogen) remain uncombined.

   c. Describe an experiment to prove the weight composition of water.

4. *a.* Show how the composition of water illustrates the Law of Definite Proportions.

   *b. Why is the volume composition of water different from its weight composition?

5. *a.* State five physical properties of water.

   b. Water is frequently called the _____ solvent.

   c. The expansion of water upon its solidification results in a (an) _____ (increase, decrease) in density.

   d. The ratio of the density of a solid or a liquid to the density of water is called _____.

6. Because extremely high temperatures are required to decompose water, it is normally a (an) _____ substance.

7. *a.* Active metals react with water to form hydrogen and _____.

   b. Some metallic oxides react with water to form _____.

   c. Some nonmetallic oxides react with water to form _____.

   d. Because water can promote certain reactions, it behaves very much like (1) an oxidizing agent (2) a reducing agent (3) a catalyst (4) a universal solvent.

   e. Complete the following word equations:
   (1) calcium + water →
   (2) barium oxide + water →
   (3) carbon dioxide + water →

8. *a.* What is meant by potable water?

   b. Solids suspended in water are removed by (1) boiling (2) adding alum (3) adding chlorine (4) adding copper sulfate.

   c. A precipitate is most conveniently removed from water by (1) aeration (2) boiling (3) distillation (4) filtration.

    d. Aeration removes *dissolved impurities.* [True or false? If false, correct the italicized term.]

    e. Water in swimming pools is purified by the addition of _____.

    f. Using a labeled diagram, describe the process of distillation.

    g. A recent, large-scale water purification method involves the use of _____.

9. *a.* A solution is a (an) _____ mixture of _____ proportions.

    b. A solution consists of a _____ dissolved in a _____.

    c. Solutions in which alcohol is the solvent are called _____.

    *d. Is the act of solution a physical or chemical change? Explain.

10. *a.* A dilute solution contains _____ (more, less) solute than solvent, while a concentrated solution contains _____ solute than solvent.

    b. A saturated solution is (1) able to dissolve more solute at a given temperature (2) unable to dissolve more solute at a given temperature (3) always dilute (4) always concentrated.

    c. A crystal of sodium chloride when added to a sodium chloride solution dissolved quickly. The solution must have been (1) concentrated (2) saturated (3) supersaturated (4) unsaturated.

    d. Calcium sulfate is slightly soluble in water. A saturated solution of calcium sulfate is (1) a concentrated (2) a dilute (3) a supersaturated (4) an unsaturated solution.

    e. A crystal of ammonium chloride dropped into a saturated solution of ammonium chloride will (1) form a supersaturated solution (2) cause ammonium chloride crystals to separate from the solution (3) cause no change in the solution (4) dissolve in the solution.

    *f. Why is it possible to make a saturated solution, but impossible to make a concentrated solution, of calcium hydroxide in water?

11. A bottle labeled sodium acetate solution contains a clear, colorless liquid. How could you determine whether this solution is unsaturated, saturated, or supersaturated?

12. *a.* As the temperature of the solvent increases, the solubility of most solids _____ (decreases, increases, remains the same).

    b. With a decrease in temperature, the solubility of all gases _____ (decreases, increases, remains the same).

    *c. Explain why some solubility curves rise or fall, while others remain horizontal.

13. *a.* One hundred grams of copper sulfate are to be dissolved in a liter of water. State three ways to hasten the speed of solution.

    b. The solubility of gases in liquids (1) decreases as temperature increases (2) is constant for all types of gases (3) is independent of the composition of the liquid (4) is not affected by pressure.

    c. Increasing the pressure increases the solubility of (1) gases (2) liquids (3) solids (4) gases and liquids   in water.

14. State four ways in which a solution differs from a suspension.

15. *a.* Define: colloidal dispersion, Brownian movement, Tyndall effect.

    b. Describe two ways to identify colloidal dispersions.

    c. How do colloids differ from suspensions and true solutions?

16. *a.* Two immiscible liquids may form (1) a solution (2) a tincture (3) an alloy (4) an emulsion.

    b. An example of an emulsion is _____.

17. *a.* All crystals (1) have water of hydration (2) have a regular internal shape (3) are found in nature (4) must be prepared in the laboratory.

   b. How do crystalline solids differ from noncrystalline solids?

   c. After crystallization takes place, the liquid in contact with the crystals is (1) a dilute (2) an unsaturated (3) a saturated (4) a supersaturated solution of the substance crystallized.

18. *a.* Heating a crystal of blue copper sulfate yields (1) a basic anhydride (2) a hydrate (3) a white powder (4) sulfur.

   b. What is a hydrate?

   *c. Describe an experiment that could be performed to determine the percentage of water of crystallization in a hydrate.

19. *a.* Distinguish between efflorescent, deliquescent, and hygroscopic substances. Give an example of each.

   b. How may deliquescent substances be used?

20. *a.* Write a word equation to illustrate the preparation of hydrogen peroxide.

   b. Write a word equation to illustrate the decomposition of hydrogen peroxide.

   *c. How are concentrated solutions of hydrogen peroxide prepared? Explain.

   d. Describe two uses of hydrogen peroxide.

21. *a.* State the Law of Multiple Proportions and illustrate the law appropriately.

   *b. Does the Law of Multiple Proportions contradict the Law of Definite Proportions? Explain.

   c. The Law of Multiple Proportions is illustrated by the compounds (1) NaI and CaI$_2$ (2) Ag$_3$PO$_4$ and Ag$_2$SO$_4$ (3) FeCl$_2$ and FeCl$_3$ (4) H$_2$O and H$_2$SO$_4$.

   d. H$_2$O is to H$_2$O$_2$ as CO is to (1) CO$_2$ (2) O$_2$ (3) H$_2$CO$_3$ (4) O$_3$.

5 ATOMIC STRUCTURE

1. THE COMPOSITION OF MATTER

In previous chapters, we studied a number of chemical changes, although we did not attempt to explain why such changes occurred. Even to the ancient Greeks it was clear that in order to understand chemical change, it was necessary to understand the composition of matter. Democritus introduced the term *atom* as the smallest, invisible, and indestructible particle of matter.

At the beginning of the 19th century, John Dalton reaffirmed the Greek belief concerning atoms. On the basis of incomplete experimentation, he attempted to describe the properties of atoms. His ideas, although essentially correct, were limited in scope. Dalton's theory, however, persisted for almost a century.

Toward the end of the 19th century, further study and experimentation led to an amplification of Dalton's ideas. *According to the modern atomic theory, we now know that the atom may be subdivided into smaller particles, some of which are electrical in nature.* It is the presence of these particles that helps us to understand the properties of elements and compounds.

2. THE DALTON THEORY

This theory, proposed in 1803, contained four major assumptions:

a. All matter is composed of extremely small, discrete particles called atoms.

b. Atoms of the same element are exactly alike in size, shape, and weight, but are different from the atoms of every other element.

c. Atoms of different elements unite in chemical changes.

d. Atoms do not subdivide during a chemical change.

3. THE ATOM AND ATOMIC WEIGHT

An **atom** is the smallest part of an element taking part in a chemical change.

Atoms, because of their size, are difficult to weigh. The actual weight of an atom is an extremely small number. Thus, *the atomic weight of an element is the relative weight of an atom of that element compared with the weight of an atom of oxygen taken as 16.*

Oxygen is used as a standard because it combines with most elements. Using 16 as a standard insures that no atomic weight will be less than 1. For example, where O = 16, the atomic weight of the lightest element, hydrogen, is approximately 1.

4. THE MOLECULE AND MOLECULAR WEIGHT

A molecule is the smallest part of a substance (element or compound) having all the properties of the substance.

Molecules of an element contain one or more atoms of the same element, while molecules of a compound contain two or more atoms of different elements. When a molecule of an element consists of only one atom, then an atom and a molecule of that element are identical.

The molecular weight is the sum of the atomic weights of all the atoms making up the molecule. Here are a few simple illustrations of finding molecular weights:

ELEMENTS

Elements may be classified as *monatomic, diatomic,* or *triatomic.* Monatomic atoms contain *one* atom to the molecule, diatomic atoms *two,* and triatomic *three.*

A molecule of helium (He) contains *one* atom of helium.

Its molecular weight is 4, the same as its atomic weight.

A molecule of oxygen (O_2) contains *two* atoms of oxygen.

Its molecular weight is $16 \times 2 = 32$.

A molecule of ozone (O_3) contains *three* atoms of oxygen.

Its molecular weight is $16 \times 3 = 48$.

COMPOUNDS

A molecule of sodium chloride (NaCl) contains *two* atoms: one of sodium and one of chlorine.

Its molecular weight is $\underset{Na}{23} + \underset{Cl}{35.5} = \underset{NaCl}{58.5}$.

A molecule of water (H_2O) contains *three* atoms: two of hydrogen and one of oxygen.

Its molecular weight is $\underbrace{1 + 1}_{2\,H} + \underset{O}{16} = 18.$

$\underset{H_2O}{}$

A molecule of sulfuric acid (H_2SO_4) contains *seven* atoms: two of hydrogen, one of sulfur, and four of oxygen.

Its molecular weight is $\underbrace{1 + 1}_{2\,H} + \underset{S}{32} + \underbrace{16 + 16 + 16 + 16}_{4\,O} = 98.$

$\underset{H_2SO_4}{}$

5. THE LAWS OF CHEMICAL COMBINATION

Dalton's theory may be used to explain the three fundamental laws of chemical combination.

a. **Law of Conservation of Matter.** Matter cannot be created or destroyed in ordinary chemical changes. Thus, in chemical reactions, the total weight of the products formed always equals the total weight of the reacting substances. According to Dalton, atoms of a given element have the same weight and do not subdivide during chemical change. All the atoms present in the reacting substances must therefore be present in the products formed. For example, if 100 atoms of carbon combine with 200 atoms of oxygen to form carbon dioxide, there must be 100 atoms of carbon and 200 atoms of oxygen present in the carbon dioxide formed. Since the total number of atoms in the reaction has not changed, there has been no change in weight. In this and other chemical changes, there is merely a rearrangement of the atoms.

b. **Law of Definite Proportions.** Every compound has a fixed composition. This means that elements must unite to form compounds in definite proportions by weight. According to Dalton, elements consist of individual atoms and each atom of a given element has the same weight. Thus, experiment shows that when carbon dioxide is formed from its elements, a specific weight of carbon combines with a specific weight of oxygen. This weight of carbon contains a fixed number of carbon atoms, which is, let us suppose, equal to 100. According to the Law of Conservation of Matter, 100 carbon atoms must also be present in the carbon dioxide formed in the reaction. Using the same reasoning, it can be shown that there must be a fixed number of oxygen atoms combining with 100 carbon atoms. Let us suppose that the number of oxygen atoms is equal to 200. Thus, 200 atoms of oxygen must be present in the carbon dioxide formed. Consequently, the carbon dioxide, having 100 carbon atoms of fixed weight and 200 oxygen atoms of fixed weight, has a definite composition.

c. Law of Multiple Proportions. When two elements form more than one compound, with the weight of one element remaining fixed, the different weights of the other element always relate to each other in a simple ratio. This ratio usually can be expressed in small whole numbers. For example, carbon forms two oxides, carbon monoxide (CO) and carbon dioxide (CO_2). The composition of carbon monoxide by weight is 12 parts of carbon to 16 parts of oxygen, while that of carbon dioxide is 12 parts of carbon to 32 parts of oxygen. The weight ratio of oxygen in the two compounds is 16:32 or, expressed in small whole numbers, 1:2.

carbon monoxide   carbon dioxide

12 : 16   12 : 32

16:32
1:2

According to Dalton, this weight ratio results from the fact that each constituent atom has a specific weight. The ratio of the weights corresponds to the ratio of the number of atoms. Thus, the ratio of the number of oxygen atoms in the two compounds is 1:2 because their weight ratio is 16:32.

6. ELECTRICAL NATURE OF MATTER

Crookes' experiments with electrical discharges through gases and the discovery of radioactivity by Becquerel suggested that the atom consisted of smaller particles which were electrical in nature. Utilizing these ideas, a number of scientists, including Bohr, Lewis, and Langmuir, developed the *electron theory*. According to the electron theory:

All matter is composed of at least three fundamental particles: protons, electrons, and neutrons. A **proton** is positively charged; an **electron** is negatively charged; and a **neutron** is uncharged.

The electron theory enables us to picture the atom as follows:

a. The protons and neutrons of an atom are located in its center, the *nucleus*. The nucleus, because of its protons, has a positive charge.

b. Around the nucleus, there are *orbits* or *rings* of electrons which are negatively charged. They are called planetary electrons because they revolve around the nucleus in much the same way that the planets revolve around the sun.

A neutron is slightly heavier than a proton, but each is about 1,837 times as heavy as an electron. Consequently, the weight of an atom is, for all practical purposes, the weight of its nucleus.

Recent research indicates the presence of other particles in the nucleus. Some information concerning these particles is summarized in the following table:

PARTICLE	CHARGE	MASS
Positron	+	Same as electron
Neutrino	0	Practically zero
Meson	+ and −	Depending upon the type, mass varies from 273 to 967 times the mass of the electron

These particles have no significance in ordinary chemical reactions. They are important, however, for a more complete understanding of the structure of the nucleus and nuclear reactions.

c. Matter is normally electrically neutral because in any atom the number of protons is exactly equal to the number of electrons. That is, the number of positive charges is balanced by the number of negative charges.

d. The size of an atom is best expressed by its atomic radius, the distance between the nucleus and the outermost orbit. Many of the properties of an element can be explained by its atomic radius.

7. SOME FUNDAMENTAL CONCEPTS IN THE ELECTRON THEORY

a. Atomic Number

The **atomic number** of an element is equal to the number of protons in the nucleus, which is the same as the number of planetary electrons.

First determined in 1913 by the English scientist Henry Moseley from studies of X-ray spectra, atomic numbers range from 1 for hydrogen to 92 for uranium—for naturally occurring elements.

b. Atomic Weight

The **atomic weight** of an element is the sum of its neutrons and protons.

***c*. Arrangement of Planetary Electrons.** The orbits in which the planetary electrons revolve are usually identified by letters: K for the one nearest the nucleus, L for the second, and so on, in alphabetic sequence. The K orbit can hold no more than 2 electrons, the L orbit no more than 8, and the M orbit no more than 8 for elements up to and including atomic number 20. An atom with an atomic number of 13, for example, would have a total of 13 electrons, with 2 in the K orbit, 8 in the L orbit, and 3 in the M orbit. The structure of the atom increases in complexity beyond atomic number 20. In elements with atomic numbers above 20, the M orbit can hold 18 electrons, the N orbit 32, and so on.

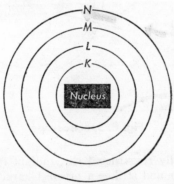

In practically all cases, the outermost orbit can contain no more than 8 electrons. The structure of this outermost orbit and the atomic radius help to determine the chemical activity of an element.

8. EMISSION OF RADIANT ENERGY

The electron orbits or rings are sometimes referred to as *energy levels*. A sodium atom has 2 electrons in the K orbit, 8 in the L orbit, and 1 in the M orbit. If sodium atoms are excited, either by heat or by electricity, the electron in the M orbit will absorb energy and shift outward to a higher energy level. *When the excited electron returns to its normal or lower energy level, radiant energy is emitted.* In the case of sodium atoms, this energy takes the form of yellow light.

Many elements can be identified by the characteristic color produced when they are heated sufficiently in the vapor state. Positive identification usually requires the aid of a special instrument called a *spectroscope*, shown in Fig. 8. The spectroscope resolves (separates) the emitted light into its component colors, the wave lengths of which can be measured. In some cases, atom excitation produces radiant energy that cannot be seen, such as ultraviolet light. Special sensitive photographic plates can record this radiation and thus detect the presence of the atoms.

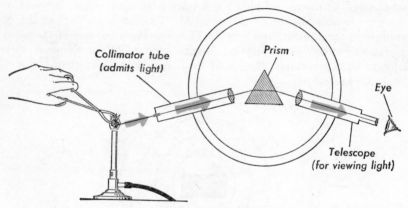

Fig. 8. Spectroscope

Through a specially constructed slit, radiant energy enters a tube called the collimator and strikes a prism. Characteristic spectra (radiant energy of specific wave lengths) are thus obtained.

9. STRUCTURAL DIAGRAMS

Using the electron theory, we may represent the structures of different atoms by means of simple diagrams in which protons are represented by +, electrons by −, and neutrons by *n*. *The number of protons, equal to the atomic number, is shown in the nucleus. An equal number of electrons is shown revolving in rings around the nucleus.* The number of electrons in the outer orbit (called valence electrons) helps us to classify the element and determine its chemical activity.

The number of neutrons in the nucleus is equal to the difference between the atomic weight and the atomic number of the element. Hydrogen is the only element whose nucleus normally contains no neutrons. Special varieties of hydrogen, called isotopes, which do contain neutrons, will be discussed later in this chapter.

Symbols of elements are written with a subscript designating the atomic number and a superscript designating the atomic weight, as shown at the right.

| atomic weight |
| Symbol |
| atomic number |

Examples of structural diagrams of several atoms follow. Note again that the atomic weight equals the sum of the protons and neutrons in the nucleus, that the atomic number equals the number of protons (or electrons), and that the number of neutrons in an atom equals the difference between the atomic weight and the atomic number.

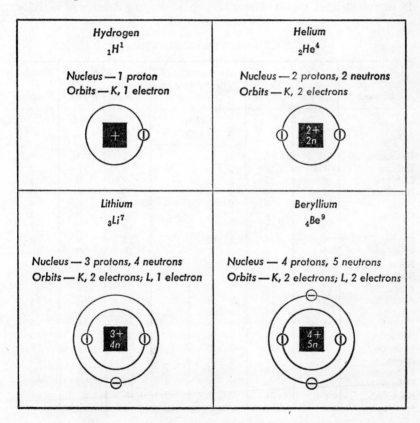

Hydrogen
$_1H^1$

Nucleus — 1 proton
Orbits — K, 1 electron

Helium
$_2He^4$

Nucleus — 2 protons, 2 neutrons
Orbits — K, 2 electrons

Lithium
$_3Li^7$

Nucleus — 3 protons, 4 neutrons
Orbits — K, 2 electrons; L, 1 electron

Beryllium
$_4Be^9$

Nucleus — 4 protons, 5 neutrons
Orbits — K, 2 electrons; L, 2 electrons

10. CHEMICAL ACTIVITY

In chemical reactions, elements tend to form compounds.

> **The chemical activity of an element is the tendency of the atoms of the element to complete their outer orbits by gaining, losing, or sharing electrons.**

If the outer shell is already complete, the atom is *inert* (totally inactive), and will not combine with any other atom. Thus, in the following table of elements of atomic numbers 1-21, numbers 2, 10, and 18 represent inert atoms. The others show varying degrees of activity.

THE FIRST 21 ELEMENTS

Element	Symbol	Atomic Number	Arrangement of Planetary Electrons				Atomic Weight	Number of Protons	Number of Neutrons
			Orbits						
			K	L	M	N			
Hydrogen	H	1	1				1	1	0
Helium	He	2	2				4	2	2
Lithium	Li	3	2	1			7	3	4
Beryllium	Be	4	2	2			9	4	5
Boron	B	5	2	3			11	5	6
Carbon	C	6	2	4			12	6	6
Nitrogen	N	7	2	5			14	7	7
Oxygen	O	8	2	6			16	8	8
Fluorine	F	9	2	7			19	9	10
Neon	Ne	10	2	8			20	10	10
Sodium	Na	11	2	8	1		23	11	12
Magnesium	Mg	12	2	8	2		24	12	12
Aluminum	Al	13	2	8	3		27	13	14
Silicon	Si	14	2	8	4		28	14	14
Phosphorus	P	15	2	8	5		31	15	16
Sulfur	S	16	2	8	6		32	16	16
Chlorine	Cl	17	2	8	7		35	17	18
Argon	A(Ar)	18	2	8	8		40	18	22
Potassium	K	19	2	8	8	1	39	19	20
Calcium	Ca	20	2	8	8	2	40	20	20
Scandium	Sc	21	2	8	9	2	45	21	24

a. **Effect of Number of Electrons in Outer Orbit.** Atoms with more than 4 electrons in their outer orbit normally tend to complete this orbit by gaining electrons. Such elements are called *nonmetals*. Atoms with less than 4 electrons in their outer orbit normally tend to lose these electrons in order to attain a completed outer orbit. Such elements are called *metals*. Atoms with just 4 electrons in the outer orbit tend to share these electrons in order to complete the outer orbit. Such elements may act as either metals or nonmetals.

In general, the fewer the number of electrons gained or lost, the more active is the element.

b. **Effect of Number of Orbits (Atomic Radius).** Because electrons are negatively charged, they are attracted to the positively charged nucleus. The electrons in orbits near the nucleus are more strongly attracted to the nucleus than are those in orbits farther away. In general, if a group or family of elements has the same number of electrons in the outer orbit, then the relative activity of these elements will depend upon the size of the atom (the number of orbits).

11. ACTIVITY OF METALS

The activity of a metal depends upon the ease with which it loses electrons. Reactions in which electrons are lost are called **oxidation**.

The ease of loss of electrons depends upon the number of electrons and the atomic radius. The fewer the electrons in the outer orbit of a metal and the larger its atomic radius, the more active a metal generally is. Thus, sodium, atomic number 11, with 1 electron in its outer orbit (M), is more active than magnesium, atomic number 12, with 2 electrons in its outer orbit (M). But potassium, atomic number 19, is more active than sodium because the 1 electron in its fourth orbit (N) is farther away from the nucleus than is the 1 electron in the third orbit (M) of the sodium atom.

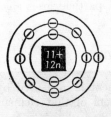

Sodium

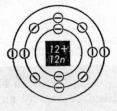

Magnesium

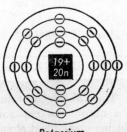

Potassium

12. ACTIVITY OF NONMETALS

The activity of a nonmetal depends upon the ease with which it gains electrons. Reactions in which electrons are gained are called **reduction.**

The ease of gain of electrons depends upon the number of electrons and the atomic radius. The greater the number of electrons in the outer orbit of a nonmetal and the smaller its atomic radius, the more active a nonmetal generally is. Thus, fluorine, atomic number 9, with 7 electrons in its outer orbit (L), is more active than oxygen, atomic number 8, with 6 electrons in its outer orbit (L). Fluorine is also more active than chlorine, atomic number 17, because a fluorine atom can attract 1 electron more readily into its second orbit (L) than a chlorine atom can attract 1 electron into its third orbit (M).

13. COMPARISON OF ACTIVITIES OF METALS AND NONMETALS

Chemical activity of metals generally increases with atomic size, while chemical activity of nonmetals generally decreases as the atomic size increases. This is the same as saying that:

In a given family of elements, metals with a higher atomic number are generally more active than metals with a lower atomic number, while nonmetals with a lower atomic number are generally more active than nonmetals with a higher atomic number.

It is not always possible to predict the activity of an element with complete accuracy solely on the basis of ease of electron gain or loss. Other factors, such as temperature or nature of the surrounding medium, may alter the activity somewhat.

From the loss and gain of electrons, we have developed our modern concept of oxidation-reduction. When a particle (atom or ion) gains electrons, it is called an *oxidizing agent*. When a particle loses electrons, it is called a *reducing agent*.

14. VALENCE—A MEASURE OF CHEMICAL ACTIVITY

The **valence** or combining capacity of an element is measured by the number of electrons gained or lost by an atom of that element during a chemical change.

The term valence is restricted to elements present in compounds. The electrons in the outer ring are called valence electrons. In general, metals tend to lose electrons and have a positive valence, while non-metals tend to gain electrons and have a negative valence. Thus, an element whose atom loses 2 electrons in a chemical action has a valence of +2, while an element whose atom gains 1 electron has a valence of −1. An element having a valence of +3 is one whose atom can lose 3 electrons, while one having a valence of −2 is an element whose atom can gain 2 electrons. Generally, the smaller the number of electrons gained or lost, the greater is the activity of the element. Inert elements, which neither gain nor lose electrons, have a valence of zero and do not react chemically.

It should be noted that protons and neutrons do not enter into chemical reactions. Protons and neutrons, however, enter into trans-mutation processes which will be considered in Chapter 23.

15. TYPES OF VALENCE

In the formation of chemical compounds, elements may gain, lose, or share valence electrons.

a. **Electrovalence.** *Compounds resulting from a gain or loss of electrons are called electrovalent, polar, or ionic compounds.* When atoms of metals lose electrons (are oxidized) and atoms of nonmetals gain electrons (are reduced), they form electrically charged particles called *ions.* Metals form positive ions, which have a deficiency of electrons, while nonmetals form negative ions, which have an excess of electrons. In any given compound derived from a metal and a nonmetal, the number of electrons lost by the metal must equal the number of electrons gained by the nonmetal. The oppositely charged ions thus formed attract each other, producing a strong chemical bond which holds the compound together. The charge on the ion corresponds to the valence of the atom from which it was derived.

Following are two examples of electrovalent compounds. Sodium (atomic number 11) combines readily with chlorine (atomic number 17), under proper conditions, to form sodium chloride. Each chlorine atom gains 1 electron to form a chloride ion, while each sodium atom loses 1 electron to form a sodium ion. The combination of 1 sodium ion and 1 chloride ion makes up a "molecule" of sodium chloride (NaCl). In reality, a single molecule of sodium chloride does not exist. The so-called molecule is probably a giant molecule consisting of sodium ions and chloride ions.

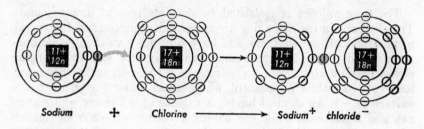

In a similar way, calcium (atomic number 20) unites with fluorine (atomic number 9) to form calcium fluoride. Each calcium atom loses 2 electrons, one of which is gained by one fluorine atom and the other by a second fluorine atom. This combination of 1 calcium ion and 2 fluoride ions makes up a "molecule" of calcium fluoride (CaF_2), as shown in the figure below.

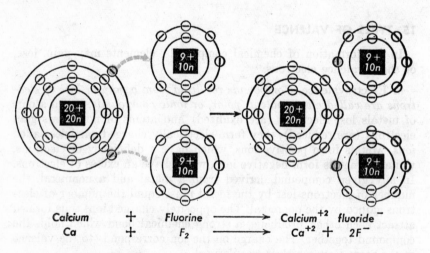

In the above examples, observe that *the total number of electrons gained by the nonmetal equals the total number of electrons lost by the metal.* Even though there are charged particles (ions) in each compound, the opposite charges balance each other, making the net electric charge of the compound zero.

As a result of the gain or loss of electrons, ions have complete outer rings. In Chapter 9, we will learn what happens when these ions become separated, as in solutions. We shall then see that ions exhibit one set of properties when they are bonded together closely in a compound, and a different set of properties when they become separated in a solution.

Electrovalent compounds are usually hard, nonvolatile solids with high melting points. Ions in these solids follow a regular arrangement, called a *crystal lattice*, shown below. In general, salts are electrovalent compounds.

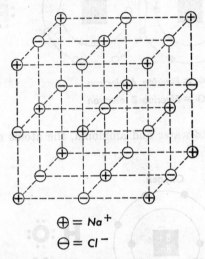

$\oplus = Na^+$

$\ominus = Cl^-$

Fig. 15a. Crystal Lattice of Sodium Chloride

b. **Covalence.** Instead of gaining or losing electrons during a chemical change, some elements may form compounds in which the atoms share one or more pairs of electrons. *Compounds in which atoms share one or more pairs of electrons are called covalent, or nonpolar.* The molecules in these compounds are composed of neutral atoms, rather than electrically charged ions. By sharing pairs of electrons, the atoms involved are considered to have completed their outer orbits without an actual transfer of electrons, as in the case of electrovalent compounds. In Chapter 21, we will discuss a large number of covalent compounds called *organic* compounds.

Covalent compounds are usually gases or liquids with low boiling points. Diatomic gaseous molecules, like those of fluorine (F_2) and hydrogen (H_2), also exhibit covalent properties.

In the fluorine molecule, each of the atoms supplies one electron to form the pair of shared electrons.

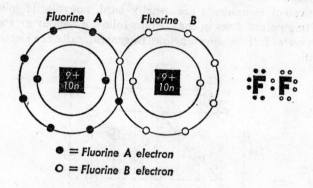

Fluorine A   **Fluorine B**

● = Fluorine A electron
○ = Fluorine B electron

In molecules like water and ammonia, the atoms are held together by covalent bonds.

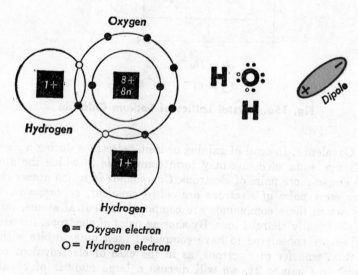

● = Oxygen electron
○ = Hydrogen electron

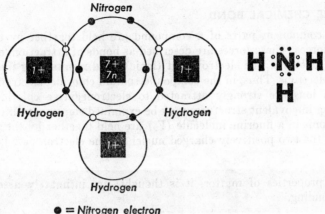

● = Nitrogen electron
O = Hydrogen electron

In the above cases, we are assuming that the electron pair is shared equally by both atoms, and so the electron pair is pictured as being equidistant between the two atoms. This is not always true. In water, the electron pair is closer to the more positively charged oxygen nucleus. The hydrogen atoms are not on opposite sides of the oxygen atom, but lie almost at right angles to each other. Water, therefore, has a kind of electrical unbalance. It is neither electrovalent nor truly covalent. Compounds such as water are called *polar covalent*. They are also referred to as *dipoles* because the molecule is thought to have one end which is positive and the other end which is negative.

A pair of electrons may also be shared by two atoms, one atom contributing both electrons. This type of valence is called *coordinate covalence*. An example of coordinate covalence is found in the structure of the ammonium ion.

Ammonia   +   Hydrogen ⟶   Ammonium
                    ion   ion

16. THE CHEMICAL BOND

The component parts of a compound are held together by electrostatic forces. These forces are described as bonds of attraction, or more simply as *bonds*. The electrovalent (ionic) bond results from the transfer of electrons. Thus, in the compound sodium chloride, electropositive sodium ions are strongly attracted to electronegative chloride ions. Bonding in covalent structures may be explained somewhat differently. The atoms in a fluorine molecule (F_2) are held together by the attraction of the two positively charged nuclei for the electron pair between them.

The properties of matter, it is thought, are intimately associated with bonding.

17. RADICALS

Groups of atoms that remain together during a chemical change, behaving almost like a single atom, are called *radicals*. Atoms in a radical are bonded (held together) by pairs of shared electrons. Except for the ammonium radical $(NH_4)^{+1}$, all common radicals have a negative valence: $(NO_3)^{-1}$, $(SO_4)^{-2}$, and so on. Some of the common radicals and their valences are listed in the following chart:

RADICAL	FORMULA AND VALENCE	RADICAL	FORMULA AND VALENCE
Ammonium	NH_4^+	Carbonate	CO_3^{-2}
Nitrate	NO_3^-	Sulfite	SO_3^{-2}
Hydroxyl	OH^-	Sulfate	SO_4^{-2}
Bicarbonate	HCO_3^-	Phosphate	PO_4^{-3}

18. ISOTOPES

Isotopes are atoms of a given element having the same atomic number but different atomic weights.

Since isotopes have similar chemical properties, they must contain the same number of electrons and therefore the same number of protons. Hence, the variation in atomic weight is due to a variation in the number of neutrons.

There are three known varieties of hydrogen, the formulas of which may be written as follows:

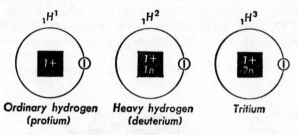

Fig. 18-A. Hydrogen Isotopes

Note that the atomic number in each case is 1, but the atomic weight varies from 1 to 3. Each of these isotopes has a special name.

As these varieties of the same element have the same number of protons as electrons, differing only in the number of neutrons, they have similar chemical properties.

Deuterium, called heavy hydrogen, unites with oxygen to form deuterium oxide, or heavy water, which has a molecular weight of 20 instead of 18.

Chlorine has two isotopes.

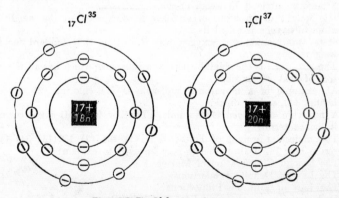

Fig. 18-B. Chlorine Isotopes

Chlorine has an atomic weight of 35.5. Since the atomic weight is equal to the total number of protons and neutrons, and must therefore be a whole number, how do we explain such fractional atomic weights? Elements that have fractional atomic weights are mixtures of isotopes. For example, chlorine is a mixture of chlorine atoms, 75% of which have an atomic weight of 35 and about 25% of which have an atomic weight of 37. Thus, the atomic weight of chlorine (35.5) is the average atomic weight of the element, based on the percentage of isotopes present.

1. *a.* Knowing the composition of matter helps us to understand the nature of _____ changes.
   b. The atom is the _____, _____, and indestructible particle of matter.
   c. The atomic theory was first proposed by _____.
   d. State the four major assumptions of this theory.
   e. In the modern atomic theory, matter is thought to be _____ in nature.
2. *a.* The _____ is the smallest part of an element taking part in a chemical change.
   b. Atoms are difficult to weigh because _____.
   c. The weight of an atom of an element compared to the weight of an atom of oxygen is called its _____.
   d. State two reasons why oxygen was chosen as the standard for atomic weights.
3. *a.* The _____ is the smallest part of a substance which has all the properties of that substance.
   b. An example of a monatomic molecule is (1) chlorine (2) oxygen (3) helium (4) carbon dioxide.
   c. A molecule of *oxygen* is triatomic. [True or false? If false, correct the italicized term.]
   d. The molecular weight of $Fe_2(SO_4)_3$ is (1) 104 (2) 152 (3) 344 (4) 400.
*4. Describe how the Dalton theory may be used to explain:
   a. The Law of Conservation of Matter
   b. The Law of Definite Proportions
   c. The Law of Multiple Proportions
5. *a.* Radioactivity was discovered by *Crookes*. [True or false? If false, correct the italicized term.]
   b. A scientist who did not work on the electron theory was (1) Bohr (2) Lewis (3) Langmuir (4) Priestley.
   c. According to the electron theory, all matter is composed of _____, _____, and _____.

   d. The nucleus of an atom consists principally of _____ and _____, and consequently has a _____ charge.

   e. Negatively charged particles are called (1) electrons (2) mesons (3) positrons (4) protons.

   f. In tabular form, compare the important properties of electrons, protons, and neutrons.

   g. Why is matter normally electrically neutral?

   h. The size of an atom is determined by its _____.

6. *a.* The atomic number of an element is equal to the number of *protons* in the nucleus. [True or false? If false, correct the italicized term.]

   b. The arrangement of atoms according to their atomic numbers was made by (1) Faraday (2) Lavoisier (3) Mendeléef (4) Moseley.

   c. Atomic numbers range from _____ for hydrogen to _____ for uranium.

   d. An atom that contains 92 protons and 143 neutrons has an atomic weight equal to (1) 51 (2) 92 (3) 143 (4) 235.

   e. The number of neutrons in the nucleus of the element of atomic number 79 and atomic weight 197 is (1) 79 (2) 118 (3) 197 (4) 276.

   f. Describe the arrangement of planetary electrons in the atom.

7. *a.* Explain why all sodium compounds impart a yellow color to the Bunsen flame.

   b. Make a labeled diagram of a simple spectroscope and explain how this instrument is used.

8. *a.* In any atom, the difference between the atomic weight and the atomic number is the number of *electrons*. [True or false? If false, correct the italicized term.]

   b. A possible structural diagram for a hydrogen atom is (1) $_1H^2$ (2) $_2H^1$ (3) $_3H^1$ (4) $_2H^4$.

9. *a.* When elements form compounds, the atoms may _____, _____, or _____ electrons.

   b. The chemical activity of an element depends on the number of electrons in the _____ orbit.

   c. If the outer shell is complete, the atom is *inactive*. [True or false? If false, correct the italicized term.]

   d. Describe, in terms of electrons, two important properties of metals and nonmetals.

   e. How is atomic radius related to chemical activity?

10. One of the elements has an atomic weight of 20 and an atomic number of 10.

   a. By means of a labeled diagram, show the possible structure of an atom of this element.

   b. Would either oxygen or sulfur react with this element? Why?

   c. Compare the chemical activity of the element having the atomic number 10 with the chemical activity of the element having the atomic number 18.

11. *a.* Metals tend to _____ electrons because they have _____ than four electrons in their outermost ring.

   b. Magnesium is _____ active than aluminum and _____ active than sodium.

12. *a.* Nonmetals tend to _____ electrons because they have _____ than four electrons in their outermost ring.

   b. Chlorine is _____ active than oxygen and _____ active than sulfur.

13. *a.* In a family of elements, as the atomic number increases, the activity of the elements _____.

   b. In a family of elements, as the atomic number decreases, the activity of the elements _____.

   c. Oxidizing agents contain particles which _____ electrons.

   d. Reducing agents contain particles which _____ electrons.

   *e. Explain why oxidation and reduction occur together in a given reaction.

14. *a.* Why is the term valence restricted to elements present in compounds only?

   b. Metals have a _____ valence, while nonmetals have a _____.

   c. The element with the atomic number 13 has a valence of _____.

   d. An element which *borrows* 2 electrons has a valence of +2. [True or false? If false, correct the italicized term.]

   e. A particle which enters into a chemical reaction is (1) an electron (2) a proton (3) a neutron (4) a positron.

15. *a.* Electron transfer results in a kind of valence called _____, producing charged particles called _____.

   b. Using electron diagrams, show the formation of magnesium fluoride.

   *c. Why is it unlikely that molecules of electrovalent compounds exist?

   d. Describe the important properties of electrovalent compounds.

16. *a.* Electron sharing results in a kind of valence called _____.

   b. The molecules in these compounds are composed of _____.

   c. Describe the important properties of covalent compounds.

   *d. Using electron diagrams, show the formation of an oxygen molecule from two oxygen atoms.

   e. What is meant by a dipole? Why is water considered a dipole?

   f. What is the essential difference between covalence and coordinate covalence?

17. *a.* Electron transfer produces a (an) _____ bond.

   b. Explain how the atoms are held together in a chlorine molecule.

18. *a.* Groups of atoms that behave as single atoms during chemical change are called _____.

   *b. Using electron diagrams, show the bonding in a nitrate radical.

19. *a.* Isotopes contain the same number of _____.

   b. Using electron diagrams, show the structures of O^{16}, O^{17}, and O^{18}.

   c. A certain element is a mixture of two isotopes, 50% of which have an atomic weight of 99 while the remaining 50% have an atomic weight of 100. The average atomic weight of this element is _____.

6 SYMBOLS, FORMULAS, AND EQUATIONS

1. CHEMICAL SYMBOLS

> A chemical symbol represents one atomic weight of the element.

A chemical symbol consists of a letter or a pair of letters representing one atom of an element. A symbol is written as a capital letter followed by a small letter if it is necessary to use a pair of letters. Whenever possible, the first letter of the name of the element is used. In other cases, especially where the names of several elements begin with the same letters, the Latin names of these elements are used.

The symbols of some common elements are listed below, but a more complete list appears in the periodic table on pages 104-105.

ELEMENT	SYMBOL	ELEMENT	SYMBOL
Aluminum	Al	Mercury (Hydrargyrum)	Hg
Antimony (Stibium)	Sb		
Arsenic	As	Nickel	Ni
Carbon	C	Oxygen	O
Chlorine	Cl	Platinum	Pt
Copper (Cuprum)	Cu	Potassium (Kalium)	K
Gold (Aurum)	Au	Silver (Argentum)	Ag
Hydrogen	H	Sodium (Natrium)	Na
Iodine	I	Sulfur	S
Iron (Ferrum)	Fe	Tin (Stannum)	Sn
Lead (Plumbum)	Pb	Zinc	Zn

2. CHEMICAL FORMULAS

> A chemical formula consists of a symbol or a group of symbols, with proper subscripts, representing one molecule of an element or a compound.

71

The subscript following the symbol of the element indicates the number of atoms of the element. When no subscript is shown, the number 1 is understood. Thus, a formula shows the *kind* and *number* of atoms present in a molecule.

As each atom represents a specific atomic weight, a given chemical formula always expresses a fixed, quantitative relationship among the atomic weights of the elements whose symbols appear in the formula. A formula therefore reveals the weight composition of a substance.

The formulas of some common substances are listed below.

ELEMENT	FORMULA	COMPOUND	FORMULA
Argon	$A(Ar)$	Carbon dioxide	CO_2
Chlorine	Cl_2	Hydrochloric acid	HCl
Helium	He	Hydrogen peroxide	H_2O_2
Hydrogen	H_2	Potassium chlorate	$KClO_3$
Neon	Ne	Sodium chloride	$NaCl$
Nitrogen	N_2	Sodium hydroxide	$NaOH$
Oxygen	O_2	Sulfuric acid	H_2SO_4
Ozone	O_3	Water	H_2O

It should be noted that some elements have only one atom in the molecule. In such cases, the atom and the molecule are identical. In these instances, also, the symbol and the formula are identical.

The molecules of the common gaseous elements such as hydrogen, oxygen, nitrogen, and chlorine contain two atoms. Exceptions are (*a*) the inert gaseous elements (such as helium, argon, neon), which contain one atom to the molecule, and (*b*) ozone, which contains three atoms to the molecule.

3. MEANING OF VALENCE

Valence has already been defined as the number of electrons one atom may gain or lose in completing its outer shell when it combines with another atom. When magnesium (atomic number 12) combines with chlorine (atomic number 17), the magnesium atom loses two electrons, while each of two chlorine atoms gains one electron. The valence of magnesium in magnesium chloride is therefore $+2$, while the valence of chlorine is -1. The formula of magnesium chloride is therefore $MgCl_2$.

The term valence is now more frequently called *valence number* to include the valences of those atoms which combine by sharing electrons. In the compound methane (CH_4), four hydrogen atoms are linked to a carbon atom by sharing four pairs of electrons.

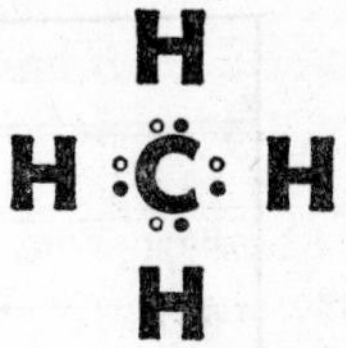

The valence number of carbon in this compound is -4, while the valence number of hydrogen is $+1$.

H

H $:\overset{..}{\underset{..}{C}}:$ H

H

● = *Carbon electron*

O = *Hydrogen electron*

From the previous examples, it can be seen that the *algebraic sum of all the valence numbers in a compound is zero.* Summarizing,

$$Mg = +2, 2\ Cl = 2(-1) = -2$$
$$Sum = 0$$

$$C = -4, 4\ H = 4(+1) = +4$$
$$Sum = 0$$

The fact that the algebraic sum of all the valence numbers in a compound is zero suggests that all compounds are electrically neutral.

Following is a table of common valence numbers:

METALLIC ELEMENTS AND RADICALS			
+1	+2	+3	+4
Ammonium NH_4^+	Barium Ba^{+2}	Aluminum Al^{+3}	Carbon C^{+4}
Copper (cup*rous*) Cu^+	Cadmium Cd^{+2}	Antimony Sb^{+3}	Silicon Si^{+4}
Hydrogen H^+	Calcium Ca^{+2}	Arsenic As^{+3}	Tin (stan*nic*) Sn^{+4}
Mercury (mercu*rous*) Hg_2^{+2}	Copper (cup*ric*) Cu^{+2}	Iron (fer*ric*) Fe^{+3}	
Potassium K^+	Iron (fer*rous*) Fe^{+2}		
Silver Ag^+	Lead Pb^{+2}		
Sodium Na^+	Magnesium Mg^{+2}		
	Manganese Mn^{+2}		
	Mercury (mercu*ric*) Hg^{+2}		
	Tin (stan*nous*) Sn^{+2}		
	Zinc Zn^{+2}		

NONMETALLIC ELEMENTS AND RADICALS			
−1	−2	−3	−4
Bicarbonate HCO_3^-	Carbonate CO_3^{-2}	Nitrogen N^{-3}	Carbon C^{-4}
Bromine Br^-	Oxygen O^{-2}	Phosphate PO_4^{-3}	Silicon Si^{-4}
Chlorate ClO_3^-	Sulfate SO_4^{-2}		
Chlorine Cl^-	Sulfite SO_3^{-2}		
Fluorine F^-	Sulfur S^{-2}		
Hydroxide OH^-			
Iodine I^-			
Nitrate NO_3^-			

4. WRITING CHEMICAL FORMULAS OF COMPOUNDS

In order to write a formula of a compound, it is necessary to know the symbols and valences of the elements in the compound.

The formulas of compounds may be written by using the following steps:

a. Write the symbols for the elements or radicals present in the compound. The element with the *positive* valence number is usually written first. Suppose the formula for aluminum oxide is required. The symbols for the elements aluminum and oxygen are written thus:

$$AlO$$

b. Above each symbol, write the proper valence number.

$$Al^{+3} \quad O^{-2}$$

c. To obtain the proper subscripts, "crisscross" the valence numbers and drop the algebraic signs.

$$\overset{+3}{Al_2} \diagdown \overset{-2}{O_3}$$

d. Where the valence numbers of both elements are 1, the formula is correct as it stands, the subscript 1 being understood. Thus, the formula for sodium chloride is:

$$\overset{+1}{Na_1} \times \overset{-1}{Cl_1} \quad \text{or} \quad NaCl$$

e. Where the valence numbers of both elements are numerically equal but *greater than 1*, the subscript 1 is understood. Thus, the formula of calcium oxide is:

$$\overset{+2}{Ca_2} \times \overset{-2}{O_2} \quad \text{or} \quad CaO$$

There are many exceptions to this rule.

f. Whenever a radical in a formula is taken *more than once*, parentheses should be placed around the radical and the correct subscript placed *outside* the parentheses. Thus, the formula for ammonium sulfate is:

$$\overset{+1}{(NH_4)_2} \times \overset{-2}{(SO_4)_1} \quad \text{or} \quad (NH_4)_2SO_4$$

Examples of other formulas obtained by following the above steps are:

$$\overset{+1}{H_2} \times \overset{-2}{O_1} \quad \text{or} \quad H_2O$$
water

$$\overset{+2}{Ca_1} \times \overset{-1}{(OH)_2} \quad \text{or} \quad Ca(OH)_2$$
calcium
hydroxide

$$\overset{+2}{Ba_3} \times \overset{-3}{(PO_4)_2} \quad \text{or} \quad Ba_3(PO_4)_2$$
barium
phosphate

5. DETERMINING VALENCE NUMBER

a. From any given formula of a binary compound (containing *two* elements), the valence numbers may be determined by reversing the crisscross procedure used to write the formula. In the formula Al_2O_3, reversing the crisscross gives aluminum a valence number of $+3$ and oxygen -2.

b. From any given formula of a ternary compound (containing *three* elements), select the two elements that behave as a radical and treat as above. In the formula Na_3PO_4, the (PO_4) group behaves as a radical with a subscript of 1: $Na_3(PO_4)_1$. The valence numbers then become $Na + 1$, $(PO_4) - 3$.

c. To find the valence number of an atom in a radical, it is necessary to know the valence numbers of the other atoms. Remember that the algebraic sum of all the valence numbers in the formula is zero. Thus, the valence number of the desired atom is that number which, when added to the valence numbers of the other atoms, produces a sum equal to zero.

To find the valence number of P in Na_3PO_4, we do the following:

(1) The valence number of Na is $+1$ and, since there are three Na atoms, the total valence number is $+3$.

(2) The valence number of oxygen is -2 and, since there are four O atoms, the total valence number is -8.

(3) The sum of $+3$ and -8 is -5.

(4) The valence number of P must be $+5$ in order that the algebraic sum of the valence numbers in the compound Na_3PO_4 equal zero.

$$\begin{array}{ccc} +3 & +5 & -8 \\ Na_3 & P & O_4 \end{array}$$

In the compound $KClO_3$, to find the valence number of Cl, we follow the same procedure.

$$\begin{array}{ccc} +1 & +5 & -6 \\ K & Cl & O_3 \end{array}$$

6. NAMING COMPOUNDS

As far as possible, the chemical name of a compound indicates the chemical composition of that compound. Some of the rules used in naming compounds are:

a. Compounds composed of only *two* elements have names ending in *-ide.*

$NaCl$ = sodium chlor*ide*	K_2S = potassium sulf*ide*
Al_2O_3 = aluminum ox*ide*	$MgBr_2$ = magnesium brom*ide*

b. When an element has more than one valence number, the *lower* valence number is indicated by the suffix *-ous* and the *higher* valence number by the suffix *-ic.*

$$\overset{+2}{\text{FeCl}_2} = \text{ferrous chloride} \qquad \overset{+1}{\text{Hg}_2\text{O}} = \text{mercurous oxide}$$

$$\overset{+3}{\text{FeCl}_3} = \text{ferric chloride} \qquad \overset{+2}{\text{HgO}} = \text{mercuric oxide}$$

Note that the suffix does not give the actual valence number. In some cases, *-ous* compounds have a valence number of +1, in others +2. A valence number of +3 is also possible. Similarly, *-ic* compounds may have valence numbers of +2, +3, +4, and +5.

c. Salts are compounds that contain a metal or metallic radical combined with an acid radical. Salts of *hydro-* acids have names ending in *-ide.* Salts of *-ous* acids end in *-ite,* and those derived from *-ic* acids end in *-ate.* Note that compounds ending in *-ite* and *-ate* always contain oxygen, the *-ite* compound containing one less atom of oxygen.

ACID		SALT	
FORMULA	NAME	FORMULA	NAME
HCl	*hydro*chloric acid	NaCl	sodium chlor*ide*
H$_2$S	*hydro*sulfuric acid	Na$_2$S	sodium sulf*ide*
HNO$_2$	nitr*ous* acid	NaNO$_2$	sodium nitr*ite*
H$_2$SO$_3$	sulfur*ous* acid	Na$_2$SO$_3$	sodium sulf*ite*
HNO$_3$	nitr*ic* acid	NaNO$_3$	sodium nitr*ate*
H$_2$SO$_4$	sulfur*ic* acid	Na$_2$SO$_4$	sodium sulf*ate*
H$_2$CO$_3$	carbon*ic* acid	Na$_2$CO$_3$	sodium carbon*ate*

d. Prefixes *mon(o)-, di-, tri-, tetr(a)-,* and *pent(a)-* are used to represent 1, 2, 3, 4, and 5 atoms respectively. These prefixes can therefore be used to distinguish two or more compounds composed of the same elements.

CO = carbon *mon*oxide   SO$_2$ = sulfur *di*oxide
CO$_2$ = carbon *di*oxide   SO$_3$ = sulfur *tri*oxide

P$_2$O$_3$ = phosphorus *tri*oxide   N$_2$O$_3$ = nitrogen *tri*oxide
P$_2$O$_5$ = phosphorus *pent*oxide   N$_2$O$_4$ = nitrogen *tetr*oxide

7. USES OF CHEMICAL FORMULAS

a. **Determination of the Atomic Composition from the Formula.** A chemical formula shows the kind and number of atoms in a molecule of an element or a compound. Thus, the formula H_2SO_4 shows that a molecule of sulfuric acid is composed of 7 atoms: 2 of hydrogen, 1 of sulfur, and 4 of oxygen.

b. **Determination of the Composition by Weight from the Formula.** If we multiply the number of atoms of each element in a molecule by the atomic weight of the element, we can determine the composition by weight. By weight, sulfuric acid (H_2SO_4) is composed of 2 parts of hydrogen (2×1), 32 parts of sulfur (1×32), and 64 parts of oxygen (4×16).

c. **Determination of the Molecular Weight from the Formula.** The molecular weight, or the relative weight of a molecule of a substance, may be determined by adding the total atomic weights of the elements making up the molecule. Sulfuric acid (H_2SO_4) has a molecular weight of 98, calculated as follows:

$$
\begin{array}{llll}
2\ H & = 2 \times & 1 & = 2 \\
1\ S & = 1 \times & 32 & = 32 \\
\underline{4\ O} & = \underline{4 \times 16} & & = \underline{64} \\
H_2SO_4 & & & = 98
\end{array}
$$

d. **Writing of Chemical Equations with Formulas.** Chemical formulas are used in writing chemical equations, which represent chemical changes.

8. CHEMICAL EQUATIONS

A chemical equation consists of a related group of formulas which represents a chemical change.

A chemical equation is a quantitative expression showing that the total molecular weight of the reacting substances (reactants) is equal to the total molecular weight of the products (resultants). Thus, a chemical equation illustrates the Law of Conservation of Matter. The formulas of the reacting substances and the products are separated by an arrow ($\rightarrow$). The formula of a gas is usually followed by an arrow pointing upward ($\uparrow$), while the formula of a precipitate is usually followed by an arrow pointing downward ($\downarrow$).

Below are shown some chemical equations together with their corresponding word equations. Note the equivalence in weights.

a. Decomposition of Mercuric Oxide

CHEMICAL EQUATION: $2\,HgO \rightarrow 2\,Hg + O_2 \uparrow$

WORD EQUATION: mercuric oxide $\rightarrow$ mercury + oxygen

WEIGHTS: $432 = 400 + 32$

b. Decomposition of Potassium Chlorate

CHEMICAL EQUATION: $2\,KClO_3 \rightarrow 2\,KCl + 3\,O_2 \uparrow$

WORD EQUATION: potassium chlorate $\rightarrow$ potassium chloride + oxygen

WEIGHTS: $245 = 149 + 96$

c. Action of Sodium on Water

CHEMICAL EQUATION: $2\,Na + 2\,H_2O \rightarrow 2\,NaOH + H_2 \uparrow$

WORD EQUATION: sodium + water $\rightarrow$ sodium hydroxide + hydrogen

WEIGHTS: $46 + 36 = 80 + 2$

9. WRITING CHEMICAL EQUATIONS

A chemical equation always represents an actual reaction. It is incorrect to write an equation for a reaction that cannot take place, such as:

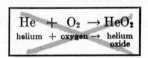

He + O₂ → HeO₂
helium + oxygen → helium oxide

In writing equations, observe the following steps:

a. The names of the reactants and resultants must be known. For example, you must know that aluminum and oxygen react to form aluminum oxide.

b. The formulas of the reactants and resultants must also be known.

$$Al + O_2 \rightarrow Al_2O_3$$

Note that since oxygen is a gaseous element, its formula is O_2. The formula for aluminum oxide (Al_2O_3) is obtained by crisscrossing the valence numbers of aluminum and oxygen.

c. Although the equation now contains the correct formulas, it does not obey the Law of Conservation of Matter. There is only one atom of aluminum on the left side of the arrow, while two atoms appear on the right side. There are also two atoms of oxygen on the left and three atoms on the right. In terms of atomic weights, note that in the *unbalanced* equation the total weight of the reactants does *not* equal the total weight of the resultant.

UNBALANCED EQUATION: $Al + O_2 \rightarrow Al_2O_3$
WEIGHTS: $27 + 32 \overset{\text{does not}}{\underset{\text{equal}}{}} 102$

The equation must be balanced so that the same number of atoms of each element appears on both sides of the equation, thus indicating that matter has been neither created nor destroyed. To balance an equation, change the coefficients in front of the formulas. *Never alter the subscripts in the formula.* Subscripts indicate the number of atoms of each element in a compound. Since a compound has a fixed composition, the subscripts in the formula never change. The formula for aluminum oxide is therefore always Al_2O_3.

The use of the proper coefficient in front of the formula will provide the correct number of atoms to balance the equation. Thus, since two atoms of aluminum are required in the formula Al_2O_3, the coefficient 2 is placed in front of the symbol for aluminum. At the same time, three atoms of oxygen are required in the formula of the product, while only two atoms of oxygen are available on the left side.

Balance may be obtained by the use of the coefficient $1\frac{1}{2}$ in front of the formula for oxygen. By using the correct atomic weights, note that the *balanced* equation follows the Law of Conservation of Matter.

BALANCED EQUATION: $2\ Al + 1\frac{1}{2}\ O_2 \rightarrow Al_2O_3$
WEIGHTS: $54 + 48 = 102$

In order to deal with whole numbers, both sides of the equation may be multiplied by 2. The equation now becomes:

BALANCED EQUATION: $4\ Al + 3\ O_2 \rightarrow 2\ Al_2O_3$
WEIGHTS: $108 + 96 = 204$

Note that the equation can be balanced by using any multiples of the above coefficients, but the smallest multiples are usually employed.

Following the steps used in balancing the previous equation, other equations may be similarly balanced.

Remember that the same number of atoms of a given element must appear on both sides of the equation. You may change coefficients, but you must not alter subscripts.

a. Burning of Hydrogen

UNBALANCED EQUATION: $H_2 + O_2 \rightarrow H_2O$

WEIGHTS: $2 + 32 \overset{\text{does not}}{\underset{\text{equal}}{}} 18$

BALANCED EQUATION: $2\,H_2 + O_2 \rightarrow 2\,H_2O$

WEIGHTS: $4 + 32 = 36$

b. Decomposition of Potassium Chlorate

UNBALANCED EQUATION: $KClO_3 \rightarrow KCl + O_2\uparrow$

WEIGHTS: $122.5 \overset{\text{does not}}{\underset{\text{equal}}{}} 74.5 + 32$

BALANCED EQUATION: $2\,KClO_3 \rightarrow 2\,KCl + 3\,O_2\uparrow$

WEIGHTS: $245 = 149 + 96$

10. TYPES OF CHEMICAL REACTIONS

a. **Direct combination, or synthesis,** is the combination of substances, usually elements, to form compounds.

This type of reaction may be generalized by using A and B as elements reacting to form compound AB.

$$A + B \rightarrow AB$$

Specific examples of this type of reaction are:

$$2\,H_2 + O_2 \rightarrow 2\,H_2O$$
$$2\,Hg + O_2 \rightarrow 2\,HgO$$

b. **Decomposition, or analysis,** is the breaking down of a compound into two or more substances, usually elements.

This type of reaction is the reverse of direct combination.

$$AB \rightarrow A + B$$

Specific examples of this type of reaction are:

$$2\,H_2O \rightarrow 2\,H_2\uparrow + O_2\uparrow$$
$$2\,HgO \rightarrow 2\,Hg + O_2\uparrow$$

c. Single replacement is the reaction between an element and a compound to form a new element and a new compound.

If A represents an element and BC represents a compound, then A reacts with BC to form compound AC and element B.

$$A + BC \rightarrow AC + B$$

Specific examples of this type of reaction are:

$$Zn + H_2SO_4 \rightarrow ZnSO_4 + H_2 \uparrow$$
$$Mg + 2\ HCl \rightarrow MgCl_2 + H_2 \uparrow$$

d. Double replacement is the reaction between two compounds to form two new compounds.

If AB and CD represent the two original compounds, then AB reacts with CD to form new compounds AD and CB.

$$AB + CD \rightarrow AD + CB$$

Specific examples of this type of reaction are:

$$NaCl + AgNO_3 \rightarrow NaNO_3 + AgCl \downarrow$$
$$NaOH + HCl \rightarrow NaCl + HOH\ (or\ H_2O)$$

11. OXIDATION-REDUCTION

Reactions involving direct combination, decomposition, and single replacement are reactions involving oxidation-reduction.

Double replacement reactions, however, do not involve oxidation-reduction; instead, a rearrangement of ions takes place.

Oxidation-reduction reactions always involve the loss and gain of electrons. The oxidized particle (atom or ion) *loses* electrons, which results in an *increase* in the valence number. The reduced particle *gains* electrons, which results in a *decrease* in the valence number. Since the number of electrons lost must equal the number of electrons gained, it follows that *for every oxidation there must be corresponding reduction.*

Let us consider the types of reactions involving oxidation-reduction.

a. Direct Combination

$$A + B \rightarrow AB$$

Since A and B are elements, each has a valence number equal to zero. As previously shown, elements have positive and negative valence numbers in compounds only. In compound AB, let us assume that A has a valence number equal to $+1$ as a result of the loss of one electron. Similarly, in compound AB, B has a valence number of -1 as a result of gaining the electron lost by A. These reactions may be summarized as follows:

$$A^0 - 1 \text{ electron } (e) \rightarrow A^+ \text{ (oxidized)}$$
$$B^0 + 1 \text{ electron } (e) \rightarrow B^- \text{ (reduced)}$$

The part of the reaction involving the loss of electrons is called *oxidation,* or oxidation partial; while the part involving the gain of electrons is called *reduction,* or reduction partial. Since oxidation and reduction take place simultaneously, all such reactions are properly called oxidation-reduction reactions.

We can now apply the same principles to decomposition and single replacement.

b. Decomposition

$$AB \rightarrow A + B$$
$$A^+ + 1 \text{ } e \rightarrow A^0 \text{ (reduction of } A^+\text{)}$$
$$B^- - 1 \text{ } e \rightarrow B^0 \text{ (oxidation of } B^-\text{)}$$

c. Single Replacement

$$A + BC \rightarrow AC + B$$
$$A^0 - 1 \text{ } e \rightarrow A^+ \text{ (oxidation of } A^0\text{)}$$
$$B^+ + 1 \text{ } e \rightarrow B^0 \text{ (reduction of } B^+\text{)}$$

We shall return to a more detailed study of types of reactions in subsequent chapters. At present we are merely concerned with recognizing the type of reaction.

1. a. A chemical symbol represents one _____ of an element.
   b. Write chemical symbols for the following elements:

   (1) aluminum   (6) oxygen
   (2) bromine   (7) iron
   (3) carbon   (8) mercury
   (4) chlorine   (9) magnesium
   (5) gold   (10) lead

2. a. A chemical formula tells the _____ and _____ of atoms present in a molecule.
   b. In the formula $Na_2CO_3 \cdot 10 \, H_2O$ there are _____ atoms.
   c. A chemical formula represents the _____ of a substance.
   d. The formula $Ca_3(PO_4)_2$ represents (1) an atom (2) an ion (3) a radical (4) a molecule.
   e. A molecule of hydrogen is represented by the formula H_2^+. [True or false? If false, correct the italicized term.]
   f. Molecules of inert gases contain _____ atom(s) per molecule.
3. a. Valence number represents the number of electrons an atom may _____, _____, or _____ in combining with other atoms.
   b. The algebraic sum of all the valence numbers in a compound is _____.
4. a. The first element that appears in a formula usually has a _____ valence number.
   b. List the important steps to be followed in writing a chemical formula.
   c. Write chemical formulas for the following:

   (1) mercuric nitrate   (6) mercurous sulfate
   (2) sulfuric acid   (7) oxygen
   (3) sodium chlorate   (8) neon
   (4) potassium chloride   (9) zinc bromide
   (5) carbon dioxide   (10) water

   d. A, B, C, D, and E represent five elements whose valence numbers are $+1$, $+2$, $+3$, -1, and -2 respectively. Write the formula for the compound formed when:
   (1) A combines with D
   (2) A combines with E
   (3) B combines with D
   (4) B combines with E
   (5) C combines with D
   (6) C combines with E
5. a. List the important steps to be followed in determining the valence number of an atom in a radical.

b. In $K_2Cr_2O_7$ the valence number of Cr is $+5$. [True or false? If false, correct the italicized term.]

c. The valence number of sulfur in K_2SO_4 is (1) -2 (2) $+2$ (3) -6 (4) $+6$.

d. Determine the valence number of the italicized element in each of the following compounds:

    (1) H_2S
    (2) Fe_2O_3
    (3) $CaSO_4$
    (4) $NaHCO_3$
    (5) $Zn_3(PO_4)_2$

e. The formula that shows chlorine with a valence number of $+7$ is (1) $HClO$ (2) $HClO_2$ (3) $HClO_3$ (4) $HClO_4$.

6. *a.* Compounds containing two elements have names ending in _____.

  b. The suffix *-ous* indicates the *lower* valence number. [True or false? If false, correct the italicized term.]

  c. Normal salts of sulfurous acid are (1) bisulfates (2) su''tes (3) sulfides (4) sulfites.

  d. Potassium chlorate is a salt of (1) chlorous acid (2) hypochlorous acid (3) chloric acid (4) perchloric acid.

  e. Three molecules of nitrogen dioxide contain a total of *five* atoms of oxygen. [True or false? If false, correct the italicized term.]

7. *a.* State four important uses of chemical formulas.

  b. In the formula $CuSO_4 \cdot 5\ H_2O$ the total number of atoms is (1) 5 (2) 9 (3) 21 (4) 33.

  c. Calculate the molecular weight of each of the following:

    (1) KBr
    (2) MgI_2
    (3) $Cu(NO_3)_2$
    (4) $Al(OH)_3$
    (5) $Cr_2(SO_4)_3$

8. *a.* A chemical equation illustrates the Law of _____.

  b. Complete and balance each of the following equations, and write the name of each substance under its formula:

    (1) $Hg + O_2 \rightarrow$ (5) $Zn + HCl \rightarrow$
    (2) $S + O_2 \rightarrow$ (6) $H_2 + O_2 \rightarrow$
    (3) $KClO_3 \rightarrow$ (7) $CuO + H_2 \rightarrow$
    (4) $Zn + H_2SO_4 \rightarrow$ (8) $Mg + O_2 \rightarrow$

  c. Write a balanced equation for each of the following reactions:

    (1) action of aluminum on hydrochloric acid
    (2) electrolysis of water
    (3) action of potassium on water
    (4) decomposition of mercuric oxide
    (5) action of steam on heated iron
    (6) decomposition of hydrogen peroxide
    (7) action of sodium peroxide on water
    (8) action of ozone on silver
    (9) reduction of lead oxide by hydrogen
    (10) decomposition of sodium chlorate

9. *a.* State the four types of chemical reactions and give two illustrations of each type.

   b. For each of the following equations, indicate the type of reaction that has occurred:

      (1) $2\ KClO_3 \rightarrow 2\ KCl + 3\ O_2\uparrow$

      (2) $Cl_2 + 2\ KI \rightarrow 2\ KCl + I_2$

      (3) $4\ P + 5\ O_2 \rightarrow 2\ P_2O_5$

      (4) $BaCl_2 + H_2SO_4 \rightarrow BaSO_4 + 2\ HCl$

      (5) $4\ Fe + 3\ O_2 \rightarrow 2\ Fe_2O_3$

10. *a.* Oxidation-reduction does not occur in reactions involving *single replacement.* [True or false? If false, correct the italicized term.]

   b. An oxidized particle always _____ (gains, loses) electrons, while a reduced particle _____ electrons.

   c. The valence number of an atom has changed from 0 to +2. The atom has been _____ (oxidized, reduced).

   d. Using electron equations, show which particle is oxidized and which particle is reduced in the following reactions:

      (1) $2\ Na + Cl_2 \rightarrow 2\ NaCl$

      (2) $CuCl_2 \rightarrow Cu + Cl_2$

  e. Using electron equations, show which particle is oxidized and which particle is reduced in the following reaction, which assumes that *A, B,* and *C* are elements:

$$2\ A + 3\ B_2C \rightarrow A_2C_3 + 6\ B$$

7 CHEMICAL CALCULATIONS

A few of the simpler types of chemical problems have been selected here for the beginning student. Other types of chemical calculations may be found in the Appendix, pages 431-436.

1. MOLECULAR WEIGHTS FROM FORMULAS

One of the most common calculations in elementary chemistry is to find the molecular weight of a substance from its chemical formula. Molecular weights are used in almost all types of problems.

METHOD   To calculate the molecular weight of a substance from its chemical formula, find the sum of the atomic weights.

In all our calculations, atomic weights are expressed to the nearest whole number.

TYPE PROBLEMS

1. Calculate the molecular weight of sodium carbonate (Na_2CO_3). [Atomic weights: $Na = 23$, $C = 12$, $O = 16$]

Molecular Weight of Na_2CO_3

1 molecular weight of Na_2CO_3 equals the sum of:

2 atomic weights of Na
1 atomic weight of C
3 atomic weights of O

$$
\begin{array}{llll}
2 \text{ atomic weights of Na} & = 2 \times 23 = & 46 \\
1 \text{ atomic weight of C} & = 1 \times 12 = & 12 \\
3 \text{ atomic weights of O} & = 3 \times 16 = & \underline{48} \\
& & 106
\end{array}
$$

Molecular weight of $Na_2CO_3 = 106$

2. Calculate the molecular weight of calcium hydroxide, $Ca(OH)_2$.
[Atomic weights: $Ca = 40$, $O = 16$, $H = 1$]

Molecular Weight of $Ca(OH)_2$

$$Ca(OH)_2 = 1\,Ca + 2\,O + 2\,H$$

$$
\begin{aligned}
1\,Ca &= 1 \times 40 = 40 \\
2\,O &= 2 \times 16 = 32 \\
2\,H &= 2 \times 1 = \underline{\;\;2\;\;} \\
&\qquad\qquad\qquad 74
\end{aligned}
$$

Molecular weight of $Ca(OH)_2 = 74$

2. WEIGHT OF ONE LITER OF A GAS

The determination of the weight of one liter of a gas is based on the principle that *the molecular weight of any gas expressed in grams (gram-molecular weight) occupies 22.4 liters (approximately) when measured at standard conditions of temperature and pressure ($0°C$ and $760\ mm$)*. The value 22.4 liters is called the *gram-molecular volume* (GMV). Thus:

The GMV is the volume occupied by the gram-molecular weight of a gas at standard conditions.

The GMV principle can be derived by a study of two laws: *The law of Gay-Lussac states that in a reaction involving gases only, the volumes of the combining gases may be expressed in ratios of small whole numbers.* In attempting to explain the small whole number ratios, Avogadro stated the law: *Equal volumes of all gases, when measured at the same temperature and pressure, contain the same number of molecules.* Avogadro's Law implies that there must be the same number of molecules in equal volumes of reacting gases. This is the same as saying that:

The numbers of molecules in reacting gases are proportional to the volumes of the gases.

Since the gram-molecular weight of all gases contains the same number of molecules, the gram-molecular volume of all gases at standard conditions (S.T.P.) is the same, namely, 22.4 liters.

It is important to remember that in order to use 22.4 liters, the molecular weight of the gas must be expressed in *grams*.

| METHOD | To find the weight of one liter of a gas, divide its gram-molecular weight by 22.4. |

TYPE PROBLEMS (assume standard conditions)

1. Find the weight of one liter of oxygen (O_2). [Atomic weight: O = 16]

   a. Molecular weight of O_2:

   $$O_2 = 2\ O = 2 \times 16 = 32$$

   b. Gram-molecular weight of O_2 is 32 grams

   c. 32 grams of O_2 occupy 22.4 liters

   d. Weight of 1 liter of $O_2 = \dfrac{32 \text{ grams}}{22.4 \text{ liters}} = 1.43$ grams

2. Find the weight of one liter of carbon dioxide (CO_2). [Atomic weights: C = 12, O = 16]

   a. Molecular weight of CO_2:

   $$\begin{aligned} 1\ C &= 1 \times 12 = 12 \\ 2\ O &= 2 \times 16 = \underline{32} \\ & 44 \end{aligned}$$

   b. Gram-molecular weight of CO_2 is 44 grams

   c. 44 grams of CO_2 occupy 22.4 liters

   d. Weight of 1 liter of $CO_2 = \dfrac{44 \text{ grams}}{22.4 \text{ liters}} = 1.96$ grams

3. PERCENTAGE COMPOSITION PROBLEMS

This type of problem may involve the calculation of: (a) the percentage of each element in a compound, (b) the percentage of one element in a compound, or (c) the percentage of a group of elements, such as water of hydration, in a compound.

METHOD	To calculate the percentage of any element or group of elements in a compound, divide the total atomic weight of the element or group of elements by the molecular weight of the compound and multiply the quotient by 100.

TYPE PROBLEMS

1. Calculate the percentage composition of sulfuric acid (H_2SO_4). [Atomic weights: $H = 1$, $S = 32$, $O = 16$]

Molecular Weight of H_2SO_4

$$2\,H = 2 \times 1 = 2$$
$$1\,S = 1 \times 32 = 32$$
$$4\,O = 4 \times 16 = \underline{64}$$
$$98$$

$$\%\,H = \frac{2\,H}{H_2SO_4} = \frac{2}{98} = 0.0204 \times 100 = \quad 2.04\%$$

$$\%\,S = \frac{1\,S}{H_2SO_4} = \frac{32}{98} = 0.3265 \times 100 = \quad 32.65\%$$

$$\%\,O = \frac{4\,O}{H_2SO_4} = \frac{64}{98} = 0.6531 \times 100 = \frac{65.31\%}{100.00\%}$$

2. Calculate the percentage of iron in hematite (Fe_2O_3). [Atomic weights: $Fe = 56$, $O = 16$]

Molecular Weight of Fe_2O_3

$$2\,Fe = 2 \times 56 = 112$$
$$3\,O = 3 \times 16 = \underline{48}$$
$$160$$

$$\%\,Fe = \frac{2\,Fe}{Fe_2O_3} = \frac{112}{160} = 0.7000 \times 100 = 70\%$$

3. Calculate the percentage of water of hydration in washing soda ($Na_2CO_3 \cdot 10\ H_2O$). [Atomic weights: $Na = 23$, $C = 12$, $O = 16$, $H = 1$]

Molecular Weight of $Na_2CO_3 \cdot 10\ H_2O$

$$
\begin{aligned}
2\,Na &= 2 \times 23 = 46 \\
1\,C &= 1 \times 12 = 12 \\
3\,O &= 3 \times 16 = 48
\end{aligned} \left.\right\} 106\ (Na_2CO_3)
$$

$$
\begin{aligned}
20\,H &= 20 \times 1 = 20 \\
10\,O &= 10 \times 16 = 160
\end{aligned} \left.\right\} 180\ (10\ H_2O)
$$

$$
\overline{286}
$$

$$
\%\ H_2O = \frac{10\ H_2O}{Na_2CO_3 \cdot 10\ H_2O} = \frac{180}{286} = 0.6293 \times 100 = 62.93\%
$$

4. STRAIGHT WEIGHT (WEIGHT-WEIGHT) PROBLEMS

Given the weight of one of the substances taking part or produced in a chemical reaction, it is a simple matter to calculate the weight of any other substance involved in the same reaction.

METHOD

a. Write a balanced chemical equation for the reaction involved.

b. Place the given weight above the corresponding formula, and an x above the formula of the substance whose weight is to be determined by calculation. In both cases, use the proper weight units.

c. Calculate the total molecular weights (molecular weight multiplied by the proper coefficient) of these two substances only. The other substances in the equation may now be disregarded.

d. Write the correct proportion and solve for x.

1. How many grams of oxygen can be obtained by the decomposition of 50 grams of mercuric oxide (HgO)? [Atomic weights: Hg = 200, O = 16]

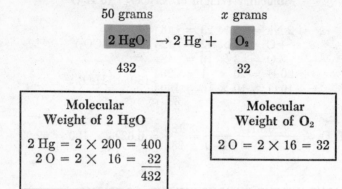

$$\text{50 grams} \qquad\qquad x \text{ grams}$$

$$2\,\text{HgO} \rightarrow 2\,\text{Hg} + O_2$$

$$\qquad 432 \qquad\qquad\qquad 32$$

Molecular Weight of 2 HgO
2 Hg = 2 × 200 = 400
2 O = 2 × 16 = 32
432

Molecular Weight of O_2
2 O = 2 × 16 = 32

The equation shows that from **432** grams of mercuric oxide we **can** obtain **32** grams of oxygen. The following proportion therefore tells **us** how much oxygen can be obtained from 50 grams of mercuric oxide.

$$\frac{50}{432} = \frac{x}{32}$$

$$432\,x = 50 \times 32$$

$$x = \frac{50 \times 32}{432}$$

$$x = 3.70 \text{ grams}$$

2. How many pounds of Chile saltpeter ($NaNO_3$) are needed to produce 500 pounds of nitric acid by heating with concentrated sulfuric acid? [Atomic weights: Na = 23, N = 14, O = 16, H = 1]

x pounds   500 pounds

$$2\ NaNO_3\ + H_2SO_4 \rightarrow Na_2SO_4 +\ 2\ HNO_3$$

170   126

Molecular Weight of 2 $NaNO_3$
2 Na = 2 × 23 = 46
2 N = 2 × 14 = 28
6 O = 6 × 16 = 96
170

Molecular Weight of 2 HNO_3
2 H = 2 × 1 =   2
2 N = 2 × 14 = 28
6 O = 6 × 16 = 96
126

$$\frac{x}{170} = \frac{500}{126}$$

$$126\,x = 500 \times 170$$

$$x = \frac{500 \times 170}{126}$$

$$x = 674.6 \text{ pounds}$$

5. WEIGHT-VOLUME PROBLEMS

In problems involving gases, the volume of a gas is sometimes required. Since all equations are based on weight relationships, it is necessary to convert molecular weights of gases into corresponding volumes. This can be done by using the gram-molecular volume, which is the volume occupied by the gram-molecular weight of a gas at standard conditions. As mentioned previously, the gram-molecular volume is 22.4 liters (22,400 cm³). The gram-molecular volume (GMV) can be used only when the weight factor given is expressed in grams. If the weight factor given is expressed in a unit other than grams, it is necessary to convert this unit into grams. (The molecular volume expressed in units other than grams can also be used. For example, the molecular volume of a gas expressed in pounds is 358 ft³.)

If the volume of a gas is to be calculated from a given number of grams of a substance, the proper proportion is set up as in the straight weight problems. The quantity 22.4 is substituted for the molecular weight of the gas and is multiplied by the number of volumes (molecules) indicated by the balanced equation. The resulting volume is expressed in liters.

METHOD

a. Write a balanced chemical equation for the reaction involved.

b. Place the given weight or volume above the corresponding formula, and an *x* above the formula of the substance whose weight or volume is being sought. In both cases, use the proper units.

c. Calculate the total molecular weight of the substance whose weight is involved, and indicate the total gram-molecular volume (22.4 multiplied by the number of molecules) under the formula of the gas whose volume is involved.

d. Write the correct proportion and solve for *x*.

TYPE PROBLEMS

1. How many liters of carbon dioxide can be produced by adding dilute hydrochloric acid to 25 grams of marble ($CaCO_3$)? [Atomic weights: $Ca = 40$, $C = 12$, $O = 16$]

$$\overset{\text{25 grams}}{CaCO_3} + 2\,HCl \rightarrow CaCl_2 + H_2O + \overset{\text{x liters}}{CO_2}$$

$$\underset{100}{} \qquad\qquad\qquad\qquad \underset{22.4}{}$$

Molecular Weight of $CaCO_3$
$1\,Ca = 1 \times 40 = 40$
$1\,C = 1 \times 12 = 12$
$3\,O = 3 \times 16 = \underline{48}$
100

$$\frac{25}{100} = \frac{x}{22.4}$$

$$100\,x = 25 \times 22.4$$

$$x = \frac{25 \times 22.4}{100}$$

$$x = 5.6 \text{ liters}$$

2. How many grams of sodium bisulfite ($NaHSO_3$) are needed to produce 10 liters of sulfur dioxide by reaction with dilute sulfuric acid?
[Atomic weights: Na = 23, H = 1, S = 32, O = 16]

x grams   10 liters

$$2\,NaHSO_3 \; + H_2SO_4 \rightarrow Na_2SO_4 + 2\,H_2O + \; 2\,SO_2$$

208   2 (22.4)
                                             44.8

Molecular Weight of 2 $NaHSO_3$

$$2\,Na = 2 \times 23 = 46$$
$$2\,H = 2 \times 1 = 2$$
$$2\,S = 2 \times 32 = 64$$
$$6\,O = 6 \times 16 = \underline{96}$$
$$208$$

$$\frac{x}{208} = \frac{10}{44.8}$$

$$44.8\,x = 208 \times 10$$

$$x = \frac{208 \times 10}{44.8}$$

$$x = 46.43 \text{ grams}$$

Weight-volume problems may also be solved as weight-weight problems, and then the weight may be converted into the corresponding
volume by using the proper density factor.

In problem 1, page 95, the weight of CO_2 obtained from 25 grams of marble can be calculated from the proportion below. [Note that the molecular weight of CO_2 (44) is used in place of the gram-molecular volume.]

$$\frac{25}{100} = \frac{x}{44}$$

$$100\,x = 1100$$

$$x = 11 \text{ grams of } CO_2$$

The density of CO_2 is 1.9 grams per liter. Since density $= \dfrac{\text{weight}}{\text{volume}}$ or since volume $= \dfrac{\text{weight}}{\text{density}}$, the volume of 11 grams of CO_2 equals:

$$\frac{11 \text{ grams}}{1.9\,\dfrac{\text{grams}}{\text{liter}}} = 5.6 \text{ liters}$$

6. STRAIGHT VOLUME (VOLUME-VOLUME) PROBLEMS

In chemical reactions involving gases, it is possible to calculate the volume of any gas in the reaction if the volume of one of the gases is known. (See Gay-Lussac's Law on page 88.) If the units in the problem are expressed in liters, the quantity 22.4 is used on both sides of the proportion. As before, it is necessary to multiply 22.4 by the number of volumes of gas in the balanced equation.

METHOD

a. Write a balanced equation for the reaction involved.

b. Above the corresponding formulas, indicate the volume given, and by an x the volume to be found. In both cases, use the proper units.

c. Write a proportion between these volumes and the numbers of molecules indicated.

d. Solve the proportion for x.

TYPE PROBLEMS

1. How many liters of hydrogen are needed to produce 100 liters of ammonia by direct combination with nitrogen?

$$x \text{ liters} \qquad 100 \text{ liters}$$

$$N_2 + \boxed{3\,H_2} \rightarrow \boxed{2\,NH_3}$$

$$3\,(22.4) \qquad 2\,(22.4)$$

Since 22.4 appears in the denominator on both sides of the equation, it may be dropped. (Arithmetically, we are multiplying both sides of the proportion by 22.4.)

$$\frac{x}{3} = \frac{100}{2}$$

$$2x = 100 \times 3$$

$$x = \frac{100 \times 3}{2}$$

$$x = 150 \text{ liters}$$

2. What volume of oxygen is needed for the complete combustion of 25 cubic feet of acetylene (C_2H_2)?

$$25 \text{ ft}^3 \qquad x \text{ ft}^3$$

$$\boxed{2\,C_2H_2} + \boxed{5\,O_2} \rightarrow 4\,CO_2 + 2\,H_2O$$

$$2 \qquad\qquad 5$$

Since cubic feet appears on both sides of the equation, the molecular volume expressed in cubic feet may be canceled out. The denominators in the proportion will therefore correspond to the volumes of gas in the balanced equation.

$$\frac{25}{2} = \frac{x}{5}$$

$$2x = 25 \times 5$$

$$x = \frac{25 \times 5}{2}$$

$$x = 62.5 \text{ ft}^3$$

Note. If the problem requires finding the volume of air needed for the combustion, then first find the volume of oxygen and multiply by 5, because air is one-fifth oxygen. In the example above, the volume of air needed for complete combustion would be 62.5×5 or 312.5 ft^3.

Study Guide

(Atomic weights will be found in the Periodic Table on pages 104-105.)

1. *a.* The molecular weight of a substance is equal to the sum of its _____.
  b. Calculate the molecular weight of each of the following:
     (1) K_2CO_3 (4) $K_4Fe(CN)_6$
     (2) $Ca(HCO_3)_2$ (5) $Fe_4[Fe(CN)_6]_3$
     (3) H_3PO_4

2. *a.* The quantity 22.4 liters is known as the _____.
  b. The _____ of all gases at standard conditions occupies 22.4 liters.
  c. Avogadro's Law states that _____.
  d. Calculate the weight of:
     (1) one liter of ammonia (NH_3)
     (2) one liter of helium
     (3) 0.5 liter of nitrogen
     (4) 0.25 liter of chlorine
     (5) 0.1 liter of sulfur dioxide (SO_2)

3. *a.* The percentage of any element in a compound may be found by dividing the _____ by the _____ and multiplying the quotient by _____.
  b. Solve the following percentage composition problems:
     (1) What is the percentage of iron in ferric sulfate, $Fe_2(SO_4)_3$?
     (2) What percentage of oxygen is present in $Al_2(SO_4)_3$?
     (3) What is the percentage of water in crystallized calcium sulfate, $CaSO_4 \cdot 2 H_2O$?
     (4) What is the percentage of water in hydrated magnesium sulfate, 5 grams of which weigh 2.44 grams after being heated?
     (5) An iron ore contains 62 per cent Fe_2O_3; what weight of iron is available from one ton of the ore?
     (6) Calculate the percentage composition of potassium chlorate, $KClO_3$.
     (7) Calculate the percentage of oxygen in ferric nitrate, $Fe(NO_3)_3$.
     (8) Calculate the percentage of oxygen in hydrogen peroxide.
     (9) What is the percentage of water in Epsom salts, $MgSO_4 \cdot 7 H_2O$?
     (10) Calculate the percentage of hydrogen in sulfuric acid.

4. *a.* In a straight weight problem, the quantities of substances taking part or produced in a reaction are expressed in _____ units.
  b. Solve the following straight weight problems:
     (1) How many grams of sodium hydroxide will be needed to react with 189 grams of nitric acid?
     (2) How many grams of sulfuric acid are needed to react with 60 grams of sodium hydroxide?
     (3) How many grams of $NaHSO_4$ will be produced when 464 grams of sodium chloride react with sulfuric acid?

(4) How many grams of magnesium oxide will be formed if 60 grams of magnesium are burned in oxygen?

(5) How many grams of sodium chloride are produced when 115 grams of sodium react with chlorine?

(6) How many tons of aluminum can be obtained from 153 tons of aluminum oxide?

(7) How many grams of calcium nitrate could be obtained by the action of an excess of nitric acid on 20 grams of calcium carbonate?

(8) How many grams of sodium sulfate are formed when sulfuric acid reacts with 32 grams of sodium hydroxide?

(9) How many grams of potassium sulfate are formed when sulfuric acid reacts with 140 grams of potassium hydroxide?

(10) How many grams of sodium sulfate are produced when 200 grams of sodium hydroxide react with a sufficient amount of sulfuric acid?

5. a. In a weight-volume problem, the quantities of substances taking part or produced in a reaction are expressed in _____ and _____ units.

   b. In order to use 22.4 liters in weight-volume problems, the weight units must be expressed in _____.

   *c. The ounce-molecular volume equals _____ ft³.

   d. Solve the following weight-volume problems:

(1) How many liters of hydrogen sulfide will react with 99.3 grams of $Pb(NO_3)_2$?

(2) How many liters of carbon dioxide are produced when 200 grams of barium carbonate react with hydrochloric acid?

(3) How many liters of sulfur dioxide are released when 189 grams of Na_2SO_3 react with hydrochloric acid?

(4) How many liters of carbon monoxide are necessary to reduce 320 grams of ferric oxide to iron?

(5) How many liters of hydrogen are produced when 117 grams of potassium react with water?

(6) How many liters of carbon dioxide could be prepared by reacting hydrochloric acid with 265 grams of sodium carbonate?

(7) How many liters of hydrogen are needed to combine completely with 42 grams of nitrogen to form ammonia?

(8) How many liters of hydrogen sulfide can be obtained by the action of hydrochloric acid on 220 grams of ferrous sulfide?

(9) How many liters of carbon dioxide can be obtained from the reaction of 2 pounds of calcium carbonate with hydrochloric acid? (454 gm = 1 lb)

(10) How many grams of sodium bicarbonate will react with hydrochloric acid to liberate 112 liters of carbon dioxide?

6. a. In a straight volume problem, the quantities of substances taking part or produced in a reaction are expressed in _____ units.

   b. Solve the following straight volume problems:

(1) How many cubic feet of oxygen will be required for the complete combustion of 17 cubic feet of carbon monoxide?

(2) How many liters of oxygen must react with sulfur dioxide to produce 175 liters of sulfur trioxide?

(3) How many liters of oxygen will be needed to react completely with 500 liters of methane, CH_4?

(4) How many liters of air are required for the complete combustion of 68 liters of hydrogen sulfide?

(5) How many liters of hydrogen are required to react with nitrogen to form 68 liters of ammonia?

(6) What volume of oxygen would completely burn 40 cubic feet of hydrogen sulfide?

(7) How many liters of carbon dioxide could be prepared by the complete combustion of 28 liters of carbon monoxide?

(8) How many liters of nitrogen will react with hydrogen to produce 30 liters of ammonia?

(9) How many cubic feet of air are needed for the complete combustion of 30 cubic feet of ethane, C_2H_6?

(10) What volume of hydrogen reacts with chlorine to produce 144 liters of hydrogen chloride?

7. Solve the following problems.

a. What volume of hydrogen is liberated from the reaction between dilute sulfuric acid and 260 grams of zinc?

b. Calculate the molecular weight of a gas from the following data: 1 gram of the gas occupies 1.4 liters under standard conditions.

c. How many tons of water can be obtained by burning 100 tons of hydrogen?

d. Calculate the weight of oxygen that is liberated by the decomposition of 1 pound of sodium chlorate.

e. What volume of hydrogen is obtained from the reaction between water and 5.75 grams of sodium?

f. Calculate the percentage composition of $Ca(ClO_3)_2$.

g. How many grams of sodium sulfate are obtained when sulfuric acid neutralizes 10 pounds of sodium hydroxide?

h. What volume will 100 grams of hydrogen chloride occupy at standard conditions?

i. Calculate the volume of chlorine that can be obtained from the reaction between hydrochloric acid and 1 pound of manganese dioxide.

j. How many grams of silver chloride will precipitate in the reaction between potassium chloride and 340 grams of silver nitrate?

k. Calculate the volume of air that is required for the complete combustion of 100 liters of hydrogen sulfide.

l. How many liters of sulfur dioxide are liberated by the reaction between concentrated sulfuric acid and 100 grams of copper?

m. How many liters of nitrogen are liberated by the decomposition of 160 grams of ammonium nitrite?

n. Calculate the percentage composition of $(NH_4)_2SO_4$.

o. The density of a gas is 1.17 grams/liter. Calculate its molecular weight.

p. Calculate the volume of carbon monoxide that is liberated when 2 kilograms of silicon carbide are produced in the electric furnace.

q. Calculate the percentage composition of $NaKC_4H_4O_6$.

r. A sample of hard water contains 10% calcium bicarbonate. What volume of carbon dioxide is liberated when 100 grams of this sample are boiled?

s. Calculate the weight of glycerine that is obtained by saponifying 50 pounds of glyceryl stearate.

t. How many liters of hydrogen chloride will react with 250 liters of ammonia?

8 THE PERIODIC CLASSIFICATION
OF THE ELEMENTS

Following the statement of the atomic theory by Dalton, chemists began to seek some relationship between atomic weights and the properties of the elements.

1. EARLY ATTEMPTS TO CLASSIFY THE ELEMENTS

a. **Döbereiner's Triads** (1829). Döbereiner, a German chemist, emphasized the similarity in properties of certain groups of three elements called *triads.* One such triad is chlorine, bromine, and iodine; another is calcium, strontium, and barium.

In the table below, note that the atomic weight of the middle member of the triad is approximately the arithmetical average (81.25) of the atomic weights of the other two members of the triad. The table also reveals that as the atomic weight of the members of the triad increases, there is a change from the gaseous to the solid state.

ELEMENT	PHYSICAL STATE	ATOMIC WEIGHT
Chlorine	Gas	35.5
Bromine	Liquid	80
Iodine	Solid	127

b. **Newlands' Law of Octaves** (1863). Newlands, an English chemist, arranged the elements in order of increasing atomic weight. He stated that:

The eighth element, starting from a given one, is a kind of repetition of the first, like the eighth note of an octave of music.

Newlands arranged the first eight elements (omitting hydrogen) as shown at the right.

Sodium appears under lithium because both elements have similar properties.

Li 7	Be 9	B 11	C 12	N 14	O 16	F 19
Na 23						

c. **Mendeléef's Periodic Law (1869).** Mendeléef, a Russian chemist, following the work of Döbereiner and Newlands, arranged all the elements known at that time in order of increasing atomic weight. He saw in this arrangement a regular repetition (periodicity) of physical and chemical properties. Mendeléef's Law stated:

> The properties of the elements are periodic functions (regular repetitions) of their atomic weights.

The Mendeléef table represented an important step in the attempt of chemists to classify matter. It aided in the prediction of new elements and served as a check on atomic weight determinations. The table, however, had some serious defects, such as the following:

(1) There was apparently no place for hydrogen.

(2) Three elements (K, Co, Te) were not in the proper place according to their atomic weights.

(3) Since this table was based on the Dalton concept of the atom, it could not account for similarities and differences in chemical behavior. These relationships are now explained by the electron theory.

2. THE MODERN PERIODIC TABLE

The electron theory, with its new approach to the composition of the atom, led to a restatement of the periodic law:

> The properties of the elements are periodic functions of their atomic numbers.

The defects in the Mendeléef table have been generally overcome in the modern periodic table.

GENERAL RELATIONSHIPS

a. Elements are arranged in eight vertical *groups*, or *families*, designated by Roman numerals I to VIII. In addition, the rare (inert) gases comprise a separate family labeled Group O.

b. Elements are also arranged in seven horizontal groups called *periods*. A period is also called a *series*.

c. Elements having similar properties fall into the same vertical group or family. Group I A consists of the alkali metals from lithium to francium. The members of this family all have one electron in their outer ring. The atomic radius, however, differs for each of these metals. Thus, they behave as reducing agents of varying ability.

I A
Li
Na
K
Rb
Cs
Fr

Group VII A is the halogen family from fluorine to astatine. In Chapter 10, it will be shown that the members of this family behave as oxidizing agents of varying ability.

VII A

F
Cl
Br
I
At

Main groups are indicated by the letter A after the group number, while subgroups contain the letter B. The elements in a subgroup resemble each other more closely than they resemble the elements in the main group. Thus, the metals in Group I B, copper, silver, and gold, resemble one another more closely than they resemble the metals in Group I A. This is due to

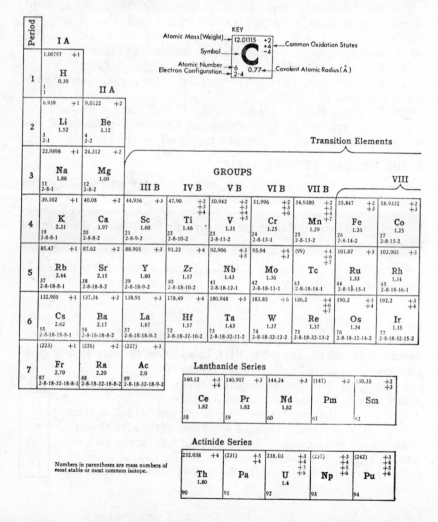

the fact that elements in subgroups have similar inner ring structures.

d. A period usually begins on the left with a metal, progresses through elements that form amphoteric compounds to a nonmetal, and terminates in a rare gas. (For the properties of amphoteric compounds, see 8*d*, page 290.)

I B
Cu
Ag
Au

In a period, there is a transition from positive to negative valence numbers. Elements near the center of the table may exhibit both positive and negative valence numbers. In the second period, lithium and

GROUPS

	III A	IV A	V A	VI A	VII A	0
					H 1.00797, −1, 0.30, 1, 1	**He** 4.0026, 0, 0.93, 2, 2
	B 10.811, +3, 0.88, 5, 2-3	**C** 12.01115, +2 +4 −4, 0.77, 6, 2-4	**N** 14.0067, +1 +2 +3 +4 +5 −2 −3, 0.70, 7, 2-5	**O** 15.9994, −2, 0.66, 8, 2-6	**F** 18.9984, −1, 0.64, 9, 2-7	**Ne** 20.183, 0, 1.12, 10, 2-8
	Al 26.9815, +3, 1.43, 13, 2-8-3	**Si** 28.086, +2 +4 −4, 1.17, 14, 2-8-4	**P** 30.9738, +3 +5 −3, 1.10, 15, 2-8-5	**S** 32.064, +4 +6 −2, 1.04, 16, 2-8-6	**Cl** 35.453, +1 +5 +7 −1, 0.99, 17, 2-8-7	**Ar** 39.948, 0, 1.54, 18, 2-8-8

Transition Elements

VIII	I B	II B	III A	IV A	V A	VI A	VII A	0
Ni 58.71, +2 +3, 1.24, 28, 2-8-16-2	**Cu** 63.54, +1 +2, 1.28, 29, 2-8-18-1	**Zn** 65.37, +2, 1.33, 30, 2-8-18-2	**Ga** 69.72, +3, 1.22, 31, 2-8-18-3	**Ge** 72.59, +2 +4, 1.22, 32, 2-8-18-4	**As** 74.9216, +3 +5 −3, 1.21, 33, 2-8-18-5	**Se** 78.96, +4 +6 −2, 1.17, 34, 2-8-18-6	**Br** 79.909, +1 +5 −1, 1.14, 35, 2-8-18-7	**Kr** 83.80, 0, 1.69, 36, 2-8-18-8
Pd 106.4, +2 +4, 1.3, 46, 2-8-18-18	**Ag** 107.870, +1, 1.44, 47, 2-8-18-18-1	**Cd** 112.40, +2, 1.49, 48, 2-8-18-18-2	**In** 114.82, +3, 1.49, 49, 2-8-18-18-3	**Sn** 118.69, +2 +4, 1.40, 50, 2-8-18-18-4	**Sb** 121.75, +3 +5 −3, 1.41, 51, 2-8-18-18-5	**Te** 127.60, +4 +6 −2, 1.37, 52, 2-8-18-18-6	**I** 126.9044, +1 +5 +7 −1, 1.33, 53, 2-8-18-18-7	**Xe** 131.30, 0, 1.90, 54, 2-8-18-18-8
Pt 195.09, +2 +4, 1.38, 78, 2-8-18-32-17-1	**Au** 196.967, +1 +3, 1.44, 79, 2-8-18-32-18-1	**Hg** 200.59, +1 +2, 1.55, 80, 2-8-18-32-18-2	**Tl** 204.37, +1 +3, 1.71, 81, 2-8-18-32-18-3	**Pb** 207.19, +2 +4, 1.75, 82, 2-8-18-32-18-4	**Bi** 208.980, +3 +5, 1.46, 83, 2-8-18-32-18-5	**Po** (210), +2 +4, 1.65, 84, 2-8-18-32-18-6	**At** (210), 1.40, 85, 2-8-18-32-18-7	**Rn** (222), 0, 2.2, 86, 2-8-18-32-18-8

Eu 151.96 +2 +3	**Gd** 157.25 +3	**Tb** 158.924 +3	**Dy** 162.50 +3	**Ho** 164.930 +3	**Er** 167.26 +3	**Tm** 168.934 +3	**Yb** 173.04 +2 +3	**Lu** 174.97 +3
2.04, 63	1.79, 64	1.77, 65	1.77, 66	1.76, 67	1.75, 68	1.74, 69	1.93, 70	1.74, 71

Am (243) +3 +4 +5 +6	**Cm** (247) +3	**Bk** (249) +3 +4	**Cf** (251) +3	**Es** (254)	**Fm** (253)	**Md** (256)	**No** (254)	**Lw** (257)
95	96	97	98	99	100	101	102	103

beryllium are strongly metallic and thus have positive valence numbers. Boron, carbon, and nitrogen may have positive or negative valence numbers, while oxygen and fluorine are strongly nonmetallic, having negative valence numbers.

2	Li	Be	B	C	N	O	F	Ne

e. The table also indicates the presence of four series of elements called *transition elements.* These elements such as scandium, titanium, and vanadium tend to complete their inner rings, while their outer rings remain unchanged. Transition series appear near the center of the table.

f. Other transition series include the rare earth group, called the lanthanides (lanthanum, cerium, etc.) and the actinides (actinium, thorium, etc.). To accommodate these elements, the modern periodic table has been widened considerably. Thus, the first period contains two elements, the second and third periods contain eight elements, the fourth and fifth periods contain eighteen elements, and the sixth period contains thirty-two elements.

The periodic table has added much to our knowledge of chemistry. By providing proper classification, it has simplified the study of chemistry and permitted quantitative predictions in the absence of experimental evidence. Do not attempt to memorize the table. Instead, try to understand the general relationships. Application of these relationships will make your study of chemistry more interesting and meaningful.

Study Guide

1.**a.* The elements lithium, sodium, and _____ make up a triad.
  b. The Mendeléef table was similar to the table proposed by (1) Dalton (2) Avogadro (3) Moseley (4) Newlands.
  c. According to Mendeléef, the properties of the elements were periodic functions of their _____.

    d. List two important limitations and three important advantages of the Mendeléef table.

    e. The modern periodic table represents the work of many scientists. Discuss the contributions of each of three such scientists.

2. *a.* According to modern concepts, the properties of the elements are periodic functions of their _____.

    *b. How has the modern periodic table overcome the limitations of the Mendeléef table?

3. *a.* Vertical groups in the periodic table are also called _____.

    b. Horizontal groups are called _____ or _____.

4. *a.* The number of electrons in the outer ring of the elements in Group II is (1) 1 (2) 2 (3) 3 (4) 4.

    b. A chemical property of rubidium (Rb) is its ability to behave as a (an) _____ (oxidizing, reducing) agent.

    c. The activity of the halogen elements _____ (decreases, increases, remains the same) as their atomic numbers increase.

    d. The halogens are considered a chemical family because they all (1) have a color (2) are active elements (3) have two electrons in their innermost orbit (4) have the same number of electrons in their outermost orbit.

    e. What is meant by a subgroup? Why are these groups necessary in the organization of the periodic table?

5. *a.* A period or series usually terminates with a (an) _____.

    b. Describe the general characteristics of the elements in the second period.

    c. Arsenic will combine with chlorine to form two chlorides, (1) $AsCl$ and $AsCl_3$ (2) $AsCl_2$ and $AsCl_3$ (3) $AsCl_3$ and $AsCl_4$ (4) $AsCl_3$ and $AsCl_5$.

    d. An element that may have either a positive or a negative valence number is (1) helium (2) mercury (3) sodium (4) sulfur.

    e. The argon atom contains the same number of electrons as the chlorine *atom.* [True or false? If false, correct the italicized term.]

6. *a.* Describe a characteristic common to transition elements.

    b. The formula for scandium (Sc) oxide is _____.

    c. The modern periodic table has been widened to accommodate the group of elements known as (1) halogens (2) alkali metals (3) lanthanides (4) inert gases.

7. *a.* Summarize the important generalizations in the modern periodic table. Give specific examples in each case.

    b. Discuss the different ways in which the periodic table can be used to make your study of chemistry more interesting and more meaningful.

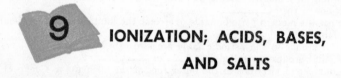

9 IONIZATION; ACIDS, BASES, AND SALTS

IONIZATION

1. CONDUCTIVITY OF SOLUTIONS

Generally speaking, we can divide chemical compounds into two categories, electrolytes and nonelectrolytes.

Electrolytes are substances which, when dissolved in water or melted, conduct an electric current. *Nonelectrolytes*, when dissolved in water or melted, do not conduct.

The conductivity apparatus in Fig. 1 is used to determine whether or not a liquid is an electrolyte. Melted compounds may be tested in the same manner. When electrolytes are tested in this way, the electric bulb lights up. Using nonelectrolytes, the bulb does not light up appreciably.

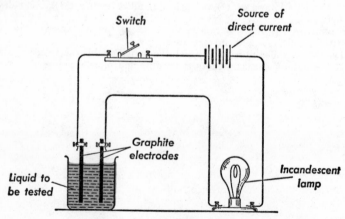

Fig. 1. Conductivity Apparatus

Since water solutions of acids, bases, and salts are generally good conductors, they are electrolytes. Since solutions of alcohol, sugar, and glycerine are nonconductors, they are nonelectrolytes.

The conductivity apparatus is not sufficiently sensitive to reveal that water will conduct electricity very slightly. If an instrument capable of measuring very small currents is used in place of the bulb, it can be shown that water is a very weak electrolyte.

2. PROPERTIES OF ELECTROLYTES

Electrolytes are solutions of acids, bases, and salts which conduct an electric current.

Electrolytes are also known as *polar compounds*. Solutions of these compounds exhibit abnormally high boiling points and abnormally low freezing points. Different electrolytes of the same concentration differ in their ability to conduct an electric current. Thus, dilute sulfuric acid is a better conductor than dilute acetic acid of the same concentration. The former is called a strong electrolyte, the latter a weak electrolyte. The stronger the electrolyte, the brighter the electric bulb lights.

Examples of strong and weak electrolytes are:

	STRONG	WEAK
ACIDS	Dilute sulfuric acid, H_2SO_4 Hydrochloric acid, HCl Nitric acid, HNO_3	Acetic acid, $HC_2H_3O_2$ Carbonic acid, H_2CO_3 Hydrosulfuric acid, H_2S
BASES	Barium hydroxide, $Ba(OH)_2$ Potassium hydroxide, KOH Sodium hydroxide, NaOH	Aluminum hydroxide, $Al(OH)_3$ Ammonium hydroxide, NH_4OH Zinc hydroxide, $Zn(OH)_2$

Solutions of salts are generally good conductors of electricity and thus are classified as strong electrolytes.

3. PROPERTIES OF NONELECTROLYTES

Nonelectrolytes do not conduct an electric current appreciably.

Nonelectrolytes are also known as *nonpolar compounds*. Solutions of these compounds exhibit normal boiling and freezing points. Under certain conditions, however, nonpolar compounds may behave as electrolytes.

4. THEORY OF IONIZATION

Although he was the first to use the terms electrolyte and nonelectrolyte, the English scientist Michael Faraday was unable to account for the differences in behavior between electrolytes and nonelectrolytes. Some fifty-five years later, in 1887, the Swedish chemist Svante Arrhenius proposed the Theory of Ionization to explain the properties of solutions of electrolytes. According to Arrhenius:

Acids, bases, and salts, when dissolved in water, break up into charged particles called **ions.**

This process, known as *ionization*, explains why electrolytes conduct electricity. Solutions that do not conduct electricity, therefore, do not ionize.

Although some of Arrhenius' ideas were faulty, much of his work is still accepted today. The modern theory of ionization, based upon the electrical structure of matter, may be summarized as follows:

a. Acids, bases, and salts ionize or dissociate into charged particles called ions. Water plays an important part in this process.

b. An ion is an atom or group of atoms which carries an electric charge. The charge is equal to the valence number of the atom or radical from which it was formed.

c. The total number of positive charges carried by the ions in solution is exactly equal to the total number of negative charges carried by the ions. As a result, the solution remains electrically neutral. The number of positive ions, however, may be equal to, less than, or greater than the number of negative ions, depending on the electrolyte which has been dissolved. The ionization of Na_2SO_4, for example, produces two sodium ions and only one sulfate ion. However, the two sodium ions have a total charge of $+2$, which is balanced by the single sulfate ion, which has a charge of -2.

$$Na_2SO_4 \rightarrow 2\,Na^+ + SO_4^{-2}$$

d. It is the ions in electrolytes which enable electrolytes to conduct an electric current. The absence of such ions in nonelectrolytes prevents the conduction of an electric current. The extent to which an electrolyte will ionize (degree of dissociation) depends upon the nature of the electrolyte, the solvent, and the concentration and temperature of the solution. Strong electrolytes are those which are completely or almost completely ionized in solution. Weak electrolytes are those which are only partially ionized in solution.

e. The passage of a direct current through an electrolyte results in the decomposition of the electrolyte. Such decomposition is called electrolysis. No electrolysis will take place, however, unless ionization precedes. Polar compounds (electrolytes) contain the necessary ions which, if provided with sufficient mobility, will undergo electrolysis. The reactions which take place in electrolysis will be considered in Chapter 11.

5. HOW IONS DIFFER FROM ATOMS

According to the electron theory, *the charge on an ion is the result of the loss or gain of electrons by an atom or group of atoms in a chemical change.* Thus, in the synthesis of sodium chloride:

a. A sodium atom loses an electron to the chlorine atom and becomes a sodium ion. Reactions in which particles lose electrons are called oxidation reactions.

$$Na^0 - 1\,e \rightarrow Na^+$$
atom   ion

Note that when a sodium atom loses one electron, it contains 11 protons and 10 electrons. The ion formed has a charge of $+1$.

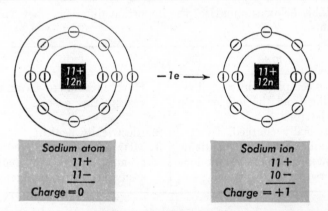

Sodium atom
11+
11−
Charge = 0

Sodium ion
11+
10−
Charge = +1

b. A chlorine atom borrows one electron from the sodium atom and becomes a chloride ion. Reactions in which particles gain electrons are called reduction reactions.

$$Cl^0 + 1\,e \rightarrow Cl^-$$
atom   ion

Note that when a chlorine atom gains one electron, it contains **17** protons and 18 electrons. The ion formed has a charge of −1.

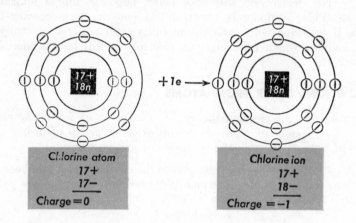

The synthesis of sodium chloride illustrates a fundamental principle:

> When oxidation occurs in a given reaction, there must be corresponding reduction.

The table below summarizes the important differences between ions and atoms.

IONS	ATOMS
1. Have complete outer shell resulting from the loss or gain of electrons.	1. Have incomplete outer shell (except rare gases).
2. Electrically charged.	2. Electrically neutral.
3. Metallic ions are oxidizing agents, while nonmetallic ions are reducing agents.	3. Metallic atoms are reducing agents, while nonmetallic atoms are oxidizing agents.

6. DISSOCIATION OF ELECTROVALENT COMPOUNDS

Compounds resulting from the gain or loss of electrons are called electrovalent, polar, or ionic compounds. Electrovalent compounds, such as salts, thus contain ions even in the solid state. Since these ions are oppositely charged, they are, in a sense, bound together and unable to move about. The process of separating these ions, that is, making them mobile, is called *dissociation*. Dissociation may be carried out in two ways:

a. **Fusing (Melting) the Solid.** The absorption of heat by the solid weakens the bonds between the ions, permitting greater mobility.

b. **Dissolving the Solid in Water.** It will be recalled (*b,* pages 64-65) that water was characterized as a polar molecule. The positive end of the water molecule attaches itself to the negative ion in the salt, while the negative end of the water molecule attaches itself to the positive ion in the salt. In this way, water weakens the electrostatic bond between the oppositely charged ions, thus permitting greater mobility of the ions. These freely moving ions conduct the electric current.

The dissociation of NaCl is indicated in the following diagram:

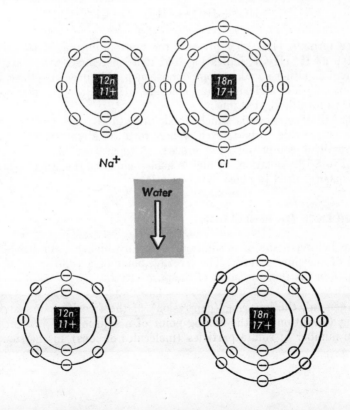

7. IONIZATION OF COVALENT COMPOUNDS

Modern research has revealed that covalent (nonpolar) compounds may react with a solvent to form charged particles. Hydrogen chloride is a covalent compound in which a pair of shared electrons binds the hydrogen to the chlorine.

● = *Chlorine electron*

O = *Hydrogen electron*

Hydrogen chloride reacts with water as follows:

$$HCl + H_2O \rightarrow (H_3O)^+ + Cl^-$$

The formula $(H_3O)^+$ represents the hydronium ion. It can also be written as $H^+(H_2O)$, indicating that it is, in reality, a hydrated hydrogen ion. Other covalent compounds, such as hydrogen sulfate, magnesium chloride, and aluminum chloride, also ionize by reacting with water to form hydrated ions.

Note that compounds which break up into charged particles when in water are said to be ionized. Where ions are already present, as in electrovalent compounds, the process of separating these ions is referred to as dissociation. In high school chemistry, the term ionization is frequently used in place of dissociation.

8. EVIDENCE OF IONIZATION

The boiling point of a solution is usually higher than the boiling point of the pure solvent. The freezing point of a solution is usually lower than the freezing point of the pure solvent.

In general, the lowering (depression) of the freezing point and the raising (elevation) of the boiling point of a solution are proportional to the number of solute particles (molecules or ions) in the solution.

The following table compares the freezing and boiling points of several different solutions with the freezing and boiling points of pure water (solvent). In each case, the solution has the same concentration, that is, one gram-molecular weight of solute is dissolved in 1,000 grams of water, a 1 molal solution (1 m).

Substance	Solute Particles	Freezing Point, °C	Freezing Point Depression, °C	Boiling Point, °C	Boiling Point Elevation, °C
Pure water	———	0	———	100	———
1 m sugar solution	1	−1.86	1.86	100.52	0.52
1 m glycerine solution	1	−1.86	1.86	100.52	0.52
1 m NaCl solution	2	−3.72	2×1.86	101.04	2×0.52
1 m CaCl₂ solution	3	−5.58	3×1.86	101.56	3×0.52

Note that for both the sugar and glycerine solutions, the freezing point depressions are the same. The boiling point elevations are also the same. Since both 1 m solutions are nonionic, each contains one molecule, or one solute particle. All nonionic solutions of the same molal concentration have the same number of solute particles. Hence, they have the same freezing point and the same boiling point.

Note that the freezing point depression of the sodium chloride solution is *twice* as great as that of the sugar or glycerine solution. The boiling point elevation is also *twice* as great as either nonionic solution.

The sodium chloride solution has two ions, one sodium ion and one chloride ion. Thus, it has *twice* as many solute particles as the sugar or glycerine solution. All solutions of the same molal concentration as sodium chloride, and containing two ions, such as potassium chloride or sodium nitrate solutions, have a freezing point and a boiling point the same as those of the sodium chloride solution.

In a similar manner, the calcium chloride solution, which has *three* ions or solute particles, depresses the freezing point *three* times as much as does the sugar or glycerine solution. The boiling point of the calcium chloride solution is also elevated *three* times as much as that of the two nonelectrolytes. Any other solution of the same molal concentration as calcium chloride, and containing three ions, such as a magnesium bromide solution, produces the same effects as the calcium chloride solution.

It should be pointed out, however, that solutions of electrolytes do not always exhibit boiling and freezing points exactly as calculated from their concentrations. The presence of charged particles causes *interionic attraction*, which produces a deviation from the calculated value.

Studies of the freezing and boiling points of solutions provide evidence of ionization. Careful measurement of conductivity also confirms the presence of ions.

9. INDICATORS

Indicators are substances which can be used to detect the presence of hydronium or hydroxyl ions.

A common indicator is litmus, a plant extract, which turns red in the presence of hydronium ions and blue in the presence of hydroxyl ions. Another indicator frequently used is phenolphthalein, which turns pink in the presence of hydroxyl ions.

ACIDS

10. WHAT ARE ACIDS?

Acids are hydrogen compounds which in water solution produce hydronium ions (H_3O^+). The ionization of an acid also produces negative ions, which may be called acid-radical ions. For the sake of simplicity, the hydronium ion is represented as a hydrogen ion (H^+). It is these hydrogen ions which give acids their sour taste, turn blue litmus red, react with metals, and neutralize bases. The formation of hydronium ions by dissolving the acid in water is illustrated by the following equations:

General Formula of an Acid

$$H^+A^-$$

$$HNO_3 + H_2O \rightarrow H_3O^+ + NO_3^- \quad [H_3O^+ = H^+ (H_2O)]$$

$$H_2SO_4 + 2 H_2O \rightarrow 2 H_3O^+ + SO_4^{-2}$$

When acids ionize, they must react with water because they are covalent compounds.

11. COMMON ACIDS

Some common acids, with their formulas and common names, are:

CHEMICAL NAME	FORMULA	COMMON NAME
Acetic acid	$HC_2H_3O_2$	Vinegar
Carbonic acid	H_2CO_3	Soda water
Hydrochloric acid	HCl	Muriatic acid
Nitric acid	HNO_3	Aqua fortis
Sulfuric acid	H_2SO_4	Oil of vitriol

12. PREPARATION OF ACIDS

a. Acids are usually prepared by heating a salt of the desired acid with an acid having a higher boiling point, such as sulfuric acid. An acid with a higher boiling point is pre-

General Method of Preparing an Acid

$$2 \text{ MA} + H_2SO_4 \rightarrow M_2SO_4 + 2 \text{ HA}$$
a salt

ferred because it remains behind in the generator, while the more volatile acid vaporizes.

To prepare hydrochloric acid, we heat sodium chloride with concentrated sulfuric acid.

$$2 \text{ NaCl} + H_2SO_4 \rightarrow Na_2SO_4 + 2 \text{ HCl}$$

To prepare nitric acid, we heat sodium nitrate with concentrated sulfuric acid.

$$2 \text{ NaNO}_3 + H_2SO_4 \rightarrow Na_2SO_4 + 2 \text{ HNO}_3$$

b. Acids may be prepared by the reaction between nonmetallic oxides and water. Such oxides are called *acid anhydrides.* Some common examples are sulfur dioxide (SO_2) and carbon dioxide (CO_2).

$$SO_2 + H_2O \rightarrow H_2SO_3$$
sulfurous
acid

$$CO_2 + H_2O \rightarrow H_2CO_3$$
carbonic
acid

Sulfur dioxide is therefore the anhydride of sulfurous acid, and carbon dioxide is the anhydride of carbonic acid.

c. Acids may also be prepared by direct union of hydrogen and a nonmetal.

$$H_2 + Cl_2 \rightarrow 2 \text{ HCl}$$

13. PROPERTIES OF ACIDS

a. All acids are composed of hydrogen ions and acid-radical ions. The hydrogen ions are replaceable by a metal.

$$\text{METAL} + \text{ACID} \rightarrow \text{A SALT} + \text{HYDROGEN}$$

$$Zn + H_2SO_4 \rightarrow ZnSO_4 + H_2 \uparrow$$

$$Mg + 2\ HCl \rightarrow MgCl_2 + H_2 \uparrow$$

b. Acids in water solution turn litmus red.

c. Water solutions of acids have a sour taste. The sour taste of some fruits is due to acidic substances in the juice. For example, the sour taste of lemons and oranges is due to the presence of citric acid.

d. Acids neutralize bases and basic anhydrides to form a salt and water.

$$\text{BASE} + \text{ACID} \rightarrow \text{A SALT} + \text{WATER}$$

$$NaOH + HCl \rightarrow NaCl + H_2O$$

$$Ca(OH)_2 + H_2SO_4 \rightarrow CaSO_4 + 2\ H_2O$$

$$\text{BASIC ANHYDRIDE} + \text{ACID} \rightarrow \text{A SALT} + \text{WATER}$$

$$Na_2O + 2\ HCl \rightarrow 2\ NaCl + H_2O$$

$$CaO + H_2SO_4 \rightarrow CaSO_4 + H_2O$$

BASES

14. WHAT ARE BASES?

Bases (sometimes called alkalies) are hydroxides of metals or metallic radicals which in water solution produce hydroxyl ions (OH^-). The ionization of a base also produces positive ions, usually metallic ions. Hydroxyl ions give bases their bitter taste, turn red litmus blue, and neutralize acids. The formation of hydroxyl ions is shown by the following equations:

General Formula of a Base

$$M^+OH^-$$

$$NaOH \rightarrow Na^+ + OH^-$$

$$KOH \rightarrow K^+ + OH^-$$

Insoluble bases do not dissolve appreciably in water. Hence, such bases do not furnish sufficient hydroxyl ions to affect red litmus.

15. COMMON BASES

Some common bases, with their formulas and common names, are:

CHEMICAL NAME	FORMULA	COMMON NAME
Ammonium hydroxide	NH_4OH	Ammonia water
Calcium hydroxide	$Ca(OH)_2$	Slaked lime
Magnesium hydroxide	$Mg(OH)_2$	Milk of magnesia
Potassium hydroxide	KOH	Caustic potash
Sodium hydroxide	NaOH	Lye or caustic soda

16. PREPARATION OF BASES

a. Soluble Bases

(1) Soluble bases may be prepared by the action of an active metal on water. Thus, sodium hydroxide may be prepared by the action of sodium on water, and calcium hydroxide by the action of calcium on water.

General Methods of
Preparing a Soluble Base

$$2 M + 2 H_2O \rightarrow 2 MOH + H_2$$
$$M_2O + H_2O \rightarrow 2 MOH$$

$$2 Na + 2 H_2O \rightarrow 2 NaOH + H_2 \uparrow$$

$$Ca + 2 H_2O \rightarrow Ca(OH)_2 + H_2 \uparrow$$

(2) Bases are formed by the reaction between metallic oxides and water. Such oxides are therefore classified as *basic anhydrides*. Examples of basic anhydrides are potassium oxide (K_2O) and calcium oxide (CaO).

$$K_2O + H_2O \rightarrow 2 KOH$$
potassium
hydroxide

$$CaO + H_2O \rightarrow Ca(OH)_2$$
calcium
hydroxide

Potassium oxide is therefore the anhydride of potassium hydroxide, and calcium oxide is the anhydride of calcium hydroxide.

b. Insoluble Bases.
Insoluble bases are prepared by precipitation, using a soluble base and a soluble salt of the desired insoluble base. Thus, ferric hydroxide can be prepared by mixing solutions of ferric chloride and sodium hydroxide.

$$FeCl_3 + 3 NaOH \rightarrow 3 NaCl + Fe(OH)_3 \downarrow$$

17. PROPERTIES OF BASES

a. All bases are composed of metallic ions (or metallic radical ions) and hydroxyl ions.

b. All bases neutralize acids or acid anhydrides, forming a salt and water.

$$\text{BASE} + \text{ACID} \rightarrow \text{A SALT} + \text{WATER}$$

$$Mg(OH)_2 + 2\ HCl \rightarrow MgCl_2 + 2\ H_2O$$

$$2\ KOH + CO_2 \rightarrow K_2CO_3 + H_2O$$

c. Soluble bases turn red litmus blue and phenolphthalein solution pink.

d. Water solutions of soluble bases have a bitter taste and a slippery feeling.

e. Strong or caustic bases (sodium and potassium hydroxides) change fats and oils to soap and glycerine. Commercial use is made of this property in the manufacture of the latter two substances. Lye or caustic soda (sodium hydroxide) is used to clean drains because it dissolves grease. Ammonia water (ammonium hydroxide) also possesses this property and is used for general household cleaning.

f. Caustic bases dissolve wool and silk but not cotton. Hence, woolen goods should not be washed in strongly basic solutions. If a sample of a so-called woolen fabric leaves a residue when boiled in sodium hydroxide solution, this indicates that the fabric contains cotton. A comparison of the weights of the sample and the dried residue would indicate the amount of cotton present.

18. MEASUREMENT OF HYDROGEN ION CONCENTRATION

The chemist uses a numerical scale (pH) to define accurately the hydrogen ion concentration of a solution. Neutral solutions have a pH of 7, acid solutions have a pH less than 7, and basic or alkaline solutions have a pH greater than 7, as shown in the pH scale below.

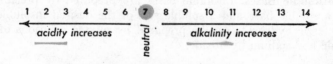

The pH values of some common acids and bases appear in the following table. Note that the concentrations of acid and base are fixed at one-tenth normal (0.1 N). (See also Table K, page 399.)

ACID	pH	BASE	pH
Hydrochloric acid	1.1	Sodium bicarbonate	8.4
Sulfuric acid	1.2	Ammonium hydroxide	11.1
Acetic acid	2.9	Sodium hydroxide	13.0
Boric acid	5.2	Potassium hydroxide	13.0

It can readily be seen that strong acids have lower pH values than weak acids, while strong bases have higher pH values than weak bases. Shrimp has a pH of 7, milk a pH of 6.6, and human blood a pH of about 7.3.

In the laboratory, pH may be measured by a special indicator called *hydrion paper*. This paper is treated in such a way as to produce a definite color for a specific pH or pH range. More accurate determination of pH can be made with an electrical instrument called a *pH meter*.

SALTS

19. NEUTRALIZATION

Neutralization is the reaction between an acid and a base, forming a salt and water. From the ionic viewpoint, neutralization is considered as the union of the hydrogen ions of an acid with the hydroxyl ions of a base to form un-ionized or undissociated water.

General Equation for Neutralization

$$HA + MOH \rightarrow MA + H_2O$$

$$H^+ + OH^- \rightarrow H_2O$$

Assuming that an acid contains hydronium ions, neutralization may be represented thus:

$$H_3O^+ + OH^- \rightarrow 2\ H_2O$$

The following equations illustrate neutralization reactions. (Note that the ionic equation can easily be written from the balanced molecular equation.)

MOLECULAR: $HCl + NaOH \rightarrow NaCl + H_2O$

IONIC: $H^+ + Cl^- + Na^+ + OH^- \rightarrow Na^+ + Cl^- + H_2O$

MOLECULAR: $HNO_3 + KOH \rightarrow KNO_3 + H_2O$

IONIC: $H^+ + NO_3^- + K^+ + OH^- \rightarrow K^+ + NO_3^- + H_2O$

MOLECULAR: $H_2SO_4 + Ca(OH)_2 \rightarrow CaSO_4 + 2\ H_2O$

IONIC: $2\ H^+ + SO_4^{-2} + Ca^{+2} + 2\ OH^- \rightarrow$
$Ca^{+2} + SO_4^{-2} + 2\ H_2O$

20. WHAT ARE SALTS?

Salts are compounds containing metal ions (or ammonium ions) and acid-radical ions. Water solutions of salts may be neutral to litmus and have a salty taste.

21. COMMON SALTS

Some common salts, with their formulas and common names, are:

CHEMICAL NAME	FORMULA	COMMON NAME
Ammonium chloride	NH_4Cl	Sal ammoniac
Magnesium sulfate	$MgSO_4 \cdot 7\ H_2O$	Epsom salts
Sodium bicarbonate	$NaHCO_3$	Baking soda
Sodium carbonate	$Na_2CO_3 \cdot 10\ H_2O$	Washing soda
Sodium chloride	$NaCl$	Table salt
Sodium tetraborate	$Na_2B_4O_7 \cdot 10\ H_2O$	Borax

Some of the salts listed above contain water of hydration, as indicated in their chemical formulas.

22. PREPARATION OF SALTS

Salts may be prepared in several ways. In each of the following cases, NaCl is the salt formed.

a. By Neutralization

$$NaOH + HCl \rightarrow NaCl + H_2O$$

b. **By Direct Combination or Synthesis**

$$2 \text{ Na} + \text{Cl}_2 \rightarrow 2 \text{ NaCl}$$

c. **By Single Replacement Such as the Action of a Metal with an Acid**

$$2 \text{ Na} + 2 \text{ HCl} \rightarrow 2 \text{ NaCl} + \text{H}_2 \uparrow$$

d. **By Action of an Acid on a Metallic Oxide**

$$\text{Na}_2\text{O} + 2 \text{ HCl} \rightarrow 2 \text{ NaCl} + \text{H}_2\text{O}$$

e. **By Double Replacement due to Volatility**

$$\text{Na}_2\text{S} + 2 \text{ HCl} \rightarrow 2 \text{ NaCl} + \text{H}_2\text{S} \uparrow$$

f. **By Double Replacement due to Insolubility**

$$\text{Na}_2\text{SO}_4 + \text{BaCl}_2 \rightarrow 2 \text{ NaCl} + \text{BaSO}_4 \downarrow$$

The following table illustrates the preparation of the salt *MA* by the six methods previously described.

a. $\text{MOH} + \text{HA} \rightarrow \text{MA} + \text{H}_2\text{O}$
b. $\text{M} + \text{A} \rightarrow \text{MA}$
c. $2 \text{ M} + 2 \text{ HA} \rightarrow 2 \text{ MA} + \text{H}_2 \uparrow$
d. $\text{M}_2\text{O} + 2 \text{ HA} \rightarrow 2 \text{ MA} + \text{H}_2\text{O}$
e. $\text{M}_2\text{S} + 2 \text{ HA} \rightarrow 2 \text{ MA} + \text{H}_2\text{S} \uparrow$
f. $\text{M}_2\text{SO}_4 + \text{BaA}_2 \rightarrow 2 \text{ MA} + \text{BaSO}_4 \downarrow$

23. TYPES OF SALTS

a. **Normal Salts.** When all the hydrogen ions of an acid are replaced by a metal, the salt formed is called a normal salt. Examples of normal salts are:

sodium chloride, NaCl
potassium sulfate, K_2SO_4
calcium phosphate, $\text{Ca}_3(\text{PO}_4)_2$

b. **Acid Salts.** When only some of the hydrogen ions of an acid are replaced by a metal, the resulting salt still contains some hydrogen ions and is called an acid salt. Examples of acid salts are:

sodium bicarbonate, NaHCO_3
sodium bisulfate, NaHSO_4

***c.* Basic Salts.** When only some of the hydroxyl ions of a base are replaced, the resulting salt still contains one or more OH ions and is called a basic salt. Examples of basic salts are:

magnesium hydroxychloride, $Mg(OH)Cl$
ferric hydroxychloride, $Fe(OH)_2Cl$

***d.* Double Salts.** Salts containing two metals and one acid radical are called double salts. Examples of double salts are the compounds called alums.

potassium aluminum sulfate (common alum)
$KAl(SO_4)_2 \cdot 12\ H_2O$ or $K_2SO_4 \cdot Al_2(SO_4)_3 \cdot 24\ H_2O$

potassium chromium sulfate (chrome alum)
$KCr(SO_4)_2 \cdot 12\ H_2O$ or $K_2SO_4 \cdot Cr_2(SO_4)_3 \cdot 24\ H_2O$

Study Guide

1. *a.* By means of a labeled diagram or a brief description, show how to determine whether or not a given substance is an electrolyte.
   b. Water is a *nonelectrolyte*. [True or false? If false, correct the italicized term.]
2. *a.* Electrolytes are solutions of _____, _____, and _____ which conduct an electric current.
   b. State three properties of electrolytes.
   c. How may strong electrolytes be distinguished from weak electrolytes?
   d. An example of a strong electrolyte is (1) sodium hydroxide (2) water (3) ammonium hydroxide (4) acetic acid.
   e. Salt solutions are classified as strong electrolytes because _____.
3. *a.* State three properties of nonelectrolytes.
   b. An example of a nonelectrolyte is (1) water (2) glycerine (3) acetic acid (4) sulfuric acid.
4. *a.* The scientist who formulated the Theory of Ionization in 1887 was _____.
   b. How did he account for the ability of electrolytes to conduct electricity?
   c. An atom bearing an electric charge is called a (an) _____.
   d. If, in a given electrolyte, there is a total of three positive charges, there must also be a total of _____ negative charges.
   e. An electrolyte has the formula $Cr_2(SO_4)_3$. The total number of ions present is (1) 2 (2) 3 (3) 5 (4) 17.

f. A weak electrolyte is one that (1) is diluted with water (2) is slightly ionized (3) is not corrosive (4) tastes sweet.

g. The degree of dissociation of an electrolyte does not depend upon the (1) nature of the electrolyte (2) concentration (3) temperature (4) pressure.

h. The _____ of an electrolyte by means of a direct current is called electrolysis.

i. Electrolysis will not take place unless it is preceded by (1) decomposition (2) oxidation (3) reduction (4) ionization.

5. *a.* Describe three ways in which atoms differ from ions.

*b. Using electron equations, show how to synthesize the hypothetical compound A_4B_3.

c. Name two ions that have the same number of electrons as an atom of argon.

6. *a.* Explain why electrovalent compounds contain ions even in the solid state.

b. A substance which contains ions in the solid state is (1) sulfur (2) sodium chloride (3) boric acid (4) sugar.

c. The process of separating ions bound together in a compound is called *ionization*. [True or false? If false, correct the italicized term.]

*d. Describe how the addition of water makes ions in a crystal of potassium nitrate more mobile. Can any other liquid be used in place of water? Explain.

7. *a.* Covalent compounds may ionize by reacting with the _____.

b. Why is dilute sulfuric acid a stronger acid than concentrated sulfuric acid?

c. Using equations, show how nitric acid and sulfuric acid ionize in water.

8. *a.* The boiling point elevation and freezing point depression of a solution are proportional to the _____ in the solution.

b. Solutions of electrolytes of a given concentration exhibit _____ (smaller, greater) boiling point elevations than solutions of nonelectrolytes of the same concentration.

c. A 1 molal copper sulfate solution will boil at approximately (1) 100°C (2) 100.52°C (3) 101.04°C (4) 103.12°C.

d. A 1 molal solution freezes at approximately −9.3°C. The solution contains (1) 2 (2) 3 (3) 4 (4) 5   ions.

*e. Explain how studies of the freezing and boiling points of solutions support the Theory of Ionization.

*f. Why does the observed boiling point of a solution differ from its calculated value?

9. *a.* Indicators may be used to detect the presence of either _____ or _____ ions.

b. Two common indicators are _____ and _____.

c. Solutions containing more H^+ than OH^- (1) turn phenolphthalein red (2) turn litmus red (3) feel slippery (4) neutralize acids.

10. *a.* All acids in water solution yield (1) chloride (2) hydronium (3) sulfate (4) hydroxyl   ions.

b. Write an equation to illustrate the ionization of phosphoric acid (H_3PO_4).

11. *a.* The common name of hydrochloric acid is (1) oil of vitriol (2) aqua fortis (3) vinegar (4) muriatic acid.

b. All acids contain (1) oxygen (2) hydrogen (3) carbon (4) sulfur.

12. *a.* Acids may be prepared by heating a salt of the desired acid with _____.

b. Describe three different ways of making acids. Write an equation to illustrate each method.

c. Anhydrides are usually (1) acids (2) bases (3) oxides (4) sulfides.

*d. Do all acids have anhydrides? Explain.

e. Hydrobromic acid may be prepared by the direct union of _____ and _____.

13. a. Describe four properties common to all acids.

b. Complete and balance each of the following equations:
  (1) $KOH + HCl \rightarrow$
  (2) $Ca(OH)_2 + HNO_3 \rightarrow$
  (3) $NaOH + H_2SO_4 \rightarrow$
  (4) $CaO + HCl \rightarrow$
  (5) $K_2O + H_3PO_4 \rightarrow$

14. a. The ionization of a base produces _____ ions, which give bases their characteristic properties.

b. Write equations to illustrate the ionization of three bases.

c. The formula for caustic soda is (1) H_2CO_3 (2) Na_2CO_3 (3) $Ca(OH)_2$ (4) $NaOH$.

15. Describe three different ways of making bases. Write an equation to illustrate each method.

16. a. All bases contain *hydronium* ions. [True or false? If false, correct the italicized term.]

b. The reaction between bases and acids always produces _____ and _____.

c. Solutions containing fewer hydrogen ions than hydroxyl ions (1) turn phenolphthalein pink (2) turn litmus red (3) have a sour taste (4) neutralize bases.

d. Strong bases convert fats to glycerine and _____.

e. Lye is used to clean drains because it _____.

f. It is not advisable to wash woolen goods in *basic* solutions. [True or false? If false, correct the italicized term.]

17. a. pH is a measure of the _____ of a solution.

b. Distilled water has a pH value close to (1) 1 (2) 6 (3) 7 (4) 14.

c. As the alkalinity of a solution decreases, its pH value _____ (decreases, increases, remains the same).

d. A solution of 0.1 N hydrochloric acid has a pH value of (1) 1.1 (2) 3.6 (3) 6.8 (4) 7.

*e. Why does a 0.1 N solution of sodium hydroxide have a higher pH value than a solution of ammonium hydroxide of the same concentration?

18. a. In neutralization reactions, water is formed from the reaction between _____ and _____ ions.

b. Equal volumes of molar solutions of hydrochloric acid and sodium hydroxide were mixed and the mixture evaporated to dryness. The residue was (1) sodium chloride and sodium hydroxide (2) sodium chloride (3) sodium hydroxide (4) hydrochloric acid.

c. Using ionic equations, show what happens in the following neutralization reactions:
  (1) $HCl + KOH \rightarrow$
  (2) $HNO_3 + Ca(OH)_2 \rightarrow$
  (3) $H_2SO_4 + NaOH \rightarrow$

19. *a.* Salts are compounds containing (1) atoms (2) molecules (3) ions (4) atoms and ions.

   b. All salts contain (1) water of hydration (2) at least two elements (3) oxygen (4) at least three elements.

   c. The chemical name for baking soda is *sodium carbonate*. [True or false? If false, correct the italicized term.]

   d. Using equations, show how potassium bromide may be prepared in five different ways.

20. *a.* An example of a normal salt is (1) NaH_2PO_4 (2) Na_2HPO_4 (3) Na_3PO_4 (4) H_3PO_4.

   b. An example of an acid salt is _____.

   c. An example of a basic salt is (1) $Cu(OH)Cl$ (2) $CuCl_2$ (3) $Cu(OH)_2$ (4) $Cu(OCl)_2$.

   d. An example of a double salt is _____.

   *e. What property of an acid determines the number of different salts that can be made from it?

   *f. What property of a base determines the number of different salts that can be made from it?

10 THE HALOGEN FAMILY

1. HALOGENS

The elements belonging to the halogen family are fluorine, chlorine, bromine, iodine, and the recently synthesized halogen, astatine. They comprise Group VII A in the periodic classification. They are called *halogens* (salt formers) because they unite readily with metals to form salts, as shown in the following general equation:

VII A
F
Cl
Br
I
At

$$2 \text{ M} + \text{X}_2 \rightarrow 2 \text{ MX}$$

univalent   halogen   univalent
metal   metallic
halide salt

A specific example is:

$$2 \text{ Na} + \text{F}_2 \rightarrow 2 \text{ NaF}$$

sodium   fluorine   sodium
fluoride

As the halogens increase in atomic weight, there is a corresponding transition in physical state. Thus, fluorine and chlorine are gases, while bromine is a liquid and iodine a solid.

Every halogen has seven electrons in its outermost orbit. The halogen atom thus tends to gain an electron in chemical changes and become a halide ion. This tendency to gain an electron decreases as the size of the atom increases. Thus:

The chemical activity of the halogens decreases with increasing atomic number.

Arranged in order of their decreasing activity, the halogens are fluorine, chlorine, bromine, and iodine. Little is known about astatine, but it is believed to be radioactive and unstable. Because they are chemically active, halogens are found combined in nature.

The halogens may be prepared from the corresponding halide ion. Since the halide ion has a complete outer ring, while the free halogen has only seven electrons, the halide ion must be oxidized to yield the free halogen. Oxidation, as previously defined, is a reaction in which a particle loses electrons. Thus:

$$2 \text{ X}^- - 2 \text{ e} \rightarrow \text{ X}_2^0$$

halide ion   free halogen

Halides may be oxidized as follows:

a. **Electrochemically.** This method is particularly effective for the most active halogen, fluorine.

b. **Using an Oxidizing Agent.** All halide ions, with the exception of fluorides, may be oxidized by suitable oxidizing agents.

FLUORINE

2. OCCURRENCE

Fluorine is found combined chiefly as fluorspar (CaF_2) and cryolite (Na_3AlF_6).

3. PREPARATION

Fluorine cannot be prepared from fluorides using an oxidizing agent. The fluoride ion is extremely stable and does not lose electrons readily.

Fluorine may be obtained by the electrolysis of a solution of potassium hydrogen fluoride dissolved in anhydrous liquid hydrogen fluoride. Fluorine is liberated at the anode by oxidation, while hydrogen is formed at the cathode by reduction. The equation for the reaction is as follows:

$$2 \text{ KHF}_2 \xrightarrow[\text{electrolysis}]{} K_2F_2 + H_2 \uparrow + F_2 \uparrow$$

Because fluorine is one of the most active elements, it attacks glass and most of the common metals. The electrolysis must therefore be carried out in apparatus which resists the action of fluorine. Moissan, the French chemist who first isolated fluorine in 1886, used a U-tube and electrodes made of an alloy of platinum and iridium. Copper electrodes are used today. The liberated fluorine forms a protective coating of copper fluoride, which resists further action.

4. PHYSICAL PROPERTIES

Fluorine is a yellowish gas with a pungent odor, denser than air, and extremely poisonous.

5. CHEMICAL PROPERTIES

Because fluorine is the halogen with the lowest atomic number, it has the greatest tendency to gain electrons. This means that fluorine can force other atoms or ions to lose electrons. Fluorine is therefore a very powerful oxidizing agent; in fact, it is the most powerful chemical oxidizing agent. In the reaction

$$Cu + F_2 \rightarrow CuF_2$$

note that fluorine forces a copper atom to lose two electrons.

$$Cu^0 - 2\,e \rightarrow Cu^{+2}$$

$$F_2 + 2\,e \rightarrow 2\,F^-$$

Fluorine reacts violently with hydrogen and with water, but reacts slowly with gold and platinum. Fluorine also reacts with glass.

6. USES

Because of its extreme chemical activity, fluorine has limited commercial use.

a. Fluorine was used during World War II to separate the uranium isotopes U^{238} and U^{235}. Fluorine converts the mixture of isotopes into a mixture of gaseous uranium hexafluorides (UF_6). The lighter isotope (U^{235}) is separated from the heavier variety by a special gaseous diffusion process.

b. Hydrofluoric acid is preferred to fluorine in the etching of glass because of its greater safety in handling.

c. Fluorides are used in insecticides and rodenticides.

d. It has been established that fluoridation of drinking water prevents dental cavities. Treatment of children's teeth with dilute fluoride solutions is also effective in reducing tooth decay.

e. Certain fluorine compounds, called *freons*, which are liquids, are used as refrigerants because they are nonpoisonous, highly volatile, and not flammable. The most commonly used freon is dichlorodifluoromethane (CCl_2F_2).

CHLORINE

7. OCCURRENCE

Chlorine, like other active elements, is not found free in nature. It is found combined chiefly in the form of sodium chloride in deposits of rock salt (halite) and in sea water (brine).

8. LABORATORY PREPARATION

Chlorine is prepared in the laboratory by the oxidation of a chloride compound.

Common chloride compounds which may be used are hydrochloric acid and sodium chloride. Since the hydrogen halide (HCl) is generally less stable than the metallic halide (NaCl), the former may be more easily oxidized. Thus, chlorine may be prepared by the oxidation of hydrochloric acid by manganese dioxide. (Other oxidizing agents, such as potassium permanganate, may also be employed.)

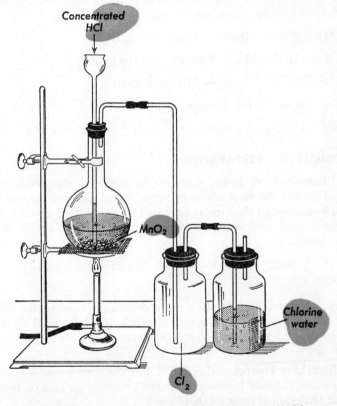

Fig. 8. Laboratory Preparation and Collection of Chlorine

Some manganese dioxide is placed in a flask, and concentrated hydrochloric acid is added through the thistle tube. The mixture is warmed gently, and the chlorine is collected in the first bottle by air displacement, as shown in Fig. 8.

The equation for the reaction is as follows:

$$4 \, HCl + MnO_2 \rightarrow MnCl_2 + 2 \, H_2O + Cl_2 \uparrow$$

Some of the excess chlorine passes into the second bottle and dissolves in the water to form a solution known as chlorine water.

Chlorine may also be prepared from sodium chloride by using sulfuric acid in addition to manganese dioxide. The reaction between sodium chloride and sulfuric acid first produces hydrochloric acid, which is oxidized by manganese dioxide as in the first method. The reactions that take place are:

(1) $2 \, NaCl + H_2SO_4 \rightarrow Na_2SO_4 + 2 \, HCl$

(2) $4 \, HCl + MnO_2 \rightarrow MnCl_2 + 2 \, H_2O + Cl_2 \uparrow$

(3) $MnCl_2 + H_2SO_4 \rightarrow MnSO_4 + 2 \, HCl$

The equation for the complete reaction follows:

$$2 \, NaCl + MnO_2 + 2 \, H_2SO_4 \rightarrow Na_2SO_4 + MnSO_4 + 2 \, H_2O + Cl_2 \uparrow$$

9. COMMERCIAL PREPARATION

a. **Electrolysis of Brine.** Chlorine is obtained commercially as a product during the electrolysis of brine. When a direct current is sent through salt water, chlorine is liberated at the carbon anode (chlorine attacks metals) and sodium hydroxide and hydrogen are liberated at the cathode.

$$\underbrace{2 \, NaCl + 2 \, H_2O}_{\text{brine}} \xrightarrow{\text{electrolysis}} 2 \, NaOH + H_2 \uparrow + Cl_2 \uparrow$$

Vorce, Nelson, and Hooker each developed electrolytic cells for the most economical commercial electrolysis of brine. This process also serves as an important commercial source of hydrogen and sodium hydroxide.

b. **Bleaching Powder and an Acid.** For the commercial bleaching of cotton cloth, chlorine is obtained by the action of an acid on bleaching powder (chloride of lime, $CaOCl_2$).

$$CaOCl_2 + H_2SO_4 \rightarrow CaSO_4 + H_2O + Cl_2 \uparrow$$

10. PHYSICAL PROPERTIES

Chlorine is a greenish-yellow gas with an irritating odor.

CAUTION	Be careful not to inhale excessive quantities of chlorine.

Chlorine is extremely poisonous, attacking the tissues of the respiratory system. Because of this property, chlorine was used in World War I as a war gas. It is two and one-half times as dense as air and is soluble in water. Hence, chlorine is collected by displacement of air. Chlorine can be readily liquefied at room temperature by pressure alone.

> Gas
> Greenish-yellow
> Irritating
> $2\frac{1}{2} \times$ air
> Soluble in water

11. CHEMICAL PROPERTIES

Next to fluorine, chlorine is the most active halogen. Because chlorine has seven electrons in its outer shell, it tends to gain electrons. This means that chlorine, like fluorine, is an oxidizing agent, second in activity only to fluorine in the halogen family.

Chlorine combines directly with many elements to form chlorides. If E represents a univalent element, the reaction between the element and chlorine can be summarized as follows:

$$2 \text{ E} + Cl_2 \rightarrow 2 \text{ ECl}$$

univalent element   chloride of univalent element

Electronically, the reaction may be represented as follows:

$$2 \text{ E} - 2 \text{ e} \rightarrow 2 \text{ E}^+$$

$$Cl_2{}^0 + 2 \text{ e} \rightarrow 2 \text{ Cl}^-$$

Note that univalent element E has lost electrons to become a positive ion, while chlorine has gained electrons to become a negative ion. Because chlorine has gained electrons, it is an oxidizing agent.

Since many of these reactions evolve heat and light, chlorine is also said to support combustion. Oxygen, therefore, is not the only gas which supports combustion.

a. **Reaction with Free Hydrogen.** If a lighted hydrogen jet is introduced into a bottle of chlorine, the flame changes color but continues to burn. The product formed is a colorless gas (hydrogen chloride) which has a choking odor and fumes when breathed upon.

Another method of reacting hydrogen with chlorine is to explode a mixture of these gases in a glass tube by an electric spark, or by placing the mixture in sunlight.

$$H_2 + Cl_2 \rightarrow 2 \ HCl \uparrow$$

Note that in this reaction, hydrogen has lost electrons while chlorine has gained electrons.

$$H_2{}^0 - 2 \ e \rightarrow 2 \ H^+$$

$$Cl_2{}^0 + 2 \ e \rightarrow 2 \ Cl^-$$

b. **Reaction with Combined Hydrogen.** Chlorine has a great affinity for combined hydrogen. It removes hydrogen from hydrocarbons such as turpentine and paraffin (candle wax) to form hydrogen chloride and carbon. When a burning candle is lowered into a bottle of chlorine, the candle continues to burn; carbon is deposited and hydrogen chloride is formed. Carbon may be recognized by its black color, while hydrogen chloride may be recognized by its choking odor or its fuming when breathed upon.

c. **Reaction with Metals.** If a metal such as powdered antimony is dropped into a bottle of chlorine, bright sparks are produced and a white cloud of antimony trichloride is formed, which settles as a powder.

$$2 \ Sb + 3 \ Cl_2 \rightarrow 2 \ SbCl_3$$

Copper foil dropped into chlorine will burn and form copper chloride.

$$Cu + Cl_2 \rightarrow CuCl_2$$

Note that both antimony and copper have lost electrons to chlorine, which demonstrates that chlorine is an oxidizing agent.

d. **Reaction with Water.** Greenish-yellow chlorine water, in the absence of organic matter and if placed in sunlight, turns colorless and releases a colorless gas. Hydrochloric acid and free oxygen are formed.

$$2 \ Cl_2 + 2 \ H_2O \rightarrow 4 \ HCl + O_2 \uparrow$$

Chlorine water should therefore be kept in brown bottles to prevent the action of light.

The reaction between chlorine and water actually takes place in a number of steps. Initially, chlorine reacts with water to form hypochlorous acid.

$$Cl_2 + H_2O \rightarrow HCl + \underset{\substack{\text{hypochlorous} \\ \text{acid}}}{HOCl}$$

Hypochlorous acid is a more powerful oxidizing agent than chlorine and will bleach certain colored materials. Dry chlorine alone is unable to bleach these materials. Salts of hypochlorous acid such as sodium hypochlorite (Clorox, Rosex, Zonite) also have an antiseptic action, which is due to the liberation of hypochlorous acid.

Hypochlorous acid is unstable and decomposes on standing.

$$2 \, HOCl \rightarrow 2 \, HCl + O_2 \uparrow$$

12. USES

a. **Bleaching Agent.** Moist chlorine is used to bleach cotton and wood pulp. The reaction between the water and chlorine liberates hypochlorous acid, which bleaches the coloring matter by oxidation. Chlorine cannot be used to bleach silk and wool; these materials are easily destroyed by it. For commercial bleaching of cotton cloth, chlorine is obtained by the action of dilute sulfuric acid on bleaching powder. (The equation for this reaction appears under *b*, page 132.) Excess chlorine which may be harmful to the fabric is removed by an *antichlor* such as sodium thiosulfate solution.

Certain ink eradicators also make use of chlorine as a bleaching agent.

b. **Water Purification.** Chlorine is added to drinking water in order to destroy harmful bacteria. This process is called chlorination. Water used in swimming pools undergoes the same treatment.

c. **Disinfectant.** Chlorine for disinfecting purposes is conveniently obtained by sprinkling chloride of lime (bleaching powder, $CaOCl_2$) in damp places. The carbon dioxide of the air unites with the moisture to form a weak acid (carbonic acid), which in turn reacts with the chloride of lime to liberate the chlorine.

$$CaOCl_2 + H_2CO_3 \rightarrow CaCO_3 + H_2O + Cl_2 \uparrow$$

d. **Antiseptic.** Solutions of sodium hypochlorite (NaOCl), such as Dakin's solution and Zonite, are used as antiseptics.

e. **Manufacture of Chlorine Compounds.** Chlorine is used to make such important compounds as chloroform ($CHCl_3$), used as an anesthetic; carbon tetrachloride (CCl_4), used as a solvent; and aluminum chloride ($AlCl_3$), used as a catalyst. Chlorine compounds used as war gases are mustard gas, phosgene, and chloropicrin.

BROMINE

13. OCCURRENCE

Bromine is found combined, chiefly as sodium bromide (NaBr) and magnesium bromide ($MgBr_2$), in salt deposits and dissolved in sea water.

14. LABORATORY PREPARATION

The laboratory preparation of bromine is similar to the preparation of chlorine. Bromine is prepared by the oxidation of a bromide compound. Because hydrobromic acid (HBr) is less stable than a metal bromide, it can be oxidized more readily. Hydrobromic acid, however, is an uncommon compound; it must first be made by the action of sulfuric acid on a metallic bromide.

A mixture of potassium bromide and manganese dioxide is placed in a test tube and moistened with concentrated sulfuric acid. (See Fig. 14.) The mixture is then heated gently, and the bromine collected in a test tube immersed in cold water. The bromine is liberated as a reddish-brown vapor and condenses to form a dark-red liquid. This method of collection is called distillation. In the preparation, the manganese dioxide oxidizes the hydrobromic acid, which is first formed by the reaction between the potassium bromide and sulfuric acid.

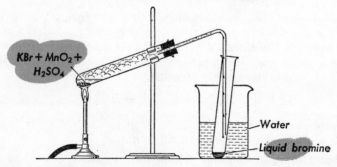

$KBr + MnO_2 + H_2SO_4$

Water

Liquid bromine

Fig 14. Laboratory Preparation and Collection of Bromine

The reactions that take place are:

(1) $2 KBr + H_2SO_4 \rightarrow K_2SO_4 + 2 HBr$

(2) $MnO_2 + 4 HBr \rightarrow MnBr_2 + 2 H_2O + Br_2 \uparrow$

(3) $MnBr_2 + H_2SO_4 \rightarrow MnSO_4 + 2 HBr$

The equation for the complete reaction follows:

$2 KBr + MnO_2 + 2 H_2SO_4 \rightarrow K_2SO_4 + MnSO_4 + 2 H_2O + Br_2 \uparrow$

15. COMMERCIAL PREPARATION

Chlorine in the presence of steam is allowed to come in contact with naturally occurring magnesium bromide ($MgBr_2$). The chlorine, because it is more active than the bromine, replaces the bromine of the magnesium bromide.

$$Cl_2 + MgBr_2 \rightarrow MgCl_2 + Br_2 \uparrow$$

16. PHYSICAL PROPERTIES

Bromine is the only nonmetallic element that is a liquid at ordinary temperatures. It is a volatile, dark-red liquid with a very irritating odor. Bromine is about three times as dense as water, and fairly soluble in water and in potassium bromide solution. Bromine is also very soluble in carbon disulfide, chloroform, and carbon tetrachloride, imparting an orange color to these solvents. This color change is used as a test for free bromine. *Bromine vapor, like that of chlorine, is pungent and poisonous.* The eyes are especially sensitive to bromine vapor.

Liquid
Dark-red
Irritating
3 × water
Fairly soluble in water;
very soluble in CS$_2$

17. CHEMICAL PROPERTIES

Bromine gains electrons more readily than iodine but not so readily as chlorine or fluorine.

Bromine is more active than iodine but less active than either fluorine or chlorine.

a. Bromine can replace iodine in an iodide compound.

$$2 KI + Br_2 \rightarrow 2 KBr + I_2$$

In terms of electrons:

$$Br_2{}^0 + 2\,e \rightarrow 2\,Br^-$$

$$2\,I^- - 2\,e \rightarrow I_2{}^0$$

Notice that bromine gains the two electrons that the iodide ions are forced to lose. Bromine can thus be considered a stronger oxidizing agent than iodine.

   b. Bromine water acts as a mild oxidizing and bleaching agent, and is used as such in the laboratory.

   c. Bromine combines with hydrogen and metals to form bromides.

$$H_2 + Br_2 \rightarrow 2\,HBr$$

$$Cu + Br_2 \rightarrow CuBr_2$$

In both of the above reactions, bromine gains electrons, thus illustrating its oxidizing action.

   d. Orange-colored bromine water becomes colorless in sunlight because of its conversion to hydrobromic acid.

$$2\,Br_2 + 2\,H_2O \rightarrow 4\,HBr + O_2 \uparrow$$

18. USES

Bromine is used in the manufacture of drugs and dyes, while bromides are used in medicines (NaBr) and in photography (AgBr).

Bromine is also used in the manufacture of ethylene dibromide ($C_2H_4Br_2$). This substance is added to leaded gasoline to convert any lead set free by combustion of the gasoline into lead bromide ($PbBr_2$). Free lead would injure the ignition points in the spark plugs.

IODINE

19. OCCURRENCE

Iodine occurs in nature in the form of iodide compounds present in sea water (brine), in seaweed (kelp), and in California oil wells. Some iodine is also found in the form of sodium iodate ($NaIO_3$) in deposits of Chile saltpeter (sodium nitrate).

20. LABORATORY PREPARATION

Iodine is prepared in the same manner as chlorine and bromine. A mixture of potassium iodide, manganese dioxide, and concentrated sulfuric acid is heated gently in a beaker. (See Fig. 20.) Sulfuric acid reacts with potassium iodide to produce hydrogen iodide. The hydrogen iodide is then oxidized by the manganese dioxide, liberating violet iodine vapor. This vapor condenses and collects on the upper, cooler walls of the beaker and bottom of the evaporating dish in the form of iodine crystals. *When a gas or vapor cools and forms a solid without passing through the liquid state, the process is called sublimation.* Iodine is thus collected by sublimation.

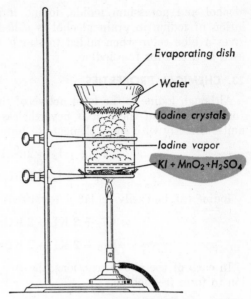

Fig. 20. Laboratory Preparation and Collection of Iodine

$$2 \text{ KI} + \text{MnO}_2 + 2 \text{ H}_2\text{SO}_4 \rightarrow \text{K}_2\text{SO}_4 + \text{MnSO}_4 + 2 \text{ H}_2\text{O} + \text{I}_2 \uparrow$$

The change from a solid to a vapor or gas without passing through the liquid state is also called sublimation. Under certain conditions, ice may sublime and form water vapor without first melting.

21. COMMERCIAL PREPARATION

Iodine is extracted from kelp by first burning the latter to an ash and then extracting the soluble iodides by dissolving them in water. This solution is evaporated to dryness and the solid iodides are treated as in the laboratory method.

Iodine may be liberated from brines by treating the brines with chlorine. The chlorine oxidizes the iodides to liberate free iodine.

$$2 \text{ NaI} + \text{Cl}_2 \rightarrow 2 \text{ NaCl} + \text{I}_2$$

22. PHYSICAL PROPERTIES

Iodine is a steel-gray crystalline solid, very slightly soluble in water. It is very soluble in carbon disulfide, carbon tetrachloride, and chloroform, producing violet solutions. This is a test for free iodine. In alcohol and potassium iodide, iodine forms brown solutions. A solution of iodine in grain alcohol is called *tincture of iodine*. Iodine gives a blue color when added to starch, so that starch may also be used as a test for free iodine.

23. CHEMICAL PROPERTIES

Although iodine is the least active of the halogens and can replace (oxidize) none of them, it is nevertheless a fairly active element. It unites directly with some elements to form iodides.

$$2\,Na + I_2 \rightarrow 2\,NaI$$

$$2\,P + 3\,I_2 \rightarrow 2\,PI_3$$

Iodine can be easily replaced (oxidized) by any other halogen.

$$Cl_2 + 2\,KI \rightarrow 2\,KCl + I_2$$

$$Br_2 + 2\,KI \rightarrow 2\,KBr + I_2$$

In each of the above reactions, the free halogen oxidizes the iodide ion to form free iodine.

24. USES

Iodine is used in the form of iodides in medicines to prevent or cure goiter, and in the making of light-sensitive emulsions for photographic plates or film. Tincture of iodine and iodoform (CHI_3) are effective antiseptics.

Radioactive iodine ($_{53}I^{131}$) is used in treating cancer of the thyroid gland.

RELATIVE ACTIVITY AND TESTS

25. RELATIVE REPLACING POWER OF HALOGENS

As has been explained, the relative ability of halogens to gain electrons depends on the size of the halogen atom. The larger the atomic radius of the halogen, the less readily the halogen can gain electrons. The order of replacement is therefore fluorine, chlorine, bromine, iodine. This is also the order of increasing atomic radius. In the reaction

$$2\,KBr + Cl_2 \rightarrow 2\,KCl + Br_2$$

chlorine can replace the bromine in KBr because chlorine, with its smaller atomic radius, gains electrons more readily than does bromine.

In the preceding reaction, chlorine forces the bromide ions to lose electrons. This is the same as saying that chlorine oxidizes the bromide ions.

The order of replacement of the halogens is based on the oxidizing power of the halogen.

Since fluorine is the most powerful oxidizing agent, it can replace any other halogen from its compound. Iodine, however, because of its poor oxidizing power, cannot replace any other halogen.

The ease with which the halogens combine with hydrogen and metallic elements to form compounds ending in -*ide* is in the same order as their replacing power. Thus, fluorides are the easiest halogen compounds to form.

26. TESTS FOR HALOGENS AND THEIR IONS

a. **Chlorine and Chloride Ions.** A greenish-yellow gas with the characteristic odor of chlorine identifies chlorine.

To test for chloride ions, add some silver nitrate solution to the solution of the compound being tested. If a white precipitate (insoluble substance) is formed, which darkens on exposure to light and is insoluble in nitric acid, the tested compound is a chloride. The addition of nitric acid is necessary to confirm the presence of a chloride because silver nitrate will form white precipitates with substances *other* than chlorides. These precipitates, however, are soluble in nitric acid. Equations for the reaction between chlorides and silver nitrate are:

$$NaCl + AgNO_3 \rightarrow NaNO_3 + \underset{\text{white}}{AgCl} \downarrow$$

$$FeCl_2 + 2\ AgNO_3 \rightarrow Fe(NO_3)_2 + 2\ \underset{\text{white}}{AgCl} \downarrow$$

The white precipitate of silver chloride is soluble in ammonium hydroxide.

b. **Bromine and Bromide Ions.** To test for free bromine, note the irritating odor of the reddish-brown liquid and add a drop of the liquid to carbon disulfide or to carbon tetrachloride, which is not flammable. If an orange solution is formed, the liquid is bromine.

To test for bromide ions, add a few drops of carbon disulfide to a water solution of the substance being tested. Add chlorine water to the mixture and shake. If an orange solution is formed in the carbon disulfide layer, the unknown is a bromide. The carbon disulfide merely acts as a solvent for the free bromine liberated by the oxidation (replacement) of bromide ions by chlorine.

c. Iodine and Iodide Ions. To test for iodine, add the solid being tested to carbon disulfide. If a violet solution is obtained, the solid is iodine. Another test for iodine is to add the solid being tested to starch paste. The formation of a blue mass indicates the presence of free iodine.

To test for iodide ions, add a few drops of carbon disulfide to a water solution of the substance being tested. Add chlorine or bromine water and shake. The formation of a violet solution in the carbon disulfide layer indicates the presence of an iodide.

HYDROGEN HALIDES AND HALOGEN ACIDS

27. PROPERTIES AND GENERAL METHOD OF PREPARATION

Chlorine combines with hydrogen to form colorless hydrogen chloride gas (HCl). Fluorine, bromine, and iodine form similar hydrogen compounds, all colorless gases. Their formulas are HF, HBr, and HI, respectively. As the most active halogen, fluorine forms the most stable compounds. Thus, of the hydrogen halides, HF is the most stable, while HI is the least stable. The concept of stability and its relationship to the prediction of chemical reactions will be considered more fully in Chapter 12.

Stability

HF
HCl
HBr
HI

The water solution of hydrogen chloride is called hydrochloric acid, and is a colorless solution. The water solutions of the other hydrogen halides are called hydrofluoric, hydrobromic, and hydriodic acids, respectively, and are all colorless solutions. Since each of these acids contains *two elements,* they are called *binary acids.* They have the typical properties of acids, listed under **13,** page 118.

FORMULA	HYDROGEN HALIDE	HALOGEN ACID
HF	Hydrogen fluoride	Hydrofluoric acid
HCl	Hydrogen chloride	Hydrochloric acid
HBr	Hydrogen bromide	Hydrobromic acid
HI	Hydrogen iodide	Hydriodic acid

All the hydrogen halides or their corresponding acids may be prepared by the action of the metallic halide on concentrated sulfuric acid. The following general reaction summarizes the preparation of any hydrogen halide:

$$2 \text{ MX} + \text{H}_2\text{SO}_4 \rightarrow \text{M}_2\text{SO}_4 + 2 \text{ HX} \uparrow$$

univalent   univalent   hydrogen
metallic   metallic   halide
halide   sulfate

28. HYDROGEN CHLORIDE AND HYDROCHLORIC ACID

The most common hydrogen halide is hydrogen chloride. In water, hydrogen chloride forms hydrochloric acid, the most important of the halogen acids because of its extensive use.

29. PREPARATION OF HYDROGEN CHLORIDE

Hydrogen chloride is prepared by gently heating a mixture of sodium chloride and concentrated sulfuric acid, as shown below. It is collected by air displacement because of its extreme solubility in water. Commercial hydrochloric acid, yellow in color due to dissolved iron, is called *muriatic acid*.

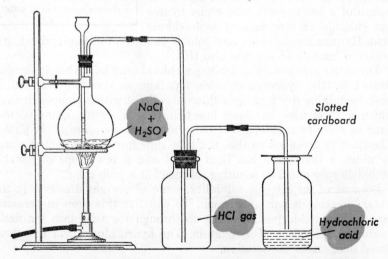

NaCl + H₂SO₄

Slotted cardboard

HCl gas

Hydrochloric acid

Fig. 29. Laboratory Preparation and Collection of HCl

The equation for the preparation is:

$$NaCl + H_2SO_4 \rightarrow NaHSO_4 + HCl \uparrow$$
sodium
bisulfate

If the temperature is raised by more vigorous heating, more sodium chloride reacts to form an additional molecule of hydrogen chloride.

$$2\ NaCl + H_2SO_4 \rightarrow Na_2SO_4 + 2\ HCl \uparrow$$
sodium
sulfate

Sodium chloride is a cheap source for the chloride ions, while sulfuric acid supplies the necessary hydrogen. Sulfuric acid also has a high boiling point ($338°C$), so that it is not liberated with the more volatile hydrogen chloride.

30. PHYSICAL PROPERTIES

Hydrogen chloride is a colorless gas with a pungent odor, and denser than air. Hydrogen chloride fumes in moist air, as may be shown by blowing one's breath across the mouth of a bottle containing either hydrogen chloride or concentrated hydrochloric

> Gas
> Colorless
> Pungent
> Denser than air
> Extremely soluble in water

acid. Hydrogen chloride is very soluble in water, forming hydrochloric acid, the formula of which is also HCl.

The extreme solubility of hydrogen chloride can be strikingly demonstrated by the hydrogen chloride fountain, as shown in Fig. 30. A flask containing dry hydrogen chloride is fitted with a stopper through which a glass tube has been inserted. (*Use a strong, round-bottom flask in order to withstand the reduction in pressure inside the flask.*) The flask is arranged so that the tube dips into a reservoir of water to which a little base has been added and a few drops of phenolphthalein solution. The resulting solution has a pink color.

Because of its extreme solubility, some of the gas dissolves in the water, creating a partial vacuum. To equalize this drop in pressure, air on the outside pushes water up through the tube into the flask, producing the effect of a fountain. The hydrochloric acid thus produced decolorizes the solution.

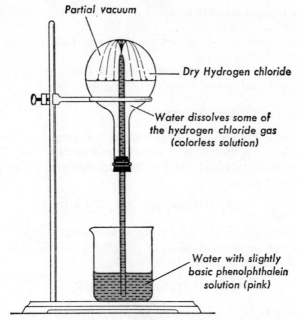

Fig. 30. The Hydrogen Chloride Fountain

31. CHEMICAL PROPERTIES

Dry hydrogen chloride is generally inactive. It will, however, react with ammonia to form a white cloud of ammonium chloride. In the laboratory, bottles of hydrochloric acid, if stored near ammonia water, will become coated with a deposit of ammonium chloride.

Hydrochloric acid is a typical acid.

The properties of acids, it is thought, are due to the formation of hydronium ions when the acid comes into contact with water.

32. USES

a. Hydrochloric acid is used to prepare chlorides, such as zinc chloride, which is used as a *soldering flux* (surface cleaner).

b. Metals are cleaned by dipping them into hydrochloric acid. This process is called *pickling.*

c. Aqua regia, a mixture of nitric and hydrochloric acids, is used to dissolve gold and platinum.

d. Hydrochloric acid is also used in the manufacture of glue and gelatine from bones.

e. Minute quantities of hydrochloric acid, found in the gastric juice of the stomach, aid in the digestion of proteins.

33. OTHER HYDROGEN HALIDES

a. **Hydrogen Fluoride.** Hydrogen fluoride is prepared by heating a mixture of calcium fluoride and concentrated sulfuric acid. This reaction is carried out in a lead dish because of the solvent action of hydrogen fluoride on glass.

$$CaF_2 + H_2SO_4 \rightarrow CaSO_4 + 2\ HF \uparrow$$

The chemical action of both hydrogen fluoride and hydrofluoric acid on glass is due to the conversion of the silicon dioxide of the glass to the gaseous compound silicon tetrafluoride.

$$SiO_2 + 4\ HF \rightarrow 2\ H_2O + SiF_4 \uparrow$$

Because of this property, both hydrogen fluoride and hydrofluoric acid are used to etch glass. Chemically, hydrofluoric acid is a weak acid because of its inability to ionize sufficiently. Hydrofluoric acid is stored in wax, rubber, or polyethylene (plastic) bottles.

b. **Hydrogen Bromide.** Pure hydrogen bromide is *not* prepared by the action of sulfuric acid on a bromide. Because it is less stable than either hydrofluoric or hydrochloric acid, hydrogen bromide is partially oxidized by sulfuric acid to free bromine. Consequently, pure hydrogen bromide is prepared by the reaction between phosphorus tribromide and water.

$$PBr_3 + 3\ H_2O \rightarrow H_3PO_3 + 3\ HBr \uparrow$$

Hydrogen bromide forms hydrobromic acid when dissolved in water.

c. **Hydrogen Iodide.** Even less stable than hydrogen bromide, hydrogen iodide is likewise partially oxidized by sulfuric acid to free iodine. Like hydrogen bromide, pure hydrogen iodide is prepared by the reaction of phosphorus tri-iodide with water.

$$PI_3 + 3\ H_2O \rightarrow H_3PO_3 + 3\ HI \uparrow$$

The water solution of hydrogen iodide is called hydriodic acid.

1. *a.* List all the common members of the halogen family and indicate the physical state of each.
   b. Why are the halogens called salt formers?
   c. Although they are all members of Group VII A, explain why the halogens differ in chemical activity.
2. *a.* If hydrofluoric acid is treated with manganese dioxide, (1) fluorine is liberated (2) water is formed (3) MnF_2 is formed (4) nothing happens.
   b. Fluorine is prepared by the _____ of potassium hydrogen fluoride.
   c. Write the equation for the reaction.
   d. The chemist who first isolated fluorine was _____.
   e. Explain why the extraction of fluorine is unusually difficult.
3. *a.* Fluorine is (1) a yellow liquid (2) nonpoisonous (3) odorless (4) denser than air.
   b. Fluorine is the halogen that has the greatest tendency to *lose* electrons. [True or false? If false, correct the italicized term.]
   c. Explain why fluorine is the most powerful chemical oxidizing agent.
   *d. Assuming that M is a trivalent metal, write two electron equations to show what happens when M reacts with fluorine. Does the reaction involve oxidation-reduction? Explain.
4. Describe three uses of fluorine and in each case state the property upon which the use depends.
5. *a.* Why is chlorine not found free in nature?
   b. The most abundant chlorine compound found in nature is _____.
6. *a.* Chlorine may be prepared by heating a mixture of hydrochloric acid and (1) a metal (2) a base (3) a catalyst (4) an oxidizing agent.
   b. Chlorine is collected by *water* displacement. [True or false? If false, correct the italicized term.]
   c. Make a labeled diagram to illustrate the laboratory preparation and collection of chlorine.
   d. Complete and balance each of the following equations:
      (1) $HCl + MnO_2 \rightarrow$
      (2) $KCl + MnO_2 + H_2SO_4 \rightarrow$
      *(3) $HCl + KMnO_4 \rightarrow MnCl_2 +$
7. *a.* Chlorine is obtained commercially from (1) HCl (2) $KClO_3$ (3) KCl (4) NaCl.
   b. An electrochemical cell used in the commercial preparation of chlorine was devised by _____.
   c. Using an equation, show how chlorine may be prepared from bleaching powder ($CaOCl_2$).
8. *a.* Chlorine is (1) a greenish-yellow liquid (2) a specific eye irritant (3) odorless (4) readily liquefied at room temperature by pressure alone.

b. Chlorine has the following approximate ratio by weight to air (1) 1:1 (2) 1:2.5 (3) 1.5:1 (4) 2.5:1.

c. Chlorine is more soluble in water at
   (1) low temperature and low pressure
   (2) low temperature and high pressure
   (3) high temperature and high pressure
   (4) high temperature and low pressure

9. a. Which is a more powerful oxidizer, chlorine or fluorine? Explain.

   b. Complete and balance each of the following equations:
      (1) $H_2 + Cl_2 \rightarrow$
      (2) $Zn + Cl_2 \rightarrow$
      (3) $Al + Cl_2 \rightarrow$
      (4) $H_2O + Cl_2 \xrightarrow{\text{sunlight}}$

   c. When a wax taper burns in chlorine, the chloride formed is (1) CCl_4 (2) $CHCl_3$ (3) $COCl_2$ (4) HCl.

   d. When metals react with chlorine, the metals _____ (lose, gain) electrons.

   e. When nonmetals react with chlorine, the nonmetals _____ (lose, gain) electrons.

   *f. Write the formulas of two chlorine compounds in which chlorine has a positive valence number. Predict whether these substances will behave as oxidizing or reducing agents.

10. a. Moist chlorine bleaches because chlorine reacts with water to form _____.

    b. A chlorine compound used as a source of chlorine for commercial bleaching is _____.

    c. Using a labeled diagram, explain the steps employed in commercial bleaching.

    d. Chlorine is added to drinking water in order to (1) improve the taste (2) improve the color (3) destroy harmful bacteria (4) remove objectionable odors.

    e. Explain how chlorine may be used as (1) a disinfectant and (2) an antiseptic.

    f. A chlorine compound used as an anesthetic is _____.

    g. A chlorine compound used widely as a solvent is $AlCl_3$. [True or false? If false, correct the italicized term.]

11. An important commercial source of bromine is _____.

12. a. The _____ (oxidation, reduction) of HBr liberates bromine.

    b. Bromine is prepared in the laboratory by heating a mixture of _____, _____, and _____.

    c. Write an equation to illustrate the laboratory preparation of bromine from (1) hydrogen bromide and (2) a metal bromide.

    d. Bromine is collected in the laboratory by (1) aeration (2) distillation (3) crystallization (4) sublimation.

    e. Make a labeled diagram to illustrate the laboratory preparation and collection of bromine.

13. a. Describe the commercial preparation of bromine from sea water.

    b. Write an equation to illustrate this process.

14. In tabular form, compare the physical properties of bromine and chlorine.

15. *a.* Bromine gains electrons more readily than _____ (fluorine, iodine).

   b. Shaking a solution of sodium bromide with free iodine and CCl_4 results in a layer of CCl_4 which is (1) blue (2) orange (3) red-brown (4) violet.

   c. By means of two electron equations, show that bromine is a stronger oxidizing agent than iodine.

   d. Complete and balance each of the following equations:

     (1) $H_2 + Br_2 \rightarrow$

     (2) $Na + Br_2 \rightarrow$

     (3) $H_2O + Br_2 \xrightarrow{\text{sunlight}}$

16. Name three bromine compounds and state a specific use for each.

17. Two sources of naturally occurring iodine are _____ and _____.

18. *a.* The proper mixture of chemicals to be used in the laboratory preparation of iodine is (1) KI, H_2O (2) KI, HCl, MnO_2 (3) KI, MnO_2 (4) KI, MnO_2, H_2SO_4.

   b. Iodine is collected in the laboratory by a process called _____.

   c. Make a labeled diagram to illustrate the laboratory preparation and collection of iodine.

19. *a.* Describe a commercial method for the extraction of iodine.

   b. Write an equation to illustrate the process.

20. *a.* At room temperature, iodine is a (1) liquid (2) solid (3) gas (4) liquid and solid.

   b. Iodine is least soluble in (1) alcohol (2) carbon disulfide (3) carbon tetrachloride (4) water.

   c. Dilute solutions of iodine in carbon tetrachloride are (1) brown (2) orange (3) violet (4) red.

   d. Solutions in which alcohol is the solvent are called _____.

21. *a.* Iodine can oxidize (1) chloride ions (2) bromide ions (3) fluoride ions (4) no other halogen ion.

   b. Complete and balance each of the following equations:

     (1) $K + I_2 \rightarrow$

     (2) $N_2 + I_2 \rightarrow$

   c. State two important uses of iodine.

   *d. Why is radioactive iodine effective in treating cancer of the thyroid gland?

22. *a.* As the atomic radius of halogens increases, the ability of the halogen to gain electrons _____ (decreases, increases, remains the same).

   b. In the reaction $2\ KBr + Cl_2 \rightarrow 2\ KCl + Br_2$, the particle that loses electrons is (1) the potassium ion (2) the bromide ion (3) chlorine (4) potassium bromide.

   c. By means of a series of experiments, explain how you would determine the relative activity of the halogens. Use balanced equations wherever possible.

23. **a.* Describe a chemical test that could be used to identify a substance as a fluoride.

   b. A greenish-yellow gas (1) must be chlorine (2) must be bromine (3) may be chlorine (4) may be bromine.

   c. Explain why a confirmatory test is necessary in testing for chloride ions.

   d. Silver chloride is soluble in (1) alcohol (2) water (3) nitric acid (4) ammonium hydroxide.

   e. By means of a chemical test, how may sodium bromide be distinguished from sodium iodide?

24. *a.* The most stable hydrogen halide is (1) HF (2) HCl (3) HBr (4) HI.

   b. The water solutions of all the hydrogen halides form acids called (1) -ic (2) -ous (3) hypo... -ous (4) hydro... -ic.

   c. All binary acids contain *oxygen*. [True or false? If false, correct the italicized term.]

   d. State two reasons why sulfuric acid is used in the preparation of other acids.

   *e. When sulfuric acid is used in the preparation of other acids, how many different sulfate salts may be formed? Explain.

25. *a.* Make a labeled diagram to illustrate the laboratory preparation and collection of hydrogen chloride.

   b. Write the equation for the reaction.

26. *a.* Hydrogen chloride is (1) insoluble in water and difficult to liquefy (2) less dense than air and colorless (3) very soluble in water and denser than air (4) very soluble in water and greenish-yellow in color.

   b. Describe a test for hydrogen chloride.

   c. Explain the action of the hydrogen chloride fountain.

27. *a.* When hydrochloric acid is added to copper, (1) copper chloride is formed (2) copper hydroxide is formed (3) hydrogen is liberated (4) nothing happens.

   b. Complete and balance each of the following equations:
   (1) $NH_3 + HCl \rightarrow$
   (2) $Al + HCl \rightarrow$
   (3) $NH_4OH + HCl \rightarrow$

28. List five important uses of hydrochloric acid.

29. *a.* Complete and balance each of the following equations:
   (1) $CaF_2 + H_2SO_4 \rightarrow$
   (2) $SiO_2 + HF \rightarrow$
   (3) $PBr_3 + H_2O \rightarrow$

   b. Hydrofluoric acid is (1) a weak acid (2) a strong acid (3) highly ionized (4) a typical halogen acid.

   c. Explain why hydrogen bromide and hydrogen iodide require a method of preparation different from other hydrogen halides.

30. Calculate the weight of hydrochloric acid needed to react with manganese dioxide to produce one ton of chlorine.

31. Calculate the volume of chlorine released during the electrolysis of 400 grams of sodium chloride.

32. Calculate the volume of hydrogen bromide produced when bromine combines with 50 cubic feet of hydrogen.

11 EFFECTS OF IONIZATION

1. IONIC EQUATIONS

In reactions involving solutions of acids, bases, and salts, it is frequently helpful to write the equations in ionic form. Neutralization equations have already been expressed in this manner.

To write an ionic equation, write the balanced molecular equation first.

The molecular equation for the neutralization of calcium hydroxide by nitric acid, for example, may be written as follows:

$$Ca(OH)_2 + 2\ HNO_3 \rightarrow Ca(NO_3)_2 + 2\ H_2O$$

The molecular equation reveals that two moles (molecular weights) of nitric acid are required. The ionic equation, hence, should show the ionization of two moles of HNO_3.

$$Ca^{+2} + 2\ OH^- + 2\ H^+ + 2\ NO_3^- \rightarrow Ca^{+2} + 2\ NO_3^- + 2\ H_2O$$

When the ionic equation is balanced, the net charge on each side of the arrow is zero.

Because the ionization of water is slight, it is written as un-ionized H_2O in neutralization equations. Under certain conditions, the slight ionization of water is sufficient to cause the salt and water to react, thus reversing the neutralization reaction. (Such reactions will be considered later in this chapter, under 3, pages 154-156.)

2. REACTIONS THAT GO TO COMPLETION

The ability of substances to ionize may cause the products of a reaction to re-form the original substances. Reactions in which both the starting substances and products are highly ionized are said to be *reversible*.

Reactions in which the products cannot re-form the original substances are called *nonreversible*.

Nonreversible reactions go to completion, or to an end.

Let us consider double replacement reactions by reviewing the neutralization of calcium hydroxide by nitric acid ionically.

$$Ca^{+2} + 2\ OH^- + 2\ H^+ + 2\ NO_3^- \rightarrow Ca^{+2} + 2\ NO_3^- + 2\ H_2O$$

Note that calcium hydroxide and nitric acid cannot be re-formed in appreciable concentration from the reaction between calcium nitrate and water. The ionic equation shows that the inability of water to furnish sufficient hydrogen and hydroxyl ions drives the reaction to completion.

Double replacement reactions will go to completion if one of the products fails to ionize appreciably.

A product may leave the field of action as a gas (volatility), a precipitate (insolubility), or as un-ionized water resulting from neutralization. Neither a gas nor a precipitate ionizes. Hence, a reaction goes to completion when any one of the products does not ionize.

Note that in ionic equations involving reactions that go to completion, the product leaving the field of action is indicated as a molecule and not as ions.

a. **Volatility.** When one of the products formed is a gas, it leaves the field of action, and the reaction goes to completion. If water is present and the gas dissolves, heat must be applied to reduce the solubility of the gas. The gas leaves the field of action, thus driving the reaction to completion. Examples of soluble gases are hydrogen chloride (HCl), hydrogen bromide (HBr), hydrogen fluoride (HF), hydrogen iodide (HI), and hydrogen sulfide (H_2S). Examples of unstable compounds which decompose to form gases are carbonic acid (H_2CO_3), sulfurous acid (H_2SO_3), and ammonium hydroxide (NH_4OH). Such compounds, usually liquids, are called volatile. The equations for their decomposition follow:

$$H_2CO_3 \rightarrow H_2O + CO_2 \uparrow$$

$$H_2SO_3 \rightarrow H_2O + SO_2 \uparrow$$

$$NH_4OH \rightarrow H_2O + NH_3 \uparrow$$

The reaction between sodium sulfide and hydrochloric acid is an example of a double replacement going to completion because of volatility.

MOLECULAR: $Na_2S + 2\ HCl \rightarrow 2\ NaCl + H_2S \uparrow$

IONIC: $2\ Na^+ + S^{-2} + 2\ H^+ + 2\ Cl^- \rightarrow$
$\qquad 2\ Na^+ + 2\ Cl^- + H_2S$

The reaction between sodium carbonate and hydrochloric acid is another example of a double replacement going to completion because of volatility.

MOLECULAR: $Na_2CO_3 + 2\ HCl \rightarrow 2\ NaCl + H_2O + CO_2 \uparrow$

IONIC: $2\ Na^+ + CO_3^{-2} + 2\ H^+ + 2\ Cl^- \rightarrow$
$\qquad 2\ Na^+ + 2\ Cl^- + H_2O + CO_2$

b. **Insolubility.** When one of the products formed is insoluble, the reaction goes to completion. The insoluble product settles out as a precipitate and hence does not ionize appreciably. Common insoluble compounds are silver chloride, $AgCl$; barium sulfate, $BaSO_4$; copper sulfide, CuS; lead sulfide, PbS; cadmium sulfide, CdS; copper hydroxide, $Cu(OH)_2$; and ferric hydroxide, $Fe(OH)_3$.

The reaction between solutions of sodium chloride and silver nitrate is an example of a double replacement going to completion because of insolubility.

MOLECULAR: $NaCl + AgNO_3 \rightarrow NaNO_3 + AgCl \downarrow$

IONIC: $Na^+ + Cl^- + Ag^+ + NO_3^- \rightarrow$
$\qquad Na^+ + NO_3^- + AgCl$

The reaction between sulfuric acid and barium chloride is another example of a double replacement going to completion because of insolubility.

MOLECULAR: $H_2SO_4 + BaCl_2 \rightarrow 2\ HCl + BaSO_4 \downarrow$

IONIC: $2\ H^+ + SO_4^{-2} + Ba^{+2} + 2\ Cl^- \rightarrow$
$\qquad 2\ H^+ + 2\ Cl^- + BaSO_4$

All nitrates, chlorates, acetates, and common compounds of sodium, potassium, and ammonium are soluble in water.

c. **Nonionization and Neutralization.** Since undissociated or unionized water is obtained as one of the products in every neutralization, such reactions go to an end. The reaction between solutions of sodium hydroxide and hydrochloric acid is an example of such a neutralization.

MOLECULAR: $NaOH + HCl \rightarrow NaCl + H_2O$

IONIC: $Na^+ + OH^- + H^+ + Cl^- \rightarrow Na^+ + Cl^- + H_2O$

3. HYDROLYSIS

Another type of reaction that may be considered an effect of ionization is hydrolysis. Essentially, this reaction is a reversal of neutralization.

Hydrolysis is the reaction between certain salts and water to produce an acid and a base.

NEUTRALIZATION: $Acid + Base \rightarrow A \; Salt + Water$

HYDROLYSIS: $A \; Salt + Water \rightarrow Acid + Base$

Hydrolysis may be attributed to the slight ionization of water, which may be written:

$$HOH \underset{\longleftarrow}{\rightarrow} H^+ + OH^-$$

Certain salts may react with these ions to produce acids and bases, which in turn will affect litmus. For example:

MOLECULAR: $Na_2CO_3 + 2 \; HOH \rightarrow 2 \; NaOH + H_2CO_3\uparrow$ (volatile)

IONIC: $2 \; Na^+ + CO_3^{-2} + 2 \; H^+ + 2 \; OH^- \rightarrow$

$2 \; Na^+ +$ $2 \; OH^-$ $+ H_2CO_3$
turns
litmus
blue

The above reaction goes to completion because H_2CO_3 is volatile and thus is only weakly ionized. This means that there are few H^+ ions in solution. On the other hand, the ionization of NaOH, which is a strong electrolyte, produces a high concentration of OH^- ions. This is the same as saying that the base produced in this reaction is stronger than the acid. Hence, the salt solution is basic and turns litmus blue.

To understand the effect of the hydrolysis of salt solutions on litmus, it is necessary to know the comparative strength of acids and bases.

In the table that follows, the strength of acids and bases is related to the ability of the acids and bases to ionize.

ACIDS			BASES	
completely or nearly completely ionized	moderately ionized	slightly ionized	completely or nearly completely ionized	slightly ionized
nitric	oxalic	hydrofluoric	potassium hydroxide	ammonium hydroxide
hydrochloric	phosphoric	acetic	sodium hydroxide	(all others)
sulfuric	sulfurous	carbonic	barium hydroxide	
hydriodic		hydrosulfuric	strontium hydroxide	
hydrobromic		(all others)	calcium hydroxide	

To predict hydrolysis reactions, the following rules may be used:

a. Salts derived from weak acids and strong bases have a basic reaction, turning litmus blue. Examples of such salts are sodium sulfide, potassium carbonate, and sodium acetate. The reaction in a sodium sulfide solution may be represented as follows:

MOLECULAR: $Na_2S + 2\ HOH \rightarrow 2\ NaOH + H_2S \uparrow$

IONIC: $2\ Na^+ + S^{-2} + 2\ H^+ + 2\ OH^- \rightarrow$

$$2\ Na^+ + \boxed{2\ OH^-} + H_2S$$

turns
litmus
blue

Hydrosulfuric acid (H_2S) is a weak acid, furnishing few H^+ ions. Since it is also volatile, it is shown in the equation as a gas leaving the reaction. On the other hand, sodium hydroxide is a strong base, furnishing many OH^- ions, and consequently turning litmus blue.

b. Salts derived from strong acids and weak bases have an acid reaction, turning litmus red. Examples of such salts are copper sulfate, zinc nitrate, and ammonium chloride. The reaction in a copper sulfate solution may be represented as follows:

MOLECULAR: $CuSO_4 + 2\ HOH \rightarrow H_2SO_4 + Cu(OH)_2$

IONIC: $Cu^{+2} + SO_4^{-2} + 2\ H^+ + 2\ OH^- \rightarrow$

$$\boxed{2\ H^+} + SO_4^{-2} + Cu(OH)_2$$

turns
litmus
red

Copper hydroxide, which is only slightly soluble, is therefore a weak electrolyte and furnishes few OH^- ions. On the other hand, sulfuric acid is a strong electrolyte, furnishing many H^+ ions, which turns litmus red.

c. Salts derived from strong acids and strong bases are neutral to litmus. They do not hydrolyze appreciably. They merely ionize.

$$NaCl \rightarrow Na^+ + Cl^-$$

d. Salts derived from weak acids and weak bases are completely hydrolyzed. The effect on litmus depends on the extent of ionization of the acid and base produced.

Hydrolysis reactions may be summarized as follows:

---

(1) No appreciable hydrolysis
        Salts of strong acids and strong bases
(2) Partial hydrolysis
        Salts of strong acids and weak bases
        Salts of weak acids and strong bases
(3) Complete hydrolysis
        Salts of weak acids and weak bases

---

4. ELECTROLYSIS

The decomposition of a substance by means of electricity is called electrolysis. In order to conduct electric current, a substance must contain ions that are free to move about. The passage of a direct current through such a substance results in a chemical change at each electrode. The changes involve both oxidation and reduction. *Oxidation,* or a loss of electrons, *always occurs at the anode,* while *reduction,* or a gain of electrons, *always occurs at the cathode.*

Electrolysis is used in the preparation of gases, in electroplating, and in the extraction of active metals from their ores. Several examples of electrolysis follow.

a. **Electrolysis of Hydrochloric Acid.** In the electrolysis of concentrated hydrochloric acid, hydrogen is liberated at the cathode and chlorine at the anode.

The equation for the electrolysis is:

$$2\,HCl \rightarrow H_2 \uparrow + Cl_2 \uparrow$$

The formation of H_2 and Cl_2 may be understood by applying our knowledge of ionization as follows:

The ionization of hydrogen chloride in solution produces hydrogen (hydronium) ions and chloride ions.

$$HCl + H_2O \rightarrow H_3O^+ + Cl^-$$

or simply $HCl \rightarrow H^+ + Cl^-$

Hydrogen ions, which have a deficiency of electrons, are attracted to the cathode, which has an excess of electrons. Each hydrogen ion regains an electron at the cathode to become a hydrogen atom. Two hydrogen atoms join to form a molecule of hydrogen gas.

$$2 H^+ + 2 e \rightarrow H_2^0$$

This reaction is called reduction because it involves a gain of electrons.

Reduction always takes place at the cathode because the cathode has an excess of electrons.

Chloride ions, which have an excess of electrons, are attracted to the anode, which has a deficiency of electrons. Each chloride ion loses an electron at the anode to become a chlorine atom. Two chlorine atoms join to form a molecule of chlorine gas.

$$2 Cl^- - 2 e \rightarrow Cl_2^0$$

This reaction is called oxidation because it involves a loss of electrons.

Oxidation always takes place at the anode because the anode has a deficiency of electrons.

b. **Electrolysis of Cupric Chloride Solution.** As in the case of hydrochloric acid, the essential reactions are as follows:

IONIZATION:	$CuCl_2 \rightarrow Cu^{+2} + 2 Cl^-$
REDUCTION AT CATHODE:	$Cu^{+2} + 2 e \rightarrow Cu^0$ (metal)
OXIDATION AT ANODE:	$2 Cl^- - 2 e \rightarrow Cl_2^0$
ELECTROLYSIS (TOTAL):	$CuCl_2 \rightarrow Cu^0 + Cl_2^0$

This example of electrolysis may be used as a practical method for electroplating copper, as discussed on pages 285-287 under *d.*

c. **Electrolysis of Sodium Chloride Solution.** In water solution, sodium ions and chloride ions are free to move about (mobile). It was formerly thought that sodium ions are attracted to the cathode, gain electrons, and form sodium metal. Recent research, however, indicates that water is reduced at the cathode to form hydroxide ions and hydrogen gas. In effect, this means that hydrogen ions from water are being reduced to form hydrogen gas, thus liberating hydroxide ions. The reactions involved in the electrolysis of sodium chloride solution may be summarized as follows:

IONIZATION: $\qquad$ $2\ NaCl \rightarrow 2\ Na^+ + 2\ Cl^-$

REDUCTION AT CATHODE: $\quad 2\ HOH + 2\ e \rightarrow 2\ OH^- + H_2^0$

OXIDATION AT ANODE: $\quad 2\ Cl^- - 2\ e \rightarrow Cl_2^0$

ELECTROLYSIS (TOTAL): $\quad 2\ NaCl + 2\ H_2O \rightarrow$
$$2\ NaOH + H_2 \uparrow + Cl_2 \uparrow$$

This reaction takes place in the Nelson, Vorce, and Hooker cells, described under *a*, page 238.

d. **Electrolysis of Water.** Because water does not conduct electricity appreciably, a little sulfuric acid is added to make it a better conductor. The reactions that take place during electrolysis may be represented as follows:

IONIZATION: $\qquad$ $HOH \rightarrow H^+ + OH^-$

REDUCTION AT CATHODE: $\quad 4\ H^+ + 4\ e \rightarrow 2\ H_2^0$

OXIDATION AT ANODE: $\quad 4\ OH^- - 4\ e \rightarrow 2\ H_2O + O_2^0$

Since four electrons are required (lost) for the oxidation, four electrons are gained during reduction. As a result, the electrolysis of water yields two volumes of hydrogen and one volume of oxygen.

$$2\ H_2O \rightarrow 2\ H_2 \uparrow + O_2 \uparrow$$

e. **Metallurgy of Active Metals.** Active metals such as potassium, sodium, calcium, magnesium, and aluminum may be extracted from their compounds by electrolysis. Since electrolysis requires the presence of mobile ions, the compounds used must be liquid. Water solutions of these compounds cannot be used because water may react with the liberated metal. The compound is therefore melted (fused) and then electrolyzed. If *MCl* represents the chloride of an active univalent metal *M*, the electrolysis reaction may be summarized as follows:

IONIZATION: $2 \text{ MCl} \rightarrow 2 \text{ M}^+ + 2 \text{ Cl}^-$

REDUCTION AT CATHODE: $2 \text{ M}^+ + 2 \text{ e} \rightarrow 2 \text{ M}^0$ (free metal)

OXIDATION AT ANODE: $2 \text{ Cl}^- - 2 \text{ e} \rightarrow \text{Cl}_2^0$

ELECTROLYSIS (TOTAL): $2 \text{ MCl} \rightarrow 2 \text{ M} + \text{Cl}_2 \uparrow$

Examples of such electrolysis reactions are:

$$2 \text{ NaCl} \rightarrow 2 \text{ Na} + \text{Cl}_2 \uparrow$$

$$2 \text{ Al}_2\text{O}_3 \rightarrow 4 \text{ Al} + 3 \text{ O}_2 \uparrow$$

Study Guide

1. *a.* When an ionic equation is balanced, the total charge on either side of the arrow is _____.
   b. Write ionization equations for each of the following reactions:
      (1) $\text{KOH} + \text{H}_2\text{SO}_4 \rightarrow$
      (2) $\text{Ba(OH)}_2 + \text{HNO}_3 \rightarrow$
      (3) $\text{NH}_4\text{OH} + \text{HCl} \rightarrow$
      (4) $\text{NaOH} + \text{H}_3\text{PO}_4 \rightarrow$
      (5) $\text{Ca(OH)}_2 + \text{HCl} \rightarrow$
2. *a.* What is meant by a reversible reaction? Illustrate.
   b. What is meant by the phrase "reactions go to completion"?
   c. State three conditions which permit reactions to go to completion. Write a balanced equation for a reaction that illustrates each condition.
3. *a.* The reaction between a salt and water is known as (1) efflorescence (2) electrolysis (3) hydrolysis (4) neutralization.
   b. Hydrolysis results from the slight ionization of *salts*. [True or false? If false, correct the italicized term.]
   c. A salt whose water solution has no effect on litmus is (1) CuSO_4 (2) Na_2CO_3 (3) NaCl (4) NaHCO_3.
   d. $\text{Mg(NO}_3)_2$ is a salt that may be prepared from a (1) strong acid and a strong base (2) strong acid and a weak base (3) weak acid and a strong base (4) weak acid and a weak base.
   e. To predict the effect of salt solutions on litmus, it is necessary to know the comparative strength of _____ and _____.

4. *a.* Salts of strong bases and weak acids turn litmus solution _____.

    b. Salts of weak bases and strong acids turn litmus solution _____.

    c. Salts of strong acids and strong bases are _____ to litmus solution.

    d. Using ionization equations, explain the effect of the following salts on litmus solution:

      *(1) sodium acetate

      (2) aluminum sulfate

      (3) barium chloride

  e. Using ionization equations, explain which of the following solutions has the highest pH:

      (1) NaOH

      (2) NaHCO₃

      (3) Na₂CO₃

5. *a.* The decomposition of a substance by means of electricity is known as _____.

    b. Solid salt will not conduct an electric current because _____.

  c. Why does electrolysis require the use of direct current?

    d. At the anode, _____ (oxidation, reduction) always takes place during electrolysis.

    e. At the cathode, _____ always takes place during electrolysis.

    f. Describe three important uses of electrolysis.

6. *a.* Why does electrolysis involve oxidation-reduction?

    b. For the electrolysis of each of the following, write the anode reaction, the cathode reaction, and the total reaction:

      (1) hydrobromic acid

      (2) zinc chloride solution

      (3) fused sodium hydroxide

      *(4) sodium hydroxide solution

    c. Explain the oxidation reaction that occurs in the electrolysis of water.

    d. During electrolysis, ions which have a deficiency of electrons are attracted to (1) the anode (2) the cathode (3) the anode and cathode (4) neither the anode nor the cathode.

12 PRINCIPLES OF REACTION

1. CONDITIONS AFFECTING REACTIONS

Whether or not a reaction will take place depends upon many factors. Some of the more common conditions determining the probability of reaction are:

    a. The activity of the elements.

    b. The stability of the compounds.

    c. The tendency of the reaction to reverse itself.

2. THE ACTIVITY OF METALS

Metals tend to lose electrons in order to complete their outer shells. The activity of a metal is therefore defined as the tendency of the metal to lose electrons.

> The greater the tendency to lose electrons, the more active is the metal.

We have previously learned that, in a given family, metals of higher atomic number generally lose electrons more readily than metals of lower atomic number. Such behavior can be explained by assuming that, as the outer ring of electrons gets farther away from the positively charged nucleus, the metal loses electrons more easily. As a result, the activity of the metal increases.

3. THE ELECTROMOTIVE (ELECTROCHEMICAL) SERIES

The electromotive series is a list of metals arranged in order of their relative activity, or their tendency to lose electrons. A portion of this list appears at the right.

Metals will react with any particle that is capable of accepting electrons. When metals replace hydrogen ions in water or in acids, the hydrogen ions accept (gain) electrons lost by the metal to become hydrogen atoms.

$$2\ H^+ + 2\ e \rightarrow H_2^0$$

K
Ca
Na
Mg
Zn
Fe
Pb
H
Cu
Ag

The rate of evolution of hydrogen may be used as a measure of the activity of a metal.

a. **Reaction of Metals with Water.** Since water contains fewer hydrogen ions than most acids, only very active metals such as potassium will react with water.

$$2 \text{ K} + 2 \text{ H}_2\text{O} \rightarrow 2 \text{ KOH} + \text{H}_2 \uparrow$$

$$2 \text{ K}^0 - 2 \text{ e} \rightarrow 2 \text{ K}^+$$

Calcium also replaces hydrogen from water, but the reaction is less vigorous. Calcium is therefore less active than potassium.

$$\text{Ca} + 2 \text{ H}_2\text{O} \rightarrow \text{Ca(OH)}_2 + \text{H}_2 \uparrow$$

$$\text{Ca}^0 - 2 \text{ e} \rightarrow \text{Ca}^{+2}$$

b. **Reaction of Metals with Acids.** Since magnesium cannot replace hydrogen from cold water, it is less active than potassium, calcium, and sodium. However, it will react vigorously with hydrochloric acid to liberate hydrogen.

$$\text{Mg} + 2 \text{ HCl} \rightarrow \text{MgCl}_2 + \text{H}_2 \uparrow$$

In order to liberate hydrogen from acids, electrons must be supplied to the hydrogen ions in the acid. Thus, when metals replace hydrogen from acids, metals lose electrons.

$$\text{Mg}^0 - 2 \text{ e} \rightarrow \text{Mg}^{+2}$$

Of all the metals listed above hydrogen in the activity series, lead reacts least readily with acids to liberate hydrogen. Copper and silver, both of which fall below hydrogen in the series, cannot replace hydrogen from acids because hydrogen loses electrons more readily than either copper or silver.

c. **Reaction of Metals with Salt Solutions.** Metals may also replace other metals from their salt solutions. In order to do this, the metal must be more active than the metal ion in the salt solution.

For example, iron will react with a copper sulfate solution.

$$Fe + CuSO_4 \rightarrow FeSO_4 + Cu$$
$$Cu^{+2} + 2\ e \rightarrow Cu^0$$
$$Fe^0 - 2\ e \rightarrow Fe^{+2}$$

Iron can replace copper from its salt solution because, as the above reaction reveals, iron loses electrons more readily than copper does. Thus, iron is more active than copper. In a similar fashion, it can be shown that:

A metal will replace any other metal below it in the electromotive series.

Thus, zinc replaces iron from its salt solution.

$$Zn + FeSO_4 \rightarrow ZnSO_4 + Fe$$

On the other hand, zinc, which is below magnesium in the electromotive series, will not replace magnesium from its salt solutions.

4. THE ACTIVITY OF NONMETALS

Nonmetals tend to gain electrons in order to complete their outer shells.

The activity of a nonmetal is defined as its tendency to gain electrons.

In any given family of nonmetals, this tendency increases with decreasing atomic number.

In a previous chapter, the activity of the halogens was discussed. The order of their activity is listed at the right. As in the electromotive series, the element above can replace the element below from its solution. Since we are dealing with nonmetals, however, the ability to replace refers to the relative tendency to *gain* electrons.

F
Cl
Br
I

$$Cl_2 + 2\ KBr \rightarrow 2\ KCl + Br_2$$

Note that in this reaction, chlorine has gained electrons while bromide ions have lost electrons.

$$Cl_2 + 2\ e \rightarrow 2\ Cl^-$$
$$2\ Br^- - 2\ e \rightarrow Br_2^0$$

Iodine, however, because it is below bromine in order of activity, will not replace bromine from its compounds.

5. OXIDIZING AND REDUCING AGENTS, AND OXIDATION-REDUCTION

The activity of an element has been defined in terms of the tendency of the element to lose or gain electrons. Reactions between elements therefore involve oxidation-reduction.

It has been stated that in a reaction where a particle loses electrons, that particle has been oxidized; in a reaction where a particle gains electrons, that particle has been reduced. In any given reaction, when one particle loses electrons, the same number of electrons must be gained by another particle. Oxidation must be accompanied by corresponding reduction. Therefore:

The oxidizing agent must contain a particle which can gain electrons (be reduced); the reducing agent must contain a particle which can lose electrons (be oxidized).

It has been shown that metals tend to lose electrons. Because metals, when losing electrons, force other particles to gain electrons, metals are called reducing agents. The more active metals are therefore the more powerful reducing agents. In the electromotive series, since potassium is the most active metal, it is also the most powerful reducing agent. In the reaction

$$K + NaCl \rightarrow KCl + Na$$

OXIDATION: $K^0 - 1 e \rightarrow K^+$

REDUCTION: $Na^+ + 1 e \rightarrow Na^0$

potassium, by losing an electron, forces a sodium ion to gain an electron. Potassium is therefore called the reducing agent, while sodium chloride is the oxidizing agent. Potassium, however, has been oxidized, while sodium chloride has been reduced.

Nonmetals tend to gain electrons and are therefore classified as oxidizing agents. Thus, in the reaction

$$Cl_2 + KI \rightarrow 2 KCl + I_2$$

OXIDATION: $2 I^- - 2 e \rightarrow I_2^0$

REDUCTION: $Cl_2^0 + 2 e \rightarrow 2 Cl^-$

chlorine atoms gain the two electrons that are lost by the iodide ions. Chlorine is therefore called the oxidizing agent, while potassium iodide is the reducing agent. Chlorine, however, has been reduced, while potassium iodide has been oxidized. Note that:

> **During oxidation-reduction, there has also been a change in valence number. This change results from the loss and gain of electrons.**

6. STABILITY OF COMPOUNDS

Energy, usually in the form of heat, is either absorbed or liberated in many chemical reactions. The heat liberated or absorbed when one gram-molecular weight of a compound is formed from its elements is called the *heat of formation* of the compound.

A table of heats of formation follows.

COMPOUND	HEAT OF FORMATION (IN CALORIES)
KCl	104,300
NaCl	98,360
HF	64,000
$CuCl_2$	51,630
HI	−6,400

The greater the heat of formation of a compound, the more energy is usually required to decompose it. Hence:

> **The higher the heat of formation, the more stable is the compound.**

In the table of heats of formation, KCl is the most stable, while HI is the least stable. (A negative heat of formation indicates relative instability.)

Examination of lists of compounds having high heats of formation reveals that these compounds are derived from active metals and active nonmetals. Active elements form stable compounds because of the ease with which electrons are transferred. The concept of heat of formation is thus part of oxidation-reduction.

7. DETERMINING THE PROBABILITY OF REACTIONS

Chemical reactions generally fall into four categories: direct combination of elements (synthesis), decomposition of compounds (analysis), single replacement, and double replacement. The prediction of the probability of a chemical reaction depends upon the *type* of reaction involved.

It has already been shown (11, pages 82-83) that reactions involving combination, decomposition, and single replacement are essentially oxidation-reduction reactions. The probability of such reactions depends upon the ease with which electrons may be transferred from one particle to another. Therefore:

The probability of such reactions depends upon the relative activity of the elements.

The concept of heat of formation may also be utilized in predicting these reactions. Generally, *reactions will proceed in the direction which produces more stable compounds.*

Let us now consider each type of reaction separately.

a. **Direct Combination.** The reaction between two elements will usually proceed if one is metallic and the other is nonmetallic. This means that the reaction will take place if electrons can be transferred from the metal to the nonmetal. The reaction

$$2 \text{ K} + \text{Cl}_2 \rightarrow 2 \text{ KCl}$$

$$2 \text{ K}^0 - 2 \text{ e} \rightarrow 2 \text{ K}^+$$

$$\text{Cl}_2{}^0 + 2 \text{ e} \rightarrow 2 \text{ Cl}^-$$

takes place because potassium atoms lose electrons and chlorine atoms gain electrons. The activity of metals and nonmetals determines the ease with which they combine.

Since active elements also form stable compounds, heats of formation can be used to predict their combination. For example, the above reaction proceeds readily because the elements are active, resulting in the formation of a stable compound. When two inactive elements combine, the product is usually unstable. The reaction between hydrogen and iodine proceeds slowly to form hydrogen iodide, which is unstable.

$$\text{H}_2 + \text{I}_2 \rightleftarrows 2 \text{ HI}$$

The instability of HI reverses the reaction, which is indicated by a double arrow ($\rightleftarrows$).

b. **Decomposition.** Since decomposition reactions are the reverse of direct combination, similar principles may be used in predicting both types of reaction.

We have shown that in the reaction

$$2 K + Cl_2 \rightarrow 2 KCl$$

electrons are transferred readily from potassium atoms to chlorine atoms. As a result, the reaction proceeds rapidly. Let us now consider the reverse reaction, namely, the decomposition of KCl. Since electrons were readily transferred in the formation of this compound, these electrons must be restored to form the original elements. Thus:

$$2 KCl \rightarrow 2 K + Cl_2 \uparrow$$

$$2 K^+ + 2 e \rightarrow 2 K^0$$

$$2 Cl^- - 2 e \rightarrow Cl_2{}^0$$

Since both potassium ions and chloride ions are very stable, the decomposition of KCl will proceed very slowly.

In the formation of KCl from its elements, 104,300 calories of heat were liberated. To decompose KCl, at least the equivalent in energy must be supplied. Thus, compounds with high heats of formation (stable compounds) decompose slowly.

c. Single Replacement. In single replacement reactions, a metal may replace a metal ion in a salt solution. Thus, in the reaction

$$Cu + 2 AgNO_3 \rightarrow Cu(NO_3)_2 + 2 Ag$$

$$Cu^0 - 2 e \rightarrow Cu^{+2}$$

$$2 Ag^+ + 2 e \rightarrow 2 Ag^0$$

copper replaces silver ions. Since copper is above silver in the electromotive series, copper loses electrons more readily than silver. The position of the metals in the electromotive series will therefore reveal whether or not single replacement can occur. Where a metal is a more powerful reducing agent than another metal, it will replace ions of that metal in a salt solution.

The difference in activity between two metals determines how rapidly single replacement reactions will occur. Thus, the reaction between zinc and silver nitrate proceeds more rapidly than the reaction between copper and silver nitrate because zinc is more active than copper. This is the same as saying that the difference in activity between zinc and silver is *greater* than the difference in activity between copper and silver.

Because a more active metal forms a more stable compound, single replacement reactions will take place if the compound formed is more stable than the starting compound. The reaction between copper and silver nitrate takes place readily because copper nitrate is more stable than silver nitrate. Again, this is the same as saying that the reaction takes place because copper is more active than silver (loses electrons more readily than silver) and will therefore replace silver from its compounds.

d. **Double Replacement.** Double replacement reactions usually take place in water solution and involve, essentially, a rearrangement of ions rather than a loss or gain of electrons.

The principles of oxidation-reduction and the concept of heat of formation are therefore *not* utilized in predicting these reactions.

Double replacement reactions may be summarized as follows:

$$AB + CD \rightarrow AD + CB$$

In order for this reaction to take place (go to completion), assuming that *AB* and *CD* are highly ionized, either *AD* or *CB* must fail to ionize or must ionize only slightly. Double replacement reactions take place if one of the products formed is a gas or volatile liquid, a precipitate, or water. Each of these substances ionizes only slightly, thus meeting the necessary condition for driving the reaction to completion. Therefore:

To predict the probability of a double replacement reaction, it is necessary to determine whether one of the products formed is volatile, insoluble, or water.

For example, the reaction

$$NH_4Cl + NaOH \rightarrow NaCl + H_2O + NH_3 \uparrow$$

goes to completion because NH_3 is volatile.

The reaction

$$Na_2CO_3 + Ba(OH)_2 \rightarrow 2\ NaOH + BaCO_3 \downarrow$$

goes to completion because $BaCO_3$ is insoluble. All neutralization reactions go to completion because water, a weak electrolyte, is formed.

8. REVERSIBLE REACTIONS

Thus far, we have considered only those reactions which tend to go to completion. In other words, we have assumed that the products of a reaction were unable to re-form the original substances. However, this is not always the case. Let us assume that the reaction

$$4 \ H_2O + 3 \ Fe \rightleftarrows Fe_3O_4 + 4 \ H_2$$

is carried out in a closed vessel at a definite temperature for a sufficient length of time. If the vessel is now opened, it will be found to contain all four substances in *fixed,* but not necessarily equal, concentrations. Such a reaction in which the products re-form the starting substances is called a *reversible reaction.* Double arrows are generally used to indicate a reversible reaction.

a. **Equilibrium.** In the preceding example, two reactions have actually taken place. Water vapor and iron have combined at some definite rate to form iron oxide and hydrogen. At the same time, iron oxide and hydrogen have combined at some definite rate to re-form water vapor and iron.

In a reversible reaction, when the rates of the opposing reactions become equal, a condition called **equilibrium** is said to exist.

To attain equilibrium, a reaction must satisfy the following conditions:

(1) The reaction must be reversible.

(2) The rate of formation of the products from the starting substances must be equal to the rate of re-formation of the starting substances from the products.

To understand the conditions which control equilibrium, it is first necessary to consider the factors which determine the velocity of a reaction.

b. **Factors Determining the Velocity of a Reaction.** The rate of reaction between different substances depends on many factors, some of which are:

(1) *Activity of the Reacting Substances (Reactants).* As has been previously explained, the relative activity of the reactants affects the speed of a reaction. Active elements combine more rapidly than in-active elements.

(2) *Temperature.* Most chemical reactions are favored by an increase in temperature. Thus, heated antimony combines more readily with chlorine than does the same weight of the metal at room temperature.

(3) *Concentration of the Reactants.* As the concentration of the reactants increases, there is an increase in reaction rate. Thus, magnesium burns more vigorously in oxygen than in air, because in air the concentration of oxygen has been reduced.

(4) *Surface Area.* As the surface area of the reactants is increased, the speed of the reaction will increase. Wood shavings or sawdust burn more readily than an equal weight of wood, because in the former case more surface area is exposed to the oxygen in air. Increasing the rate of contact between particles therefore increases the reaction rate.

(5) *Pressure.* Reactions involving gases will increase in velocity as the pressure is increased. Thus, hydrogen and chlorine react violently under increased pressure because the rate of contact has been increased.

(6) *Catalysts.* Catalysts are substances which alter the speed of a reaction without undergoing any permanent change. Catalysts may hasten reactions, such as the more rapid decomposition of potassium chlorate in the presence of manganese dioxide. Some catalysts retard a reaction and are known as negative catalysts, or *inhibitors.* For example, ordinary 3% hydrogen peroxide, on standing, tends to decompose into water and oxygen, thus lessening its usefulness. An inhibitor such as acetanilid is added to prevent this deterioration, thus keeping the peroxide potent for a longer period of time.

***c.* The Law of Mass Action.** The relationship between the speed of a reaction and concentration was established by Guldberg and Waage in 1867. This relationship later became known as the Law of Mass Action, which states that:

At a constant temperature, the speed of a reaction is directly proportional to the concentration of the reacting substances.

The Law of Mass Action enables the chemist to calculate the concentrations of starting substances and products for a reaction that has reached equilibrium. The information is especially useful in industrial processes in which reversible reactions occur.

d. Conditions Which Control Equilibrium. Once equilibrium has been attained, only that factor which affects the velocity of opposing reactions *differently* will upset the equilibrium. Surface area and the presence of catalysts affect the velocity of the opposing reactions *equally*. However, changes in concentration, temperature, and pressure may affect the velocity of these reactions differently. Hence, *the factors which control equilibrium are concentration, temperature, and pressure.* How these factors affect equilibrium may be understood by applying Le Chatelier's principle.

e. Le Chatelier's Principle. This principle states that:

> **If an equilibrium is subjected to a stress or strain, it reacts so as to remove the stress or strain.**

A stress or strain usually refers to a change in concentration, temperature, or pressure.

Let us consider the reaction between nitrogen and hydrogen to produce ammonia.

$$N_2 + 3 \ H_2 \rightleftarrows 2 \ NH_3$$

Under special conditions of temperature and pressure and in the presence of a catalyst, equilibrium is attained. At equilibrium, there is a definite concentration of nitrogen, hydrogen, and ammonia, depending upon the rate of reaction for the production of these substances. Commercially, it is desirable to increase the yield of ammonia. To do this, it is necessary to upset the equilibrium temporarily by subjecting it to a stress or strain. This is the same as saying that some change in concentration, temperature, or pressure will upset or "shift" the equilibrium toward the right (formation of more ammonia).

Le Chatelier's principle enables us to predict the effect of these changes. For example, an increase in pressure shifts the equilibrium to the right, causing an increase in the yield of ammonia. Note that in the equation, only two volumes of ammonia are produced from a total of one volume of nitrogen and three volumes of hydrogen (four volumes). The effect of an increase in pressure (stress) is to favor that reaction which produces a smaller volume, thus relieving the stress. An increase in pressure therefore favors the production of more ammonia. In actual practice, a pressure of about 1,000 atmospheres and a temperature of about 500°C convert 50% of the nitrogen into ammonia.

f. **Common Ion Effect.** The common ion effect deals with the effect of a strong electrolyte on a solution of a weak electrolyte where the strong electrolyte provides an ion common to the weak electrolyte. We are dealing here essentially with the effect of a change in concentration (stress) on an equilibrium. Again, Le Chatelier's principle may be used to predict the result.

It has already been noted that acetic acid is a weak acid. The ionization of acetic acid may be written thus:

$$\text{Acetic acid} \xrightleftharpoons{} \text{Hydrogen ions} + \text{Acetate ions}$$

Because it is a weak acid, acetic acid furnishes only a small number of hydrogen (hydronium) ions. These ions will barely turn blue litmus red. If sodium acetate, a strong electrolyte, is added to the acetic acid, the acetate ion concentration (common ion) is increased, upsetting the equilibrium. To offset this change, acetate ions will combine with hydrogen ions to form more molecular acetic acid. As a result, the ionization of acetic acid may be lessened (repressed) so much as to furnish insufficient hydrogen ions to turn blue litmus red. Thus, *the addition of a common ion from a strong electrolyte always results in the repression of the ionization of the weak electrolyte.*

The common ion effect has considerable application and usefulness in chemical analysis.

Study Guide

1. *a.* Describe the conditions which determine the probability of a chemical reaction.
   b. Give two examples of each condition.
2. *a.* The activity of a metal is the tendency of the metal to _____ (gain, lose) electrons.
   b. In a given family, as the atomic numbers of metals increase, the activity of the metals generally _____ (decreases, increases, remains the same).
   c. In a given family, as the atomic radii of metals decrease, the activity of the metals generally _____ (decreases, increases, remains the same).

3. *a.* The letters *A, B, C,* and *D* represent metals of varying activity. Describe an experiment to determine the relative activity of each metal.

 b. On the basis of the experiment, which metal loses electrons most readily?

 c. Water is most rapidly decomposed by (1) potassium (2) zinc (3) aluminum (4) calcium.

 *d. Why will magnesium react more readily with hot water than with cold water?

 e. Hydrogen may be obtained by the reaction of hydrochloric acid with (1) copper (2) mercury (3) silver (4) iron.

 f. Prove that hydrochloric acid is an oxidizing agent.

 g. A metal that will react with an iron sulfate solution is (1) copper (2) lead (3) silver (4) zinc.

 h. One of the substances formed when a strip of zinc is placed in a solution of copper sulfate is (1) copper sulfide (2) zinc sulfide (3) zinc sulfate (4) sulfur.

4. *a.* The activity of a nonmetal is the tendency of the nonmetal to _____ (gain, lose) electrons.

 b. In a given family, as the atomic numbers of nonmetals increase, the activity of the nonmetals generally _____ (decreases, increases, remains the same).

 c. In a given family, as the atomic radii of nonmetals decrease, the activity of the nonmetals generally _____ (decreases, increases, remains the same).

 d. The letters *E, F, G,* and *H* represent nonmetals of varying activity. Describe an experiment to determine the relative activity of each nonmetal.

 e. On the basis of the experiment, which nonmetal gains electrons most readily?

5. *a.* Distinguish between the following pairs of terms:
  (1) oxidation and oxidizing agent
  (2) reduction and reducing agent

 b. For each of the following equations, indicate the oxidized and reduced particles, the oxidizing and reducing agents:
  (1) $Mg + 2\ HCl \rightarrow MgCl_2 + H_2 \uparrow$
  (2) $2\ KClO_3 \rightarrow 2\ KCl + 3\ O_2 \uparrow$
  **(3) $2\ KMnO_4 + 16\ HCl \rightarrow 2\ KCl + 2\ MnCl_2 + 8\ H_2O + 5\ Cl_2 \uparrow$

 c. The change from the *-ous* to the *-ic* state involves _____ (oxidation, reduction).

 d. In a reaction, the reducing agent is always *reduced*. [True or false? If false, correct the italicized term.]

6. *a.* What is meant by heat of formation?

 b. Stable compounds have _____ (high, low) heats of formation.

 c. Inactive elements form *stable* compounds. [True or false? If false, correct the italicized term.]

 d. The compound from which oxygen can be liberated by using the least amount of energy is (1) Al_2O_3 (2) ZnO (3) Fe_2O_3 (4) PbO.

 *e. Show how the concept of heat of formation is related to oxidation-reduction.

7. *a.* Four types of chemical reaction are _____, _____, _____, and _____.

  b. Oxidation-reduction takes place in all types of chemical reaction except _____.

  c. State the principles used in predicting each of the types of chemical reaction.

  d. Using the code letters *R* for proceeds rapidly, *S* for proceeds slowly, and *X* for no reaction, predict what will happen in each of the following reactions: (In each case, give a reason for your choice and, where a reaction occurs, write the balanced equation.)

(1) $K + Cl_2 \rightarrow$	(6) $Zn + HgCl_2 \rightarrow$	(11) $NaCl + Ba(NO_3)_2 \rightarrow$
(2) $Ag + Au \rightarrow$	(7) $Cu + AgNO_3 \rightarrow$	(12) $K_2CO_3 + H_2SO_4 \rightarrow$
(3) $Zn + Br_2 \rightarrow$	(8) $Fe + Al_2O_3 \rightarrow$	(13) $Na_2CO_3 + H_2O \rightarrow$
(4) $P + I_2 \rightarrow$	(9) $Pb + HCl \rightarrow$	(14) $AgF + CaCl_2 \rightarrow$
(5) $N_2 + H_2 \rightarrow$	(10) $Al + CuSO_4 \rightarrow$	(15) $CdSO_4 + H_2S \rightarrow$

8. *a.* An equilibrium mixture contains definite but not necessarily _____ concentrations of reactants and resultants.

  b. At equilibrium, the velocities of the forward and backward reactions become _____.

  c. Describe two conditions a reaction must satisfy to attain equilibrium.

9. *a.* As the temperature increases, the velocity of a reaction usually _____ (decreases, increases, remains the same).

  b. As the concentration of reactants is increased, there is (1) an increase in concentration of resultants (2) a decrease in concentration of resultants (3) no change in the rate of reaction (4) a decrease in the rate of reaction.

  c. Decreasing the surface area of reactants generally _____ (increases, decreases) the rate of reaction.

  d. Reactions involving gases will decrease in velocity as the _____ is decreased.

  e. Catalysts may _____ or _____ the rate of reaction.

10. *a.* State the Law of Mass Action.

  *b. How can this law be used to determine the concentration of an equilibrium mixture?

  c. Two factors which affect the rate of reaction but have no effect on an equilibrium are _____ and _____.

  d. State Le Chatelier's principle.

  *e. Show how this principle may be applied to the equilibrium:

$$CO + Cl_2 \rightleftarrows COCl_2$$

  *f. Show how this principle may be used to explain why an increase in pressure aids in melting ice.

  g. The common ion effect deals with the effect of a change in _____ on an equilibrium.

  *h. Explain why hydrogen sulfide in the presence of dilute acid has a lower sulfide ion concentration than hydrogen sulfide alone.

13 SULFUR AND ITS COMPOUNDS

SULFUR

1. OCCURRENCE

Sulfur is found abundantly both free and combined in nature. It is found free in Texas and Louisiana, and in Sicily. It is found combined with metals in the form of sulfides and sulfates. Combined sulfur is more abundant than free sulfur.

2. EXTRACTION

In Sicily, sulfur is found in volcanic rock. The rock is ignited, causing much of the sulfur to melt. The melted sulfur is further purified by distillation.

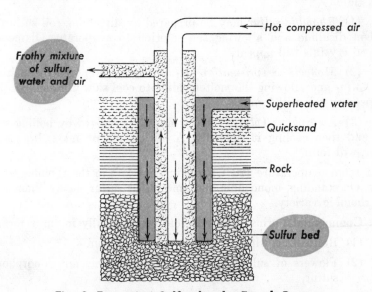

Fig. 2. Extracting Sulfur by the Frasch Process

Sulfur in this country cannot be extracted by the Sicilian process because the sulfur beds are too deep in the ground. Where deposits are under layers of clay and quicksand, several hundred feet below the surface, the Frasch process (Fig. 2) is employed.

In the Frasch process, the low melting point of sulfur (114.5°C) permits its extraction.

Three concentric pipes are sunk to the sulfur bed. Superheated water (water heated under pressure) at a temperature of 167°C is sent down the outermost pipe to melt the sulfur. Hot compressed air is forced down the innermost pipe to make the melted sulfur light and frothy, and to force it to the surface through the middle pipe. The melted sulfur is then run into large wooden bins, where it is allowed to solidify. The sulfur obtained by this process is over 99% pure.

3. FORMS OF SULFUR

a. **Allotropic Forms.** Sulfur, like oxygen and carbon, exists in several allotropic forms. *The allotropic forms of an element are varieties of the element, differing mainly in physical properties.* The different forms of sulfur are called rhombic, monoclinic (prismatic), and amorphous (plastic).

(1) *Rhombic sulfur* may be prepared by dissolving roll sulfur in carbon disulfide and allowing the solution to evaporate. Diamond-shaped crystals will appear.

(2) *Monoclinic (prismatic) sulfur* may be prepared by melting roll sulfur and allowing the molten sulfur to cool slowly. Long, needle-shaped crystals will form.

(3) *Amorphous (plastic) sulfur* may be prepared by boiling sulfur and then cooling it suddenly. A sticky, plastic mass, brown in color, will form.

At room temperature (20°C), sulfur can exist in the rhombic form only. On standing, monoclinic and amorphous sulfur slowly change to the rhombic variety.

b. **Commercial Forms.** Sulfur is sold commercially in three forms.

(1) Roll sulfur, which is largely rhombic sulfur.

(2) Flowers of sulfur, which contains rhombic and amorphous sulfur.

(3) Milk of sulfur, which is largely amorphous sulfur.

4. PHYSICAL PROPERTIES

Sulfur is a yellow solid, odorless, and practically insoluble in water. Its physical properties are summarized in the following table:

	RHOMBIC	MONOCLINIC	AMORPHOUS
Color	Yellow	Yellow	Yellow to amber
Density	2.07	1.96	1.92
Solubility	Soluble in carbon disulfide	Soluble in carbon disulfide	Slightly soluble in carbon disulfide
Stability	Below 96°C	96°C to 114.5°C	Above 114.5°C

5. CHEMICAL PROPERTIES

Because they are members of the same family in the periodic table (Group VI A), sulfur and oxygen closely resemble one another in their chemical properties. Both elements contain six electrons in their outermost ring. As a result, they are nonmetals with a usual valence number of -2. However, sulfur also has positive valence numbers of $+4$, as in sulfur dioxide (SO_2); and $+6$, as in sulfur trioxide (SO_3). The tendency to gain electrons makes sulfur, like oxygen, an oxidizing agent. Under certain conditions, sulfur can behave as a reducing agent.

VI A

O
S
Se
Te
Po

a. As sulfur has an additional ring (larger atomic radius), it is a milder oxidizing agent than oxygen. In the presence of heat, sulfur vaporizes and oxidizes many metals to form metallic sulfides.

$$Fe + S \rightarrow FeS$$

$$Cu + S \rightarrow CuS$$

$$Zn + S \rightarrow ZnS$$

The metal is oxidized while the sulfur is reduced. The production of heat and light in the above reactions also indicates that sulfur vapor supports combustion.

b. All the allotropic forms of sulfur burn in air or oxygen with a blue flame to form sulfur dioxide. This reaction proves that oxygen is a stronger oxidizing agent than sulfur, because an oxide rather than a sulfide is formed.

$$S + O_2 \rightarrow SO_2 \uparrow$$

6. USES

a. The manufacture of sulfuric acid is probably the most important use of sulfur.

b. Sulfur is used to make sulfur dioxide, which is used for fumigation and bleaching, and in the making of sulfuric acid.

c. Sulfur is used to vulcanize rubber, a process which makes it harder, stronger, and therefore more durable.

d. Lime-sulfur sprays are used to kill insects and fungi which attack plants.

e. Sulfur is used in the manufacture of sulfa drugs, such as sulfanilamide and sulfathiazole.

HYDROGEN SULFIDE

7. OCCURRENCE

Hydrogen sulfide is present in volcanic gases and found dissolved in mineral waters. It is formed when organic matter containing sulfur decays.

8. PREPARATION

Hydrogen sulfide is prepared in the laboratory and commercially by the action of an acid on any metallic sulfide. Ferrous sulfide is commonly used because it is abundant. The gas is usually collected by displacement of air.

$$FeS + 2\ HCl \rightarrow$$
$$FeCl_2 + H_2S \uparrow$$

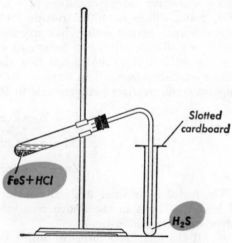

Fig. 8. Laboratory Preparation and Collection of Hydrogen Sulfide

9. PHYSICAL PROPERTIES

> Gas
> Colorless
> Odor of rotten eggs
> Denser than air
> Moderately soluble in water

Hydrogen sulfide is a colorless gas, denser than air, fairly soluble in water, and easily identified by its most striking physical property—its disagreeable (rotten egg) odor.

Because hydrogen sulfide is exceedingly toxic, considerable care must be exercised in its preparation and use. *Volume for volume, hydrogen sulfide is more poisonous than carbon monoxide.*

> **CAUTION**   Be careful not to inhale excessive quantities of hydrogen sulfide.

10. CHEMICAL PROPERTIES

a. The products formed by the burning of hydrogen sulfide depend upon the available air or oxygen. Note, however, that water is always produced.

> Hydrogen sulfide:
> 1. Is a reducing agent.
> 2. Precipitates metallic sulfides.

INCOMPLETE COMBUSTION (limited supply of air):

$$2 \ H_2S + O_2 \rightarrow 2 \ H_2O + 2 \ S \downarrow$$

COMPLETE COMBUSTION (unlimited supply of air):

$$2 \ H_2S + 3 \ O_2 \rightarrow 2 \ H_2O + 2 \ SO_2 \uparrow$$

b. Hydrogen sulfide can reduce hydrogen peroxide to form water and a precipitate of sulfur.

$$H_2S + H_2O_2 \rightarrow 2 \ H_2O + S \downarrow$$

c. Hydrogen sulfide dissolves in water to form hydrosulfuric acid, a weak acid. On exposure to air, hydrosulfuric acid is incompletely oxidized to form water and sulfur. To obtain the acid, therefore, the solution must be freshly prepared.

d. Hydrogen sulfide reacts with metals to form sulfides and hydrogen. With silver, it forms black silver sulfide (silver tarnish).

$$2 \text{ Ag} + H_2S \rightarrow Ag_2S + H_2 \uparrow$$

In this reaction, it appears that silver is replacing hydrogen, which, according to the electromotive series, is impossible. Actually, silver will not tarnish unless air or oxygen is present. Silver is probably changed to an oxide, which then reacts with hydrogen sulfide. Thus:

$$4 \text{ Ag} + O_2 \rightarrow 2 \text{ Ag}_2O$$

$$Ag_2O + H_2S \rightarrow Ag_2S + H_2O$$

Objects made of silver will tarnish on exposure to foods or air containing sulfur or sulfur compounds. Most other metals tarnish or rust by combining with the oxygen in the atmosphere.

e. Hydrogen sulfide reacts with solutions of salts to form precipitates of metallic sulfides which have characteristic colors, as shown by the following equations:

$$Pb(NO_3)_2 + H_2S \rightarrow 2 \text{ HNO}_3 + \underset{\text{black}}{PbS \downarrow}$$

$$Cd(NO_3)_2 + H_2S \rightarrow 2 \text{ HNO}_3 + \underset{\text{yellow}}{CdS \downarrow}$$

$$Zn(NO_3)_2 + H_2S \rightarrow 2 \text{ HNO}_3 + \underset{\text{white}}{ZnS \downarrow}$$

$$2 \text{ SbCl}_3 + 3 \text{ H}_2S \rightarrow 6 \text{ HCl} + \underset{\text{orange}}{Sb_2S_3 \downarrow}$$

$$2 \text{ Bi}(NO_3)_3 + 3 \text{ H}_2S \rightarrow 6 \text{ HNO}_3 + \underset{\text{brown}}{Bi_2S_3 \downarrow}$$

$$CuSO_4 + H_2S \rightarrow H_2SO_4 + \underset{\text{black}}{CuS \downarrow}$$

$$2 \text{ AgNO}_3 + H_2S \rightarrow 2 \text{ HNO}_3 + \underset{\text{black}}{Ag_2S \downarrow}$$

11. USES

The formation of sulfide precipitates with characteristic colors aids the analytical chemist in identifying metal ions. For example, the formation of a white precipitate, when hydrogen sulfide is bubbled into a solution, indicates the presence of a zinc compound (zinc ions). Some colored sulfides, such as yellow cadmium sulfide, may be used as paint pigments.

12. TESTS FOR HYDROGEN SULFIDE AND SULFIDE IONS

Hydrogen sulfide can be identified by its characteristic odor of rotten eggs. Hydrogen sulfide will also darken a piece of paper that has been saturated with lead acetate.

The addition of hydrochloric acid to an unknown, resulting in the formation of hydrogen sulfide, is a test for sulfide ions.

SULFUR DIOXIDE

13. OCCURRENCE

Sulfur dioxide occurs in small quantities in air as a result of the burning of sulfur compounds. Certain mineral waters and some volcanic gases also contain traces of sulfur dioxide.

14. LABORATORY PREPARATION

Sulfur dioxide is prepared in the laboratory by the decomposition of unstable sulfurous acid (H_2SO_3).

$$H_2SO_3 \rightarrow H_2O + SO_2 \uparrow$$

a. **Acid and a Sulfite.** Sulfurous acid may be prepared by the action of a dilute acid on a sulfite or bisulfite salt. (See Fig. 14*a*.)

$$Na_2SO_3 + 2\,HCl \rightarrow 2\,NaCl + H_2SO_3$$

sodium
sulfite

$$\downarrow$$

$$H_2O + SO_2 \uparrow$$

$$2\,NaHSO_3 + H_2SO_4 \rightarrow Na_2SO_4 + 2\,H_2SO_3$$

sodium
bisulfite

$$\downarrow$$

$$2\,H_2O + 2\,SO_2 \uparrow$$

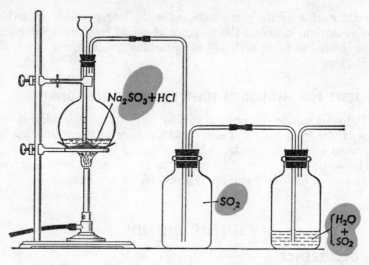

Fig. 14a. Laboratory Preparation and Collection of Sulfur Dioxide

Sulfur dioxide is collected by air displacement because it is soluble in water.

b. **Hot, Concentrated Sulfuric Acid and a Metal.** Sulfurous acid may also be prepared by heating concentrated sulfuric acid with copper. Hydrogen is not obtained under these conditions because hot, concentrated sulfuric acid is an oxidizing agent.

$$Cu + 2\,H_2SO_4 \rightarrow CuSO_4 + 2\,H_2O + SO_2\uparrow$$

15. COMMERCIAL PREPARATION

a. Sulfur dioxide is obtained commercially by burning sulfur in air.

$$S + O_2 \rightarrow SO_2\uparrow$$

b. Large quantities of sulfur dioxide are also produced by roasting sulfide ores.

$$2\,ZnS + 3\,O_2 \rightarrow 2\,ZnO + 2\,SO_2\uparrow$$
$$\text{zinc blende}$$

$$4\,FeS_2 + 11\,O_2 \rightarrow 2\,Fe_2O_3 + 8\,SO_2\uparrow$$
$$\text{iron pyrites}$$

16. PHYSICAL PROPERTIES

> Gas
> Colorless
> Choking odor
> $2 \times$ air
> Very soluble in water

Sulfur dioxide is a colorless gas with a choking odor. It is more than twice as dense as air, very soluble in water, and easily liquefied. Its extreme solubility is shown by the fact that if a test tube of sulfur dioxide is inverted in a pan of water, the water rises in the test tube. This same effect can be demonstrated by a fountain similar to the hydrogen chloride fountain (Fig. 30, page 145).

17. CHEMICAL PROPERTIES

a. Sulfur dioxide is an acid anhydride. *An acid anhydride is a non-metallic oxide which combines with water to form an acid.* Sulfur dioxide, because it combines with water to form sulfurous acid, is called sulfurous anhydride. Since sulfurous acid is unstable, the reaction is reversible. Note the use of the longer arrow to indicate that the backward reaction predominates.

> Sulfur dioxide is:
> 1. A reducing agent.
> $S^{+4} - 2e \rightarrow S^{+6}$
> 2. An oxidizing agent.
> $S^{+4} + 4e \rightarrow S^{0}$

$$SO_2 + H_2O \underset{}{\overset{\rightharpoonup}{\leftharpoondown}} H_2SO_3$$
$$\text{sulfurous} \qquad\qquad \text{sulfurous}$$
$$\text{anhydride} \qquad\qquad \text{acid}$$

b. Sulfur dioxide (sulfurous anhydride) combines with oxygen to form sulfur trioxide (sulfuric anhydride) if the temperature is carefully regulated and if platinum is present as a catalytic agent. In this reaction, sulfur dioxide behaves as a reducing agent.

$$2\,SO_2 + O_2 \xrightarrow{\text{platinum}} 2\,SO_3$$

Note that sulfur trioxide (SO_3) and the sulfite ion (SO_3)$^{-2}$, although similar in composition, are two different particles. The former (SO_3) is a compound in which sulfur has a valence number of $+6$, while the latter (SO_3)$^{-2}$ is an ion in which sulfur has a valence number of $+4$.

c. Sulfur dioxide may also behave as an oxidizing agent.

$$2\,H_2S + SO_2 \rightarrow 3\,S + 2\,H_2O$$

d. Sulfur dioxide is not combustible and generally does not support combustion.

18. CHEMICAL PROPERTIES OF SULFUROUS ACID

a. Sulfurous acid exhibits the usual properties of an acid, such as turning litmus red and neutralizing bases.

> H_2SO_3 (S^{+4}) resembles SO_2 (S^{+4}) in chemical properties.

$$H_2SO_3 + Ca(OH)_2 \rightarrow CaSO_3 + 2\ H_2O$$

b. Sulfurous acid is also a reducing agent.

(1) It will reduce hydrogen peroxide to water, while it itself is oxidized to sulfuric acid.

$$H_2SO_3 + H_2O_2 \rightarrow H_2SO_4 + H_2O$$

The bleaching of a purple solution of potassium permanganate by sulfurous acid also shows the reducing action of the latter.

(2) Sulfurous acid in small quantities is oxidized to sulfuric acid on exposure to air.

$$2\ H_2SO_3 + O_2 \rightarrow 2\ H_2SO_4$$

19. USES OF SULFUR DIOXIDE

a. **Manufacture of Sulfuric Acid.** The most important use of sulfur dioxide is in the manufacture of sulfuric acid by the *contact process.*

b. **Disinfectant.** Sulfur dioxide is used for disinfecting and fumigating because it destroys bacteria. The sulfur dioxide is obtained for these purposes by burning sulfur.

c. **Refrigeration.** Sulfur dioxide was at one time widely used as a refrigerant because it could be liquefied at low pressures. Modern electric refrigerators, however, use freon, an organic halogen compound, because it is less toxic.

d. **Bleaching.** Straw, silk, wool, and fruits are bleached by sulfur dioxide. Chlorine cannot be used safely to bleach these materials because it destroys them. Chlorine is used to bleach cotton only. Moist chlorine and hydrogen peroxide bleach by *oxidizing* the dye, while moist sulfur dioxide (sulfurous acid) bleaches by *reducing* the dye. Bleaching with sulfur dioxide is not permanent. Oxidation causes the color to return on exposure to air.

e. **Paper Manufacture.** From sulfur dioxide we can prepare calcium bisulfite, which, in turn, is used in the processing of wood pulp for paper making.

20. TESTS FOR SULFUR DIOXIDE AND SULFITE IONS

Sulfur dioxide can be identified by its characteristic choking odor. Sulfur dioxide will also bleach a purple solution of potassium permanganate. The addition of hydrochloric acid to an unknown, resulting in the formation of sulfur dioxide, is a test for sulfite or bisulfite ions.

SULFURIC ACID

21. COMMERCIAL PREPARATION

The preparation of sulfuric acid involves, essentially, changing $SO_2(S^{+4})$ to $SO_3(S^{+6})$.

a. **Lead Chamber Process.** The older method for making sulfuric acid, which is still used today, is the *lead chamber process*. In this process, sulfur dioxide combines with certain oxides of nitrogen to yield *nitrosyl sulfuric acid*. When this substance is dissolved in water, *dilute* sulfuric acid is obtained. Most of our sulfuric acid, however, is made by the contact process.

b. **Contact Process.** The anhydride of sulfuric acid is sulfur trioxide (SO_3). In the preparation of sulfuric acid by the contact process, it is necessary first to make sulfur trioxide. Sulfur trioxide is prepared in the following manner:

(1) Sulfur is burned in air, forming sulfur dioxide.

$$S + O_2 \rightarrow SO_2 \uparrow$$

(2) The sulfur dioxide is then purified and dried, mixed with air, and brought into contact with a catalyst, which may be finely divided platinum or vanadium pentoxide (V_2O_5). The temperature in the catalytic chamber is about 450°C. The sulfur dioxide is thus oxidized to sulfur trioxide.

$$2 SO_2 + O_2 \xrightarrow[\text{platinum}]{} 2 SO_3$$

As sulfur trioxide is not appreciably soluble in water, it is dissolved in concentrated sulfuric acid, forming fuming sulfuric acid (oleum).

$$SO_3 + H_2SO_4 \rightarrow H_2SO_4 \cdot SO_3$$
fuming
sulfuric acid

(3) Water is added to the fuming sulfuric acid, forming almost pure concentrated sulfuric acid.

$$H_2SO_4 \cdot SO_3 + H_2O \rightarrow 2\ H_2SO_4$$

Note that *one* molecule of sulfuric acid is used to make *two* molecules of sulfuric acid.

22. LABORATORY PREPARATION

The laboratory preparation of sulfuric acid follows each step of the contact process. As shown in Fig. 22, a mixture of SO_2 and air is purified, dried, and passed into a tube containing heated platinized asbestos. However, in the laboratory, it is unnecessary to dissolve the sulfur trioxide in concentrated sulfuric acid. Enough sulfur trioxide will dissolve in water to produce a quantity of sulfuric acid which will respond to a chemical test. In commercial practice, the sulfur trioxide is dissolved in concentrated sulfuric acid in order to increase the final yield of acid.

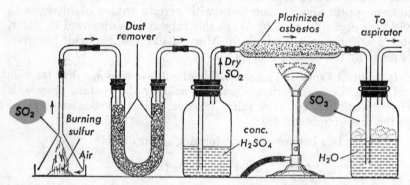

Fig. 22. Laboratory Preparation and Collection of Sulfuric Acid

23. PHYSICAL PROPERTIES

Sulfuric acid, commonly called "oil of vitriol," is an oily liquid almost twice as dense as water and with a high boiling point (338°C). It is colorless and odorless when pure. Sulfuric acid is a hygroscopic substance because it absorbs moisture on exposure to air. Hence, an open bottle completely

> Liquid
> Colorless
> Odorless
> Almost 2 × water
> Soluble in water

filled with the concentrated acid overflows on standing exposed to air. Sulfuric acid can be diluted with water in all proportions.

CAUTION	When diluting concentrated sulfuric acid, pour the acid slowly into a large volume of water with constant stirring.

The above procedure dissipates the considerable heat liberated during dilution and thereby prevents spattering. As shown below, the acid may be safely poured into water along the surface of a stirring rod.

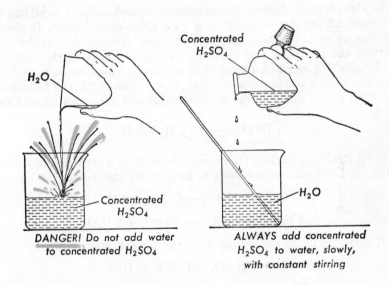

DANGER! Do not add water to concentrated H_2SO_4

ALWAYS add concentrated H_2SO_4 to water, slowly, with constant stirring

24. CHEMICAL PROPERTIES

a. **Action on Metals.** Dilute sulfuric acid behaves as a typical acid and reacts with certain metals to liberate hydrogen and form sulfates.

$$Zn + H_2SO_4 \rightarrow ZnSO_4 + H_2 \uparrow$$
$$Fe + H_2SO_4 \rightarrow FeSO_4 + H_2 \uparrow$$

Dilute H_2SO_4 is a typical acid.
Concentrated H_2SO_4 is:
1. A dehydrating agent.
2. An oxidizing agent.

$$S^{+6} + 2\,e \rightarrow S^{+4}$$
$$S^{+6} + 8\,e \rightarrow S^{-2}$$

Hot, concentrated sulfuric acid behaves as an oxidizing agent and reacts with metals such as copper and silver to liberate sulfur dioxide. In such reactions, the metal reduces the sulfuric acid.

$$Cu + 2 \underset{\text{conc.}}{H_2SO_4} \rightarrow CuSO_4 + 2 H_2O + SO_2 \uparrow$$

When a more active metal such as zinc is used, hydrogen sulfide is liberated. Since zinc is more active than copper (that is, is a more powerful reducing agent), the sulfuric acid is further reduced.

$$4 Zn + 5 \underset{\text{conc.}}{H_2SO_4} \rightarrow 4 ZnSO_4 + 4 H_2O + H_2S \uparrow$$

b. Dehydrating Action. Because concentrated sulfuric acid has a powerful affinity for water, it is a good dehydrating agent. It chars substances such as wood, paper, and sugar (carbohydrates) by removing the hydrogen and oxygen as water and leaving the carbon. *A dehydrating agent is, therefore, a substance which removes hydrogen and oxygen in the form of water from a compound.* The following equation shows the reaction between sugar and concentrated sulfuric acid:

$$\underset{\text{cane sugar}}{C_{12}H_{22}O_{11}} \xrightarrow{\text{H}_2\text{SO}_4} 11 H_2O + 12 C$$

c. Neutralizing Action. Dilute sulfuric acid, as a typical acid, turns litmus red and neutralizes bases to form a salt and water.

$$Ca(OH)_2 + H_2SO_4 \rightarrow CaSO_4 + 2 H_2O$$

$$2 NaOH + H_2SO_4 \rightarrow Na_2SO_4 + 2 H_2O$$

It also reacts with metallic oxides to form a salt and water.

$$CaO + H_2SO_4 \rightarrow CaSO_4 + H_2O$$

d. Action on Salts to Form Acids. Because of its high boiling point, concentrated sulfuric acid is used to make other acids.

$$2 NaCl + H_2SO_4 \rightarrow Na_2SO_4 + 2 HCl$$

$$2 NaNO_3 + H_2SO_4 \rightarrow Na_2SO_4 + 2 HNO_3$$

25. USES

Sulfuric acid, the "King of Chemicals," is the most widely used chemical. Its uses are so numerous that only the more important ones are listed here.

a. Because of its high boiling point, sulfuric acid is used in the preparation of other acids, such as nitric and hydrochloric acids.

b. It is used in the manufacture of explosives, drugs, and dyes.

c. Before metals are electroplated, they are cleaned of rust or tarnish by dipping them into dilute sulfuric acid. This process is called *pickling,* and depends on the action of the acid on metallic oxides.

d. It is used to convert insoluble rock phosphate into soluble monocalcium phosphate (superphosphate), which is used as a fertilizer.

e. It is used in the lead storage battery as the electrolyte.

f. Large quantities of sulfuric acid are used in the refining of petroleum.

g. It is used to dry moist gases because it is a hygroscopic substance.

26. TEST FOR SULFATE IONS

Any soluble sulfate reacts with a solution of barium chloride to form a white precipitate of barium sulfate, which is insoluble in hydrochloric acid. This reaction may be used as a test for sulfate ions.

$$H_2SO_4 + BaCl_2 \rightarrow 2\ HCl + BaSO_4 \downarrow$$

$$Na_2SO_4 + BaCl_2 \rightarrow 2\ NaCl + BaSO_4 \downarrow$$

Study Guide

1. *a.* Texas, Louisiana, and Sicily are sources of _____ (free, combined) sulfur.

   b. Combined sulfur occurs in the form of metallic _____ and _____.

2. *a.* How is sulfur extracted from Sicilian deposits?

   b. Why is it not practical to extract sulfur in this country in the same manner?

   c. Using a labeled diagram, describe the Frasch process.

3. *a.* The element (1) oxygen (2) hydrogen (3) sulfur (4) carbon does not have allotropic forms.

   b. Rhombic sulfur is soluble in (1) alcohol (2) carbon disulfide (3) kerosene (4) water.

   c. _____ sulfur may be prepared by the slow cooling of melted sulfur.

   d. _____ sulfur may be prepared by the rapid cooling of boiling sulfur.

   e. On long standing, all forms of sulfur revert to the *monoclinic* form. [True or false? If false, correct the italicized term.]

   f. A variety of sulfur which is not a commercial form is (1) rhombic sulfur (2) roll sulfur (3) flowers of sulfur (4) milk of sulfur.

4. *a.* The allotropic forms of sulfur generally have *similar* physical properties. [True or false? If false, correct the italicized term.]

    b. The form of sulfur least soluble in carbon disulfide is _____ sulfur.

5. *a.* Chemically, sulfur most closely resembles _____.

    b. Predict some of the chemical properties of sulfur on the basis of its position in the periodic table.

    *c. Compare the chemical properties of sulfur with at least two other members of Group VI A.

    d. Write a balanced equation for each of the following reactions:

        (1) $Na + S \rightarrow$

        (2) $Pb + S \rightarrow$

        (3) $Al + S \rightarrow$

    e. In the above reactions, is sulfur an oxidizing or reducing agent? Explain.

    f. The product formed by burning the different allotropic forms of sulfur (1) is chiefly SO_2 (2) is chiefly SO_3 (3) is chiefly H_2S (4) varies with the form of sulfur used.

6. *a.* The most important use of sulfur is in the manufacture of _____.

    b. The formula of a sulfur compound used in bleaching is _____.

    c. An example of a sulfa drug is _____.

7. How does hydrogen sulfide occur in nature?

8. *a.* Hydrogen sulfide may be prepared in the laboratory by the action of an acid on (1) sulfur (2) any sulfide (3) a metallic sulfide (4) sulfur dioxide.

    b. Make a labeled diagram to illustrate the laboratory preparation and collection of hydrogen sulfide.

    c. Write the balanced equation for the reaction that occurs in *b*.

9. *a.* Hydrogen sulfide has the odor of (1) burning sulfur (2) rotten eggs (3) battery acid (4) sulfur.

    b. Explain why extreme caution must be exercised in the preparation and use of hydrogen sulfide.

10. *a.* The combustion of hydrogen sulfide always yields _____.

    b. Write a balanced equation to illustrate each of the following:

        (1) incomplete combustion of hydrogen sulfide

        (2) complete combustion of hydrogen sulfide

        (3) air oxidation of hydrosulfuric acid

        (4) formation of silver tarnish

    c. Silver will be tarnished by hydrogen sulfide only in the presence of _____.

    d. Write balanced equations to show what happens when hydrogen sulfide is bubbled into solutions of (1) lead nitrate, (2) cadmium sulfate, and (3) zinc chloride.

    *e. Explain why hydrogen sulfide cannot behave as an oxidizing agent, while sulfur can behave either as an oxidizing agent or a reducing agent.

11. *a.* The formation of a black precipitate when hydrogen sulfide is bubbled into a solution indicates that (1) copper is present (2) lead is present (3) zinc is present (4) lead may be present.

    b. Hydrogen sulfide can be recognized by its characteristic *color*. [True or false? If false, correct the italicized term.]

12. *a.* Sulfur dioxide can be prepared in the laboratory by the action of dilute sulfuric acid on (1) any metal (2) a sulfide (3) a sulfite (4) a sulfate.

    b. Sulfur dioxide is the anhydride of (1) hydrosulfuric acid (2) sulfurous acid (3) sulfuric acid (4) sulfur trioxide.

    c. Make a labeled diagram to illustrate the laboratory preparation and collection of sulfur dioxide.

    d. Write the balanced equation for the reaction that takes place in *c.*

13. *a.* Two commercial sources of sulfur dioxide are _____ and _____.

    b. Write a balanced equation to show the formation of sulfur dioxide from each source in *a.*

14. *a.* Sulfur dioxide is (1) odorless (2) slightly soluble in water (3) yellow (4) easily liquefied.

    b. The formula for sulfurous anhydride is (1) SO_2 (2) SO_3 (3) $(SO_3)^{-2}$ (4) H_2SO_3.

    c. The catalytic oxidation of sulfur dioxide yields _____.

    d. The anhydride of sulfuric acid is (1) SO_2 (2) SO_3 (3) $(SO_3)^{-2}$ (4) H_2SO_4.

    e. Write a balanced equation to show what happens when sulfur dioxide is bubbled into a solution of barium hydroxide.

    *f. Using balanced equations wherever possible, explain why sulfurous acid can behave either as an oxidizing or a reducing agent.

15. Describe three uses of sulfur dioxide and for each use state the property which makes the use possible.

16. Describe two tests to prove that an unknown substance contains sulfite ions.

17. *a.* The final product in the lead chamber process is (1) dilute sulfuric acid (2) concentrated sulfuric acid (3) nitrogen dioxide (4) sulfur trioxide.

    b. In the contact process, it is first necessary to make _____.

    c. By means of balanced equations, show how sulfuric acid is manufactured by the contact process.

    d. A catalyst used in the contact process is _____.

    e. Explain the use of sulfuric acid in the contact process.

18. *a.* The specific gravity of chemically pure sulfuric acid is (1) 0.78 (2) 1.0 (3) 1.84 (4) 13.6.

    b. The physical property of sulfuric acid that makes it valuable in preparing other acids is its _____.

    c. Why does an open bottle completely filled with concentrated sulfuric acid overflow upon exposure to air?

    d. In diluting concentrated sulfuric acid, always add the _____ to the _____.

19. **a.* When sulfuric acid of any concentration reacts with metals, the sulfuric acid behaves as an oxidizing agent. Explain.

    b. Write a balanced equation for each of the following reactions:

      (1) $Fe + H_2SO_4 \rightarrow$
         dilute

      (2) $Ag + H_2SO_4 \rightarrow$
         conc.

      (3) $Zn + H_2SO_4 \rightarrow$
         conc.

    *c. Explain why sulfuric acid can behave only as an oxidizing agent and not as a reducing agent.

    d. Litmus paper dipped into concentrated sulfuric acid turns black because sulfuric acid (1) is a strong acid (2) has a high boiling point (3) is an oxidizing agent (4) is a dehydrating agent.

 e. Write a balanced equation for each of the following reactions:

(1) $C_6H_{12}O_6 \xrightarrow[H_2SO_4]{}$

(2) $Ba(OH)_2 + H_2SO_4 \rightarrow$
    dilute

(3) $Na_2O + H_2SO_4 \rightarrow$
    dilute

(4) $KNO_3 + H_2SO_4 \rightarrow$
    dilute

20. *a.* Give the reason for the use of sulfuric acid in each of the following:

(1) cleaning metals before electroplating

(2) making superphosphate fertilizer from phosphate rock

*(3) as the electrolyte in the lead storage battery

(4) drying moist gases

 b. By means of chemical tests, distinguish between a sulfite salt and a sulfate salt. Write balanced equations for the reactions involved.

21. Calculate the weight of aluminum sulfide formed from the reaction between aluminum and 160 grams of sulfur.

22. Calculate the volume of sulfur dioxide released when hydrochloric acid is added to 210 grams of sodium sulfite.

23. Calculate the weight of sulfuric acid that can be obtained from 800 pounds of sulfur.

14 NITROGEN AND ITS COMPOUNDS

THE ATMOSPHERE

The atmosphere is a layer of gases extending several hundred miles into space. With increased altitude, the density of air decreases. Above three or four miles, the air becomes so thin that special equipment for aviators is required.

1. COMPOSITION

The atmosphere is a mixture of nitrogen, oxygen, and many other different substances in widely varying proportions. The components of air, their relative amounts, and their importance are described below.

Composition of Air

Composition of Air
Nitrogen
Oxygen
Carbon dioxide
Inert gases
Water vapor
Dust
Organisms

a. **Nitrogen.** Air is composed of about 78% nitrogen by volume. The nitrogen serves to dilute the oxygen, thus preventing too rapid burning. Some nitrogen is removed from the air by nitrogen-fixing bacteria and during lightning storms, but is constantly returned to the air through the decay of plant and animal matter.

b. **Oxygen.** Air is composed of about 21% oxygen by volume. Oxygen is removed from air during plant and animal respiration and by the process of burning. Plants return oxygen to the air during the process of *photosynthesis.*

c. **Carbon Dioxide.** Air usually contains about 0.04% carbon dioxide by volume. Green plants utilize the carbon dioxide present in air during photosynthesis. Carbon dioxide is returned to the air as a product of respiration, by the decay of plant and animal matter, and when most fuels are burned.

During respiration, living things remove oxygen from the air and release carbon dioxide. The carbon dioxide is used by the green plants for photosynthesis. Oxygen, a product of photosynthesis, is then returned to the air, thus completing the *carbon dioxide-oxygen cycle.*

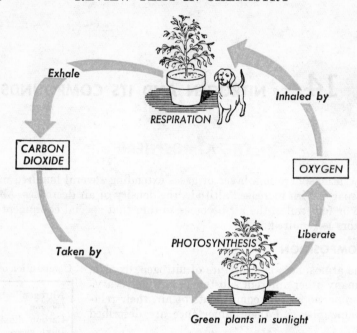

Fig. 1c. The Carbon Dioxide-Oxygen Cycle

d. **Inert Gases.** There are several inert (rare) gases in air that are completely inactive:

(1) *Argon,* the most abundant of these gases, makes up 0.9% of air by volume. Argon is used with nitrogen to fill electric light bulbs. The presence of argon retards the evaporation of the lamp filament.

(2) *Helium* is used in airships because of its low density and incombustibility.

(3) *Neon* is used in electric (neon) signs because of its characteristic glow during electric discharge.

(4) *Krypton* and *xenon,* the least abundant gases in air, are also used to fill electric light bulbs.

e. **Water Vapor.** The amount of water vapor that air can hold is variable, depending upon atmospheric conditions of temperature, pressure, and the degree of saturation. Air can hold more water vapor as its temperature rises and its pressure and degree of saturation decrease.

Under certain conditions, such as a drop in temperature, condensation or precipitation may take place. Some of the water vapor is thus removed from air as fog, rain, hail, sleet, or snow. Water vapor returns to the air by evaporation of water from lakes, rivers, and oceans. Air saturated with water vapor, especially in summer, makes people uncomfortable. Under such conditions, perspiration evaporates very slowly.

Relative humidity is a percentage which expresses the amount of moisture in the air compared to the amount of moisture needed to saturate the air at a given temperature. Air is most comfortable when the relative humidity is about 50% at a temperature of 68°F.

f. Dust. The dust in air may easily be made visible by permitting a beam of sunlight to enter a darkened room. Each particle of dust reflects and scatters the light. (See Tyndall effect, **b**, pages 41-42.)

Dust particles also act as nuclei around which water vapor condenses to form raindrops.

g. Organisms. Air acts as a medium for the transmission of bacteria, the spores of fungi, and pollen.

2. DETERMINING THE COMPOSITION OF AIR

A small piece of yellow phosphorus is placed on a cork covered with asbestos. (See Fig. 2.) The cork is floated in water. The phosphorus is then ignited and immediately covered with a large gas measuring tube, which encloses a definite volume of air. The phosphorus combines with the oxygen of the air, forming white phosphorus pentoxide, which dissolves in the water. Impure nitrogen remains in the cylinder.

$$4 P + 5 O_2 \rightarrow 2 P_2O_5$$

Water rises approximately one-fifth the height of the cylinder to take the place of the oxygen consumed during the burning of the phosphorus. The remaining four-fifths is largely nitrogen. *Thus, by volume, air is composed of approximately four-fifths (78%) nitrogen and one-fifth (21%) oxygen; about 1% consists of other substances.*

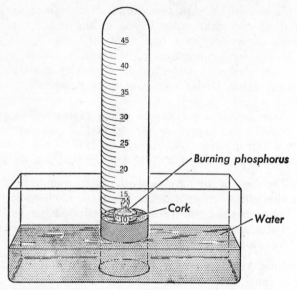

Fig. 2. Determining the Composition of Air

3. AIR IS A MIXTURE

Air, earth, fire, and water were considered by the ancients to be the only elements. We now know that none of these is an element.

> Air is a mixture of different substances, and not a compound.

Proofs that air is a mixture:

a. The composition of the air varies. If air were a compound, it would have a definite composition by weight.

b. The components of air may be separated by physical means. When air is liquefied and allowed to evaporate, the nitrogen evaporates at a lower temperature than the oxygen, thus separating from the oxygen. If air were a compound, it would liquefy or evaporate completely at one given temperature and not at different temperatures.

c. When air is dissolved in water, the oxygen and nitrogen dissolve at different rates.

d. Both the nitrogen and oxygen in air retain their original properties. If air were a compound, these gases would lose their original properties when they combined.

NITROGEN

4. OCCURRENCE

Nitrogen is found free in the air to the extent of about 78% by volume, and combined in Chile saltpeter ($NaNO_3$) and in all proteins.

5. LABORATORY PREPARATION

a. **Burning of Phosphorus in Air.** (See figure, page 196.)

b. **Decomposition of Ammonium Nitrite (NH_4NO_2).** Pure nitrogen may be conveniently obtained in the laboratory from the decomposition of ammonium nitrite. Since ammonium nitrite is very unstable, it is customary to heat a mixture of ammonium chloride (NH_4Cl) and sodium nitrite ($NaNO_2$). This reaction probably produces ammonium nitrite, which decomposes into water and nitrogen. The nitrogen formed is collected by displacement of water.

$$NH_4Cl + NaNO_2 \rightarrow NaCl + NH_4NO_2$$

$$NH_4NO_2 \rightarrow 2\ H_2O + N_2 \uparrow$$

6. COMMERCIAL PREPARATION

Large quantities of nitrogen and oxygen are obtained commercially by the fractional distillation of liquid air.

7. PHYSICAL PROPERTIES

Nitrogen is a colorless, odorless, and tasteless gas, a little less dense than air and slightly soluble in water.

8. CHEMICAL PROPERTIES

Nitrogen is the lightest member of Group V A in the periodic table. Because nitrogen contains five electrons in its outermost shell, its usual valence numbers are +5 and −3. Nitrogen tends to form covalent compounds.

V A
N
P
As
Sb
Bi

a. Nitrogen is an inactive gas which neither burns nor supports combustion under ordinary conditions.

b. Under special conditions, nitrogen can be made to unite with hydrogen to form ammonia.

$$N_2 + 3\ H_2 \rightarrow 2\ NH_3 \uparrow$$

c. Nitrogen reacts with oxygen under special conditions to form nitric oxide.

$$N_2 + O_2 \rightarrow 2\ NO \uparrow$$

d. At high temperatures, certain metals will combine with nitrogen. A piece of burning magnesium, for example, will continue to burn in nitrogen, forming a nitride.

$$3 \ Mg + N_2 \rightarrow \underset{\substack{magnesium \\ nitride}}{Mg_3N_2}$$

The conversion of a nitride into ammonia by the addition of water may serve as a test for nitrogen.

$$Mg_3N_2 + 6 \ H_2O \rightarrow 3 \ Mg(OH)_2 + 2 \ NH_3 \uparrow$$

e. Nitrogen combines with hot calcium carbide to form calcium cyanamid.

$$CaC_2 + N_2 \rightarrow CaCN_2 + C$$

Calcium cyanamid is a cheap source of ammonia.

9. USES

Commercially, nitrogen is used to make ammonia and nitric acid, from which other important compounds may be made.

In nature, certain bacteria convert nitrogen into useful compounds. This process, called *nitrogen-fixation*, will be discussed later.

AMMONIA

10. OCCURRENCE

Ammonia is produced in nature by the bacterial decomposition of plant and animal matter.

11. LABORATORY PREPARATION

Ammonia may be prepared in the laboratory by the action of a base on any ammonium salt.

$$(NH_4)_2SO_4 + 2 \ NaOH \rightarrow Na_2SO_4 + 2 \ H_2O + 2 \ NH_3 \uparrow$$

$$2 \ NH_4Cl + Ca(OH)_2 \rightarrow CaCl_2 + 2 \ H_2O + 2 \ NH_3 \uparrow$$

Ammonia is usually obtained by heating a mixture of ammonium chloride and calcium hydroxide (slaked lime), as shown in Fig. 11. The ammonium hydroxide formed is unstable and decomposes into ammonia and water. The ammonia is collected by displacement of air because ammonia is lighter than air and very soluble in water.

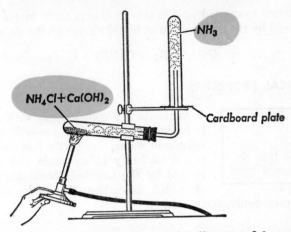

Fig. 11. Laboratory Preparation and Collection of Ammonia

12. COMMERCIAL PREPARATION

a. **Destructive Distillation of Soft Coal.** Ammonia is obtained as a by-product during the destructive distillation of soft coal.

> **Destructive distillation** is the process whereby a substance is heated in the absence of air and decomposes.

The decomposition products of destructive distillation are usually gases, liquids, and solids.

b. **Haber Process.** Ammonia can be made synthetically from its elements: nitrogen and hydrogen. Because this reaction is reversible and reaches equilibrium, special conditions must be maintained to insure a satisfactory yield. These conditions include high pressure (about 1,000 atmospheres), moderately high temperature (about 500°C), and a catalyst, usually finely divided iron. (For a fuller description of the Haber process, see *e*, page 171.)

$$N_2 + 3 H_2 \rightleftarrows 2 NH_3$$

c. **Cyanamid Process.** Ammonia can also be made by reacting calcium cyanamid ($CaCN_2$) with steam.

$$CaCN_2 + 3 H_2O \rightarrow CaCO_3 + 2 NH_3 \uparrow$$

The calcium cyanamid used in this process is made by passing nitrogen, obtained by the evaporation of liquid air, over hot calcium carbide.

$$CaC_2 + N_2 \rightarrow CaCN_2 + C$$

13. PHYSICAL PROPERTIES

> Gas
> Colorless
> Pungent
> Less dense than air
> Very soluble in water

Ammonia is a colorless gas with a pungent, irritating odor. It is less dense than air, very soluble in water, and easily liquefied. The extreme solubility of ammonia can be demonstrated by the ammonia fountain, the action of which resembles the hydrogen chloride fountain. (See figure, page 145.)

14. CHEMICAL PROPERTIES OF AMMONIA

a. Ammonia combines with water to form ammonium hydroxide (ammonia water), a weak base.

> At room temperature, ammonia gas is generally an inactive substance.

$$NH_3 + H_2O \rightleftharpoons NH_4OH$$

b. Ammonia unites directly with acids to form ammonium salts.

$$NH_3 + HCl \rightarrow NH_4Cl$$

$$2\,NH_3 + H_2SO_4 \rightarrow (NH_4)_2SO_4$$

$$NH_3 + HNO_3 \rightarrow NH_4NO_3$$

c. Ammonia does not support combustion. It can, however, be oxidized to nitric oxide if white-hot platinum is present as a catalyst (Ostwald process).

$$4\,NH_3 + 5\,O_2 \rightarrow 6\,H_2O + 4\,NO \uparrow$$
$$\text{nitric oxide}$$

d. Ammonia also reacts with metals at high temperatures, forming nitrogen compounds.

$$2\,NH_3 + 3\,Mg \rightarrow Mg_3N_2 + 3\,H_2 \uparrow$$

$$2\,NH_3 + 2\,Na \rightarrow 2\,NaNH_2 + H_2 \uparrow$$
$$\text{sodium amide}$$

15. CHEMICAL PROPERTIES OF AMMONIUM HYDROXIDE

a. The solution of ammonia in water is commonly called ammonium hydroxide. Since it is doubtful if any molecular ammonium hydroxide exists, it is more accurate to call this

> Ammonium hydroxide:
> 1. Is a weak base.
> 2. Has the properties of a base.

solution ammonia water ($NH_3 + H_2O$). The ionization of ammonia water can be represented thus:

$$NH_3 + H_2O \rightleftharpoons NH_4^+ + OH^-$$

Note the shorter arrow, which indicates that ionization of ammonia water is limited. As a result of this limited ionization, few hydroxyl ions (OH^-) are produced. Thus, the solution of ammonia in water is a weak base. For the sake of simplicity, we shall refer to this solution as ammonium hydroxide.

b. Ammonium hydroxide neutralizes acids, forming an ammonium salt and water.

$$NH_4OH + HCl \rightarrow NH_4Cl + H_2O$$

c. Ammonium hydroxide precipitates insoluble bases.

$$3\ NH_4OH + FeCl_3 \rightarrow 3\ NH_4Cl + Fe(OH)_3 \downarrow$$

d. Ammonium hydroxide dissolves fats and greases, thus making it a good cleansing agent.

e. Ammonium hydroxide is unstable. On standing, it decomposes into water and ammonia.

$$NH_4OH \rightarrow H_2O + NH_3 \uparrow$$

16. USES OF AMMONIA

a. **Refrigeration.** Because it is easily liquefied, ammonia is used in refrigeration and in the manufacture of artificial ice. When liquid ammonia is allowed to evaporate, it absorbs large quantities of heat from its surroundings. Modern household refrigerators, however, use freon, which is less toxic than either ammonia or sulfur dioxide.

b. **Manufacture of Ammonia Water.** Ammonia is passed into water to make ammonia water. Ammonia water, or ammonium hydroxide, is extensively used as a household cleansing agent because it is a good solvent for grease and fat, it does not injure cloth, and any excess decomposes and evaporates.

c. **Manufacture of Ammonium Compounds.** Ammonia is used to make other important ammonium compounds, such as ammonium sulfate $(NH_4)_2SO_4$, used as a fertilizer; and ammonium chloride (NH_4Cl), used as an electrolyte in dry cells.

d. **Solvay Process.** Large quantities of ammonia are used in the manufacture of sodium bicarbonate (baking soda) and sodium carbonate (washing soda) by the Solvay process. (For a discussion of the Solvay process, see *e,* page 225.)

e. **Ostwald Process.** In this process, nitric acid is made by the oxidation of ammonia in the presence of platinum as a catalyst. (The Ostwald process is described on page 203, under *a.*)

17. TESTS FOR AMMONIA AND AMMONIUM IONS

A gas with a pungent odor that turns moist red litmus blue and forms white fumes in the presence of hydrochloric acid must be ammonia. If heated with a soluble base (NaOH), an unknown substance that evolves a gas having the properties named above must contain ammonium ions.

NITRIC ACID (AQUA FORTIS)

18. LABORATORY PREPARATION

Nitric acid is obtained in the laboratory by gently heating a mixture of sodium nitrate (Chile saltpeter) and concentrated sulfuric acid.

Because nitric acid is a volatile liquid, it is collected by distillation. (See Fig. 18.) Sulfuric acid is used because it furnishes hydrogen ions and has a high boiling point. Sodium nitrate is the cheapest compound that can furnish nitrate ions.

The equation for the reaction is:

$$NaNO_3 + H_2SO_4 \rightarrow NaHSO_4 + HNO_3 \uparrow$$

At higher temperatures, the reaction proceeds as follows:

$$2\,NaNO_3 + H_2SO_4 \rightarrow Na_2SO_4 + 2\,HNO_3 \uparrow$$

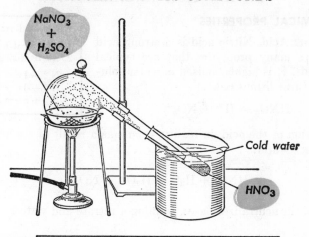

Fig. 18. Laboratory Preparation and Collection of Nitric Acid

19. COMMERCIAL PREPARATION

a. **Ostwald Process.** This process consists of oxidizing ammonia in the presence of platinum as a catalyst to produce nitric oxide (NO).

$$4 NH_3 + 5 O_2 \rightarrow 6 H_2O + 4 NO \uparrow$$

Nitric oxide with additional oxygen and water forms nitric acid.

$$4 NO + 3 O_2 + 2 H_2O \rightarrow 4 HNO_3$$

b. **Arc Process.** The first synthetic method for making nitric acid was the arc process. A huge electric arc was used to combine atmospheric nitrogen and oxygen to form nitric oxide. The addition of more oxygen and water produced nitric acid. This process is obsolete today because it cannot compete economically with the Ostwald process.

20. PHYSICAL PROPERTIES

Pure nitric acid is a colorless, odorless liquid with a low boiling point (86°C) and is almost twice as dense as water. Commercial nitric acid contains about 68% nitric acid in water solution. The acid is sometimes yellow because of dissolved oxides of nitrogen, formed by the partial decomposition of the acid.

> Liquid
> Colorless
> Odorless
> Almost 2 × water
> Soluble in water

21. CHEMICAL PROPERTIES

a. **Strong Acid.** Nitric acid is a strong acid and shows many properties that are typical of all acids. It is highly ionized in water solution and turns litmus red.

$$HNO_3 \rightarrow H^+ + NO_3^-$$

> Nitric acid is:
> 1. A typical acid.
> 2. An oxidizing agent.
> $$N^{+5} + 1\,e \rightarrow N^{+4}$$
> $$N^{+5} + 3\,e \rightarrow N^{+2}$$
> $$N^{+5} + 8\,e \rightarrow N^{-3}$$

Ionization of the acid, in reality, occurs as a result of the acid combining with water.

$$HNO_3 + H_2O \rightarrow H_3O^+ + NO_3^-$$

Nitric acid neutralizes bases, forming a nitrate and water.

$$NaOH + HNO_3 \rightarrow NaNO_3 + H_2O$$

b. **Oxidizing Agent.** Nitric acid is a powerful oxidizing agent. It will be remembered from a previous chapter that the presence of a reducible particle in a substance makes this substance an oxidizing agent. In nitric acid, the reducible particle is the nitrate ion, which can be reduced to a variety of products such as nitrogen dioxide, nitric oxide, or ammonia.

In the discussion that follows, the nitrate ion, for the sake of simplicity, will be represented as N^{+5}. Similarly, the reduction products of nitrate ion will be represented as N^{+4}, N^{+2}, and N^{-3}.

The extent to which nitrate ions can be reduced is a relative measure of the oxidizing power of nitric acid. This is the same as saying that *as nitrate ions gain electrons more readily, the oxidizing power of nitric acid increases.* The oxidizing power of nitric acid depends largely upon two factors:

(1) *Concentration.* With concentrated nitric acid, copper will liberate brown nitrogen dioxide (NO_2).

$$Cu + 4\,HNO_3 \rightarrow Cu(NO_3)_2 + 2\,H_2O + 2\,NO_2 \uparrow$$

REDUCTION OF NITRATE ION: $\underset{\substack{\text{nitrate} \\ \text{ion}}}{N^{+5}} + 1\,e \rightarrow \underset{\substack{\text{nitrogen} \\ \text{dioxide}}}{N^{+4}}$

OXIDATION OF COPPER: $Cu^0 - 2\,e \rightarrow Cu^{+2}$

As the acid becomes more dilute, nitrate ions gain more electrons. With dilute nitric acid, copper will liberate colorless nitric oxide (NO).

$$3 \text{ Cu} + 8 \text{ HNO}_3 \rightarrow 3 \text{ Cu(NO}_3)_2 + 4 \text{ H}_2\text{O} + 2 \text{ NO} \uparrow$$

$$N^{+5} + 3 \text{ e} \rightarrow N^{+2}$$
nitrate   nitric
ion   oxide

$$Cu^0 - 2 \text{ e} \rightarrow Cu^{+2}$$

Note that nitrate ions gain electrons more readily when nitric acid is diluted.

(2) *Nature of the Reducing Agent.* As the strength of the reducing agent is increased, the reduction of nitrate ions also increases. Note that in the presence of zinc, nitrate ions gain electrons more readily than they do in the presence of copper.

$$4 \text{ Zn} + 10 \text{ HNO}_3 \rightarrow 4 \text{ Zn(NO}_3)_2 + 3 \text{ H}_2\text{O} + \text{NH}_4\text{NO}_3$$

$$N^{+5} + 8 \text{ e} \rightarrow N^{-3}$$
nitrate   ammonium
ion   ion

$$Zn^0 - 2 \text{ e} \rightarrow Zn^{+2}$$

Thus, because of its oxidizing power, nitric acid reacts with all metals except gold and platinum. Gold and platinum do not react with nitric acid because they do not lose electrons readily enough to reduce nitrate ions. Hydrogen, normally, cannot be formed as a reduction product of nitric acid because hydrogen is easily oxidized to water by the nitric acid. If an active metal is used and the acid is extremely dilute, hydrogen may be liberated.

c. **Action of Aqua Regia.** No single acid can dissolve gold or platinum. However, *aqua regia*, which is a mixture of one part concentrated nitric acid and three parts concentrated hydrochloric acid, will dissolve these metals.

It was believed that the reaction between hydrochloric and nitric acids produced an oxidizing agent (nitrosyl chloride, NOCl) more powerful than nitric acid. It is now thought, however, that in the presence of hydrochloric acid, metals like gold and platinum become more active (more powerful reducing agents), thus increasing the oxidizing power of nitric acid.

d. **Unstable Compound.** Nitric acid is unstable and readily decomposes on being heated. Nitric acid decomposes partially when acted upon by sunlight, forming nitrogen dioxide, which gives the acid a yellow color.

$$4 HNO_3 \rightarrow 2 H_2O + O_2 \uparrow + 4 NO_2 \uparrow$$

22. USES

a. **Manufacture of Explosives.** Nitric acid is used in the manufacture of such explosives as nitroglycerine, TNT (trinitrotoluene), and guncotton. Potassium nitrate is an important ingredient in gunpowder. The use of nitrogen compounds as explosives is based on their instability.

b. **Manufacture of Fertilizer.** Nitric acid is used to make nitrates for use as fertilizers.

c. **Manufacture of Aqua Regia.** As already noted, the mixture of nitric and hydrochloric acids, called aqua regia, is used to dissolve gold and platinum. Nitric acid alone is used to separate gold from silver in a mixture of these metals, and to distinguish between gold and brass.

d. **Manufacture of Dyes.** Many synthetic dyes are made from aniline ($C_6H_5NH_2$). Aniline is made from nitrobenzene ($C_6H_5NO_2$), which is obtained by treating benzene with a mixture of nitric and sulfuric acids.

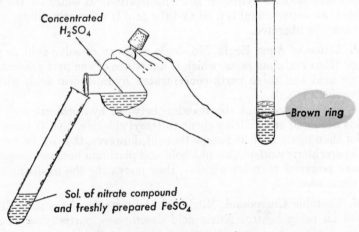

Concentrated H₂SO₄

Brown ring

Sol. of nitrate compound and freshly prepared FeSO₄

Fig. 23. Test for Nitrate Ions

23. TEST FOR NITRATE IONS

To test a compound for nitrate ions, add some *freshly prepared* ferrous sulfate solution to a solution of the compound being tested. Then pour concentrated sulfuric acid slowly down the side of the test tube. The formation of a *brown ring,* as shown in Fig. 23, indicates the presence of nitrate ions.

OXIDES OF NITROGEN

24. NITROUS OXIDE (N₂O)

a. **Preparation.** Nitrous oxide is obtained by the gentle heating and decomposition of ammonium nitrate (NH_4NO_3).

$$NH_4NO_3 \rightarrow 2 H_2O + N_2O \uparrow$$

CAUTION	Exercise extreme care during the heating of ammonium nitrate because it is unstable.

Since nitrous oxide is only slightly soluble, it can be collected by displacement of water.

b. **Properties.** Nitrous oxide is a colorless gas with a rather sweet odor. It is denser than air and only slightly soluble in water. Nitrous oxide supports combustion almost as well as oxygen does, and causes a glowing splint to burst into flame. Sulfur, however, burns somewhat more brightly in oxygen than in nitrous oxide.

c. **Use.** Commonly known as laughing gas, nitrous oxide is used as an anesthetic.

25. NITRIC OXIDE (NO)

a. **Preparation.** Nitric oxide is prepared in the laboratory by the reaction between copper and dilute nitric acid. It is collected by the displacement of water.

$$3 Cu + 8 HNO_3 \rightarrow 3 Cu(NO_3)_2 + 4 H_2O + 2 NO \uparrow$$

b. **Properties.** Nitric oxide is a colorless gas, slightly denser than air, and only slightly soluble in water. Unlike nitrous oxide, it does not support combustion. When exposed to the air, it unites readily with oxygen to form a brown gas, nitrogen dioxide (NO_2).

$$2 NO + O_2 \rightarrow 2 NO_2 \uparrow$$

Nitrogen dioxide is first formed in a nitric oxide generator because the colorless nitric oxide combines with the oxygen of the air in the generator. This brown gas dissolves in the water of the collecting bottle and is not collected.

c. **Use.** Nitric oxide is used in the manufacture of nitric acid.

26. TESTS FOR NITRIC AND NITROUS OXIDES

A colorless gas which turns brown on exposure to air *must* be nitric oxide. A colorless gas which causes a glowing splint to burst into flame *might* be nitrous oxide or oxygen.

To distinguish one from the other, *nitric oxide* is mixed with the gas to be tested. If the mixture of gases remains colorless, the tested gas is nitrous oxide. If the mixture of gases is brown, the tested gas is oxygen.

27. NITROGEN DIOXIDE (NO_2)

a. **Preparation.** Nitrogen dioxide is conveniently obtained by exposing nitric oxide to the air.

$$2 NO + O_2 \rightarrow 2 NO_2 \uparrow$$

Nitrogen dioxide may also be obtained by the reaction between copper and concentrated nitric acid.

$$Cu + 4 HNO_3 \rightarrow Cu(NO_3)_2 + 2 H_2O + 2 NO_2 \uparrow$$

b. **Properties.** Nitrogen dioxide is a brown, toxic gas with an irritating odor. When the gas is cooled, the brown color slowly becomes lighter until a colorless gas is formed. This change in color is due to the formation of nitrogen tetroxide (N_2O_4). This gas may be considered another oxide of nitrogen or merely a form of nitrogen dioxide.

$$2 NO_2 \underset{\text{warm}}{\overset{\text{cool}}{\rightleftarrows}} N_2O_4$$

Nitrogen dioxide is denser than air and soluble in water. It combines with water to form a mixture of nitrous and nitric acids.

$$2 NO_2 + H_2O \rightarrow HNO_2 + HNO_3$$

Excess nitrogen dioxide will oxidize the nitrous acid to nitric acid.

c. **Use.** Nitrogen dioxide is used in the manufacture of nitric acid.

28. OXIDES OF NITROGEN AND THE LAW OF MULTIPLE PROPORTIONS

Four oxides of nitrogen, including nitrogen tetroxide, have been described. Two other oxides of nitrogen are nitrogen trioxide and nitrogen pentoxide. Nitrogen trioxide (N_2O_3) is the anhydride of nitrous acid and is called nitrous anhydride.

$$N_2O_3 + H_2O \rightarrow 2\ HNO_2$$

Nitrogen pentoxide (N_2O_5) is the anhydride of nitric acid and is called nitric anhydride.

$$N_2O_5 + H_2O \rightarrow 2\ HNO_3$$

Taken *individually*, the composition by weight of each oxide of nitrogen illustrates the Law of Definite Proportions. Taken *together*, the composition by weight of the oxides of nitrogen illustrates the Law of Multiple Proportions. It is convenient to fix the weight of the nitrogen in each of the oxides of nitrogen by writing the formula of nitric oxide as N_2O_2 and nitrogen dioxide as N_2O_4.

NAME	FORMULA	NUMBER OF ATOMS		WEIGHT ($N = 14$; $O = 16$)		RATIO OF OXYGEN
		N	O	N	O	
Nitrous oxide	N_2O	2	1	28	16	$\frac{16}{16} = 1$
Nitric oxide	$2\ NO = N_2O_2$	2	2	28	32	$\frac{32}{16} = 2$
Nitrogen trioxide	N_2O_3	2	3	28	48	$\frac{48}{16} = 3$
Nitrogen dioxide	$2\ NO_2 = N_2O_4$	2	4	28	64	$\frac{64}{16} = 4$
Nitrogen pentoxide	N_2O_5	2	5	28	80	$\frac{80}{16} = 5$

CONVERTING AND RESTORING FREE NITROGEN

29. NITROGEN-FIXATION

Nitrogen-fixation is any process by which the free nitrogen of the air is converted into useful nitrogen compounds.

Nitrogen-fixation occurs in nature and is also carried out in industry in the following ways:

a. **In Nature.** Leguminous plants such as the pea, bean, clover, and alfalfa have certain bacteria living on their roots. The bacteria are able to convert the free nitrogen of the air into nitrogen compounds which the plants can use. These bacteria are called nitrogen-fixing bacteria.

Lightning flashes produce a small amount of nitric acid. The chemical actions taking place are the same as those in the arc process for the preparation of nitric acid. The resulting nitric acid reacts with the rocks of the soil, forming nitrates.

b. **In Industry.** The Haber process, already described as a commercial method for the manufacture of ammonia, is an industrial nitrogen-fixation process. In this process, ammonia is made by the direct combination of the nitrogen of the air with hydrogen, under special conditions.

The cyanamid process is another industrial nitrogen-fixation process. In this process, nitrogen from liquid air is made to react with calcium carbide to form calcium cyanamid, which forms ammonia when treated with steam. (See *c,* pages 199-200, for the equations of the process.)

30. NITRIFICATION AND DENITRIFICATION

In addition to nitrogen-fixation processes, nitrates may be restored to the soil by *nitrification*. Nitrification is a decomposition process in which complex nitrogen compounds (proteins) present in organic waste materials are converted by nitrifying bacteria into simpler nitrates. The action of denitrifying bacteria upon these nitrates helps to restore nitrogen to the atmosphere. This process is called *denitrification*.

31. THE NITROGEN CYCLE

The processes of nitrogen-fixation and nitrification are combined in nature to furnish the soil with a constant supply of nitrates. Denitrification restores nitrogen to the atmosphere. This series of changes is called the *nitrogen cycle*. A summary of the important changes in the nitrogen cycle follows:

a. Atmospheric nitrogen is converted into nitrates that can be utilized by plants for the production of plant protein.

b. Animals feed on this plant protein, ultimately developing animal protein.

c. The bacterial decay of animal protein restores nitrogen to the atmosphere, thus allowing the cycle to continue.

Study Guide

1. *a.* The gases in the atmosphere extend *three or four* miles into space. [True or false? If false, correct the italicized term.]
   b. With increased altitude, the density of air _____ (decreases, increases, remains the same).
   c. The two chief components of air are _____ and _____.
   d. By volume, air contains (1) one-fifth (2) two-fifths (3) three-fifths (4) four-fifths   nitrogen.
   e. Nitrogen is removed from air by _____, but is constantly returned by _____.
   f. In air, there is approximately _____ per cent of oxygen by volume.
   g. Oxygen is returned to the air by plants during the process of _____.
2. *a.* In the manufacture of starch, green plants utilize (1) oxygen (2) nitrogen (3) argon (4) carbon dioxide.
   b. Using a labeled diagram, describe how the amounts of atmospheric oxygen and carbon dioxide remain relatively constant.
   c. State the name of an inert gas that has each of the following properties:
      (1) used in electric signs because of characteristic glow during electric discharge
      (2) the most abundant inert gas in the air
      (3) low density and incombustibility
   d. Three factors that determine the amount of water vapor that air can hold are _____, _____, and _____.
   e. Explain how the amount of water vapor in air remains relatively constant.
   f. Relative humidity expresses the amount of moisture in air compared to

   *g. As the temperature falls, relative humidity _____ (decreases, increases, remains the same).

3. *a.* Describe an experiment that can be used to determine the volume composition of air.

   **b.* Is the volume composition of air the same as its weight composition? Explain.

4. *a.* Substances considered by the ancients to be elements were air, earth, water, and _____.

   b. Describe three proofs that air is a mixture.

   c. State one important application that results from the fact that air is a mixture.

5. *a.* Using balanced equations, show how nitrogen may be prepared in the laboratory from sodium nitrite.

   b. Large quantities of nitrogen are extracted from air by (1) evaporation (2) boiling (3) electrolysis (4) fractional distillation.

6. *a.* The density of nitrogen compared to the density of air is approximately (1) 0.5 (2) 0.9 (3) 2 (4) 22.4.

   b. If 39 volumes of sulfur dioxide will dissolve in one volume of water at room temperature, the number of volumes of nitrogen that will dissolve in the same volume of water at the same temperature is approximately (1) .015 (2) 0.1 (3) 78 (4) 445.

7. *a.* Nitrogen, atomic number 7, has _____ valence electrons.

   b. Nitrogen tends to form compounds by _____ electrons.

   c. The valence number of nitrogen in the compound Mg_3N_2 is (1) —3 (2) +3 (3) —5 (4) +5.

   d. Write a balanced equation for each of the following reactions:

      (1) $N_2 + H_2 \rightarrow$

      (2) $Al + N_2 \rightarrow$

      (3) $Mg_3N_2 + H_2O \rightarrow$

      (4) $CaC_2 + N_2 \rightarrow$

8. Two important substances which can be made from nitrogen are _____ and _____.

9. The bacterial decomposition of plant and animal matter to yield ammonia suggests that all organic matter contains the elements hydrogen and _____.

10. *a.* Make a labeled diagram to illustrate the laboratory preparation and collection of ammonia.

   b. Write a balanced equation for the reaction in *a.*

   c. Ammonia is not collected by water displacement because it (1) forms an acid in solution (2) dissolves in water (3) is easily decomposed (4) is less dense than air.

11. *a.* Ammonia may be obtained from coal by *destructive distillation.* [True or false? If false, correct the italicized term.]

   b. Synthetically, ammonia may be prepared from (1) nitrogen and oxygen (2) nitrogen, oxygen, and hydrogen (3) ammonium hydroxide (4) nitrogen and hydrogen.

   c. The formation of ammonia in the Haber process represents a reversible reaction which reaches _____.

   d. Write a balanced equation to show how ammonia may be prepared from calcium cyanamid.

12. *a.* Ammonia is most readily identified by (1) its color (2) its odor (3) its density (4) chemical analysis.

    b. Ammonia is very soluble in water and (1) denser than air (2) odorless (3) greenish-yellow (4) easily liquefied.

    c. The formula for the ammonium radical is (1) NH_3 (2) NH_4^+ (3) NH_4 (4) NH_4OH.

13. *a.* As the temperature of ammonia water rises, the concentration of the solution _____ (decreases, increases, remains the same).

    b. Ammonia water is (1) liquid ammonia (2) a refrigerant (3) a strong base (4) a weak base.

    c. Write balanced equations to show how ammonia reacts directly with acids.

    d. Write a balanced equation for each of the following reactions:
      (1) catalytic oxidation of ammonia
      (2) conversion of ammonia into a metallic amide

14. *a.* Phenolphthalein turns _____ in the presence of ammonia water.

    b. List three chemical properties of ammonium hydroxide.

15. *a.* State the property of ammonia which makes each of the following uses possible:
    (1) refrigerant
    (2) household cleansing agent
    (3) source of nitric acid

    b. Name two important ammonium compounds and state a use for each.

16. The presence of ammonium ions in a compound may be detected by converting the compound into _____, which forms white fumes in the presence of _____.

17. *a.* Nitric acid can be prepared by the reaction between (1) calcium nitrate and hydrochloric acid (2) ammonium chloride and sulfuric acid (3) sodium nitrite and hydrochloric acid (4) zinc nitrate and sulfuric acid.

    b. Because nitric acid is volatile, it is collected by _____.

    c. The generator that is most commonly used in the laboratory preparation of nitric acid is a (1) beaker (2) flask (3) retort (4) test tube.

    d. Make a labeled diagram to illustrate the laboratory preparation and collection of nitric acid.

    e. Write balanced equations for two reactions that may occur in *d.*

18. **a.* Explain why the conversion of ammonia into nitric acid must involve oxidation-reduction.

    b. By means of balanced equations, describe the Ostwald process.

    c. A lightning flash through air may result in the formation of (1) ammonia (2) carbon dioxide (3) nitric oxide (4) water.

19. *a.* Pure nitric acid is (1) less dense than water (2) nonvolatile (3) colored (4) colorless.

    b. The yellow color of commercial nitric acid is due to the presence of impurities such as _____.

20. *a.* *Concentrated* nitric acid is highly ionized. [True or false? If false, correct the italicized term.]

    b. Write a balanced equation for each of the following reactions:
      (1) $HNO_3 + H_2O \rightarrow$
      (2) $HNO_3 + KOH \rightarrow$
      (3) $HNO_3 + Al(OH)_3 \rightarrow$

    c. Why does nitric acid behave as an oxidizing agent?

    d. Two factors that determine the oxidizing power of nitric acid are _____ and _____.

    e. As nitric acid becomes more dilute, the power of nitrate ions to gain electrons _____ (decreases, increases, remains the same).

    f. Why is nitric acid a more powerful oxidizing agent with zinc than with copper?

    g. Nitric acid will not react with gold because _____.

    h. Aqua regia is a mixture of _____ and _____.

    i. Explain why gold and platinum will dissolve in aqua regia.

    j. Write an equation to show what happens when nitric acid is exposed to light.

21. *a.* Two nitrogen compounds used in explosives are _____ and _____.

    b. A reagent that can be used to distinguish gold from brass is (1) aqua regia (2) nitric acid (3) hydrochloric acid (4) silver nitrate.

    c. Aniline compounds may be used in the manufacture of (1) fertilizers (2) explosives (3) aqua regia (4) dyes.

22. *a.* Describe the test for nitrate ions.

    *b. Why must the ferrous sulfate used in the nitrate test be freshly prepared?

23. *a.* Write a balanced equation for the laboratory preparation of nitrous oxide.

    b. Why is this reaction dangerous?

    c. A chemical property common to nitrous oxide and oxygen is that both gases _____.

    d. The common name of nitrous oxide is _____.

24. *a.* Write a balanced equation for the laboratory preparation of nitric oxide.

    b. Unlike nitrous oxide, nitric oxide (1) is a gas (2) is denser than air (3) is slightly soluble in water (4) does not support combustion.

    c. Nitric oxide readily unites with oxygen to form *nitrous oxide*. [True or false? If false, correct the italicized term.]

25. *a.* The reagent that can be used to distinguish between NO and N_2O is _____.

    b. The reagent that can be used to distinguish between N_2O and O_2 is _____.

26. *a.* Write a balanced equation for the laboratory preparation of NO_2.

    *b. Why is nitrogen peroxide the incorrect name for NO_2?

    c. Upon cooling, nitrogen dioxide is changed into (1) nitrous oxide (2) nitric oxide (3) nitrogen tetroxide (4) nitrogen pentoxide.

    d. Nitrogen dioxide is not the true anhydride of nitric acid. Explain.

27. *a.* The anhydride of nitrous acid is _____.

    b. The anhydride of nitric acid is _____.

    c. Name five oxides of nitrogen and write the chemical formula of each.

    d. State the chemical law illustrated by this series of oxides.

    e. Explain how these oxides illustrate this law.

28. *a.* Nitrogen-fixation means converting free nitrogen into _____.

    b. Nitrogen-fixing bacteria are found on the roots of (1) celery (2) corn (3) peas (4) potatoes.

    c. Two examples of industrial nitrogen-fixation processes are _____ and _____.

    d. Distinguish between nitrification and denitrification.

    e. Describe the important steps in the nitrogen cycle.

29. Calculate the volume of air required to convert phosphorus into 710 grams of phosphorus pentoxide.

30. Calculate the weight of ammonia that can be obtained from 100 grams of ammonium bicarbonate.

31. Calculate the volume of nitric oxide that can be obtained by the oxidation of 100 liters of ammonia.

15 CARBON AND ITS OXIDES

CARBON

1. OCCURRENCE

Carbon is found free in nature as coal, graphite, and diamond. It is found combined in nature in the carbon dioxide of the air, carbonates, natural gas, petroleum, and in the protoplasm of plants and animals.

2. ALLOTROPIC FORMS

Carbon, like oxygen and sulfur, has several allotropic forms, which differ mainly in physical properties. The allotropic forms of carbon are amorphous carbon, graphite, and diamond.

a. **Amorphous Carbon.** This form of carbon is noncrystalline in structure, and is represented by such varieties as coal, coke, charcoal, boneblack, lampblack, and carbon black. Recent X-ray studies, however, indicate that amorphous carbon may consist of submicroscopic crystals of graphite.

(1) *Coal.* Coal is a product of prehistoric times. The plant matter of previous ages became buried deep in the ground, where it was subjected to tremendous heat and pressure. Initially, peat, a partially decomposed plant material containing considerable water, was formed. With continued heat and pressure, lignite, also called brown coal, was produced. Continued loss of volatile materials, such as hydrocarbons (compounds of carbon and hydrogen), resulted in the formation of coal.

The two most common varieties of coal are hard (anthracite) and soft (bituminous). They differ mainly in the amount of free (uncombined) carbon they contain. Anthracite contains over 85% free carbon, while bituminous has over 60% free carbon; the remainder of the carbon is combined in the form of hydrocarbons. Anthracite is used chiefly as a fuel in the home. It burns more uniformly, with a smaller flame, and produces less smoke than bituminous coal. Bituminous coal is used as an industrial fuel, and in the manufacture of coke. It is also an important source of ammonia. Because it contains a greater percentage of combustible hydrocarbons, bituminous coal has a higher heat content than anthracite on an equal weight basis.

(2) *Coke.* When soft coal is heated in airtight retorts to temperatures between 800° and 1,000°C, volatile products are driven out and a porous solid, coke, remains. This process represents a chemical change and is called *destructive distillation.* (For the definition of destructive distillation, see *a,* page 199.)

Coke is used both as an industrial and domestic fuel. It is used as a reducing agent in the extraction of metals from their oxide ores, and in the manufacture of water gas. Coke is preferred as a reducing agent in the extraction of iron because it can sustain the crushing weight it is subjected to in the blast furnace. It is also used in the manufacture of carbides, which will be discussed later in this chapter.

The volatile products of the destructive distillation of soft coal include a liquid, coal tar, and a number of gases such as coal gas, ammonia, and hydrogen sulfide. By subjecting coal tar to fractional distillation, benzene, toluene, and phenol, invaluable to the dye and drug industries, are obtained.

Fractional distillation is the separation by distillation of a complex mixture of liquids into simpler mixtures in the order of their increasing boiling points.

The most volatile fractions distill off first.

(3) *Charcoal.* Like coal, when wood is heated in the absence of air, volatile products are driven out and a solid, charcoal, remains.

Charcoal is light, porous, and burns with practically no flame. It is used as a fuel, in sketching, and to remove coloring matter and undesirable gases by adsorption. *Adsorption is the process whereby impurities are attracted and held on the surface of the adsorbing agent.* As the surface area of the adsorbing agent increases, the ability to adsorb also increases. As an adsorbent, charcoal is used in gas masks to remove poisonous gases from air, and in refrigerators to take up undesirable odors. Treating charcoal with steam removes some of the tars present and increases the surface area of the charcoal. This variety of charcoal, called *activated charcoal,* is therefore a better adsorbent than ordinary charcoal.

The volatile products of the destructive distillation of wood include a liquid, wood tar, also called pyroligneous acid; and wood gas, which is a mixture of hydrocarbons and oxides of carbon. Like coal tar, wood tar may be fractionally distilled to yield wood alcohol, acetone, and acetic acid.

(4) *Boneblack.* Boneblack, or animal charcoal, is produced by the destructive distillation of bones. In addition to carbon, boneblack also contains a high percentage of calcium phosphate. Because boneblack is so finely divided, it presents a large surface area useful for adsorption. Large quantities of boneblack are consumed in the decolorization of sugar during the refining process. See Fig. (4) below.

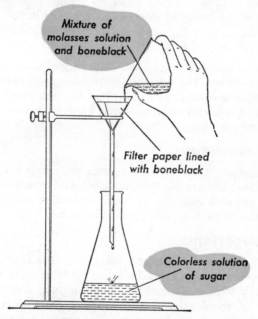

Fig. (4). Decolorizing Action of Boneblack

(5) *Lampblack and Carbon Black.* Lampblack is obtained by the incomplete combustion of hydrocarbon oils, that is, by burning these oils in a limited supply of air. When natural gas is used as the hydrocarbon source, a form of lampblack, called carbon black or gas carbon, is obtained. Carbon black is finer and less tarry than lampblack and is slowly replacing lampblack in many of its uses.

Large quantities of lampblack, however, are still used in the manufacture of inks, shoe polish, and paints. Carbon black is added to rubber tires to make them more resistant to wear and abrasion.

b. **Graphite.** Graphite is found in nature, and is also made artificially by heating anthracite coal in the electric furnace. Graphite is black, soft, and crystalline in structure. Its tiny crystals slide over one another very easily, making it useful as a lubricant, especially at high temperatures where oils would normally deteriorate. Because of its extreme softness, graphite leaves a mark on paper and is therefore used in "lead" pencils. "Lead" pencils also contain varying amounts of clay to reduce the softness of the graphite, thus making the "lead" harder. Because it is a refractory substance, that is, has a high melting point, graphite is used to make crucibles for high-temperature reactions. As a good conductor of electricity, it is used in the manufacture of electrodes for electric furnaces, and brushes for motors. In nuclear reactors, graphite is used as a moderator to slow down neutrons.

c. **Diamond.** Diamond, the purest form of carbon, is crystalline in structure and colorless. Because they disperse light to produce brilliant colors, diamonds are used as gems. The hardest natural substance known, diamond is useful as an abrasive. Faulty diamonds and impure black diamonds are used to cut other diamonds, and in wire dies.

3. PHYSICAL PROPERTIES

All the allotropic forms of carbon, with the exception of diamond, are black solids. They are odorless, tasteless, and generally denser than water. They are also insoluble in water and other common solvents. Small quantities of carbon will dissolve in molten iron.

4. CHEMICAL PROPERTIES

IV A

| C |
| Si |
| Ge |
| Sn |
| Pb |

Carbon, the lightest member of Group IV A, has four electrons in its outer ring. As a result, carbon tends to share electrons, especially with other carbon atoms, forming a tremendous number of covalent compounds. These compounds are part of a special branch of chemistry called organic chemistry, and will be discussed in Chapter 21.

The chemical properties of carbon depend largely on temperature.

a. At ordinary temperatures, carbon is inactive and does not react with oxygen, acids, or bases.

b. All forms of carbon, when moderately heated, burn in air to produce carbon dioxide. (Diamond will burn only in pure oxygen.) This proves that all the allotropic forms of carbon are the same element.

$$C + O_2 \rightarrow CO_2 \uparrow$$

c. When moderately heated, carbon is an excellent reducing agent. It is used in the extraction of metals from their oxide ores. As shown in Fig. 4c, charcoal will reduce copper oxide to form copper and carbon dioxide.

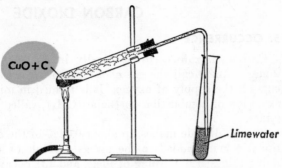

Fig. 4c. Reduction of Copper Oxide

$$2 \, CuO + C \rightarrow 2 \, Cu + CO_2 \uparrow$$

d. At the high temperature of an electric furnace, carbon reacts with other substances to form important commercial products.

(1) *Silicon carbide* (SiC) is made by heating a mixture of sand (SiO$_2$) and coke in the electric furnace.

$$SiO_2 + 3 \, C \rightarrow SiC + 2 \, CO \uparrow$$

Silicon carbide is used as an abrasive in grinding wheels and sharpening stones for tools. It is commonly known as carborundum.

(2) *Calcium carbide* (CaC$_2$) is made by heating a mixture of quicklime (CaO) and coke in the electric furnace.

$$CaO + 3 \, C \rightarrow CaC_2 + CO \uparrow$$

Water added to calcium carbide produces acetylene (C$_2$H$_2$), which may be used as an illuminant, and as a fuel in the oxyacetylene blowtorch.

$$CaC_2 + 2 \, H_2O \rightarrow Ca(OH)_2 + C_2H_2 \uparrow$$

(3) *Carbon disulfide* (CS$_2$) is made by reacting coke with sulfur in an electric furnace from which air has been excluded. The absence of air prevents the ignition of this highly flammable sulfide.

$$C + 2 \, S \rightarrow CS_2$$

Carbon disulfide is an important organic solvent. It is also used in the manufacture of viscose rayon and in the preparation of carbon tetrachloride.

CARBON DIOXIDE

5. OCCURRENCE

Carbon dioxide occurs naturally in air, in spring waters, and in mines. Miners call the gas *choke damp* because it is so dense that it cuts off the supply of oxygen. It is formed in mines as a result of the explosion of combustible methane (CH_4), called *fire damp*, present in mines.

Carbon dioxide makes up about 0.04% of the atmosphere. It is continually being added to the air as a result of (1) respiration in all living things, (2) burning of fuels, and (3) decay of plant and animal matter. Green plants remove carbon dioxide from the air and release oxygen during the process of photosynthesis (*f*, page 225). As a result of this carbon dioxide-oxygen cycle, the proportion of these two gases in the air is fairly constant. (See figure, page 194.)

6. LABORATORY PREPARATION

Carbon dioxide may be prepared in the laboratory by the action of a carbonate or bicarbonate on an acid.

$$(CO_3)^{-2} + 2\,H^+ \rightarrow H_2O + CO_2 \uparrow$$

$$(HCO_3)^- + H^+ \rightarrow H_2O + CO_2 \uparrow$$

Carbon dioxide is usually obtained by treating calcium carbonate in the form of marble chips with dilute hydrochloric acid. (See Fig. 6.) Sulfuric acid should not be used because of the formation of insoluble calcium sulfate, which slows down the further decomposition of the marble.

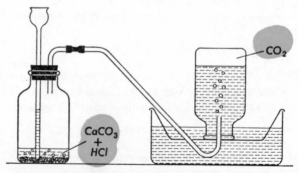

Fig. 6. Laboratory Preparation and Collection of Carbon Dioxide

The reaction takes place in two steps. Double replacement first occurs, resulting in the formation of unstable carbonic acid (H_2CO_3).

$$CaCO_3 + 2\ HCl \rightarrow CaCl_2 + H_2CO_3$$

The H_2CO_3 then decomposes into water and carbon dioxide.

$$H_2CO_3 \rightarrow H_2O + CO_2 \uparrow$$

Adding the preceding equations, we get:

$$CaCO_3 + 2\ HCl \rightarrow CaCl_2 + H_2O + CO_2 \uparrow$$

Carbon dioxide may be collected by displacement of air or by displacement of water because it is only moderately soluble in water.

7. COMMERCIAL PREPARATION

Large quantities of carbon dioxide may be obtained by:

a. **Burning of Carbon**

$$C + O_2 \rightarrow CO_2 \uparrow$$

b. **Heating and Decomposition of Calcium Carbonate in Lime Kilns**

$$CaCO_3 \rightarrow CaO + CO_2 \uparrow$$

c. **As a By-product of Fermentation.** The fermentation of sugars, with the aid of special catalysts called *enzymes,* produces ethyl (grain) alcohol and carbon dioxide. Yeast is used to supply the enzyme, zymase.

$$\underset{\text{glucose}}{C_6H_{12}O_6} \xrightarrow[\substack{\text{in yeast}}]{\text{zymase}} \underset{\substack{\text{ethyl} \\ \text{alcohol}}}{2\ C_2H_5OH} + 2\ CO_2 \uparrow$$

8. PHYSICAL PROPERTIES

Carbon dioxide is a colorless, odorless, and tasteless gas. It is nonpoisonous, about one and one-half times as dense as air, and moderately soluble in water, but much more soluble under increased pressure. Carbon dioxide is easily liquefied and solidified.

Gas
Colorless
Odorless
$1\frac{1}{2} \times$ air
Moderately soluble in water

9. CHEMICAL PROPERTIES

> 1. At *ordinary* temperatures, CO_2 is inactive and does not support combustion.
> 2. At *high* temperatures, CO_2 supports combustion (is an oxidizing agent).
>
> $$C^{+4} + 4e \rightarrow C^0$$

a. Carbon dioxide is a stable compound. It does not burn, and does not support combustion under ordinary conditions. However, if a piece of burning magnesium is lowered into a bottle of carbon dioxide, the metal continues to burn, forming a black deposit of carbon. This indicates that carbon dioxide supports combustion at high temperatures. The equation for the reaction is as follows:

$$CO_2 + 2\,Mg \rightarrow 2\,MgO + C$$

Note that in this reaction, carbon dioxide has oxidized the magnesium.

b. Carbon dioxide can also be reduced to carbon monoxide by hot carbon.

$$CO_2 + C \rightarrow 2\,CO \uparrow$$

c. Carbon dioxide is an acid anhydride because it combines with water to form carbonic acid (H_2CO_3), a weak acid.

$$CO_2 + H_2O \xrightleftharpoons{} H_2CO_3$$

d. Carbon dioxide, when passed through limewater, $Ca(OH)_2$, causes the limewater to turn milky as a result of the formation of a white precipitate of calcium carbonate.

$$CO_2 + Ca(OH)_2 \rightarrow H_2O + \underset{white}{CaCO_3 \downarrow}$$

e. An excess of carbon dioxide passed through limewater causes this white precipitate to dissolve, forming soluble calcium bicarbonate, $Ca(HCO_3)_2$.

$$CO_2 + H_2O + CaCO_3 \rightarrow Ca(HCO_3)_2$$

10. USES

The uses of carbon dioxide depend on the specific properties it possesses as either a gas, liquid, or solid.

Fire extinguishers
Carbonated beverages
Refrigeration
Source of pressure
Solvay process
Photosynthesis
Leavening agent

a. **Fire Extinguishers.** Because carbon dioxide is a stable, noncombustible gas which does not support combustion at ordinary temperatures, it is used in certain fire extinguishers.

(1) In the soda-acid type of fire extinguisher, carbon dioxide is generated by the action of concentrated sulfuric acid on a saturated solution of sodium bicarbonate (baking soda, $NaHCO_3$).

$$2\ NaHCO_3 + H_2SO_4 \rightarrow Na_2SO_4 + 2\ H_2O + 2\ CO_2 \uparrow$$

A cylindrical copper tank with a screw head contains the sodium bicarbonate solution, while the acid is contained in a bottle with a lead gravity stopper. When the extinguisher is inverted, the lead stopper falls out of the bottle, permitting the two liquids to mix. The liberated carbon dioxide, being under great pressure, forces out the solution which extinguishes the fire.

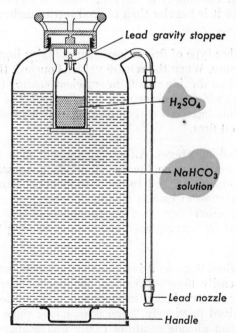

Lead gravity stopper

H_2SO_4

$NaHCO_3$ solution

Lead nozzle

Handle

Fig. 10a(1). Soda-acid Fire Extinguisher

Sodium bicarbonate is preferred to sodium carbonate as the source of carbon dioxide, because pound for pound sodium bicarbonate furnishes more gas with the same weight of acid.

A soda-acid fire extinguisher should not be used on electrical fires because it expels a solution which conducts electricity. This type of extinguisher should also not be used on fires where molten metals are present. At these high temperatures, carbon dioxide will support combustion.

(2) The foamite type of fire extinguisher is especially effective in fighting oil fires. It resembles the soda-acid fire extinguisher, except that a licorice extract (foam stabilizer) is mixed with the sodium bicarbonate solution, and a solution of alum takes the place of the sulfuric acid. The hydrolysis of the alum solution produces enough sulfuric acid to react with the bicarbonate of soda. The carbon dioxide thus produced is trapped in a frothy foam which floats on the burning oil, shutting off the supply of oxygen. Water is ineffective in fighting oil fires because it is heavier than oil and settles underneath the burning oil.

(3) Another type of fire extinguisher contains liquid carbon dioxide under pressure. When the release valve is opened, the rapid expansion of the carbon dioxide results in sufficient cooling to produce solid carbon dioxide, which emerges as a fine "snow." The evaporation of this solid produces gaseous carbon dioxide, which effectively smothers electrical and oil fires.

b. **Carbonated Beverages.** Although carbon dioxide is tasteless, the carbonic acid formed when the gas dissolves gives water a pleasant taste. Carbon dioxide is used to make carbonated beverages, such as soda water (solution of carbon dioxide in water). Tremendous quantities of carbon dioxide are used for this purpose. The carbon dioxide is manufactured by burning coke and then carefully purifying the resulting product.

c. **Refrigeration.** Because it is a colorless, odorless, nonpoisonous gas which can be easily liquefied, carbon dioxide has been used in place of ammonia or sulfur dioxide in electrical refrigeration on ships. As has been explained previously, freon is replacing these gases. Because carbon dioxide solidifies easily and changes directly from the solid to the gaseous form, it is used as a portable refrigerant for icing freight cars and for freezing ice cream. Solid carbon dioxide is called "dry ice." Its temperature of about −79°C makes it much too cold to be used as a household refrigerant. It can, however, be used where such low temperatures are desirable. It has also been successfully used in cloud seeding to produce rain artificially.

d. **As a Source of Pressure.** Sealed containers of dry ice develop tremendous pressures. These pressures can be utilized as a source of power to operate emergency brakes and to inflate life rafts.

e. **Solvay Process.** Carbon dioxide is used to manufacture sodium bicarbonate and sodium carbonate by the Solvay process. Carbon dioxide and ammonia are forced under pressure into a saturated sodium chloride solution, and under these conditions sodium bicarbonate precipitates out. Although this reaction is essentially ionic, it is written below in molecular form for the sake of simplicity.

$$(1) \quad NaCl + H_2O + NH_3 + CO_2 \rightarrow NH_4Cl + NaHCO_3 \downarrow$$

Sodium bicarbonate is converted into sodium carbonate by heat.

$$(2) \quad 2\,NaHCO_3 \rightarrow Na_2CO_3 + H_2O + CO_2 \uparrow$$

Carbon dioxide is prepared for the Solvay process by the decomposition of limestone ($CaCO_3$) at red-heat.

$$CaCO_3 \rightarrow CaO + CO_2 \uparrow$$

The calcium oxide produced is converted into calcium hydroxide by reaction with water.

$$CaO + H_2O \rightarrow Ca(OH)_2$$

The resulting calcium hydroxide is then heated with the ammonium chloride, produced in equation (1), to yield ammonia.

$$Ca(OH)_2 + 2\,NH_4Cl \rightarrow CaCl_2 + 2\,H_2O + 2\,NH_3 \uparrow$$

With the exception of salt, the substances needed for the Solvay process can be manufactured from the products of this process. This makes the process economical and efficient.

f. **Photosynthesis.** Green plants combine carbon dioxide from the air and water from the soil to form simple sugar and liberate oxygen. The plant then converts some of the sugar into starch. The process of photosynthesis requires sunlight and takes place in the presence of chlorophyll, the green coloring matter in plants.

$$6\,CO_2 + 6\,H_2O \rightarrow \underset{\substack{simple \\ sugar}}{C_6H_{12}O_6} + 6\,O_2 \uparrow$$

g. **Leavening Agent.** Carbon dioxide is used as a leavening agent in baking, because the small bubbles of carbon dioxide generated in the dough expand considerably during the baking process and make the product porous and more digestible. Carbon dioxide for leavening may be generated by using either baking powder alone or a mixture of sour milk and baking soda, or by the action of yeast on sugar or flour.

(1) Baking powder is a mixture of baking soda ($NaHCO_3$) and an acid salt. The acid salts commonly used are cream of tartar ($KHC_4H_4O_6$) or monocalcium phosphate $Ca(H_2PO_4)_2$. Alum, $K_2SO_4 \cdot Al_2(SO_4)_3 \cdot 24 H_2O$, is sometimes substituted for the acid salt because, by hydrolysis, sufficient acid is produced. Since baking powder is decomposed by the moisture in air, starch is always added to help keep the mixture dry and thus prevent decomposition. When water is added to flour that has been mixed with baking powder, the following reaction takes place between the baking soda and the cream of tartar:

$$\underbrace{\underset{\substack{\text{baking}\\\text{soda}}}{NaHCO_3} + \underset{\substack{\text{cream of}\\\text{tartar}}}{KHC_4H_4O_6}}_{\text{baking powder}} \rightarrow KNaC_4H_4O_6 + H_2O + CO_2 \uparrow$$

(2) When sour milk is used in leavening, it should be added to flour that has been mixed with baking soda. The lactic acid of sour milk liberates the carbon dioxide of baking soda.

(3) In baking bread with yeast, carbon dioxide is generated by the fermenting action of yeast on sugar or starch (flour), producing grain alcohol as an additional product. Since leavening by yeast is a slow process, the dough is allowed to stand for several hours.

11. TESTS FOR CARBON DIOXIDE AND CARBONATE IONS

a. **Carbon Dioxide.** Bubble the gas being tested into limewater, $Ca(OH)_2$. A white precipitate indicates the presence of carbon dioxide. (Sulfur dioxide, which behaves in a similar manner, can be distinguished from carbon dioxide by its characteristic odor.)

b. **Carbonate Ions.** Add dilute hydrochloric acid to the solid being tested, and pass the liberated gas into limewater. A white precipitate indicates that the solid may be a carbonate. It may also be a bicarbonate. To distinguish between the two:

(1) Subject both solids to moderate heat. The evolution of a gas which turns limewater milky indicates that the substance is a bicarbonate.

(2) Compare the weights of carbon dioxide released by equal weights of both solids. Bicarbonate releases more carbon dioxide than does carbonate.

CARBON MONOXIDE

12. SOURCES OF CARBON MONOXIDE IN AIR

a. **Automobile Exhaust.** Carbon monoxide in automobile exhausts results from the incomplete combustion of gasoline. *Keeping an automobile engine running in a closed garage may produce sufficient poisonous carbon monoxide to cause death.*

b. **Coal Furnace.** Coal may be burned in a furnace or stove in such a way that carbon monoxide may be produced. At the grate, where there is a plentiful supply of air, carbon dioxide is first produced.

$$C + O_2 \rightarrow CO_2 \uparrow$$

In the middle of the bed of white-hot coal, the carbon dioxide formed is reduced by the hot carbon to carbon monoxide.

$$CO_2 + C \rightarrow 2\ CO \uparrow$$

This carbon monoxide may escape into a room in dangerous quantities. Supplying a sufficient volume of air to the top of the bed of white-hot coal brings about the oxidation of the carbon monoxide, which burns with a blue flame to form carbon dioxide.

$$2\ CO + O_2 \rightarrow 2\ CO_2 \uparrow$$

c. **Gas Leaks.** Where household gas is of the manufactured variety and not natural gas, a gas leak will evolve carbon monoxide to the air. Heaters utilizing kerosene or other hydrocarbon fuels may also produce carbon monoxide by incomplete combustion.

13. PREPARATION

a. **Incomplete Combustion of Carbon.** This may be accomplished by burning carbon in a limited supply of air.

$$2\ C + O_2 \rightarrow 2\ CO \uparrow$$

b. **Reduction of Carbon Dioxide.** Carbon dioxide passed over hot carbon is reduced to carbon monoxide.

$$CO_2 + C \rightarrow 2\ CO \uparrow$$

If all the carbon dioxide is not reduced, it may contaminate the carbon monoxide. Excess carbon dioxide is removed by bubbling the mixture through a sodium hydroxide solution. The carbon dioxide is absorbed, and the carbon monoxide passes through unaffected.

c. **Preparation in the Laboratory.** Pure carbon monoxide is usually obtained in the laboratory by the dehydration of formic acid (HCOOH), using concentrated sulfuric acid as the dehydrating agent. (See figure below.)

$$HCOOH \xrightarrow[\substack{conc. \\ H_2SO_4}]{} H_2O + CO \uparrow$$

Because it is only slightly soluble in water, carbon monoxide is collected by water displacement.

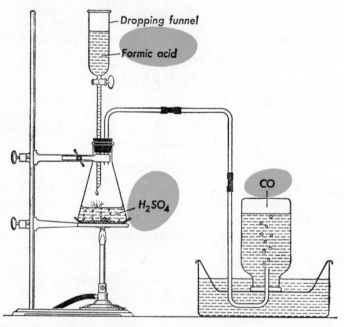

Fig. 13c. Laboratory Preparation and Collection of Carbon Monoxide

14. PHYSICAL PROPERTIES

Carbon monoxide is a colorless, odorless, and tasteless gas, slightly less dense than air, and only slightly soluble in water.

15. CHEMICAL PROPERTIES

a. Carbon monoxide is extremely poisonous when inhaled. A concentration of 1 part carbon monoxide in 100 parts of air may be fatal if inhaled for a few minutes. It unites readily with the hemoglobin of the blood to form a very stable compound, so that the hemoglobin cannot carry oxygen to the tissues.

CAUTION	Be careful not to inhale excessive quantities of carbon monoxide.

b. Carbon monoxide burns readily in air with a blue flame to form carbon dioxide.

$$2\ CO + O_2 \rightarrow 2\ CO_2 \uparrow$$

Since hydrogen also burns with a blue flame, it is sometimes necessary to distinguish carbon monoxide from hydrogen. If the unknown gas is burned and the product is bubbled through limewater, the formation of a white precipitate indicates that the original gas was carbon monoxide.

c. Carbon monoxide is a good reducing agent, uniting with the oxygen of metallic oxides to form carbon dioxide and liberating the metal. Thus, it is used in extracting iron from its oxide ore.

$$Fe_2O_3 + 3\ CO \rightarrow 2\ Fe + 3\ CO_2 \uparrow$$

d. Carbon monoxide also reacts with such metals as nickel and iron to form compounds called *carbonyls.*

$$Ni + 4\ CO \rightarrow \underset{\text{nickel carbonyl}}{Ni(CO)_4}$$

This reaction is utilized in the purification of nickel from its ores (Mond process).

e. Carbon monoxide reacts with hydrogen in the presence of a catalyst to form wood alcohol (methyl alcohol).

$$CO + 2\ H_2 \rightarrow \underset{\substack{\text{methyl} \\ \text{alcohol}}}{CH_3OH}$$

16. USES

a. **Fuel.** Carbon monoxide is an important component of some widely used gaseous fuels such as water
gas and producer gas.

Gaseous Fuels
Water gas
Producer gas
Natural gas
Coal gas
Hydrogen
Acetylene

(1) *Water Gas.* When steam is passed over heated
coke, a mixture of carbon monoxide and hydrogen,
called water gas, is formed.

$$C + H_2O \rightarrow CO \uparrow + H_2 \uparrow$$

The introduction of steam lowers the temperature of the heated carbon, thus reducing the efficiency of the process. From time to time, hot
air is passed over the coke to raise it to the proper temperature.

To increase its heat value, water gas is *enriched* by the addition of
certain hydrocarbons such as propane (C_3H_8) and butane (C_4H_{10}).

Although water gas as a household fuel has been replaced by natural gas, water gas is still an important industrial fuel.

(2) *Producer Gas.* When steam and hot air are passed over heated
coke or hard coal, a mixture of carbon monoxide, hydrogen, and nitrogen, called producer gas, is formed. The presence of a considerable
concentration of nitrogen distinguishes producer gas from water gas.
The presence of nitrogen also lowers the heat value of producer gas.
However, its economical preparation makes it a widely used commercial fuel gas.

A table of other common fuel gases appears below.

FUEL	COMPOSITION	SOURCE
Natural gas	largely CH_4	Decomposition of plant matter
Coal gas	$H_2 + CH_4 + CO$	Destructive distillation of soft coal
Hydrogen	H_2	Electrolysis of water or brine From water gas
Acetylene	C_2H_2	Action of calcium carbide on water: $CaC_2 + 2 H_2O \rightarrow Ca(OH)_2 + C_2H_2 \uparrow$

b. **Reducing Agent.** Carbon monoxide is used as a reducing agent in extracting metals from oxide ores.

17. HOW TO DISTINGUISH BETWEEN CO AND CO_2

Carbon monoxide is slightly less dense than air, burns with a blue flame, and has no effect upon limewater. Carbon dioxide is denser than air, is not combustible, does not support combustion normally, and turns limewater milky.

Study Guide

1. *a.* A natural source of uncombined carbon is (1) petroleum (2) carbonates (3) diamond (4) protoplasm.
    b. A natural source of combined carbon is (1) coal (2) graphite (3) soot (4) carbon dioxide.
2. *a.* The allotropic forms of carbon are _____, _____, and _____.
    b. All forms of amorphous carbon are generally _____ in structure.
3. *a.* Describe how coal has been produced in nature.
    b. Hard coal differs from soft coal in the amount of _____.
    c. Explain why soft coal has a higher heat content than hard coal on an equal weight basis.
4. *a.* Destructive distillation involves a chemical change because _____.
    b. List three important uses of coke.
    c. A substance that is not a volatile product of the destructive distillation of soft coal is (1) coke (2) coal tar (3) ammonia (4) hydrogen sulfide.
    d. Fractional distillation represents a *chemical* change. [True or false? If false, correct the italicized term.]
    e. Charcoal is made by the destructive distillation of (1) coke (2) petroleum (3) soft coal (4) wood.
    f. State two uses of charcoal and for each use indicate the property that makes the use possible.
    g. What is activated charcoal? Why is it superior to ordinary charcoal as an adsorbent?
    h. A substance that is not a volatile product of the destructive distillation of wood is (1) pyroligneous acid (2) charcoal (3) wood gas (4) carbon dioxide.
    i. The fractional distillation of wood tar yields (1) phenol (2) benzene (3) toluene (4) acetic acid.
5. In tabular form, list the source, composition, and important uses of bone-black and lampblack.

6. *a.* Graphite may be produced artificially in the electric furnace from _____.

  b. State four uses of graphite and for each use indicate the property which makes the use possible.

  c. The purest form of carbon is (1) graphite (2) boneblack (3) lampblack (4) diamond.

  d. The property of diamond which makes it useful as an abrasive is its _____.

  e. Why do diamond and graphite differ so much in hardness?

7. A physical property common to all the forms of carbon is their (1) black color (2) low density (3) solid state (4) combustibility in oxygen.

8. *a.* The bonding in carbon compounds is generally (1) ionic (2) electrovalent (3) covalent (4) coordinate covalent.

  b. At ordinary temperatures, carbon is *inert*. [True or false? If false, correct the italicized term.]

  c. The product formed by burning the different allotropic forms of carbon in oxygen is _____.

  d. Write two equations to illustrate the reducing activity of carbon.

  e. Carborundum is formed by the reaction between coke and (1) galena (2) gypsum (3) limestone (4) sand.

  f. The substance formed when calcium carbide reacts with nitrogen is (1) calcium cyanide (2) calcium cyanamid (3) ammonia (4) acetylene.

  g. The missing term X in the equation $CaC_2 + 2\ H_2O \rightarrow C_2H_2 + X$ is (1) $CaCO_3$ (2) $Ca(HCO_3)_2$ (3) CaO (4) $Ca(OH)_2$.

  h. How does the manufacture of carbon disulfide differ from the manufacture of most electric furnace products?

9. *a.* Carbon dioxide is constantly being restored to the atmosphere as a result of _____, _____, and _____.

  b. Explain why the amount of carbon dioxide in air remains relatively constant.

10. *a.* Make a labeled diagram to illustrate the laboratory preparation and collection of carbon dioxide.

  b. Write the balanced equation for the reaction in *a*.

  c. Why is it undesirable to use sulfuric acid in the laboratory preparation of carbon dioxide?

  d. Write a balanced equation for each of the following:
    (1) $(CO_3)^{-2} + H^+ \rightarrow$ \qquad (2) $(HCO_3)^- + H^+ \rightarrow$

11. By means of balanced equations, describe three methods for preparing carbon dioxide commercially.

12. *a.* Carbon dioxide is (1) easily solidified (2) less dense than air (3) more soluble in water under reduced pressure (4) pungent.

  b. Why is carbon dioxide easily liquefied?

13. *a.* Under ordinary conditions, carbon dioxide (1) supports combustion (2) is combustible (3) is unstable (4) is stable.

  b. In the reaction $CO_2 + 2\ Mg \rightarrow 2\ MgO + C$, Mg behaves as a (an) _____ agent.

  c. Passing carbon dioxide into a red litmus solution results in (1) bleaching (2) a blue solution (3) no change in color (4) precipitation.

  d. Write a balanced equation for each of the following reactions:
    (1) $CO_2 + C \rightarrow$ \quad (2) $CO_2 + Ca(OH)_2 \rightarrow$ \quad (3) $CO_2 + H_2O + CaCO_3 \rightarrow$

*e. A gas that will probably react with limewater in the same manner as carbon dioxide will react with limewater is (1) carbon monoxide (2) hydrogen chloride (3) ammonia (4) sulfur dioxide.

14. a. Make a labeled diagram of the soda-acid fire extinguisher.
   b. Write a balanced equation for the reaction that occurs in a.
   c. In the foamite fire extinguisher, the hydrolysis of the alum solution produces sufficient _____ to react with the sodium bicarbonate.
   d. All carbonated beverages contain (1) sugar (2) carbonic acid (3) bicarbonate of soda (4) amorphous carbon.
   e. Solid carbon dioxide is called _____. It cannot be used as an ordinary household refrigerant because _____.
   f. Two important products of the Solvay process are _____ and _____.
   g. Write a balanced equation for each of the following reactions:
      (1) $NaCl + H_2O + NH_3 + CO_2 \rightarrow$ (2) $NaHCO_3 \rightarrow$
   h. Why is the Solvay process economical and efficient?
   i. The products of photosynthesis are _____ and _____.
   j. All baking powders contain _____.
   k. Write a balanced equation for the reaction that occurs in a cream of tartar baking powder.

15. a. Testing sea shells by the addition of hydrochloric acid results in the rapid evolution of a colorless gas. This indicates that the sea shells probably contain a (1) carbonate (2) chloride (3) phosphate (4) sulfate.
   b. How can you distinguish between a carbonate and a bicarbonate?

16. Describe three sources of carbon monoxide.

17. a. Carbon monoxide may be formed by the incomplete combustion of _____.
   b. Carbon monoxide may be separated from a mixture of carbon monoxide and carbon dioxide by bubbling the mixture of gases through _____.
   c. Make a labeled diagram to illustrate the laboratory preparation and collection of carbon monoxide.
   d. Write a balanced equation for the reaction that occurs in c.

18. a. Carbon monoxide is poisonous because it (1) causes severe throat irritation (2) destroys lung tissue (3) is odorless (4) prevents the red cells from distributing oxygen.
   b. Write a balanced equation to show that carbon monoxide is combustible.
   c. Describe a test to distinguish carbon monoxide from hydrogen.
   d. When carbon monoxide acts as a reducing agent, _____ is always formed.
   e. Carbon monoxide reacts with such metals as nickel and iron to form *carbides*. [True or false? If false, correct the italicized term.]
   f. In the presence of a catalyst, carbon monoxide reacts with hydrogen to form _____.

19. Describe two uses of carbon monoxide.

20. Compare water gas and producer gas as to composition and heat value.

21. An oxide of carbon which has no effect on limewater is probably _____.

22. a. Calculate the volume of carbon dioxide that will be liberated from:
      (1) 100 grams of limestone
      (2) 100 grams of sodium carbonate
      (3) 100 grams of sodium bicarbonate
   b. Calculate the weight of carbon dioxide that will be liberated from 100 grams of baking powder, 90% of which contains baking soda.

16 SODIUM, POTASSIUM, AND THEIR COMPOUNDS

1. THE ALKALI METALS

This family of elements consists of lithium, sodium, potassium, rubidium, cesium, and the most recently discovered radioactive element, francium. These elements form Group I A of the periodic table. Because these elements are metallic and tend to form strong bases, they are called the *alkali metals*. Since all the members of this family contain only one electron in their outermost orbit, they tend to lose this electron readily in chemical reactions. As a result:

I A
Li
Na
K
Rb
Cs
Fr

The alkali metals are powerful reducing agents, forming ions with a charge of +1.

As the atomic radius increases, chemical activity generally increases correspondingly. Thus, potassium, which has a larger atomic radius, is more active than sodium. Lithium, however, is an exception to this rule. Of all the alkali metals, lithium has the smallest atomic radius and should therefore be the least active. It has been previously pointed out that particles may react with water during the process of hydration, liberating considerable energy. (See **11,** page 37.) The very small lithium ion is very strongly attracted to the water dipole, forming a hydrated lithium ion. Thus, lithium loses electrons more readily than might be suspected from its position in Group I A.

Because sodium and potassium are the most common of the alkali metals, this chapter will be restricted to a study of only these metals and their compounds.

2. SODIUM

a. **Occurrence.** Sodium, like most other active elements, is never found free in nature. It is found abundantly in combined form, chiefly as sodium chloride (NaCl) and sodium nitrate ($NaNO_3$).

b. **Commercial Preparation.** Sodium is obtained commercially in the *Downs cell* by the electrolysis of fused or molten sodium chloride.

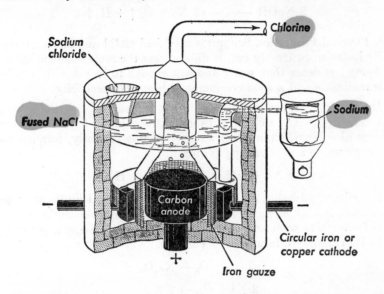

Fig. 2b. Electrolysis of Fused Sodium Chloride in the Downs Cell

Because the melting point of sodium chloride is somewhat high (800°C), sodium carbonate is added to lower the melting point to about 600°C.

Sodium chloride, like other fused salts, is ionic. *Since metallic ions have a deficiency of electrons (are positively charged), the extraction of the free metal always involves the restoring of electrons to the metallic ion.* This means that the metallic ion must be reduced in order to be liberated. At the same time, the nonmetallic ion is oxidized.

IONIZATION:	$2\ NaCl \rightarrow 2\ Na^+ + 2\ Cl^-$
REDUCTION AT CATHODE:	$2\ Na^+ + 2\ e \rightarrow 2\ Na^0$
OXIDATION AT ANODE:	$2\ Cl^- - 2\ e \rightarrow Cl_2{}^0$
ELECTROLYSIS (TOTAL):	$2\ NaCl \rightarrow 2\ Na + Cl_2 \uparrow$

Sodium metal collects at the cathode, while chlorine gas is liberated at the anode.

Sodium may also be obtained by the electrolysis of fused sodium hydroxide.

$$2 \text{ NaOH} \xrightarrow[\text{electrolysis}]{} 2 \text{ Na} + \text{O}_2 \uparrow + \text{H}_2 \uparrow$$

c. Physical Properties. Sodium is a typical metal and has a silvery-white luster when freshly cut. It differs from the more common metals by being less dense than water and soft enough to be cut with a knife. It is malleable and a good conductor of heat and electricity.

d. Chemical Properties. Because it reacts readily with the oxygen and moisture in air, sodium is usually stored under kerosene. When a piece of sodium is placed in water, it reacts violently, forming sodium hydroxide and liberating hydrogen.

$$2 \text{ Na} + 2 \text{ H}_2\text{O} \rightarrow 2 \text{ NaOH} + \text{H}_2 \uparrow$$

As sodium hydroxide is a base, it may be identified by its effect on red litmus. It may be recovered as a white solid by evaporation.

Sodium reacts with an excess of oxygen to form sodium peroxide, and with chlorine to form sodium chloride.

$$2 \text{ Na} + \text{O}_2 \rightarrow \text{Na}_2\text{O}_2$$

$$2 \text{ Na} + \text{Cl}_2 \rightarrow 2 \text{ NaCl}$$

e. Uses. Sodium is used in the manufacture of such compounds as sodium peroxide (Na_2O_2), used as an oxidizing agent; and sodium cyanide (NaCN), used in electroplating. A list of important sodium compounds appears at the right. Sodium is also used in the preparation of antiknock compounds for gasoline, and in the manufacture of dyes such as indigo. It is also used in the sodium vapor lamp to provide nonglare highway illumination.

NaCl
NaOH
NaHCO$_3$
Na$_2$CO$_3$
NaNO$_3$

3. SODIUM CHLORIDE

a. Occurrence. Sodium chloride is the most abundant naturally occurring sodium compound. It is found in salt deposits in New York State, Michigan, and several European countries. It is also found dissolved in sea water and in salt lakes.

b. Extraction

(1) *Salt Mines.* When the salt deposit is found near the surface of the earth, the rock salt (halite) is mined in much the same manner as coal.

(2) *Salt Wells.* Salt is obtained from deposits deep in the earth by drilling wells. Water is used to dissolve the salt, and the resulting brine (salt water) is then pumped to the surface. The salt is recovered from the brine by evaporation.

(3) *Sea Water.* In warm countries, salt is obtained by allowing the sun's heat to evaporate sea water. In cold countries, sea water is allowed to freeze. The ice formed on the surface is removed, thus reducing the quantity of solvent. This procedure is repeated several times until a concentrated salt solution is obtained, from which the salt may be more economically recovered by evaporation with heat.

c. **Purification.** Table salt usually contains small quantities of magnesium chloride, a deliquescent impurity, which causes the salt to cake on a humid day. Caking may be prevented by adding starch or rice, which are hygroscopic substances (substances which absorb moisture without becoming wet). Table salt may be purified by recrystallization from its saturated solution, or by passing hydrogen chloride into this solution. The pure salt precipitates in the latter process by application of the common ion effect. (The common ion effect is discussed under *f,* page 172.)

d. **Physical Properties.** Pure sodium chloride is a white, crystalline solid, slightly more soluble in hot water than in cold water. Its crystals contain no water of hydration.

e. **Chemical Properties.** Sodium chloride does not decompose appreciably upon heating. However, when fused, it may be decomposed by electrolysis to form sodium and chlorine.

Sodium chloride reacts with sulfuric acid to form hydrogen chloride, which in water solution forms hydrochloric acid.

When heated with manganese dioxide and sulfuric acid, sodium chloride liberates chlorine.

f. **Uses.** Sodium chloride, essential to the diet, is used as a seasoning for food. It is also used as a food preservative, and with ice to make freezing mixtures. It is used in the manufacture of important sodium compounds such as sodium hydroxide ($NaOH$), sodium bicarbonate ($NaHCO_3$), and sodium carbonate (Na_2CO_3). In the laboratory and commercially, sodium chloride is used to prepare chlorine and hydrochloric acid.

4. SODIUM HYDROXIDE

a. **Commercial Preparation.** Sodium hydroxide is prepared chiefly by the electrolysis of brine. The Vorce, Nelson, and Hooker electrochemical cells are used commercially to prepare sodium hydroxide in this way. Although the cells used in these processes differ somewhat, the chemical reactions that occur are the same.

As shown in Fig. 4a, when a direct current is passed through brine, chlorine is liberated at the anode; sodium ions remain unchanged. At the cathode, hydrogen is formed; hydroxyl ions remain unaffected. Thus, chlorine, hydrogen, and sodium hydroxide are formed. (See *c*, page 158, for a fuller discussion.)

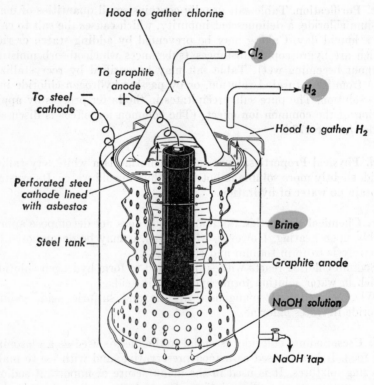

Fig. 4a. The Nelson Cell

$$2 \text{ NaCl} + 2 \text{ H}_2\text{O} \xrightarrow[\text{electrolysis}]{} 2 \text{ NaOH} + \text{H}_2 \uparrow + \text{Cl}_2 \uparrow$$

The electrolysis of brine is one of the most important processes in the chemical industry. By the electrolysis of a cheap substance, such as salt water, three products of great commercial value may be manufactured.

Sodium hydroxide may also be prepared by the *Lye process*. The reaction for this process is as follows:

$$Na_2CO_3 + Ca(OH)_2 \rightarrow 2\ NaOH + CaCO_3 \downarrow$$

The sodium hydroxide solution is first filtered to separate it from the insoluble calcium carbonate. By evaporation, solid sodium hydroxide is obtained.

b. **Properties.** Sodium hydroxide is a white, deliquescent solid. It is very soluble in water, liberating considerable heat during the process of solution. Sodium hydroxide is known as caustic soda because of its corrosive action on the skin. It is also known as lye when sold in the form of a concentrated solution. The concentrated solution, because it attacks glass, should not be stored in bottles with glass stoppers. The water solution of sodium hydroxide forms a typical base, which turns litmus blue, has a bitter taste and a soapy feeling, and neutralizes acids. Sodium hydroxide solution dissolves silk and wool readily, but reacts very slowly with cotton.

c. **Uses.** Soap is manufactured by boiling sodium hydroxide with fats or oils. Because it dissolves organic matter, sodium hydroxide in the form of lye is used to clean sinks and drains. In the petroleum industry, sodium hydroxide is used to neutralize acids. In the textile industry, it is used to distinguish silk and wool from cotton, dissolving the former but not the latter. Sodium hydroxide is also used in the manufacture of rayon and mercerized cotton. (See Chapter 22.)

5. SODIUM BICARBONATE

a. **Commercial Preparation.** Sodium bicarbonate is prepared commercially by the Solvay process, discussed fully under *e*, page 225.

b. **Properties.** Sodium bicarbonate ($NaHCO_3$), commonly known as baking soda, is a white, crystalline solid, slightly soluble in water. Its water solution turns litmus blue, a basic reaction due to hydrolysis. It reacts with acids to liberate carbon dioxide.

c. **Uses.** Sodium bicarbonate is used with sulfuric acid in fire extinguishers to liberate carbon dioxide, as shown in the following equation:

$$2\ NaHCO_3 + H_2SO_4 \rightarrow Na_2SO_4 + 2\ H_2O + 2\ CO_2 \uparrow$$

It is used in baking powders with acid salts, such as potassium acid tartrate (cream of tartar), to liberate carbon dioxide. It is also used to neutralize excess acid in the stomach.

6. SODIUM CARBONATE

a. **Commercial Preparation.** Sodium carbonate is also prepared commercially by the Solvay process.

b. **Properties.** Sodium carbonate in crystalline form is known commonly as washing soda and has the chemical formula $Na_2CO_3 \cdot 10 H_2O$. When exposed to the air, it loses its water of hydration, showing that it is efflorescent. The anhydrous form of sodium carbonate is known as soda ash. The water solution of sodium carbonate turns litmus blue as a result of hydrolysis. Because it does not contain hydrogen ions, sodium carbonate is more basic than sodium bicarbonate.

$$NaHCO_3 \rightarrow Na^+ + H^+ + (CO_3)^{-2}$$

$$Na_2CO_3 \rightarrow 2 Na^+ + (CO_3)^{-2}$$

c. **Uses.** Sodium carbonate is used for washing because it acts as a solvent for grease and softens hard water. It is used in the manufacture of soap powders, glass, sodium hydroxide, and in the refining of petroleum.

7. SODIUM NITRATE

a. **Occurrence.** Sodium nitrate ($NaNO_3$), commonly called Chile saltpeter, is found in large deposits in Chile. It is obtained from these deposits by evaporating dissolved crude saltpeter. It is then purified by recrystallization. Sodium nitrate may also be obtained synthetically from the reaction between nitric acid and soda ash.

b. **Properties.** Sodium nitrate is a white, hygroscopic, crystalline salt, extremely soluble in water. It gives off oxygen when heated, leaving a residue of sodium nitrite.

$$2 NaNO_3 \rightarrow 2 NaNO_2 + O_2 \uparrow$$

c. **Uses.** Sodium nitrate is used directly as a fertilizer and in the manufacture of nitric acid and explosives. It reacts with potassium chloride to produce potassium nitrate (KNO_3), commonly called saltpeter. Sodium nitrate is required for the manufacture of sodium nitrite, which in turn is used in the preparation of many dyes and drugs.

8. OTHER SODIUM COMPOUNDS

COMPOUND	FORMULA	USES
Borax	$Na_2B_4O_7 \cdot 10\ H_2O$	Flux in soldering; preparation of boric acid (H_3BO_3)
Sodium hypochlorite	NaClO	Bleach
Sodium phosphate (trisodium phosphate, T.S.P.)	Na_3PO_4	Cleansing agent
Sodium sulfate (Glauber's salt)	$Na_2SO_4 \cdot 10\ H_2O$	Manufacture of paper
Sodium thiosulfate (hypo)	$Na_2S_2O_3 \cdot 5\ H_2O$	Antichlor; photographic fixing agent

9. POTASSIUM

Potassium, like sodium, is never found free in nature. Combined, it occurs much less abundantly than sodium. The most common compounds are potassium chloride, potassium sulfate, and feldspar rock (a complex potassium magnesium silicate). Potassium resembles sodium in its preparation and properties. Because of its larger atomic radius, potassium is chemically more active than sodium. Potassium has few specific uses for which sodium will not serve equally as well.

10. POTASSIUM COMPOUNDS

COMPOUND	FORMULA	USES
Potassium carbonate (potash)	K_2CO_3	Glass manufacture
Potassium chloride	KCl	Fertilizers
Potassium hydroxide (caustic potash)	KOH	Preparation of soaps; electrolyte in batteries (Edison cells)
Potassium nitrate (saltpeter)	KNO_3	Manufacture of gunpowder; preservative for meats

Study Guide

1. *a.* The most recently discovered alkali metal is _____.
   b. All the alkali metals form (1) strong acids (2) strong bases (3) weak acids (4) weak bases.
   c. All the alkali metals (1) are reducing agents (2) are oxidizing agents (3) form ions with a charge of −1 (4) have complete outer rings.
   d. As the atomic radius of the alkali metals increases, their activity generally _____ (decreases, increases, remains the same).
2. A sodium compound occurring abundantly in nature is sodium (1) hydroxide (2) carbonate (3) bicarbonate (4) nitrate.
3. *a.* Make a labeled diagram to illustrate a commercial process for extracting metallic sodium from sodium chloride.
   b. Why is sodium carbonate used in this process?
   c. By means of electron equations, show that the reaction that occurs in *a* involves oxidation-reduction.
4. *a.* Sodium differs from most metals in density and _____.
   b. Sodium is sometimes stored under *water*. [True or false? If false, correct the italicized term.]
   c. Evaporation of a solution of sodium hydroxide results in the formation of (1) sodium (2) sodium oxide (3) solid sodium hydroxide (4) sodium peroxide.
   d. The valence number of oxygen in the compound sodium peroxide is _____.
5. List three important uses of sodium.
6. The most abundant naturally occurring sodium compound is _____.
7. *a.* Describe three methods of extracting sodium chloride from naturally occurring salt.
   b. The impurity which causes salt to stick in a salt shaker is (1) sodium iodide (2) sodium chloride (3) magnesium chloride (4) magnesium nitrate.
8. *a.* As the temperature of the water increases, the amount of sodium chloride that will dissolve (1) increases considerably (2) decreases (3) increases slightly (4) remains the same.
   b. Sodium chloride reacts with sulfuric acid and manganese dioxide to form (1) chlorine (2) hydrogen chloride (3) sulfur dioxide (4) sulfur trioxide.
9. *a.* Why is sodium chloride useful in making freezing mixtures?
   b. Three important sodium compounds that can be made from common salt are _____, _____, and _____.
10. *a.* Make a labeled diagram of the Nelson cell.
    b. Write a balanced equation for the reaction that occurs in *a.*
    c. Write a balanced equation to illustrate the Lye process.
11. *a.* Sodium hydroxide is *a deliquescent* solid. [True or false? If false, correct the italicized term.]

  b. A common name for sodium hydroxide is (1) caustic potash (2) soda ash (3) Chile saltpeter (4) lye.

  c. List three chemical properties of sodium hydroxide.

12. *a.* Soap is made by boiling sodium hydroxide with (1) fats (2) glycerine (3) salt (4) organic matter.

  b. Sodium hydroxide is used in the manufacture of _____ and _____.

13. The chief products in the Solvay process are (1) sodium chloride and sodium hydroxide (2) sodium carbonate and sodium nitrate (3) sodium chloride and sodium bicarbonate (4) sodium bicarbonate and sodium carbonate.

14. *a.* The formula for baking soda is Na_2CO_3. [True or false? If false, correct the italicized term.]

  b. A water solution of sodium bicarbonate is alkaline due to (1) decomposition (2) ionization (3) hydrolysis (4) neutralization.

15. The reaction in the soda-acid fire extinguisher and the reaction in baking powders both produce (1) sodium bicarbonate (2) sodium carbonate (3) carbon monoxide (4) carbon dioxide.

16. *a.* The formula $Na_2CO_3 \cdot 10\ H_2O$ represents (1) a hydrate (2) a mixture (3) baking powder (4) soda ash.

  *b. Using equations wherever possible, explain which of the following is the most alkaline and which is the least alkaline:

    (1) sodium hydroxide
    (2) sodium bicarbonate
    (3) sodium carbonate

17. *a.* The common name of sodium nitrate is *saltpeter*. [True or false? If false, correct the italicized term.]

  b. Heating sodium nitrate produces (1) nitrous oxide (2) nitric oxide (3) nitrogen dioxide (4) oxygen.

  c. Explain how sodium nitrate is used to prepare potassium nitrate.

18. Fill in the blank spaces in the following chart of sodium and potassium compounds:

COMPOUND	FORMULA	USE
	$Na_2B_4O_7 \cdot 10\ H_2O$	
Trisodium phosphate		
		Bleach
	$Na_2S_2O_3 \cdot 5\ H_2O$	
Caustic potash		
		Manufacture of gunpowder

17 CALCIUM AND ITS COMPOUNDS

1. THE ALKALINE EARTH METALS

This family of elements, comprising Group II A of the periodic table, consists of beryllium, magnesium, calcium, strontium, barium, and the radioactive element radium. Called the *alkaline earth metals*, they form bases in the same manner as do the alkali metals of Group I A. The bases formed by the metals in Group II A, however, are generally less soluble and not so strong as those formed by the metals in Group I A.

II A

| Be |
| Mg |
| Ca |
| Sr |
| Ba |
| Ra |

Chemically, the alkaline earth metals tend to lose two electrons, forming positive ions with a charge of +2.

The activity of the alkaline earth metals generally increases with an increase in atomic radius.

We shall limit our discussion in this chapter to calcium and its compounds because of their abundance and usefulness.

2. CALCIUM

a. **Occurrence.** Calcium is never found free in nature because of its activity. It is found abundantly in many compounds, such as carbonates, sulfates, and phosphates.

b. **Commercial Preparation.** Calcium is obtained by the electrolysis of molten calcium chloride. Just as in the electrolytic extraction of sodium and potassium, the metal deposits on the cathode.

$$CaCl_2 \xrightarrow{\text{electrolysis}} Ca + Cl_2 \uparrow$$

c. **Physical Properties.** Calcium is a silvery metal, about one and one-half times as dense as water and somewhat softer than lead.

d. **Chemical Properties.** Calcium combines with oxygen, forming calcium oxide.

$$2 \; Ca + O_2 \rightarrow 2 \; CaO$$

It also reacts with water, more slowly than does sodium or potassium, forming calcium hydroxide and liberating hydrogen.

$$Ca + 2 H_2O \rightarrow Ca(OH)_2 + H_2 \uparrow$$

e. **Uses.** Calcium is used as a purifying agent in the metallurgy of copper, nickel, and aluminum. Alloyed with lead, calcium forms special low-friction metals. A list of important calcium compounds appears at the right.

CaCO$_3$
CaO
Ca(OH)$_2$
CaSO$_4$
CaOCl$_2$

3. CALCIUM CARBONATE

a. **Occurrence.** Calcium carbonate ($CaCO_3$) is the most abundant calcium compound in nature. It is found in the form of limestone and marble. Dolomite is a mixture of calcium and magnesium carbonate. Other forms of $CaCO_3$ are chalk, shell, coral, and calcite.

b. **Properties.** Pure calcium carbonate is white. Crystalline calcium carbonate, in the form of calcite, is colorless, clear, and transparent.

(1) Calcium carbonate is decomposed by heat to produce quicklime (CaO) and liberate carbon dioxide.

$$CaCO_3 \rightarrow CaO + CO_2 \uparrow$$

(2) Calcium carbonate reacts with dilute acids to liberate carbon dioxide.

$$CaCO_3 + 2 HCl \rightarrow CaCl_2 + H_2O + CO_2 \uparrow$$

(3) All varieties of calcium carbonate are insoluble in water, but dissolve readily in water containing dissolved carbon dioxide (carbonic acid). In nature, soil water carrying carbon dioxide from the air or from decaying plant matter dissolves calcium carbonate to form soluble calcium bicarbonate, Ca(HCO$_3$)$_2$.

$$CaCO_3 + H_2O + CO_2 \rightarrow Ca(HCO_3)_2$$

This reaction helps to explain the formation of limestone caves.

c. **Limestone Caves.** Limestone caves are produced in nature by the action of soil water containing dissolved carbon dioxide on deposits of limestone. The limestone is dissolved, forming soluble calcium bicarbonate. When the solution of calcium bicarbonate trickles from the roof of the cave, it undergoes decomposition, resulting in a deposit of calcium carbonate.

$$Ca(HCO_3)_2 \rightarrow CaCO_3 \downarrow + H_2O + CO_2 \uparrow$$

The hanging masses of calcium carbonate that develop from the roof of the cave are called *stalactites,* while the mounds formed on the floor of the cave are called *stalagmites.* Stalactites and stalagmites may join and re-form the original limestone deposit.

d. **Uses.** Because of their durability and beauty, limestone and marble are used as building materials. Limestone is also used as a flux in the extraction of iron from its oxide ore, to make quicklime (CaO), to neutralize (sweeten) acid soil, and in the manufacture of glass and cement.

4. CALCIUM OXIDE (QUICKLIME)

a. **Preparation.** Calcium oxide (CaO) is obtained commercially by the heating and decomposition of limestone in a special furnace called a lime kiln, as shown in Fig. 4a.

The reaction that takes place is as follows:

$$CaCO_3 \rightarrow CaO + CO_2 \uparrow$$

b. **Properties.** Calcium oxide is a white, amorphous solid that is practically infusible (does not melt). When heated to incandescence in the oxyhydrogen flame, it produces a brilliant white light called limelight.

(1) Calcium oxide is a basic anhydride, uniting readily with water to form slaked lime, $Ca(OH)_2$, and liberating a great deal of heat. This process is called the *water slaking of lime.*

$$CaO + H_2O \rightarrow Ca(OH)_2$$

(2) On exposure to air, quicklime is first converted to slaked lime by moisture. The carbon dioxide in the air then converts the slaked lime to calcium carbonate.

$$CO_2 + Ca(OH)_2 \rightarrow H_2O + CaCO_3 \downarrow$$

Air-slaked lime is therefore a mixture of calcium hydroxide and calcium carbonate.

(3) Calcium oxide, when heated with coke in the electric furnace, produces calcium carbide, which reacts with water to form acetylene. The equations for these reactions appear under (2), page 219.

c. **Uses.** Calcium oxide is used to make slaked lime, mortar, bleaching powder, glass, and calcium carbide. It is also used in the manufacture of paper and rubber.

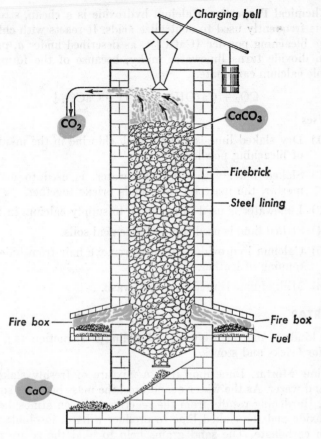

Fig. 4a. The Lime Kiln

5. CALCIUM HYDROXIDE (SLAKED LIME)

a. **Preparation.** Calcium hydroxide, $Ca(OH)_2$, is obtained by the addition of water to quicklime. This reaction is accompanied by the liberation of a large amount of heat.

$$CaO + H_2O \rightarrow Ca(OH)_2$$

b. **Physical Properties.** Calcium hydroxide is a white solid, only slightly soluble in water. A saturated solution of calcium hydroxide is called limewater, while a suspension of calcium hydroxide is called milk of lime.

c. **Chemical Properties.** Calcium hydroxide is a cheap, strong base which is frequently used to neutralize acids. It reacts with chlorine to produce bleaching powder ($CaOCl_2$), as described under *a,* page 249. Carbon dioxide turns limewater milky, because of the formation of insoluble calcium carbonate.

$$CO_2 + Ca(OH)_2 \rightarrow H_2O + CaCO_3 \downarrow$$

d. **Uses**

(1) Dry slaked lime is treated with chlorine in the manufacture of bleaching powder.

(2) Slaked lime, with sand and water, is used to make lime mortar, the material that holds bricks together.

(3) Limewater is used in medicine to supply calcium in the diet.

(4) Slaked lime is used to neutralize acid soils.

(5) Calcium hydroxide is used to remove hair from hides in the tanning of leather.

(6) Milk of lime is used as a whitewash.

6. MORTAR

Two kinds of mortar are used in building construction as a binding agent for bricks and stones.

a. **Lime Mortar.** Lime mortar is a mixture of freshly slaked lime, sand, and water. As the water evaporates, the mass becomes somewhat porous. Hardening results from the reaction between atmospheric carbon dioxide and the slaked lime to produce a hard, insoluble mass of calcium carbonate. The sand grains help to bind the entire mixture, providing added strength.

b. **Cement Mortar and Concrete.** Cement mortar is a mixture of cement, sand, and water. As in the case of lime mortar, the sand acts as a binder. Cement is a complex mixture of limestone and clay-containing materials. The hardening of cement mortar results from the reaction between the cement and water, which forms hydrates. Cement mortar can therefore be used for underwater structures. Lime mortar cannot be similarly used. Cement mortar is replacing lime mortar in building construction because it is more versatile and generally stronger.

Concrete is made from cement, sand, crushed stone, and water. Concrete may be reinforced with iron or steel rods.

Engineers have recently developed a new type of concrete called *pre-stressed* concrete. It is made by pouring concrete around special steel rods which are under considerable tension. After the concrete has set, the tension on the steel is released, compressing the concrete. Pre-stressed concrete is stronger than reinforced concrete and can be molded into any desired shape. The use of this new building material in roofs, domes, and girders makes it unnecessary to use large quantities of steel.

7. CALCIUM SULFATE

a. **Gypsum, $CaSO_4 \cdot 2 H_2O$.** Gypsum is hydrated calcium sulfate and is found in nature. It is used as a fertilizer, as a building material, and in the manufacture of plaster of Paris.

b. **Plaster of Paris, $(CaSO_4)_2 \cdot H_2O$.** Plaster of Paris is made by heating gypsum until it loses three-fourths of its water of hydration.

$$2 \underbrace{CaSO_4 \cdot 2 H_2O}_{\text{gypsum}} \rightarrow \underbrace{(CaSO_4)_2 \cdot H_2O}_{\text{plaster of Paris}} + 3 H_2O$$

The addition of water to plaster of Paris results in a thick paste which sets or hardens to form a solid. This is brought about by combination with the water to form an artificial gypsum. Exposure to air is not necessary for the hardening of wet plaster of Paris.

$$\underbrace{(CaSO_4)_2 \cdot H_2O}_{\text{plaster of Paris}} + 3 H_2O \rightarrow 2 \underbrace{CaSO_4 \cdot 2 H_2O}_{\text{gypsum}}$$

Plaster of Paris is used to make plaster casts and surgical casts because it expands on hardening. It is also used for plastering walls and in making wallboard.

8. BLEACHING POWDER

a. **Preparation.** Bleaching powder ($CaOCl_2$) is made by passing chlorine over dry slaked lime. Bleaching powder is also known as chloride of lime.

$$Cl_2 + Ca(OH)_2 \rightarrow CaOCl_2 + H_2O$$

Recent studies have revealed that bleaching powder is not a pure compound, but probably a more complex material. For the sake of simplicity, it will be considered a compound in this discussion.

***b*. Properties.** Bleaching powder reacts readily with acids to liberate chlorine.

$$CaOCl_2 + 2\ HCl \rightarrow CaCl_2 + H_2O + Cl_2 \uparrow$$

Upon standing exposed to air, bleaching powder reacts slowly with moisture and carbon dioxide to liberate chlorine.

$$CaOCl_2 + H_2O + CO_2 \rightarrow CaCO_3 + H_2O + Cl_2 \uparrow$$

Hence, bleaching powder should be stored in airtight containers.

***c*. Uses.** Bleaching powder is used as a source of chlorine for bleaching cotton materials, for disinfecting, and for water purification.

9. HARD WATER

***a*. Composition.** Soap is a mixture of soluble organic salts of which sodium stearate is an example. When these salts dissolve in water, they form a lather necessary for the cleansing action of soap. Water in which soap will dissolve freely to produce an abundant lather is called *soft water*. However, if soap (sodium stearate) is added to water containing soluble calcium, magnesium, or iron salts, a precipitate of insoluble stearates will be formed instead of lather. This kind of water is called *hard water*. The formation of insoluble stearates is caused by the reaction between the metal ions in the hard water (Ca^{+2}, Mg^{+2}, Fe^{+2}) and the soap.

$$\underbrace{\text{sodium stearate}}_{\text{soap}} + Ca^{+2} \rightarrow \underbrace{\text{calcium stearate} \downarrow}_{\substack{\text{insoluble}\\\text{stearate}}} + Na^{+}$$

$$2\ NaC_{17}H_{35}CO_2 + Ca^{+2} \rightarrow Ca(C_{17}H_{35}CO_2)_2 \downarrow + 2\ Na^{+}$$

Hard water is a sample of water which most often contains Ca^{+2}, Mg^{+2}, or Fe^{+2}, but may contain any ion capable of forming insoluble stearates.

Natural waters used for drinking or washing may contain the bicarbonates or sulfates of calcium, magnesium, or iron. Although limestone is insoluble in water, it may be converted into the soluble bicarbonate by the action of soil water containing carbon dioxide on the deposits over which it flows. In this manner, bicarbonates enter the water supply.

$$CaCO_3 + H_2O + CO_2 \rightarrow Ca(HCO_3)_2$$

The sulfates of calcium, magnesium, or iron are more soluble than the corresponding carbonates, and are dissolved by soil water which flows over the natural deposits of these compounds. Hence, hard waters may contain either the bicarbonates or sulfates of calcium, magnesium, or iron.

b. Disadvantages of Using Hard Water

(1) Hard water is uneconomical for washing because large quantities of soap must be used before suds can be obtained. The soap is actually wasted in softening the hard water.

(2) Some hard water in steam boilers deposits insoluble carbonates, called *boiler scale,* on the walls of the boiler. This deposit or scale decreases the capacity and efficiency of the boiler and clogs the pipes. Explosions may result.

(3) Hard water is injurious to laundry. The stearates that are precipitated stick to clothes and, if iron is present, may also stain.

(4) Hard water is also harmful to certain dyes, because it reacts with the dye to form insoluble compounds. Uneven dyeing results.

c. Softening Hard Water

Since hardness in water is caused by the presence of certain ions, the softening of hard water is merely a process for the removal of these ions.

As we learned in Chapter 12, ions may be removed from the field of action by the addition of a substance capable of precipitating these ions. The failure of the precipitate to ionize appreciably results in the removal of these ions.

There are two kinds of hard water, temporary and permanent. The difference between the two varieties depends upon the composition and also the specific method employed to soften the water.

d. Temporary Hard Water.

Temporary hard water usually contains bicarbonates of calcium and magnesium in solution, and can be softened in two ways:

(1) Boiling drives off water and carbon dioxide, and precipitates the insoluble carbonates.

MOLECULAR: $Ca(HCO_3)_2 \rightarrow CaCO_3 \downarrow + H_2O + CO_2 \uparrow$

IONIC: $Ca^{+2} + 2 (HCO_3)^- \rightarrow CaCO_3 \downarrow + H_2O + CO_2 \uparrow$

MOLECULAR: $Mg(HCO_3)_2 \rightarrow MgCO_3 \downarrow + H_2O + CO_2 \uparrow$

IONIC: $Mg^{+2} + 2 \ (HCO_3)^- \rightarrow MgCO_3 \downarrow + H_2O + CO_2 \uparrow$

(2) Addition of limewater also softens temporary hard water, as shown in the following equation:

MOLECULAR: $Ca(HCO_3)_2 + Ca(OH)_2 \rightarrow 2 \ CaCO_3 \downarrow + 2 \ H_2O$

IONIC: $Ca^{+2} + 2 \ (HCO_3)^- + Ca^{+2} + 2 \ (OH)^- \rightarrow$
$2 \ CaCO_3 \downarrow + 2 \ H_2O$

In each of the above cases, note that the ion responsible for hardness was removed by the formation of an insoluble compound.

e. Permanent Hard Water. Permanent hard water commonly contains the sulfates of calcium and magnesium in solution, and cannot be softened by boiling. Some naturally occurring hard waters may also contain chlorides of these metals.

Permanent hard waters may be softened by adding sodium carbonate, which removes the Ca^{+2} and Mg^{+2} ions in the form of their insoluble carbonates.

MOLECULAR: $CaSO_4 + Na_2CO_3 \rightarrow Na_2SO_4 + CaCO_3 \downarrow$

IONIC: $Ca^{+2} + SO_4^{-2} + 2 \ Na^+ + CO_3^{-2} \rightarrow$
$2 \ Na^+ + SO_4^{-2} + CaCO_3 \downarrow$

MOLECULAR: $MgCl_2 + Na_2CO_3 \rightarrow 2 \ NaCl + MgCO_3 \downarrow$

IONIC: $Mg^{+2} + 2 \ Cl^- + 2 \ Na^+ + CO_3^{-2} \rightarrow$
$2 \ Na^+ + 2 \ Cl^- + MgCO_3 \downarrow$

f. Commercial Water Softeners. Hard waters may be softened on a large scale in the following ways:

(1) Using commercial water softeners, such as permutit. Permutit belongs to a class of compounds called *zeolites*, which are naturally occurring mineral silicates.

The Na^+ ions of the permutit (sodium zeolite) replace the Ca^{+2} and the Mg^{+2} ions of the hard water, forming insoluble calcium or magnesium zeolite.

$Ca^{+2} + 2 \ Na^+ + 2 \ (zeolite)^- \rightarrow Ca \ (zeolite)_2 \downarrow + 2 \ Na^+$

$Mg^{+2} + 2 \ Na^+ + 2 \ (zeolite)^- \rightarrow Mg \ (zeolite)_2 \downarrow + 2 \ Na^+$

The permutit becomes used up (precipitated) when all the sodium zeolite has been converted to calcium zeolite. Treatment with sodium chloride solution is used to regenerate the permutit, as shown in the following equation:

$$\text{Ca (zeolite)}_2 + 2\,\text{Na}^+ \rightarrow \underbrace{2\,\text{Na}^+ + 2\,\text{(zeolite)}^-}_{\text{permutit}} + \text{Ca}^{+2}$$

This reaction is merely the reverse of the above reaction, re-forming the original zeolite.

(2) Hard waters may also be softened on a much larger scale by treatment with *ion exchange resins*. These resins are synthetic organic compounds capable of removing all the positive and negative ions present in hard water by an exchange of ions. Since these resins tend to become used up, they must be regenerated from time to time. Water treated in this way is almost as pure as distilled water and is used as a substitute for it.

SUMMARY OF HARD WATERS

	TEMPORARY	PERMANENT
Composition	Bicarbonates of calcium, magnesium, and iron	Sulfates of calcium, magnesium, and iron
Softening	Boiling	Treatment with Na_2CO_3, permutit, or ion-exchange resins

g. Tests for Hard Water

(1) *Hard Water*. Hardness in water may be ascertained by the addition of a small quantity of soap solution to the sample being tested. The formation of a curd, or the absence of permanent lather, indicates the presence of hard water.

(2) *Temporary Hard Water*. To prove that a sample contains temporary hard water, it is necessary to employ two tests. Hardness is first established by utilizing the test previously described. In addition, another portion of the same sample must be boiled until the formation of gas bubbles ceases. If a precipitate forms, and the resulting filtrate is shaken with a small quantity of soap solution, a permanent lather will result. Since boiling removed the hardness, the sample contains temporary hard water.

(3) *Permanent Hard Water.* To prove that a sample contains permanent hard water, again establish its hardness and boil another portion of the same sample. In this instance, boiling produces no change in hardness. No precipitate is formed, and the addition of a small quantity of soap solution produces no permanent lather. Since the sample was hard water and did not become soft on boiling, permanent hardness is present.

(4) *Both Temporary and Permanent Hardness.* To prove the presence of both temporary and permanent hardness in water, the tests previously described are combined. A small quantity of soap solution is added to a portion of the sample. If a precipitate is obtained, it proves that the sample contains hard water. Boiling another portion will produce gas bubbles and a white precipitate. This indicates the presence of temporary hardness. The boiled solution is filtered and a little soap solution is added to the filtrate. The formation of a white precipitate indicates that boiling failed to remove all the hardness present in the sample. Thus, the sample also contains permanent hard water.

10. OTHER CALCIUM COMPOUNDS

COMPOUND	FORMULA	USES
Calcium arsenate	$Ca_3(AsO_4)_2$	Insecticide
Calcium chloride	$CaCl_2$	A deliquescent material used to dry gases and settle dust on roads
Calcium fluoride	CaF_2	Used in glass manufacture and to remove impurities in steel
Calcium phosphate (rock phosphate)	$Ca_3(PO_4)_2$	Source of phosphorus, phosphoric acid, and superphosphate fertilizers
Monocalcium phosphate	$Ca(H_2PO_4)_2$	Acid salt in baking powder, and as a fertilizer

Study Guide

1. *a.* Calcium, barium, radium, and (1) zinc (2) cadmium (3) mercury (4) strontium   are members of Group II A.
   b. From its position in the periodic table, predict some chemical properties of barium.
   c. In what way does radium differ from all the other alkaline earth metals?
   d. As the chemical activity of the alkaline earth metals decreases, the atomic radius _____ (decreases, increases, remains the same).
2. Metallic calcium is extracted commercially by the electrolysis of _____.
3. *a.* A surface coating on a piece of calcium is probably calcium (1) oxide (2) sulfide (3) carbonate (4) nitrate.
   b. The compound formed when calcium reacts with water is (1) hydrogen (2) oxygen (3) calcium oxide (4) calcium hydroxide.
   c. State two uses of calcium.
4. *a.* The most abundant naturally occurring calcium compound is _____.
   b. The chemical composition of marble is the same as that of (1) limestone (2) granite (3) dolomite (4) firebrick.
5. *a.* One of the products formed when calcium carbonate is heated strongly is (1) calcium (2) calcium carbide (3) calcium oxide (4) calcium hydroxide.
   b. All forms of calcium carbonate (1) are soluble in water (2) are unstable (3) react with dilute bases (4) dissolve in soil water containing carbon dioxide.
   c. Write a balanced equation to explain the formation of limestone caves.
   d. Distinguish between stalactites and stalagmites.
   e. *Limestone* is used as a flux in metallurgical processes. [True or false? If false, correct the italicized term.]
6. *a.* Quicklime is made commercially by heating _____.
   b. Make a labeled diagram of a lime kiln.
   c. Write a balanced equation for the reaction that occurs in *b*.
   d. Write a balanced equation for each of the following reactions:
      (1) water slaking of lime
      (2) air slaking of lime
      (3) preparation of calcium carbide
   e. Calcium oxide is used commercially to make (1) limestone (2) plaster of Paris (3) cement (4) bleaching powder.
7. *a.* Slaked lime is most conveniently prepared from calcium (1) carbonate (2) bicarbonate (3) oxide (4) sulfate.
   b. A saturated solution of calcium hydroxide in water is called _____.
   c. State the property of calcium hydroxide which makes each of the following uses possible:
      (1) neutralization of acid soils
      (2) test for carbon dioxide
      (3) preparation of mortar

*d. In the reaction between calcium hydroxide and chlorine, is it possible to obtain an oxychlorine compound other than bleaching powder? Explain.

8. In tabular form, compare the composition, hardening, and versatility of lime mortar and cement mortar.

9. a. A recently developed building material that can be used in place of steel is _____.
   b. How is this building material prepared?

10. a. The formula of gypsum is _____.
    b. State two uses of gypsum.
    c. Write a balanced equation to show how plaster of Paris may be prepared from gypsum.
    d. The hardening of plaster of Paris produces (1) limestone (2) gypsum (3) calcium sulfate (4) lime.
    *e. Why does plaster of Paris expand on hardening?

11.*a. What is the valence number of chlorine in $CaOCl_2$?
    b. Write a balanced equation for each of the following reactions:
       (1) $Cl_2 + Ca(OH)_2 \rightarrow$ (2) $CaOCl_2 + HCl \rightarrow$ (3) $CaOCl_2 + H_2CO_3 \rightarrow$

12. a. Sodium stearate is an example of a *fat*. [True or false? If false, correct the italicized term.]
    b. Hard water contains ions of (1) sodium (2) potassium (3) ammonium (4) calcium.
    c. Describe how magnesium bicarbonate may enter natural waters.
    d. List three disadvantages of using hard water in the home.

13. a. State the chemical principle that is utilized in softening hard water.
    b. Temporary hard water can be softened by _____.
    c. Write a balanced equation for the reaction that occurs in b.
    d. Permanent hard water may contain (1) sodium chloride (2) calcium chloride (3) calcium bicarbonate (4) sodium sulfate.
    e. Write a balanced equation for each of the following reactions:
       (1) softening permanent hard water in the laboratory
       (2) action of zeolites on hard water
       (3) regeneration of zeolites
    f. What is meant by ion exchange?
    g. Describe how hard water may be softened by using ion exchange resins.

14. a. A substance used in testing for the presence of hard water is _____.
    b. How may temporary hard water be distinguished from permanent hard water?

15. Fill in the blank spaces in the following chart of calcium compounds:

COMPOUND	FORMULA	USE
		Source of phosphoric acid
	CaF_2	
Monocalcium phosphate		
Calcium chloride		

18 METALS AND METALLURGY

1. ABUNDANCE OF THE ELEMENTS

The following table shows the average composition by weight of the crust of the earth:

ELEMENT	PERCENTAGE	ELEMENT	PERCENTAGE
Oxygen	49.2	Magnesium	1.9
Silicon	25.6	Hydrogen	0.9
Aluminum	7.4	Titanium	0.6
Iron	4.7	Chlorine	0.2
Calcium	3.4	Phosphorus	0.1
Sodium	2.5	Manganese	0.1
Potassium	2.4	All others	1.0

Analysis of the above table reveals that thirteen elements, eight of which are metallic, account for 99% of the weight of the earth's crust. The metals alone account for almost 25% of this weight. The most abundant metal present in the crust of the earth is aluminum, while the most abundant nonmetal is oxygen.

2. METALS IN THE PERIODIC TABLE

The periodic table reveals the presence of approximately **73 metals**, which tend to occupy, generally, the left side of the table.

Metals usually contain less than four valence electrons, and consequently lose electrons in chemical reactions to form positively charged ions. Some metals, such as manganese and chromium, which appear more toward the right side of the table, may also form negatively charged ions by sharing electrons with elements like oxygen. Manganese, for example, may form positively charged ions by losing two electrons, as in Mn^{+2}, or it may become part of the negative permanganate ion $(MnO_4)^-$ by sharing electrons with four oxygen atoms.

3. PHYSICAL PROPERTIES

A crystal of sodium chloride has already been shown to consist of a characteristic, repeated arrangement of sodium ions and chloride ions. (See figure, page 63.) This structure, called a *lattice*, is also characteristic of metals. X-ray analysis reveals that metals consist of a lattice of positive ions surrounded by a cloud of mobile valence electrons. This cloud of valence electrons is free to shift from one metal atom to another. Some of the physical properties of metals, such as conductivity, luster, malleability, and ductility, may be explained on the basis of the structure of the metal lattice.

Physical Properties of Metals

Conductivity
Luster
Malleability
Ductility
Hardness
Tenacity
Specific gravity

a. **Conductivity.** The constant shifting of electrons from atom to atom permits metals to conduct heat and electricity. The best conductors are silver, copper, gold, and aluminum, in that order.

b. **Luster.** Metals are easily recognized by their shiny appearance or metallic luster. The luster of the more active metals is usually dulled by oxide and carbonate coatings.

c. **Malleability.** The property which enables us to hammer or bend metals into any desired shape, or roll them into thin sheets, is called malleability. Most metals are malleable, gold being the most malleable.

d. **Ductility.** Because most metals may be easily drawn out into a wire, they are said to be ductile. Tungsten and copper are very ductile.

e. **Hardness.** Hardness means the ability of metals to scratch one another. Hard metals will scratch softer metals. Metals vary a great deal in their degree of hardness. Some, such as sodium and potassium, are very soft, while iron and steel are two of the hardest metals.

f. **Tenacity.** The resistance that a substance offers to being pulled apart is called its tenacity, or tensile strength. Metals vary a great deal in their strength, or tenacity. Steel wire can be made strong enough to withstand a pull of 120 tons on every square inch of cross section.

g. **Specific Gravity.** The number of times a substance is as heavy as an equal volume of water is called its specific gravity. Lithium, potassium, and sodium are lighter than an equal volume of water, while most of the other metals are heavier. Platinum is more than twenty-one times as heavy as an equal volume of water.

The specific gravity of a number of common substances is:

SUBSTANCE	SP. GR.	SUBSTANCE	SP. GR.
Lithium	0.5	Tin	7.3
Potassium	0.8	Iron	7.8
Sodium	0.9	Copper	8.9
WATER	**1.0**	Lead	11.3
Calcium	1.7	Uranium	18.7
Aluminum	2.7	Platinum	21.4

4. CHEMICAL PROPERTIES

Since metals tend to lose electrons, they will react with any particle which can accept electrons.

a. **Reactions of Metals and Salt Solutions.** In the electromotive series, discussed in Chapter 12, the elements were arranged in a table in order of their decreasing activity. In the electromotive series, the elements above replace the elements below from their compounds. The elements near the top of the table, such as potassium, calcium, and sodium, are powerful reducing agents. For example, in the following reaction, potassium can replace sodium because it is more active than sodium and hence loses electrons more readily. The sodium ions accept these electrons.

$$K + NaCl \rightarrow KCl + Na$$

$$\underset{\text{metal}}{K^0} - 1\,e \rightarrow \underset{\text{ion}}{K^+}$$

$$\underset{\text{ion}}{Na^+} + 1\,e \rightarrow \underset{\text{metal}}{Na^0}$$

In the reaction

$$Fe + 2\ AgNO_3 \rightarrow Fe(NO_3)_2 + 2\ Ag$$

iron replaces silver because it is more active than silver and hence loses electrons more readily than silver.

$$\underset{\text{metal}}{Fe^0} - 2\,e \rightarrow \underset{\text{ion}}{Fe^{+2}}$$

$$\underset{\text{ion}}{2\,Ag^+} + 2\,e \rightarrow \underset{\text{metal}}{2\,Ag^0}$$

Thus, the metal which loses electrons more readily is the more powerful reducing agent. It will be shown in later chapters how reducing action may be utilized in extracting metals from their ores.

b. **Reactions of Metals and Acids.** The electromotive series also reveals which metals will replace hydrogen from acids. All metals above hydrogen in the electromotive series will liberate hydrogen from certain acids. Thus, in the reaction

$$Zn + 2\ HCl \rightarrow ZnCl_2 + H_2 \uparrow$$

zinc replaces hydrogen ions in the acid. Zinc is a more powerful reducing agent than hydrogen, which is the same as saying that zinc loses electrons more readily than hydrogen. As a result, the hydrogen ions in the acid gain electrons to become hydrogen gas.

$$\underset{\text{metal}}{Zn^0} - 2\ e \rightarrow \underset{\text{ion}}{Zn^{+2}}$$

$$\underset{\text{ion}}{2\ H^+} + 2\ e \rightarrow \underset{\text{gas}}{H_2{}^0}$$

c. **Reactions of Metals and Bases.** Metals like aluminum and zinc lose electrons when they react with strong bases to produce hydrogen and an aluminate or zincate compound. Thus:

$$2\ Al + 6\ NaOH \rightarrow 2\ \underset{\substack{\text{sodium} \\ \text{aluminate}}}{Na_3AlO_3} + 3\ H_2 \uparrow$$

$$Zn + 2\ NaOH \rightarrow \underset{\substack{\text{sodium} \\ \text{zincate}}}{Na_2ZnO_2} + H_2 \uparrow$$

d. **Reactions of Metals and Water.** Only active metals like potassium and sodium will replace hydrogen from water. The tendency of these metals to lose electrons is sufficiently great to offset the very small number of hydrogen ions present in water.

$$2\ Na + 2\ HOH \rightarrow 2\ NaOH + H_2 \uparrow$$

$$\underset{\text{metal}}{2\ Na^0} - 2\ e \rightarrow \underset{\text{ion}}{2\ Na^+}$$

$$\underset{\text{ion}}{2\ H^+} + 2\ e \rightarrow \underset{\text{gas}}{H_2{}^0}$$

e. **Reactions of Metals and Nonmetals.** Metals also lose electrons when they react with certain nonmetals to form salts.

$$2\ K + Cl_2 \rightarrow 2\ KCl$$

5. OCCURRENCE OF METALS

a. Ores

Minerals are generally inorganic substances in the earth's crust having a definite chemical composition.

When minerals contain large quantities of a metal which may be economically extracted, they are called *ores*.

b. Types of Ores. The less active metals are found free or uncombined in nature. These metals are said to be in their *native* state. Some metals found uncombined are silver, platinum, and gold. The more active metals are found combined in nature in the form of carbonates, oxides, and sulfides. They are never found in the free state.

The chemical formulas and common names of the ores of some of the more common metals are:

TYPES OF ORES	FORMULAS	COMMON NAMES
Carbonates	$FeCO_3$	Siderite
	$ZnCO_3$	Smithsonite
Oxides	Fe_2O_3	Hematite
	Fe_3O_4	Magnetite
	Fe_3O_4	Taconite
	ZnO	Zincite
	Al_2O_3	Bauxite
Sulfides	FeS_2	Iron pyrites
	$CuFeS_2$	Chalcopyrites
	Cu_2S	Chalcocite
	ZnS	Zinc blende
	PbS	Galena
	HgS	Cinnabar

6. EXTRACTION OF METALS

The means by which a metal is extracted from its ore (metallurgy) depends chiefly upon the composition of the ore.

When the percentage of metal present in the ore is small, the ore is first concentrated in order to remove impurities.

Impurities in ores are called *gangue*. The percentage of gangue in the ore must be lowered to a point where the extraction of the metal becomes economical and efficient.

a. Removal of Impurities

(1) *Froth Flotation*. The rock mass, or impure ore, is ground to a fine powder and mixed with air, water, and oil. The particles of ore are adsorbed by the oil-covered air bubbles, while the particles of gangue become water-wetted. Since oil is less dense than water, the ore rises to the surface and may be floated off, while the gangue settles to the bottom.

(2) *Gravity Separation* (*Panning*). The rock is ground to a fine powder and treated with running water. The heavier ore particles sink to the bottom and the lighter gangue is washed away.

(3) *Magnetic Separation*. Certain ores, notably magnetite (Fe_3O_4), have magnetic properties. Since the gangue is generally nonmagnetic, separation can be easily effected.

(4) *Electrostatic Separation*. The gangue-containing ore is finely ground and electrically charged. Since the metallic ore is a conductor, it does not retain electrostatic charges as long as does the nonmetallic gangue, which is a nonconductor. The gangue will therefore cling to a conveyor belt, while the ore is led into storage hoppers.

b. Reduction of Metal Ores.

After impurities have been removed from combined metals in ores, the ore must be reduced.

Since the metal in an ore is deficient in electrons, any process of metallurgy must restore these electrons.

This means that the metal combined in the ore must gain electrons, that is, reduction must take place. Ores may be reduced as follows:

(1) *Reduction by a More Active Element*. The electromotive series reveals that one method of reduction is the use of a more active element as a reducing agent. For example, lead can be extracted from lead ores by the use of zinc as a reducing agent. Thus:

$$Zn + PbO \rightarrow ZnO + Pb$$

$$\underset{\text{metal}}{Zn^0} - 2\ e \rightarrow \underset{\text{ion}}{Zn^{+2}}$$

$$\underset{\text{ion}}{Pb^{+2}} + 2\ e \rightarrow \underset{\text{metal}}{Pb^0}$$

In order to extract lead from its ore (liberate lead from its compound), lead must gain electrons. Since zinc is a more active metal, it loses electrons more readily than does lead, thus forcing lead in the ore to gain electrons. In actual practice, it is more economical to use carbon in the form of coke as a reducing agent.

(2) *Reduction by Electrolysis.* If the ore contains an active metal, such as magnesium in magnesium oxide, a metal more active than magnesium would have to be used in the extraction process. However, the use of very active metals poses so many additional problems that reduction is accomplished more efficiently in another manner. It will be recalled from a previous chapter that, during electrolysis, reduction takes place at the cathode. Active metals such as potassium, calcium, sodium, magnesium, and aluminum may be extracted by the electrolysis of their melted (fused) ores. In the case of magnesium oxide, magnesium metal is liberated at the cathode, where reduction takes place as follows:

$$\underset{\text{ion}}{Mg^{+2}} + 2\ e \rightarrow \underset{\text{metal}}{Mg^0}$$

Other active metals, like aluminum, may be extracted in a similar manner.

If the ore is not an oxide, reduction is usually preceded by *roasting,* which consists of heating the ore in air. Sulfide and carbonate ores are commonly converted into oxides by roasting.

$$2\ ZnS + 3\ O_2 \rightarrow 2\ ZnO + 2\ SO_2 \uparrow$$

$$ZnCO_3 \rightarrow ZnO + CO_2 \uparrow$$

7. CONSERVATION OF METALS

The wise use of our natural resources is called *conservation.* Some of the methods presently used for conserving metals are briefly described below.

a. **Substitute Materials.** Natural and synthetic materials may be substituted for metals for many uses. Glass, wood, and plastics are being used in place of metals in many industries. Electrical appliances, automobiles, and electronic equipment use many of these substitute materials.

b. **Reclaiming of Scrap.** Scrap metal is an important source of nickel, iron, lead, and tin. These metals can be readily reclaimed and used over and over again. Scrap iron and scrap steel are continually being used in the open-hearth process, which produces 85% of our steel.

c. **Metals from the Sea.** Magnesium is now being extracted in commercial quantities from the magnesium chloride found in sea water (Dow process). In the future, it may be necessary to extract other metals from the sea.

d. **Low-grade Ores.** When complete exhaustion of the natural supply of high-grade ores is threatened, it is necessary to work low-grade ores. The United States is already obtaining some iron from low-grade taconite, because our supply of high-grade hematite is gradually being exhausted. Low-grade ores may be concentrated to make the extraction of the metal commercially feasible.

e. **Prevention of Corrosion.** Corrosion or rusting is caused by weathering, which results from the action of oxygen, carbon dioxide, and water vapor present in air. The corrosion of metals changes the properties of the metals, frequently destroying or limiting their usefulness. Corrosion affects metals differently. The corrosion of aluminum and copper produces a surface coating which adheres to the metal, forming a protective film. The rusting of iron, however, produces a compound which flakes off and actually hastens further corrosion.

Rusting may be explained by assuming that the surface of the iron contains, in addition to iron, various impurities surrounded by a film of water containing dissolved carbon dioxide, which forms carbonic acid. In effect, the presence of two dissimilar metallic substances, iron and iron oxide, in contact with an electrolyte, carbonic acid, constitutes an *electrochemical cell*. In such cells, oxidation-reduction takes place. (See 4, page 156.) This action is sometimes called "couple action." The couple represents the two dissimilar metals or metallic substances in contact with the electrolyte. The more active metal corrodes because it loses electrons and becomes oxidized. In rusting, the oxidation of iron results in the formation of ferrous ions, which may oxidize in air to form ferric ions. The ferric ions may react further with water and carbon dioxide to form complex mixtures of hydroxides and carbonates. As long as any free iron remains, the action continues until all the metal has softened and crumbled into a powder.

Some methods in use to prevent corrosion are:

(1) Using rust-resistant metal coatings, such as zinc (galvanizing) and tin (tinning).

(2) Electroplating the metal surface with rust-resistant metals, such as nickel and chromium. These metals may also be pre-mixed in the molten state with the metal to be protected. Such combinations of metals are called alloys.

(3) Applying rust-resistant nonmetal coatings, such as paints and lacquers.

8. TESTS FOR METALS

Certain metals present in compounds may be identified by a *borax bead test*. Make a borax bead by melting some borax in a small loop on a platinum wire. The heated bead is then dipped into a very small quantity of the unknown and reheated in an oxidizing flame. The metal oxide formed reacts with the borax bead to produce borate compounds having characteristic colors: cobalt—blue, chromium—green, iron—yellow, manganese—violet, nickel—brown.

Other tests for metals are discussed on pages 291 and 294.

1. *a.* The most abundant metal in the crust of the earth is _____.
   b. The most abundant nonmetal in the crust of the earth is _____.
2. *a.* Metals occupy, generally, the _____ (left, right) side of the periodic table.
   b. Metal M loses three electrons to form an ion, the symbol of which is _____.
   c. A metal that may form a negative ion by covalent linkage with oxygen is (1) potassium (2) calcium (3) gold (4) chromium.
   d. The valence number of manganese in the permanganate $(MnO_4)^-$ ion is (1) +2 (2) +4 (3) +7 (4) −1.
3. *a.* What is meant by the term lattice structure?
   b. Describe the metal lattice.
   c. How does the metal lattice explain some physical properties of metals?
   d. Of the following metals, the best conductor of electricity is (1) silver (2) gold (3) copper (4) aluminum.
   e. A substance responsible for dulling a copper surface is probably copper (1) carbonate (2) sulfate (3) sulfide (4) silicate.
   f. The most malleable metal is _____.
   g. The ability of a metal to be drawn into fine wire is called _____.
   h. The hardness of a metal refers to its *specific gravity*. [True or false? If false, correct the italicized term.]
   i. Of the following, the substance that has the highest tenacity is (1) nylon (2) cotton (3) sodium (4) copper.
4. *a.* Metals are arranged in order of their activity in the _____ series.
   b. Assume that the order of decreasing activity of three metals, X, Y, and Z,

is Z, X, Y. It therefore follows that (1) Y can replace X from its compound (2) Z cannot replace Y from its compound (3) Y can reduce X ions but not Z ions (4) X can reduce Y ions but not Z ions.

 c. In the reaction $K + NaCl \rightarrow KCl + Na$, (1) K is the oxidizing agent (2) NaCl is oxidized (3) K gains electrons (4) K loses electrons.

 d. In the reaction $Fe + 2\ AgNO_3 \rightarrow Fe(NO_3)_2 + 2\ Ag$, Fe is a more powerful *oxidizing* agent than Ag. [True or false?]

 e. Describe what happens when:
  (1) a strip of iron is placed in a solution of magnesium chloride
  (2) a strip of aluminum is placed in a solution of silver nitrate

 f. If a reaction occurs in *e*, show that oxidation-reduction has taken place.

 g. Write a balanced equation for each of the following reactions:
  (1) $Al + NaOH \rightarrow$ (2) $Li + H_2O \rightarrow$ (3) $B + O_2 \rightarrow$

5. *a.* Distinguish between minerals and ores.

 b. A metal usually found free in nature is (1) Li (2) Ca (3) Pt (4) Al.

 c. Metals are frequently found combined in nature as (1) carbonates (2) cyanides (3) peroxides (4) sulfites.

 **d.* Why is copper found both free and combined in nature?

 e. Why do many ores occur as oxides and sulfides?

6. *a.* The extraction of a metal depends largely upon the _____ of the ore.

 b. Impurities in ores may be removed by _____ and _____ methods.

7. *a.* The extraction of metals from ores is usually preceded by a process which _____ (increases, decreases) the amount of gangue present.

 b. Describe the important principle of each of the following metallurgical processes: (1) froth flotation (2) panning (3) electrostatic separation.

8. *a.* Combined metals are always extracted from their ores by (1) electrolysis (2) oxidation (3) reduction (4) froth flotation.

 b. A metal usually extracted from its ore with the aid of a reducing agent is (1) calcium (2) gold (3) potassium (4) lead.

 c. Active metals may be economically extracted from their ores by (1) use of a reducing agent (2) roasting (3) flotation (4) electrolysis.

 d. Write a balanced equation for each of the following reactions:
  (1) $Zn + PbO \rightarrow$ (4) $MgO \xrightarrow{\text{electrolysis}}$
  (2) $C + SnO_2 \rightarrow$
  *(3) $H_2 + WO_3 \rightarrow$ (5) $KOH \xrightarrow{\text{electrolysis}}$

 e. Before carbonate and sulfide ores are reduced, they are first _____.

 f. Write a balanced equation for each of the following reactions:
  (1) $PbS + O_2 \rightarrow$ *(2) $HgS + O_2 \rightarrow$

9. *a.* What is meant by conservation?

 b. Why must metals be conserved?

 c. List four methods of conserving metals.

 d. Three common metal substitutes are _____, _____, and _____.

 e. A metal extracted in large quantities from the sea is _____.

 f. Shortages of hematite have led to the increasing use of another iron ore called (1) siderite (2) taconite (3) galena (4) bauxite.

 g. Corrosion is not caused by the presence in air of (1) oxygen (2) carbon dioxide (3) argon (4) water vapor.

 h. Explain how corrosion may be beneficial to certain metals.

 i. Corrosion may be prevented by the use of _____ coatings.

10. *a.* Describe how a borax bead test may be carried out in the laboratory.

 b. A green borax bead indicates the presence of _____.

19 IRON AND STEEL

1. EXTRACTING IRON FROM ITS ORES

a. **Ores of Iron.** Iron, the second most abundant metal, makes up about 5% of the earth's crust by weight. It is found combined chiefly with oxygen in several varieties of oxides. The most important ores of iron are:

Fe_2O_3 hematite $\qquad\qquad$ $FeCO_3$ siderite

Fe_3O_4 $\begin{cases} \text{magnetite} \\ \text{taconite} \end{cases}$ $\quad$ $2\,Fe_2O_3 \cdot 3\,H_2O$ limonite

Most of the iron in this country has been obtained from the hematite ore in the open-pit Mesabi mines in Minnesota. Since it is expected that these mines will become completely exhausted someday, chemists have been seeking other sources. They have recently begun to extract iron from taconite, a low-grade magnetite ore. At present, the largest known reserve of hematite is in South America.

b. **Principles of Extraction.** There are two main steps in extracting iron from its ores:

(1) *Reduction.* The moderate activity of iron suggests that it can be extracted from its ores by reduction, using a reducing agent of greater activity than iron. In practice, carbon in the form of coke or carbon monoxide is used as the reducing agent.

> In extracting iron from its ores, the essential reaction that takes place is:
>
> $$Fe^{+3} + 3\,e \rightarrow \underset{\text{metal}}{Fe^0}$$

(2) *Removal of Impurities.* As even high-grade ores contain a considerable amount of impurities, the process of extraction must also include some treatment to remove or lessen these impurities. The chief

impurity in hematite is sand (SiO_2), an acidic oxide. This is removed by combination with calcium oxide, a basic oxide, obtained by the decomposition of limestone in the actual blast-furnace operation. The combination of these oxides results in the formation of a glassy material called *slag*, which can be easily separated from the iron.

2. THE BLAST FURNACE

The blast furnace is used to extract iron from its ores.

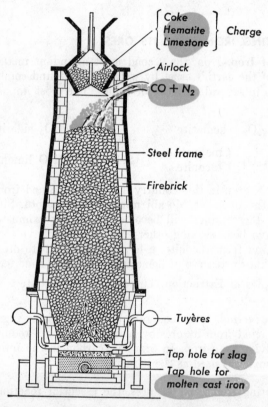

{ Coke
Hematite
Limestone } Charge

Airlock

$CO + N_2$

Steel frame

Firebrick

Tuyères

Tap hole for *slag*

Tap hole for molten cast iron

Fig. 2a. The Blast Furnace

a. **Construction.** Made of riveted steel plates, the blast furnace is about 100 feet in height and 30 feet in diameter. The interior of the furnace is lined with firebrick. Near the bottom are pipes in which cold water circulates to prevent overheating. Near the bottom also are air pipes (tuyères) through which blasts of hot air are permitted to enter. The heated air permits combustion and provides the proper temperature for the operation of the furnace. Under the tuyères are two tap holes, one for the removal of the molten iron and the other for the removal of the molten slag. The airlock arrangement at the top of the furnace makes it possible to charge the furnace with little loss of heat.

b. **Charge.** The charge in the blast furnace is a mixture of:

Charge in
Blast Furnace

(1) *Ore*—hematite, chiefly ferric oxide containing sand as an impurity.

Hematite
Coke
Limestone

(2) *Reducing agent*—coke, which serves as the source of carbon monoxide. The carbon monoxide is the chief reducing agent in this process.

(3) *Flux*—limestone, which decomposes to form the basic oxide, calcium oxide (CaO). This oxide combines with impurities such as sand and other acidic oxides to form slag. A flux, therefore, removes impurities.

c. **Important Reactions.** A number of chemical reactions take place in the different temperature zones of the furnace.

(1) The coke is first oxidized to form carbon dioxide.

$$C + O_2 \rightarrow CO_2 \uparrow$$

(2) The carbon dioxide thus formed is then reduced by the hot coke to form carbon monoxide.

$$CO_2 + C \rightarrow 2\ CO \uparrow$$

(3) The reduction reactions resulting in the formation of iron can be summarized as follows:

$$3\ Fe_2O_3 + CO \rightarrow 2\ Fe_3O_4 + CO_2 \uparrow$$

$$Fe_3O_4 + CO \rightarrow 3\ FeO + CO_2 \uparrow$$

$$FeO + CO \rightarrow Fe + CO_2 \uparrow$$

The carbon dioxide thus formed is reduced by the hot coke to form more carbon monoxide as shown in step (2).

The molten iron resulting from these reactions collects at the bottom of the blast furnace, where it is tapped off. The molten iron may be moved directly to the steel mill, or it may be cast into blocks called *pig iron.*

(4) The limestone undergoes decomposition as follows:

$$CaCO_3 \rightarrow CaO + CO_2 \uparrow$$

(5) The resulting calcium oxide unites with the sand in the iron ore to form slag.

$$CaO + SiO_2 \rightarrow CaSiO_3$$

The slag, composed chiefly of calcium silicate ($CaSiO_3$), floats on the molten iron at the bottom of the furnace, preventing its reoxidation. The slag is tapped off at regular intervals.

d. **Cast Iron.** The iron tapped off from the blast furnace is called *cast iron,* or pig iron.

(1) *Composition*

Cast iron is the most impure form of iron.

Cast iron contains from 3 to 5% carbon and about 1% manganese, both of which are desirable impurities; and smaller quantities of silicon, sulfur, and phosphorus, which are undesirable impurities. The high carbon content is due to the fact that molten iron is a good solvent for the coke used in the furnace.

(2) *Properties.* Cast iron varies in color and is crystalline in structure. It melts readily at about 1,200°C and is easily cast because it expands during solidification, thus producing an exact reproduction of the mold. Cast iron is hard but brittle, can neither be welded nor tempered, cannot withstand sudden shock or vibration, and corrodes rapidly in air.

Welding consists of melting the edges of two pieces of metal until they become plastic and fuse together. *Tempering,* which means varying the hardness by heat treatment and subsequent cooling, will be considered on page 277, under 9.

Although cast iron cannot be tempered, its properties may be varied by changing the rate of cooling of the molten iron. When cooled rapidly, *white cast iron* is formed. In this variety of cast iron, the carbon present is dissolved as *cementite* (Fe_3C), making the iron hard and brittle. When cooled slowly, *gray cast iron* is formed. The cementite breaks up to form iron and carbon in the form of graphite. Consequently, gray cast iron is not so hard and brittle as the white variety.

(3) *Uses.* Where massiveness and little tensile strength are required and where brittleness can be tolerated, cast iron may be used.

Thus, cast iron is used in the manufacture of stoves, radiators, frames, and machine supports.

Wrought iron and steel are also made from cast iron by methods that can be considered as refining processes.

WROUGHT IRON AND STEEL

3. PRINCIPLES OF REFINING

The manufacture of wrought iron and steel requires the removal of the chief impurities present in cast iron, namely, carbon, manganese, sulfur, silicon, and phosphorus.

There are two essential steps in the refining of iron: controlled oxidation and neutralization.

a. **Controlled Oxidation.** The impurities are oxidized carefully so that the iron itself remains unaffected. The two gaseous oxides formed, carbon dioxide and sulfur dioxide, pass off into the air. The remaining oxides are solid oxides of silicon, manganese, and phosphorus and need further treatment, usually neutralization.

b. **Neutralization.** Since silicon dioxide and phosphorus pentoxide are acidic oxides, they are removed by reaction with basic oxides, such as calcium oxide or ferric oxide.

$$SiO_2 + CaO \rightarrow CaSiO_3$$

$$P_2O_5 + Fe_2O_3 \rightarrow 2\ FePO_4$$

If metallic impurities such as manganese are present, the oxides formed can be removed by reaction with acidic oxides, such as silicon dioxide.

$$MnO + SiO_2 \rightarrow MnSiO_3$$

Refining furnaces are therefore lined with acidic and basic oxides in the form of firebrick to carry out neutralization. After reaction, the impurities form a slag which can later be separated from the molten metal. As the firebrick lining takes part in the reaction, it is replaced from time to time.

4. WROUGHT IRON

a. Manufacture

The manufacture of wrought iron is a refining process whereby the carbon content of cast iron is reduced to less than 0.2% and the amounts of the other impurities are reduced to traces.

Wrought iron is so called because it is the iron used by the blacksmith and ornamental ironworker and can be wrought (worked) into various shapes.

Wrought iron was once made by hand in a special furnace, called a reverberatory or puddling furnace, shown below.

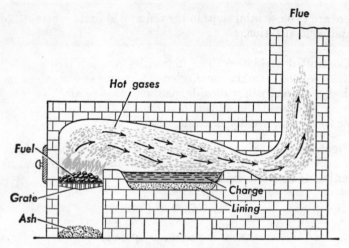

Fig. 4a. The Reverberatory (Puddling) Furnace

Cast iron was heated on a layer of ferric oxide, which acted as a flux to remove acidic oxide impurities. Today, cast iron is poured into molten slag and oxidized until most of the impurities are removed. Most of the slag is then squeezed out by hammering, but some slag is allowed to remain in order to give wrought iron its many desirable properties.

b. Composition

Wrought iron is the purest form of iron.

Wrought iron contains less than 0.2% carbon and only traces of silicon, sulfur, and phosphorus. The slag is not an impurity but an important ingredient of wrought iron, giving it the quality of toughness.

c. **Properties.** Wrought iron is relatively soft, malleable, and ductile. It is fibrous in structure. It can be welded and forged, but can be neither cast nor tempered.

d. **Uses.** Wrought iron, because of its many desirable properties, has more uses than cast iron. It is used to make bolts, chains, machine parts, wire, nails, and other hardware. Electromagnets are made of wrought iron because it loses its magnetism easily. It does not rust as readily as the more impure cast iron and therefore is used in anchors and boiler pipes.

5. THE MANUFACTURE OF STEEL

Steel is a form of iron in which the carbon content has been carefully controlled and to which fixed amounts of certain metals have been added to give the steel desired properties.

Generally, steel has a carbon content ranging from 0.2 to 2% and also contains traces of undesirable impurities, chiefly phosphorus.

The manufacture of steel is essentially a process involving the refining of cast iron. The impurities in cast iron are removed or reduced by careful oxidation and subsequent conversion to slag. There are two major processes of steel manufacture in this country. The older *Bessemer process* manufactures only about 5% of the total steel produced, while the *open-hearth process* accounts for 85%. The remaining 10% is limited to processes that manufacture precision steel for special uses.

6. BESSEMER STEEL

In the Bessemer process, both carbon and the undesirable impurities are simultaneously removed by oxidation. The desired amount of carbon is added to the furnace later.

a. **Bessemer Process.** Molten cast iron taken directly from the blast furnace may be converted into steel in a Bessemer converter, shown in Fig. 6*a*. The converter is made of wrought iron or steel and is lined with firebrick. It holds only about 20 tons of metal, which therefore limits its usefulness.

Charge in
Bessemer Furnace

Molten cast iron
Spiegeleisen

Blasts of air of 10 or 15-minute duration are forced through the molten cast iron, oxidizing only the carbon and other impurities but not the iron itself. A calculated amount of *spiegeleisen*, an iron-manganese alloy rich in carbon, is then added to give the resulting steel the desired carbon content. The manganese adds to the hardness of the product and also removes any air trapped in the molten metal.

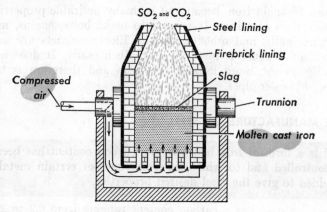

Fig. 6a. The Bessemer Converter

The converter is mounted on an axle called a trunnion, so that the finished product can be conveniently poured out. The molten steel is cast into bars or ingots, which are then rolled or drawn while still hot.

b. **Composition.** Bessemer steel contains about 1% carbon and only traces of silicon, sulfur, and phosphorus.

c. **Properties.** Since Bessemer steel ranks between cast iron and wrought iron in carbon content, it has many of the desirable properties of each. Bessemer steel is moderately hard and tough, malleable and ductile, and can be cast, forged, welded, and tempered.

d. **Uses.** The composition of Bessemer steel is difficult to control carefully, due to the speed with which impurities are removed. Consequently, batches of Bessemer steel may contain sufficient phosphorus and sulfur to render the steel brittle. Bessemer steel must either be further refined or limited in use to the manufacture of products in which corrosion and resistance to shock are unimportant. Because it is malleable and ductile, Bessemer steel is used to make wire, sheets, and rods.

7. OPEN-HEARTH STEEL

The object of the open-hearth process is to reduce slowly and carefully the carbon content of cast iron to between 0.2% and 2%, with only traces of silicon, sulfur, and phosphorus. This is accomplished by the use of an oxidizing agent in the form of hematite (Fe_2O_3). By oxidation, the carbon content is lessened to the desired quantity. At the same time, the undesirable impurities are converted to oxides, which are removed in the form of slag by acid or basic furnace linings. Scrap steel is frequently added to the charge to increase the total steel output.

The open-hearth process has many advantages over the Bessemer process. Small samples of steel may be analyzed periodically, thus maintaining more accurate control over the composition of the steel. The open-hearth process is also more economical in operation; the furnaces can handle larger quantities of steel and a special heating process cuts down on fuel cost.

***a*. Open-hearth Process.** The open-hearth furnace (see Fig. 7a) has a bed or hearth capable of holding from 50 to 150 tons of steel. To meet the huge increase in the demand for steel, open-hearth furnaces capable of holding much larger quantities of steel are being built.

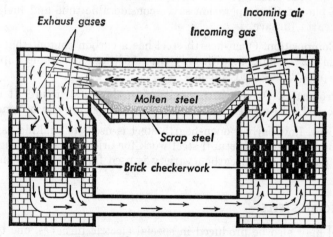

Fig. 7a. The Open-hearth Furnace

Depending on the impurities present, the furnace has either a basic lining of magnesium oxide or an acid lining of silicon dioxide. The hearth is heated by a *regenerative heating system,* which uses the heat contained in the exhaust gases to preheat the incoming fuel gas and air mixture. On both sides of the bed is a pair of flues, surrounded by a checkerwork of firebrick. Producer gas and air are preheated and passed through one pair of flues. The hot gas and air mix as they pass over the bed, resulting in a flame of very high temperature. The hot products of combustion pass out through the other pair of flues, heating the checkerwork. The flow of gas and air is then reversed and passes up through the newly heated flues, over the bed, and out through the first pair of flues.

The charge placed on the acid or basic lining of the hearth is first scrap steel, then pig iron, and finally hematite. The carbon and undesirable impurities are oxidized by the hematite, and the oxides formed either escape as gases or combine with the basic lining to form a slag. The process is continued until the samples of steel, taken from time to time, show the desired percentage of carbon.

Charge in
Open-hearth Furnace

Scrap steel
Pig iron
Hematite

When the sample of cast iron has an excessive phosphorus content, a combination or *duplex* process is employed. Most of the impurities except phosphorus are first removed in a Bessemer converter. The charge is then transferred to an open-hearth furnace for the removal of phosphorus. This operation saves considerable time and fuel in the open-hearth furnace.

b. **Composition.** Open-hearth steel has a carbon content that varies between 0.2% and 2%, with only traces of the undesirable impurities sulfur, phosphorus, and silicon.

c. **Properties.** Open-hearth steel is granular in structure. It can be cast, forged, and welded and the high-carbon variety can be tempered.

d. **Uses.** Low-carbon open-hearth steel is used for making cannons, rails, boiler plates, structural steel work for bridges and buildings, and armor plate. The high-carbon variety is used for cheap tools and cutlery.

8. SPECIAL STEELS

Steel may also be produced in special electric furnaces, one type of which is shown in Fig. 8. In such furnaces, higher temperatures and more careful control of impurities can be obtained. Electric-furnace steels are considerably more expensive to produce. This process is therefore limited to the production of alloy steels of the finest quality.

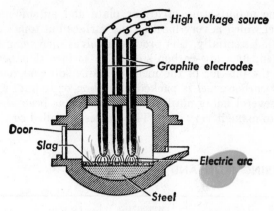

Fig. 8. The Electric Furnace

9. HARDNESS OF STEEL

The hardness of steel depends upon the carbon content.

High-carbon steels are harder than low-carbon steels. The hardness also depends on the percentage of combined carbon as well as of free carbon. The greater the amount of combined carbon, the harder the steel. The addition of certain metals such as manganese, chromium, or nickel to an ordinary carbon steel increases the hardness of that steel. Steel may be hardened in several ways:

(1) A steel with a certain percentage of carbon may have its hardness changed by *tempering,* so that the same billet of steel may be used for manufacturing razor blades or saw blades. Tempering is the process by which the hardness of a given carbon steel is varied by heat treatment and subsequent cooling. Such treatment varies the ratio of free to combined carbon in the steel. The process consists of two steps. The steel is first heated to a cherry-red color and plunged into cold water. This makes the steel hard but brittle. The steel is then reheated to withdraw little or much of the hardness, depending on the use for which it is intended. It is again plunged into cold water. A slight reheating, indicated by the formation of a yellow film on the steel, would make the steel suitable for razor blades. A longer reheating, indicated by the formation of a blue film on the steel, would make the steel suitable for saw blades.

(2) The manufacture of armor plate and automobile parts requires a steel which is very hard on the surface but tough in the body of the metal. Essentially, this process involves increasing the surface carbon content of a low-carbon steel. The surface thus becomes very hard, while the interior of the metal remains soft and tough. In this process, low-carbon steel is packed in carbon or sodium cyanide and heated for several hours until enough carbon has been absorbed into the surface to make it very hard. This process is called *case-hardening*.

10. COMPARING IRON AND STEEL

FORM	PROCESS	IMPURITIES	PROPERTIES	USES
Cast (pig) iron	Blast furnace	3-5% C, 1% Mn, some Si, S, P	Crystalline, brittle, hard; easily cast, cannot be welded or tempered	Stoves, radiators, frames
Wrought iron	Reverberatory (puddling) furnace	Less than 0.2% C, traces of Si, S, P	Fibrous structure, soft, ductile, malleable	Chains, electromagnets, anchors
Steel	Bessemer converter	About 1% C, traces of Si, S, P	Tough, malleable, ductile; can be cast, welded, and tempered	Wire, sheets, rods
	Open-hearth furnace	0.2-2% C, traces of Si, S, P	Granular structure; can be forged, welded, and tempered	Rails, armor plate, bridges
	Electric furnace	% C varied to meet specific use	Uniform quality, free from oxides or adsorbed gases	Alloy steels

11. ALLOYS

Alloys are substances that have metallic properties and consist of two or more elements, at least one of which is a metal. Analysis and study with X-rays have revealed that some alloys are probably solid solutions, while others appear to be complex chemical compounds. The properties of alloys, such as mechanical strength and electrical conductivity, are quite different from the properties of the constituent elements. It is thought that differences in these properties are due to the different arrangement of atoms in the alloy. Thus, from about 40 common metals, several thousand alloys have been prepared, offering a wide variety of uses.

The following tables list the composition and uses of some common alloys and alloy steels:

ALLOYS

ALLOY	COMPOSITION	USES
Brass	Cu-Zn	Sheets, tubing, ornamental fixtures, plumbing
Bronze	Cu-Sn	Valves, fittings, statues
Duralumin	Al-Cu	Airplane and auto parts
German silver (nickel brass)	Cu-Zn-Ni	Tableware, rheostats
Gold (18-carat)	Au-Cu (3:1)	Jewelry
Invar	Fe-Ni	Low coefficient of expansion; used in precision instruments
Magnalium	Mg-Al	Airplane parts, scientific instruments
Monel	Ni-Cu-Fe	Resists corrosion; used in acid tanks and propeller blades
Nichrome	Ni-Cr	Electrical heating devices
Silver amalgam	Ag-Hg	Dental fillings
Solder	Pb-Sn	Joining metals
Wood's metal	Pb-Sn-Cd-Bi	Low-melting point alloy; used in fire-sprinkling systems

ALLOY STEELS

ALLOY STEEL	COMPOSITION	PROPERTIES	USES
Chrome steel	Fe-Cr-Si-Mn	Hard, strong	Gears, armor plate
Manganese steel	Fe-Mn	Hard, tough	Safes, rock crushers
Molybdenum steel	Fe-Mo	Strong, tough	Auto frames, structural steel
Nickel steel	Fe-Ni-C	Strong, tough, resists corrosion	Structural steel, rails, battleships
Silicon steel (Duriron)	Fe-Si	Very magnetic	Armatures, transformer cores, acid tanks
Stainless steel	Fe-Cr	Resists corrosion	Cutlery, surgical instruments
Tungsten steel	Fe-W-Cr	Hard, magnetic	Permanent magnets, cutting tools, hacksaw blades
Vanadium steel	Fe-V	Strong, durable, very elastic	Axles, springs, tools, bearings

COMPOUNDS OF IRON

12. CHEMICAL PROPERTIES OF IRON

The position of iron in the electromotive series indicates that it is moderately active.

a. **Ferrous and Ferric Compounds.** Iron forms two types of compounds. In ferrous compounds, iron has a valence number of $+2$; in ferric compounds, iron has a valence number of $+3$.

(1) The change from the ferrous state to the ferric state involves the process of oxidation. When a metal ion becomes more positively

charged ($Fe^{+2} \rightarrow Fe^{+3}$), electrons must be lost. Thus, in the reaction

$$2 \text{ FeCl}_2 + \text{Cl}_2 \rightarrow 2 \text{ FeCl}_3$$

chlorine gas oxidizes the ferrous chloride to ferric chloride.

$$2 \text{ Fe}^{+2} - 2 \text{ e} \rightarrow 2 \text{ Fe}^{+3}$$

$$\text{Cl}_2{}^0 + 2 \text{ e} \rightarrow 2 \text{ Cl}^-$$

(2) The change from the ferric to the ferrous state involves reduction. When a metal ion becomes less positively charged ($Fe^{+3} \rightarrow Fe^{+2}$), electrons must be gained. Thus, in the reaction

$$2 \text{ FeCl}_3 + \text{H}_2 \rightarrow 2 \text{ FeCl}_2 + 2 \text{ HCl}$$

hydrogen gas reduces the ferric chloride to ferrous chloride.

$$2 \text{ Fe}^{+3} + 2 \text{ e} \rightarrow 2 \text{ Fe}^{+2}$$

$$\text{H}_2{}^0 - 2 \text{ e} \rightarrow 2 \text{ H}^+$$

b. **Tests for Iron Salts**

(1) *Test for Ferrous Salts.* The addition of potassium *ferricyanide*, $K_3Fe(CN)_6$, to a ferrous salt produces a dark-blue precipitate (Turnbull's blue).

$$2 \text{ K}_3\text{Fe(CN)}_6 + 3 \text{ FeCl}_2 \rightarrow 6 \text{ KCl} + \text{Fe}_3[\text{Fe(CN)}_6]_2 \downarrow$$

(2) *Test for Ferric Salts.* The addition of potassium *ferrocyanide*, $K_4Fe(CN)_6$, to a ferric salt produces a dark-blue precipitate (Prussian blue).

$$3 \text{ K}_4\text{Fe(CN)}_6 + 4 \text{ FeCl}_3 \rightarrow 12 \text{ KCl} + \text{Fe}_4[\text{Fe(CN)}_6]_3 \downarrow$$

Note that a dark-blue precipitate is obtained only when the reagent containing the *opposite* ion is used. Thus, *ferrous* salts produce a dark-blue precipitate with potassium *ferric*yanide, while *ferric* salts produce a dark-blue precipitate with potassium *ferro*cyanide. Although the precipitates are both dark-blue, they do not have the same composition.

SUMMARY OF IRON COMPOUNDS

ION	FORMULA	REAGENT FOR TEST
Ferrous	Fe^{+2}	Potassium ferricyanide
Ferric	Fe^{+3}	Potassium ferrocyanide

1. *a.* Iron may be extracted from the ore (1) cinnabar (2) cryolite (3) galena (4) magnetite.
 b. The most common iron ore found in this country is _____.
 c. Two reducing agents that can be used to extract iron from its ores are _____ and _____.
 d. The chief impurity in hematite is (1) iron oxide (2) coke (3) calcium carbonate (4) silicon dioxide.
 e. Impurities in iron ore are removed in the form of _____.

2. *a.* Make a labeled diagram of the blast furnace for the extraction of iron from its ores.
 b. Describe the function of each of the following parts of the furnace:
 (1) firebrick lining
 (2) tuyères
 (3) air lock
 c. The charge in the blast furnace is (1) ore, coke, and sand (2) ore, limestone, and sand (3) coke, limestone, and sand (4) ore, coke, and limestone.
 d. The function of a flux is _____.
 e. Write balanced equations for the important reactions that take place in the blast furnace.
 f. The density of slag is _____ (less, greater) than the density of molten iron.

3. *a.* The largest impurity in cast iron is *carbon.* [True or false? If false, correct the italicized term.]
 b. A substance which is not an impurity in cast iron is (1) oxygen (2) silicon (3) phosphorus (4) sulfur.
 c. When molten cast iron solidifies, it (1) first expands, then contracts (2) first contracts, then expands (3) expands only (4) contracts only.
 d. Cast iron (1) can be tempered (2) can be welded (3) has high tensile strength (4) is crystalline.
 e. Distinguish between welding and tempering.
 *f. What determines whether or not a sample of metal can be welded or tempered?
 g. How does the rate of cooling of molten cast iron affect its composition?
 h. Cast iron cannot be used in the manufacture of (1) train rails (2) machine supports (3) radiators (4) stoves.

4. *a.* The chief raw material used to make wrought iron is _____.
 b. Describe two important principles involved in the refining of cast iron.
 c. For each principle described in *b,* write two balanced equations.

5. *a.* The carbon content of wrought iron is *greater* than the carbon content of cast iron. [True or false? If false, correct the italicized term.]

b. The desirable properties of wrought iron are due to the presence of _____.

c. Wrought iron cannot be **(1)** hammered **(2)** welded **(3)** cast **(4)** drawn into wire.

d. State three important uses of wrought iron and for each use indicate the property which makes the use possible.

6. *a.* The carbon content of steel is generally *higher* than the carbon content of wrought iron. [True or false? If false, correct the italicized term.]

b. Steelmaking processes involve the refining of _____.

c. In the manufacture of steel, phosphorus is removed by **(1)** oxidation only **(2)** direct conversion to slag **(3)** distillation **(4)** oxidation and subsequent conversion to slag.

d. The furnace which produces the most steel in this country is the **(1)** Bessemer **(2)** duplex **(3)** open-hearth **(4)** electric.

7. *a.* Make a labeled diagram of the Bessemer converter.

b. State a reason for the use of each of the constituents of the charge in the Bessemer converter.

c. Spiegeleisen is used in this furnace to provide the steel with _____.

d. List the important properties of Bessemer steel.

e. Four impurities that may remain in Bessemer steel are _____.

f. State two uses of Bessemer steel.

8. *a.* List three advantages of the open-hearth process over the Bessemer process.

b. The object of the open-hearth process is to provide an accurate control of _____ content.

c. Make a labeled diagram of the open-hearth furnace.

d. State a reason for the use of each of the constituents of the charge in the open-hearth furnace.

e. An important similarity between the Bessemer and open-hearth processes is the **(1)** time of operation **(2)** heating system **(3)** furnace capacity **(4)** method of removal of impurities.

f. What is the function of the duplex process?

g. Low-carbon open-hearth steel cannot be **(1)** cast **(2)** forged **(3)** tempered **(4)** welded.

h. State two uses of open-hearth steel for which Bessemer steel is inadequate. Explain why.

9. *a.* Precision steels are manufactured in special furnaces called _____ furnaces.

b. Why do precision steels require special steelmaking furnaces?

10. *a.* As the amount of combined carbon in steel increases, the hardness _____ (decreases, increases, remains the same).

b. Hardness in steel may be varied by **(1)** casting **(2)** forging **(3)** tempering **(4)** welding.

c. Describe the two important steps in the process of tempering.

d. The surface carbon content of low-carbon steel may be increased by a process called _____.

11. In tabular form, compare the composition, properties, and uses of cast iron, wrought iron, and steel.

12. *a.* An alloy always contains at least **(1)** two metals **(2)** one metal and a nonmetal **(3)** two nonmetals **(4)** two elements.

*b. Why do the properties of alloys differ from their constituent elements?

  c. An element common to brass and bronze is (1) copper (2) zinc (3) tin (4) nickel.

  d. Alloys used in making airplane parts contain (1) zinc and aluminum (2) copper and zinc (3) magnesium and zinc (4) magnesium and aluminum.

  e. An element common to nichrome and German silver is (1) chromium (2) nickel (3) copper (4) silver.

  f. Amalgams always contain (1) silver (2) copper (3) mercury (4) gold.

  g. Low-melting point alloys usually contain lead and (1) copper (2) mercury (3) tin (4) zinc.

13. a. All alloy steels contain _____.

  b. In tabular form, indicate the name, composition, and one important use for each of five alloy steels.

14. a. In ferrous compounds, iron has a valence number of _____; while in ferric compounds, iron has a valence number of _____.

  b. Write a balanced equation for each of the following reactions:
   (1) $FeCl_2 + Cl_2 \rightarrow$
   (2) $FeCl_3 + H_2 \rightarrow$

  c. For each reaction in b, write the oxidation and reduction equations.

  d. For each reaction in b, indicate the
   (1) oxidized particle
   (2) reduced particle
   (3) oxidizing agent
   (4) reducing agent

15. a. Write the valence number of iron in:
   (1) $K_3Fe(CN)_6$
   (2) $K_4Fe(CN)_6$

  b. Write a balanced equation for each of the following reactions:
   (1) $K_3Fe(CN)_6 + FeCl_2 \rightarrow$
   *(2) $K_4Fe(CN)_6 + Fe_2(SO_4)_3 \rightarrow$

  c. How does the formation of a dark-blue precipitate in testing for iron salts indicate the presence of ferrous or ferric ions?

16. Calculate the weight of iron that can be obtained from 100 tons of taconite, 30% of which is iron oxide.

17. Calculate the volume of chlorine required to oxidize 635 grams of ferrous chloride.

20 COPPER, ZINC, ALUMINUM, AND OTHER METALS

COPPER

1. METALLURGY

a. **Ores.** Copper is probably our most important *nonferrous* metal; its annual production exceeds one million tons.

Copper occurs in the free and combined states. It is found combined in considerable quantities as the oxide, cuprite (Cu_2O) and the sulfide, chalcocite (Cu_2S). It also occurs as the basic carbonate, malachite, $Cu(OH)_2 \cdot CuCO_3$.

b. **Extraction.** Ores containing native copper are concentrated; the impurities are removed by reaction with a flux such as limestone.

Sulfide ores yield about 70% of the copper produced in this country. The low copper content of these ores, coupled with the presence of impurities that are difficult to remove, makes the extraction of copper a complex process. Essentially, the process involves flotation, roasting, and reduction. The copper thus obtained, called *blister copper*, varies in purity from 95 to 99% and contains silver, gold, and arsenic as impurities. Since most of the copper produced is used for electrical purposes, it is necessary to refine the copper further. The presence of even small amounts of impurities enormously increases the resistance of the copper, thus reducing its conductivity considerably.

c. **Refining.** Copper is refined by an electrolytic process which increases its purity to 99.95%. This process, shown in Fig. 1c, can be summarized as follows:

Thick, impure copper slabs are used as anodes, while thin sheets of pure copper are used as cathodes. The electrolyte is a solution of copper sulfate and sulfuric acid. When the electrical circuit is completed, the copper anode is oxidized and goes into solution. At the same time, the copper ions in the electrolyte are reduced to form free copper, which is deposited on the cathode. The less active metals, gold and silver, which are more difficult to plate out, settle at the bottom of the tank as a sludge or mud. The metals are then recovered from the sludge.

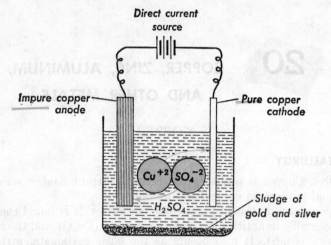

Fig. 1c. Electrolytic Refining of Copper

ANODE REACTION: $Cu^0 - 2\,e \rightarrow Cu^{+2}$

CATHODE REACTION: $Cu^{+2} + 2\,e \rightarrow Cu^0$

d. **Electroplating.** The electro-refining of copper is essentially an electroplating process. Using the same principles, it is possible to plate with many metals. A typical setup is shown in Fig. 1*d*.

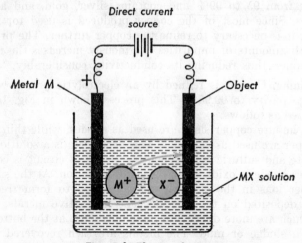

Fig. 1d. Electroplating

To electroplate metal M on an object, the object is connected to the cathode, while metal M is connected to the anode. A salt solution of M (MX) serves as the electrolyte.

In this manner, copper, gold, or silver may be plated on objects as follows:

KIND OF PLATING	ANODE	CATHODE	ELECTROLYTE
Copper	Copper	Object	Solution of copper sulfate
Gold	Gold	Object	Solution of potassium gold cyanide
Silver	Silver	Object	Solution of potassium silver cyanide

2. PHYSICAL PROPERTIES

Next to silver, copper is the best conductor of heat and electricity. Copper is very malleable and extremely ductile. It is thus readily converted into sheets and wire.

3. CHEMICAL PROPERTIES

The position of copper in the electromotive series reveals that it cannot replace hydrogen from acids. However, copper reacts with concentrated sulfuric acid to form sulfur dioxide and with concentrated nitric acid to form nitrogen dioxide.

$$Cu + 2\ H_2SO_4 \rightarrow CuSO_4 + 2\ H_2O + SO_2 \uparrow$$

$$Cu + 4\ HNO_3 \rightarrow Cu(NO_3)_2 + 2\ H_2O + 2\ NO_2 \uparrow$$

4. USES

Because copper is ductile and a good electrical conductor, it is used extensively as wire for conducting an electric current. Because it is malleable and forms a protective coating on rusting, it is used in the manufacture of gutters, roofing, and screens. Being both malleable and a good heat conductor, copper is used to manufacture boilers, kettles, and stills. It alloys readily with other metals. Copper is added to gold and silver to make a harder alloy for the production of coins and jewelry. 18-carat gold contains $\frac{18}{24}$ or 75% gold and 25% copper by weight.

5. COPPER COMPOUNDS

Copper exhibits two valence numbers in its compounds. In cuprous compounds, copper has a valence number of +1; while in cupric compounds, copper has a valence number of +2. The most common compound of copper is hydrated copper sulfate, commonly called blue vitriol ($CuSO_4 \cdot 5 H_2O$). Blue vitriol is used to purify water because it kills algae and other small plants which give water an offensive odor.

White anhydrous copper sulfate, formed by heating the blue crystalline variety until the water of crystallization has been driven out, is used as a test for the presence of water. On dissolving, the anhydrous salt forms a blue solution because of the presence of the copper ion. If such a solution is evaporated carefully, the crystalline form will again be obtained.

SUMMARY OF COPPER

Ores: Cuprite, chalcocite, malachite
Metallurgy: Extraction by roasting and reduction, refining by electrolysis
Properties: Most common electrical conductor; below hydrogen in the electromotive series
Common compounds: Cu_2O, $CuSO_4 \cdot 5 H_2O$
Uses: Electric wire, alloys

ZINC

6. METALLURGY

a. **Ores.** The United States is the largest producer of zinc in the world. Because of its chemical activity, zinc does not occur in nature in the free state. The most important zinc ores are zinc blende, also called sphalerite (ZnS); zincite (ZnO); and smithsonite ($ZnCO_3$).

b. **Extraction.** Zinc is extracted from its ores as follows:

(1) The ore is concentrated by either flotation or magnetic separation, both of which are discussed under *a,* page 262.

(2) Nonoxide ores are converted to the oxide by roasting in furnaces. (For the equations involved, see page 263.)

(3) Zinc, which is only moderately active, is extracted from its oxide ore by reduction with carbon, usually in the form of powdered hard coal.

$$ZnO + C \rightarrow Zn + CO \uparrow$$

Since zinc melts at 419°C and boils at 950°C, it is possible to collect it by distillation. The condensed zinc vapor formed in the furnace flues is called *zinc dust*. Other commercial forms of zinc are *granulated (mossy) zinc*, produced by pouring molten zinc into water; and *zinc bars (spelter)*, made by pouring molten zinc into molds.

More recently, zinc is being extracted from sulfide ore by electrolytic processes. The sulfide ore is first roasted and the zinc oxide produced is dissolved in sulfuric acid. The zinc sulfate thus formed is subjected to electrolysis. Metallic zinc plates out on an aluminum cathode. As in the case of copper, electrolytic zinc has exceptionally high purity and is preferred in the manufacture of alloys.

7. PHYSICAL PROPERTIES

Zinc in the form of spelter is a bluish-white metal, crystalline in structure, and brittle at ordinary temperatures. At higher temperatures, about 150°C, zinc becomes malleable and may be rolled into sheets. When heated to about 300°C, zinc once more loses its malleability and becomes brittle.

8. CHEMICAL PROPERTIES

a. Zinc is a moderately active metal. It unites readily with nonmetals such as oxygen, sulfur, and chlorine.

$$2\,Zn + O_2 \rightarrow 2\,ZnO$$

$$Zn + S \rightarrow ZnS$$

$$Zn + Cl_2 \rightarrow ZnCl_2$$

b. Zinc reacts readily with hydrochloric acid and dilute sulfuric acid to liberate hydrogen.

$$Zn + 2\,HCl \rightarrow ZnCl_2 + H_2 \uparrow$$

$$Zn + H_2SO_4 \rightarrow ZnSO_4 + H_2 \uparrow$$

c. Zinc reacts with bases to form a soluble zincate and hydrogen.

$$Zn + 2\,NaOH \rightarrow Na_2ZnO_2 + H_2 \uparrow$$
$$\text{sodium}$$
$$\text{zincate}$$

d. When soluble zinc salts are treated with a soluble base such as sodium hydroxide, a precipitate of zinc hydroxide is first formed. Addition of excess sodium hydroxide causes the insoluble zinc hydroxide to dissolve.

$$ZnCl_2 + 2 \ NaOH \rightarrow 2 \ NaCl + Zn(OH)_2 \downarrow$$

$$Zn(OH)_2 + 2 \ NaOH \rightarrow Na_2ZnO_2 + 2 \ H_2O$$

Because zinc hydroxide dissolves in excess base, it is an *amphoteric compound.* Amphoteric compounds may act either as acids or bases. The slight ionization of zinc hydroxide may be written thus:

$$Zn^{+2} + 2 \ (OH)^- \rightleftharpoons Zn(OH)_2 \rightleftharpoons 2 \ H^+ + ZnO_2^{-2}$$

As a result of this dual property, zinc hydroxide will react with acids and bases and thus dissolve in them.

IN ACIDS: $Zn(OH)_2 + 2 \ HCl \rightarrow ZnCl_2 + 2 \ H_2O$

IN BASES: $Zn(OH)_2 + 2 \ NaOH \rightarrow Na_2ZnO_2 + 2 \ H_2O$

Note in the above cases that insoluble zinc hydroxide can dissolve in acid or base, but not in water. When solution takes place in substances other than water, a chemical change probably occurs. Where water is the solvent, a chemical change may occur, as described under **11,** page 37.

9. USES

a. **Alloys.** Brass, bronze, and German silver are important alloys containing zinc.

b. **Galvanizing.** Galvanizing consists of coating sheet iron with zinc in order to prevent rusting. The zinc corrodes on exposure to air, forming a protective coating of zinc oxide, which prevents the rusting of the iron.

c. **Dry Cells.** The container of a dry cell is made of zinc and serves as the cathode. Oxidation-reduction takes place in this cell, resulting in an excess of electrons at the cathode and a deficiency at the anode. The electrical energy obtained from the cell is the result of this difference of potential.

d. **Manufacture of Zinc Compounds**

(1) Zinc oxide, or zinc white, is prepared by oxidizing zinc. It is used as a paint base where white lead would blacken.

(2) Lithopone, a mixture of zinc sulfide and barium sulfate, is a pigment used in permanent white paints.

(3) Zinc chloride reacts with and dissolves metallic oxides, making it useful as a flux in soldering.

10. COBALT NITRATE TEST FOR ZINC COMPOUNDS

The compound to be tested is placed in a cavity in a charcoal block and heated with a blowpipe until it becomes white-hot. When the mass has cooled, a drop of cobalt nitrate solution is added. The formation of a green mass (cobalt zincate) indicates the presence of a zinc compound.

SUMMARY OF ZINC

Ores: Sphalerite, zincite, and smithsonite
Metallurgy: Roasting, reduction, and distillation; electrolysis
Properties: Moderately active metal; forms amphoteric compounds
Common compounds: ZnO, $ZnCl_2$
Uses: Alloys, galvanizing, dry cells
Test: Cobalt nitrate test yields *green* cobalt zincate

ALUMINUM

11. METALLURGY

a. Ores. Aluminum is the most abundant metal found in the crust of the earth. Because of its chemical activity, aluminum always occurs combined with other elements, chiefly as clay, which is a complex silicate; as bauxite (Al_2O_3); and as cryolite (Na_3AlF_6). Technical difficulties in the extraction process limit the extraction of aluminum at the present time to its oxide ore, bauxite.

b. Extraction. Because aluminum is an active metal, its compounds cannot be reduced by carbon. The use of more active metals, such as sodium or potassium, is not commercially practical. Instead, aluminum is extracted from its ore by electrolysis. The process now in use was devised by a young American chemist, Charles Martin Hall, in 1886, while he was a student at Oberlin College.

As shown in Fig. 11*b*, the electrolysis is carried out in an iron box lined with carbon. The carbon lining acts as the cathode. The anodes are a series of carbon (graphite) rods dipping into an electrolyte consisting of bauxite dissolved in molten cryolite (Na_3AlF_6).

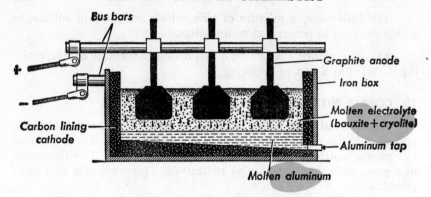

Fig. 11b. Hall Process for the Extraction of Aluminum

IONIZATION:	$2 Al_2O_3 \rightarrow 4 Al^{+3} + 6 O^{-2}$
REDUCTION AT CATHODE:	$4 Al^{+3} + 12 e \rightarrow 4 Al^0$
OXIDATION AT ANODE:	$6 O^{-2} - 12 e \rightarrow 3 O_2$
TOTAL REACTION:	$2 Al_2O_3 \rightarrow 4 Al + 3 O_2 \uparrow$

The oxygen produced reacts with the carbon anodes to produce carbon monoxide, which, at the temperature of the furnace, burns to form carbon dioxide. As a result, these anodes are gradually consumed and must be replaced from time to time. The molten metal, being denser than the electrolyte, collects at the bottom of the box and is tapped periodically. Since only aluminum ions are discharged at the cathode, the purity of the metal produced may be close to 100%.

12. PHYSICAL PROPERTIES

Aluminum is a silvery-white metal about one-third as dense as iron or copper. Its usually dull surface is due to an oxide coating. It is malleable, ductile, and an excellent conductor of heat and electricity.

13. CHEMICAL PROPERTIES

Aluminum is an active metal, as indicated by the following:

a. Aluminum reacts with hydrochloric acid or dilute sulfuric acid to form a salt and hydrogen.

$$2 Al + 6 HCl \rightarrow 2 AlCl_3 + 3 H_2 \uparrow$$

$$2 Al + 3 H_2SO_4 \rightarrow Al_2(SO_4)_3 + 3 H_2 \uparrow$$

b. Aluminum is a powerful reducing agent. When a mixture of aluminum and powdered iron oxide is properly ignited, the reaction will generate enough heat to melt the iron produced. The mixture of aluminum and iron oxide is called *thermite*.

$$\underbrace{Fe_2O_3 + 2\ Al}_{\text{thermite}} \rightarrow Al_2O_3 + 2\ Fe$$

Aluminum will similarly reduce oxides of manganese and chromium.

$$3\ MnO_2 + 4\ Al \rightarrow 2\ Al_2O_3 + 3\ Mn$$

$$Cr_2O_3 + 2\ Al \rightarrow Al_2O_3 + 2\ Cr$$

The thermite reaction was formerly used in welding processes and during World War II as an incendiary bomb.

c. Aluminum reacts with bases to form soluble aluminates and hydrogen.

$$2\ Al + 6\ NaOH \rightarrow 2\ \underset{\substack{\text{sodium} \\ \text{aluminate}}}{Na_3AlO_3} + 3\ H_2 \uparrow$$

d. Aluminum, like zinc, forms an amphoteric hydroxide, $Al(OH)_3$, which reacts with and dissolves in acids and bases.

IN ACIDS: $Al(OH)_3 + 3\ HCl \rightarrow AlCl_3 + 3\ H_2O$

IN BASES: $Al(OH)_3 + 3\ NaOH \rightarrow Na_3AlO_3 + 3\ H_2O$

14. USES

a. **Utensils.** Aluminum is used in kitchen utensils because it is a good heat conductor, does not tarnish, and is not acted upon by ordinary foods.

b. **Aluminum Alloys.** Duralumin and magnalium are widely used aluminum alloys.

c. **Transportation Vehicles.** Aluminum alloys have the tensile strength of steel with only one-third the density. Consequently, much aluminum, in the form of alloys, goes into the manufacture of airplane parts, railroad train bodies, and automobile engine pistons.

d. **Aluminum Foil.** Because of its malleability and cheapness, aluminum foil competes with wax paper as a wrapping for perishable foods. Aluminum foil can be used as an insulating material because it reflects a great deal of light and heat.

e. **Paints.** Aluminum powder is used in paints for the protection of both wooden and metallic surfaces.

f. **Reducing Agent.** Because of its chemical activity, aluminum may be used to extract such metals as manganese and chromium from their ores.

15. ALUMINUM COMPOUNDS

a. **Aluminum Hydroxide.** Aluminum hydroxide is a white, jelly-like precipitate formed by the reaction between the solutions of a soluble base and a soluble aluminum salt. An excess of certain bases, such as sodium hydroxide, should be avoided because aluminum hydroxide is amphoteric and will dissolve.

(1) Aluminum hydroxide is used as a *mordant* in the dyeing of cotton cloth. (See *c,* page 341, for the process of mordant dyeing.) A mordant acts as a binder between the dye and the cloth by absorbing the dye and forming an insoluble substance called a *lake.* Ammonium hydroxide is used as the precipitating base.

$$Al_2(SO_4)_3 + 6 \ NH_4OH \rightarrow 3 \ (NH_4)_2SO_4 + 2 \ Al(OH)_3 \downarrow$$

(2) Aluminum hydroxide is also used as a coagulant for clarifying water because the gelatinous precipitate settles down, carrying with it any germs or suspended matter. Calcium hydroxide is used as the precipitating base.

$$Al_2(SO_4)_3 + 3 \ Ca(OH)_2 \rightarrow 3 \ CaSO_4 + 2 \ Al(OH)_3 \downarrow$$

b. **Alums.** *An alum is a double salt composed of a sulfate of a trivalent metal, such as aluminum, and a sulfate of a monovalent metal, such as sodium or potassium.* An example of an alum is potassium alum, $K_2SO_4 \cdot Al_2(SO_4)_3 \cdot 24 \ H_2O$. This formula may also be written as $KAl(SO_4)_2 \cdot 12 \ H_2O$. Potassium alum is used in baking powders and as a styptic (to stop bleeding). It is also used in the purification of water.

16. COBALT NITRATE TEST FOR ALUMINUM COMPOUNDS

The compound to be tested is placed in a cavity in a charcoal block and heated with a blowpipe until it becomes white-hot. When the mass has cooled, a drop of cobalt nitrate solution is added. The formation of a blue mass (cobalt aluminate) indicates the presence of an aluminum compound.

SUMMARY OF ALUMINUM

Ores: Bauxite, cryolite
Metallurgy: Electrolysis (Hall process)
Properties: Excellent conductor of heat and electricity; active metal (powerful reducing agent); forms amphoteric compounds
Common compounds: $Al(OH)_3$, alums
Uses: Kitchen utensils, alloys
Test: Cobalt nitrate test yields *blue* cobalt aluminate

SPECIAL METALS WITH IMPORTANT USES

17. GERMANIUM

Germanium is a member of the carbon family, Group IV A. It is one of several substances classified as semiconductors. Semiconductors in the pure state act as electrical insulators, while in the impure state they behave as conductors. This property is utilized in the manufacture of a tiny vacuum tube substitute called a *transistor*. Because the conductivity of transistors can be varied and because they require the use of very small currents for operation, they are replacing ordinary vacuum tubes for many purposes, including radios and hearing aids.

18. TITANIUM

Titanium, in the form of titanium oxide (TiO_2), is becoming an increasingly important white paint pigment. This pigment is very white, has superior covering power, does not blacken in the presence of hydrogen sulfide, and is nonpoisonous.

19. URANIUM

The important ores of uranium are pitchblende, which is an oxide of uranium; and carnotite, which is a complex mixture of potassium, vanadium, and uranium oxides. (The use of uranium in the release of nuclear energy is discussed fully in Chapter 23.)

20. OTHER METALS

The table on the next page lists other important metals, their sources, methods of extraction, properties, and uses.

METAL	ORES	EXTRACTION
Gold	Native but alloyed with silver and platinum	Similar to silver
Lead	Galena (PbS)	Roasting and reduction
Magnesium	Carnallite ($MgCl_2 \cdot KCl \cdot 6\ H_2O$) Complex silicates, such as talc and asbestos	Electrolysis of fused chloride or oxide
Mercury	Cinnabar (HgS)	Roasting and distillation $HgS + O_2 \rightarrow Hg + SO_2 \uparrow$
Platinum	Native but alloyed with other metals, such as iridium and osmium	Presence of related metals makes extraction extremely complex
Silver	Native but alloyed with copper, mercury, and gold Mixed with copper, lead, and gold ores	Recovered from lead ores which contain silver (Parke's process) By-product in the electrolytic refining of copper
Tin	Cassiterite (SnO_2)	Concentration and reduction

PROPERTIES	USES
Most malleable and ductile of all metals Resistant to any single common acid Soluble in aqua regia	Manufacture of jewelry and coinage
Soft, heavy metal Low melting point Generally resistant to acids except nitric and acetic Forms amphoteric compounds	Low-melting point alloys Electrode in storage batteries Paint pigments, such as white lead (basic lead carbonate), and red lead (Pb_3O_4)
Lightest of the structurally useful metals Burns vigorously in air with a dazzling light $$2 \, Mg + O_2 \rightarrow 2 \, MgO$$ Decomposes hot water or steam $$Mg + 2 \, H_2O \rightarrow Mg(OH)_2 + H_2 \uparrow$$	Structural alloys Incendiary and photographic flash powders
Only common metallic element liquid at room temperature Exhibits almost uniform expansion and contraction with changes in temperature Forms -*ous* salts (Hg_2^{+2}) and -*ic* salts (Hg^{+2})	Manufacture of mercury alloys, called amalgams Manufacture of important compounds, such as calomel (Hg_2Cl_2), used medicinally; and corrosive sublimate ($HgCl_2$), a deadly poison used in very dilute solutions as an antiseptic
Very malleable and ductile High melting point Unaffected by air or any single acid Soluble in aqua regia	Manufacture of jewelry Catalyst
Best conductor of heat and electricity Extremely malleable and ductile Reacts readily with HNO_3 to form oxides of nitrogen Tarnishes in air because of the presence of H_2S and forms black Ag_2S Forms light-sensitive compounds ($AgBr$)	Silver coin Photographic industry Mirrors
Low melting point Resistant to the action of air and acids	Manufacture of alloys Forms rust-resistant coatings

1. *a.* The most widely used nonferrous metal is (1) copper (2) zinc (3) aluminum (4) lead.

   b. An ore that does not contain copper is (1) malachite (2) chalcocite (3) cuprite (4) hematite.

2. *a.* Most of the copper produced in this country is extracted from (1) oxide (2) carbonate (3) sulfide (4) sulfate ores.

   b. List the three important steps in the extraction of copper from its ores.

   c. Impure copper, called _____ copper, is refined by a (an) _____ process.

   d. Why does commercial copper require a very high degree of purity?

   e. Make a labeled diagram to illustrate how impure copper is refined.

   f. Write electron equations for the important reactions that occur in *e.*

   g. Make a labeled diagram to illustrate how to silver plate a graphite bar.

   h. Give a reason for the use of each material in *g.*

   i. Why is a solution of silver nitrate not used as the electrolyte in electroplating silver?

3. *a.* The most useful physical property of copper is *malleability.* [True or false? If false, correct the italicized term.]

   b. How does the position of copper in the electromotive series reveal its chemical properties?

   c. List three uses of copper and for each use indicate the property upon which the use depends.

   d. 18-carat gold contains _____ (more, less) copper than 14-carat gold.

4. *a.* Why is copper not a member of Group I A of the periodic table?

   b. The two common valence numbers for copper are (1) +1, +2 (2) +1, +3 (3) +2, +3 (4) +2, +4.

   c. A copper compound used in water purification is _____.

   d. The color of anhydrous copper sulfate is _____.

5. *a.* Zinc does not occur in the free state because _____.

   b. An example of a zinc ore is (1) sphalerite (2) cassiterite (3) magnetite (4) galena.

6. *a.* Prior to the extraction of zinc metal, carbonate and sulfide ores of zinc are converted into (1) oxides (2) sulfates (3) sulfites (4) carbides.

   b. Zinc is extracted from its oxide ore by (1) hydrolysis (2) electrolysis (3) amalgamation (4) reduction.

   c. Zinc may be collected by distillation because it has a
   (1) low melting point and high boiling point
   (2) low melting point and low boiling point
   (3) high melting point and high boiling point
   (4) high melting point and low boiling point

   d. Describe an electrolytic process for extracting zinc.

   e. What special property does electrolytic zinc possess and how is this property utilized?

7. *a.* At room temperature, zinc is _____ (malleable, brittle).

   b. Write a balanced equation for each of the following reactions:
   (1) Zn + trivalent nonmetal $X \rightarrow$
   (2) Zn + acid $HX \rightarrow$
   (3) Zn + $NaOH \rightarrow$
   (4) $ZnCl_2$ + excess $NaOH \rightarrow$

   c. By means of ionization equations, show how zinc hydroxide can behave as an amphoteric base.

8. *a.* Zinc is not present in the alloy (1) brass (2) bronze (3) solder (4) German silver.

   b. Explain how galvanizing iron with zinc prevents the iron from rusting.

   *c. Explain the function of zinc in the dry cell.

   d. List two uses of zinc and for each use indicate the property which makes the use possible.

*9. By means of a series of equations, show how green cobalt zincate is formed in the cobalt nitrate test.

10. *a.* Aluminum is the _____ (least, most) abundant metal found in the earth's crust.

   b. Aluminum is presently extracted from its (1) silicate (2) oxide (3) fluoride (4) carbonate ore.

11. *a.* Because of its activity, aluminum must be extracted from its ore by _____.

   b. Make a labeled diagram to illustrate the extraction of aluminum from its ore.

   c. Give a reason for the use of each material used in *b*.

   d. Write a balanced equation for the reaction in *b*.

   e. Why is the purity of aluminum produced in the Hall process close to 100%?

12. *a.* Aluminum is a silvery-white metal, *denser* than water. [True or false? If false, correct the italicized term.]

   b. The coating on an aluminum surface is probably aluminum (1) sulfide (2) sulfate (3) carbonate (4) oxide.

   c. Write a balanced equation for each of the following reactions:
   (1) Al + $HCl \rightarrow$
   (2) Al + dilute $H_2SO_4 \rightarrow$
   *(3) Al + conc. $H_2SO_4 \rightarrow$
   *(4) Al + dilute $HNO_3 \rightarrow$

   d. Why is aluminum a powerful reducing agent?

   e. Write a balanced equation for each of the following reactions:
   (1) Fe_2O_3 + $Al \rightarrow$
   (2) Cr_2O_3 + $Al \rightarrow$
   (3) MnO_2 + $Al \rightarrow$
   (4) Al + $NaOH \rightarrow$

   f. By means of ionization equations, show how aluminum hydroxide can behave as an amphoteric base.

13. *a.* List three properties which make aluminum useful in kitchen utensils.

   b. An important alloy composed of aluminum, copper, and magnesium is (1) bronze (2) duralumin (3) magnalium (4) monel.

    c. Because of its low density, aluminum is used in the manufacture of _____.

    d. State the property of aluminum which makes it useful in the manufacture of:
      (1) foil
      (2) paints
      (3) screening

14.**a.* Why does aluminum hydroxide dissolve in excess sodium hydroxide but not in excess ammonium hydroxide?

    b. Describe how aluminum hydroxide is used as a mordant.

    c. Aluminum hydroxide is a good coagulant because it is (1) a base (2) amphoteric (3) gelatinous (4) unstable.

    d. Alums are (1) acid (2) basic (3) double (4) acid or basic   salts.

    e. The formula for chrome alum is _____.

    f. List two uses of potassium alum and for each use indicate the property which makes the use possible.

    g. The composition of the blue mass produced in the cobalt nitrate test for an aluminum compound is _____.

15. *a.* An element used as a semiconductor in transistors is _____.

    b. Transistors require _____ (small, large) currents for operation.

    c. List four properties of titanium oxide which account for its increasing use as a white paint pigment.

    d. An important ore of uranium is (1) carnallite (2) taconite (3) chalcocite (4) pitchblende.

16. *a.* The most malleable and ductile of all metals is (1) tungsten (2) gold (3) aluminum (4) silver.

    b. A metal which forms amphoteric compounds and is a constituent of low-melting point alloys is (1) aluminum (2) cadmium (3) lead (4) zinc.

    c. A structurally useful metal prepared by electrolysis is (1) iron (2) manganese (3) magnesium (4) sodium.

    d. The roasting of cinnabar yields (1) mercury (2) mercuric oxide (3) sulfur (4) mercurous oxide.

    e. A metal which occurs in nature associated with iridium and osmium is _____.

    f. Parke's process is used to recover (1) copper (2) lead (3) silver (4) zinc.

    g. A light-sensitive compound used in photography is (1) magnesium oxide (2) calcium oxide (3) silver sulfide (4) silver bromide.

    h. The reduction of cassiterite yields (1) tin (2) mercury (3) iron (4) lead.

17. Calculate the volume of oxygen required to liberate 100 liters of sulfur dioxide during the roasting of sphalerite.

18. Calculate the weight of aluminum that can be obtained during the electrolysis of one ton of aluminum oxide.

21   ORGANIC CHEMISTRY

1. THE SCOPE OF ORGANIC CHEMISTRY

It was formerly believed that substances produced by plants and animals could not be prepared in the laboratory. Chemists explained this by the *vital force doctrine,* a theory which stated that some mysterious life force was present in substances produced by living things. The branch of chemistry that dealt with the products of living things was called organic chemistry.

The vital force doctrine was overthrown in 1828 by the experiments of the German scientist Friedrich Wöhler. Wöhler synthesized the organic compound urea, $CO(NH_2)_2$, an animal waste product, from the inorganic compound ammonium cyanate (NH_4OCN). This was the first time that a product was made in the laboratory that previously had been made only by living things. As a result of this experiment, the scope of organic chemistry was no longer restricted to the products of living things. Instead:

Organic chemistry became known as the branch of chemistry dealing with the study of all carbon compounds, both those found in nature and those produced artificially.

Since Wöhler's historic experiment, thousands of organic compounds have been synthesized in the laboratory from substances not produced by living things. Some of these substances made by man are vitamins, drugs, dyes, explosives, textiles, and rubber. At present, there are over a million organic compounds, to which there is the prospect of adding 10,000 new compounds each year. When compared with the approximately 25,000 noncarbon (inorganic) compounds, the number of organic compounds takes on added significance.

2. SOURCES OF ORGANIC COMPOUNDS

In addition to plants and animals, the most important sources of organic compounds in nature are petroleum, bituminous (soft) coal, and natural gas. Some of the processes employed to obtain useful organic compounds from these natural sources include:

a. fractional distillation
b. destructive distillation
c. fermentation
d. polymerization
e. cracking
f. hydrogenation

These processes will be described later in this chapter.

3. REASONS FOR THE LARGE NUMBER OF ORGANIC COMPOUNDS

We learned in Chapter 8 that in a given period the activity of elements generally decreases as we go toward the center of the table. The central position of carbon suggests that its activity would be extremely limited. We must therefore consider other properties of the carbon atom to account for the existence of so many compounds of carbon.

a. Carbon Atoms May Form Covalent Bonds

(1) *With Atoms Other Than Carbon.* Carbon, atomic number 6, has four electrons in its outer ring. Theoretically, a carbon atom should be able to achieve ring completeness by the loss or gain of four electrons. Carbon compounds, however, do not generally exhibit the properties of electrovalent substances because the compounds usually have *not* been formed by the gain or loss of electrons. Instead, these compounds are nonionic, indicating that they have been formed by the sharing of electrons and thus contain covalent bonds.

In the following electronic formula for the hydrocarbon methane (CH_4), note how carbon completes its outer ring by sharing its four valence electrons with four hydrogen atoms.

● = Carbon electron
○ = Hydrogen electron

Thus:

> Carbon atoms may form covalent linkages with hydrogen, nitrogen, sulfur, oxygen, and other atoms, resulting in the formation of large numbers of compounds.

(2) *With Other Carbon Atoms.* In the electronic formula for ethane (C_2H_6), appearing at the right, note how two carbon atoms combine with each other and with hydrogen. To distinguish the carbon atoms, they are numbered differently. The valence electrons associated with each atom are labeled x, z, and o.

X = Carbon 1 electron
Z = Carbon 2 electron
O = Hydrogen electron

Carbon 1 shares three pairs of electrons with three hydrogen atoms and one pair of electrons with carbon 2. Carbon 2, in turn, shares three pairs of electrons with three more hydrogen atoms. Each carbon atom now has a complete outer ring.

Other carbon compounds formed in the same way may be long chains of carbon atoms. Some may consist of groups of carbon atoms with side chains, called *branches,* and some compounds may consist of carbon atoms linked together as rings.

> Carbon may form compounds in which there are large numbers of carbon-to-carbon linkages through pairs of shared electrons.

b. Organic Compounds Having the Same Composition May Have Different Arrangements of the Atoms

> By rearranging the atoms of an organic compound, it is possible to form a new compound having the same molecular formula but a different structure.

Two or more compounds having the same molecular formula but with a different arrangement of the atoms within their molecules are called isomers. This property, known as isomerism, can best be understood by representing the arrangement of the atoms within a molecule by means of a *graphic formula.* In this type of formula, the pairs of shared electrons are indicated by dashes.

Using graphic formulas, we can represent butane (C_4H_{10}) as:

(1)

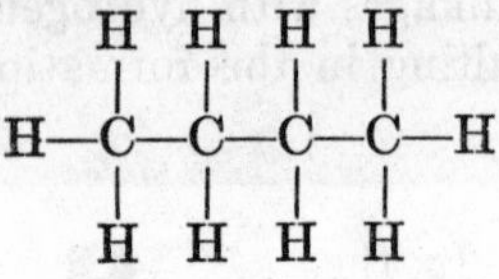

$$H-\overset{\overset{H}{|}}{\underset{\underset{H}{|}}{C}}-\overset{\overset{H}{|}}{\underset{\underset{H}{|}}{C}}-\overset{\overset{H}{|}}{\underset{\underset{H}{|}}{C}}-\overset{\overset{H}{|}}{\underset{\underset{H}{|}}{C}}-H$$

or

(2)

$$H-\overset{\overset{H}{|}}{\underset{\underset{H}{|}}{C}}-\overset{\overset{H}{|}}{\underset{\underset{H-C-H}{|}}{C}}-\overset{\overset{H}{|}}{\underset{\underset{H}{|}}{C}}-H$$

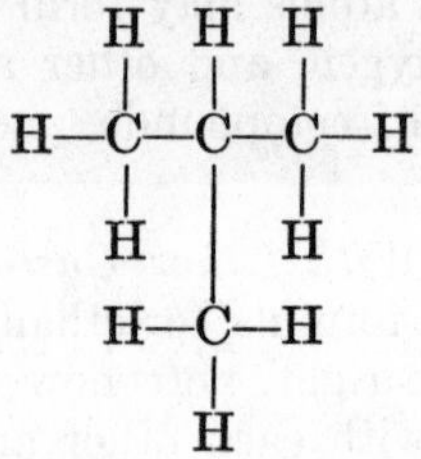

Organic compounds in which the carbon atoms are arranged in a straight chain, such as compound (1), are called *normal*. Compound (1) is therefore known as normal butane. Compounds in which the carbon atoms are arranged in a branched chain, such as compound (2), are called *iso-*. Compound (2) is therefore known as isobutane.

From the graphic diagram, we can see that both normal butane and isobutane have the same molecular formula, C_4H_{10}. However, since the arrangement of the carbon and hydrogen atoms differs, normal butane and isobutane are isomers. This difference also becomes evident when the formula of normal butane is written as $CH_3CH_2CH_2CH_3$, while the formula of isobutane is written as $CH_3CHCH_3CH_3$.

As the number of carbon atoms in compounds increases, the number of different possible structures also increases, thus resulting in a larger number of isomers. For example, the compound C_8H_{18} has 18 isomers, while $C_{10}H_{22}$ has 75 isomers.

4. STRUCTURAL FORMULAS

The existence of isomers limits the usefulness of the molecular formula in describing a carbon compound. A special graphic method of indicating an organic compound, known as a *structural formula*, is therefore used.

A **structural formula** indicates not only the kind and number of atoms in a molecule, but also the arrangement of the atoms.

On page 73, we used graphic formulas in which shared electrons were represented by dots. In this chapter, the pairs of shared electrons are represented by dashes, each dash indicating a single valence bond. Since the use of dashes is considerably simpler, we shall, wherever possible, use this technique to represent structural formulas. The structural formulas for two common organic compounds are:

$$
\begin{array}{ccc}
& H & \\
& | & \\
H-&C&-H \\
& | & \\
& H &
\end{array}
\qquad
\begin{array}{ccccc}
& H & & H & \\
& | & & | & \\
H-&C&-&C&-H \\
& | & & | & \\
& H & & H &
\end{array}
$$

Methane   Ethane

5. SOME DIFFERENCES BETWEEN ORGANIC AND INORGANIC COMPOUNDS

The fundamental laws and principles which apply to inorganic chemistry also apply to organic chemistry. There are, however, some differences:

a. There are marked differences between the solubilities of inorganic and organic compounds. Many inorganic compounds are soluble in water, while organic compounds are generally insoluble in water. Organic compounds are usually soluble in organic solvents such as ether, alcohol, chloroform, benzene, and carbon tetrachloride.

b. Organic compounds decompose at relatively lower temperatures than do inorganic compounds. Organic compounds are generally less stable than inorganic compounds.

c. Many organic compounds can burn, whereas only a small number of inorganic compounds are combustible.

d. Organic compounds may have isomers. The property of isomerism is rare in inorganic compounds.

e. Reactions involving organic compounds usually proceed more slowly than do reactions between inorganic compounds. The presence of ions in many inorganic reactions tends to accelerate the reactions.

6. CHARACTERISTICS OF ORGANIC COMPOUNDS

a. **Molecular Structure.** Atoms in molecules of organic compounds are generally linked by covalent bonds. Each covalent bond is the equivalent of a single pair of shared electrons. Since such molecules do not contain charged particles (ions), organic compounds are generally nonionic.

b. **Saturation.** When adjacent carbon atoms in a molecule of an organic compound are joined by only a single pair of shared electrons, the compound is said to be *saturated*. If any two adjacent carbon atoms are linked by two or more pairs of shared electrons, the compound is *unsaturated*.

Ethane (C_2H_6) is a saturated compound, while ethylene (C_2H_4) and acetylene (C_2H_2) are unsaturated compounds. To represent the structural formulas of these compounds, we use a single valence bond (—) to stand for a pair of shared electrons, a double valence bond (=) to stand for two pairs of shared electrons, and a triple valence bond (≡) to represent three pairs of shared electrons. Thus,

$$
\begin{array}{ccc}
\begin{array}{c}
\text{H} \quad \text{H} \\
| \quad | \\
\text{H—C—C—H} \\
| \quad | \\
\text{H} \quad \text{H}
\end{array}
&
\begin{array}{c}
\text{H} \quad \text{H} \\
| \quad | \\
\text{H—C=C—H}
\end{array}
&
\text{H—C≡C—H}
\end{array}
$$

(Saturated)	**(Unsaturated)**	**(Unsaturated)**
Ethane, C_2H_6	**Ethylene, C_2H_4**	**Acetylene, C_2H_2**

Unsaturated compounds can also be formed when atoms such as nitrogen or sulfur are linked to carbon atoms by more than one pair of shared electrons.

TYPE	STRUCTURE
Saturated compound	Single pair of shared electrons between two atoms
Unsaturated compound	More than one pair of shared electrons between two atoms

***c.* Chemical Activity.** Reactions between organic compounds are generally slow because of their nonionic nature.

Unsaturated compounds are more active than saturated compounds, because unsaturated compounds are more unstable.

The relative instability of unsaturated compounds may be explained by considering a valence bond to be a strain resulting from holding carbon atoms together. The greater the number of valence bonds between carbon atoms, the greater the strain and, therefore, the greater the tendency of the compound to overcome the strain. Thus, ethylene is more active than ethane.

7. CLASSIFYING ORGANIC COMPOUNDS

To simplify the study of organic chemistry, organic compounds are grouped in two main divisions: *aliphatic compounds* and *aromatic com-*

pounds. Aliphatic compounds are carbon compounds in which the carbon atoms are arranged in straight or branched chains. Aromatic compounds, also known as ring or cyclic compounds, have their carbon atoms arranged in one or more rings.

Organic compounds may be further subdivided into classes, or families, based on their chemical and physical properties.

a. hydrocarbons
b. alcohols
c. aldehydes, ketones, and ethers
d. organic acids

e. esters
f. soaps
g. carbohydrates

HYDROCARBONS, R—H

8. WHAT ARE HYDROCARBONS?

Hydrocarbons are compounds containing only hydrogen and carbon, and may be represented by the family formula R—H. In this formula, *R* is an organic radical, examples of which appear in **29**, page 324.

It will be shown later in this chapter that many organic compounds are actually or theoretically derived from hydrocarbons. The organic radical *R* will therefore appear in other family formulas.

There are many hydrocarbons which have similar chemical properties. These related compounds are grouped together as families, or series. In each series of compounds, there is a fixed relationship between the number of carbon and hydrogen atoms. Such a related series is called an *homologous series.*

9. METHANE (PARAFFIN) SERIES

The methane series is the simplest series of saturated, aliphatic hydrocarbons. The members of the methane series are characterized by their chemical inactivity. The first eight members are:

CH_4	methane	C_5H_{12}	pentane
C_2H_6	ethane	C_6H_{14}	hexane
C_3H_8	propane	C_7H_{16}	heptane
C_4H_{10}	butane	C_8H_{18}	octane

From these formulas, we see that the number of hydrogen atoms in each compound is two more than double the number of carbon atoms.

If we let n represent the number of carbon atoms, then the general formula for any member compound of the methane series becomes C_nH_{2n+2}. A general formula can always be used to represent an homologous series.

The structural formulas of the first five members of the methane series are:

$$
\begin{array}{ccc}
\text{H} & \text{H H} & \text{H H H} \\
| & |\ \ | & |\ \ |\ \ | \\
\text{H--C--H} & \text{H--C--C--H} & \text{H--C--C--C--H} \\
| & |\ \ | & |\ \ |\ \ | \\
\text{H} & \text{H H} & \text{H H H}
\end{array}
$$

Methane, CH_4 Ethane, C_2H_6 Propane, C_3H_8

$$
\begin{array}{cc}
\text{H H H H} & \text{H H H H H} \\
|\ \ |\ \ |\ \ | & |\ \ |\ \ |\ \ |\ \ | \\
\text{H--C--C--C--C--H} & \text{H--C--C--C--C--C--H} \\
|\ \ |\ \ |\ \ | & |\ \ |\ \ |\ \ |\ \ | \\
\text{H H H H} & \text{H H H H H}
\end{array}
$$

Butane, C_4H_{10} Pentane, C_5H_{12}

Of the eight members of the series listed, the first four are normally gases, while the remaining four are liquids. As the number of carbon and hydrogen atoms increases and the hydrocarbons become heavier, they become solids.

Let us now consider in detail some paraffin hydrocarbons.

a. **Methane** (CH_4). Methane is commonly called marsh gas because it is often found in swamps and marshes, where it is formed as a result of plant decay. In coal mines, it forms explosive mixtures with air and is referred to as fire damp. Natural gas is composed mainly of methane and is widely used as an industrial and commercial fuel. Coal gas formed by the destructive distillation of soft coal also contains methane.

The complete combustion of methane, or of any other hydrocarbon, forms water and carbon dioxide.

$$CH_4 + 2\,O_2 \rightarrow 2\,H_2O + CO_2 \uparrow$$

The incomplete combustion of a hydrocarbon also results in the formation of water, and either carbon monoxide or carbon, depending on the extent to which the supply of air or oxygen is limited.

$$2\,CH_4 + 3\,O_2 \rightarrow 4\,H_2O + 2\,CO \uparrow$$

$$CH_4 + O_2 \rightarrow 2\,H_2O + C$$

Saturated hydrocarbons, like methane, may also react with elements where atoms of the element are substituted for hydrogen in the hydrocarbon. Such reactions, called *substitution*, will be considered later.

b. **Petroleum and Gasoline.** Petroleum, a mixture of long-chain hydrocarbons, is an important source of many hydrocarbons. By the process of fractional distillation, petroleum is separated into a number of important substances. Arranged in the order of their increasing boiling point or decreasing volatility, they are: gasoline, benzine, kerosene, fuel oil, lubricating oil, vaseline, paraffin.

(1) *Manufacturing Processes.* Practically all these petroleum derivatives are mixtures of hydrocarbons of the methane series. The yield of gasoline, the most valuable of these products, has been increased by a process called *cracking.* By means of heat and increased pressure, the heavy hydrocarbons of petroleum are broken down into lighter and more volatile hydrocarbons, such as pentane, hexane, heptane, and octane. Heptane and octane are normally present in gasoline.

Gasoline has also been manufactured by the hydrogenation of powdered coal.

Still another method of producing gasoline is to combine molecules of simpler hydrocarbons to produce the more complex hydrocarbons found in gasoline. The process of combining small, light molecules (monomers) to form large, heavy molecules (polymers) is called *polymerization.*

(2) *Knocking.* Multiple explosions in the cylinders of a gasoline engine—rather than a single, uniform, controlled explosion—result in what is commonly called *knocking.* The rapid burning of very volatile gasoline may produce knocking. The tendency of gasoline to knock is expressed by the *octane rating* of the gasoline. To determine the octane rating of a given grade of gasoline, it is necessary to burn the gasoline in a test engine and compare the extent of knocking with standard mixtures of iso-octane and heptane. A sample that is 100% iso-octane and 0% heptane is assigned an arbitrary octane rating of 100. Let us suppose that a prepared mixture of 90% iso-octane and 10% heptane produces a certain knock. If the tested sample of gasoline produces the same knock, the gasoline has an octane rating of 90.

Standard auto gasolines have an octane rating of about 70-80. Aviation gasoline gives 20% better performance than iso-octane, and therefore has an octane rating of 120. Gasolines of high octane number have a lesser tendency to knock and consequently have greater power. Antiknock compounds, such as tetraethyl lead, $Pb(C_2H_5)_4$, are added to gasoline to increase the octane rating. The antiknock compounds apparently behave as negative catalysts during the combustion of the gasoline.

(3) *Care in Handling Gasoline. Gasoline is extremely volatile and forms explosive mixtures with air.* In addition, gasoline has a low kindling temperature. Large quantities are therefore stored in underground tanks. Gasoline should not be handled near an open flame.

When used in the automobile, gasoline undergoes incomplete combustion, producing poisonous carbon monoxide. Engines, therefore, should not be kept running in a closed garage.

10. ETHYLENE SERIES

Another homologous series of hydrocarbons is the ethylene series. All members of the ethylene series are unsaturated hydrocarbons, that is, two adjacent carbon atoms share two pairs of electrons. This sharing is indicated by a double bond. Each member of the ethylene series has two hydrogen atoms less than its corresponding member of the methane series. The general formula for compounds of the ethylene series is therefore C_nH_{2n}, where n stands for the number of carbon atoms in the molecule.

Ethylene (C_2H_4). The simplest member of this series is ethylene, whose structural formula is:

$$\begin{array}{ccc} H & & H \\ | & & | \\ H-C & = & C-H \end{array}$$

Ethylene is a colorless gas found in natural gas and formed in the refining of petroleum. As a typical unsaturated hydrocarbon, ethylene reacts by breaking the double bond, allowing one additional atom to join each carbon atom. This type of reaction, called *addition*, will be considered later.

Ethylene is used as an anesthetic, in the artificial ripening of fruits, and in the manufacture of the permanent antifreeze, ethylene glycol, $C_2H_4(OH)_2$.

Some additional members of the ethylene series are propylene (C_3H_6) and butylene (C_4H_8).

11. ACETYLENE SERIES

All members of this series of highly unsaturated hydrocarbons are characterized by a triple bond between adjacent carbon atoms. The general formula for members of the acetylene series is C_nH_{2n-2}.

Acetylene (C_2H_2). The simplest member of this series, acetylene, has the following structural formula:

$$H—C\equiv C—H$$

The presence of the triple bond makes acetylene more unsaturated and, under certain conditions, more active than ethylene. Acetylene readily enters into addition reactions.

Acetylene may be prepared by the action of water on calcium carbide. See $4d(2)$, page 219.

Since acetylene burns readily in air or oxygen, producing a great deal of heat and a brilliant white light, it is used both as a fuel and as an illuminant. Acetylene lamps are still used for illumination, while the oxyacetylene blowtorch is used in the welding and cutting of metals. The complete combustion of acetylene takes place as follows:

$$2\ C_2H_2 + 5\ O_2 \rightarrow 2\ H_2O + 4\ CO_2 \uparrow$$

Acetylene is also used in the production of many organic compounds and as a starting material for making certain types of synthetic rubber.

12. BENZENE SERIES

Each of the members of this series is characterized by a closed or ring structure (aromatic), unlike the open or chain structure (aliphatic) of the hydrocarbons previously studied. All members of this series are also unsaturated hydrocarbons having the general formula C_nH_{2n-6}.

Benzene (C_6H_6). The structural formula for the simplest member of this series, benzene, reveals the ring structure characteristic of the series.

The structural formula of benzene may be simplified by writing it as a hexagon.

Benzene, sometimes called benzol, is a coal-tar derivative. Coal tar is one of the products obtained when soft coal is heated in the absence of air. This process of destructive distillation also yields coke, coal gas, ammonia, and hydrogen sulfide. When coal tar, which is a mixture, is fractionally distilled, each component or fraction distills off at its own boiling point, thus separating the mixture into simpler parts. Some of the products of the fractional distillation of coal tar are benzene, phenol, and toluene.

Benzene, which is a definite chemical compound (C_6H_6), should be distinguished from *benzine,* which is a mixture of volatile hydrocarbons derived from the fractional distillation of *petroleum.* Benzene is a colorless liquid which burns with a smoky flame. It is used as an organic solvent and as a raw material in the synthesis of many organic compounds.

Another member of the benzene series is toluene (C_7H_8). Toluene is also obtained from the fractional distillation of coal tar. It is an important organic solvent and is used in the manufacture of trinitro-toluene (TNT).

13. NAPHTHALENE SERIES

The most common member of this complex ring hydrocarbon series is naphthalene ($C_{10}H_8$), also derived from the fractional distillation of coal tar. It should not be confused with *naphtha,* which, like benzine, is a mixture of hydrocarbons.

Naphthalene in the form of flakes or moth balls was formerly used to protect woolens against destruction by moths. It is being replaced for this purpose by another organic compound, paradichlorobenzene, commonly called "para" ($C_6H_4Cl_2$). Naphthalene is an important raw material in the manufacture of dyes.

HYDROCARBONS, R—H

SATURATED SERIES	UNSATURATED SERIES
Paraffin, C_nH_{2n+2} 1. Methane, CH_4 2. Ethane, C_2H_6	Ethylene, C_nH_{2n} 1. Ethylene, C_2H_4 2. Propylene, C_3H_6 Acetylene, C_nH_{2n-2} 1. Acetylene, C_2H_2 2. Propyne, C_3H_4 Benzene, C_nH_{2n-6} 1. Benzene, C_6H_6 2. Toluene, C_7H_8

14. SUBSTITUTION AND ADDITION REACTIONS

We have already learned that organic compounds react less readily than inorganic compounds. Under certain conditions, however, organic compounds may react readily. Two common types of reaction are called *substitution* and *addition*.

***a*. Substitution Reactions of Hydrocarbons.** Saturated hydrocarbons react generally by substitution. In a substitution reaction, atoms of an element or a group of elements are substituted for hydrogen atoms in the hydrocarbon. An example of such a reaction is the substitution of a chlorine atom for a hydrogen atom in the hydrocarbon ethane.

$$C_2H_6 \quad + Cl_2 \rightarrow \quad C_2H_5Cl \quad + HCl$$

ethane — ethyl chloride

$$\begin{array}{ccc} \text{H} & \text{H} & \\ | & | & \\ \text{H--C--C--H} + Cl_2 \rightarrow & \text{H--C--C--Cl} + HCl \\ | & | & \\ \text{H} & \text{H} & \end{array}$$

***b*. Addition Reactions of Hydrocarbons.** Unsaturated hydrocarbons react generally by addition. In an addition reaction, atoms are added to molecules of the unsaturated hydrocarbon. The double or triple bond opens to permit the additional atoms to join the chain. As a result of an addition reaction, unsaturated compounds become saturated. Because of the greater instability of unsaturated compounds, addition reactions take place more readily than do substitution reactions.

The manufacture of ethylene dibromide, used in the gasoline industry, illustrates an addition reaction.

$$\begin{array}{cc} \text{H H} & \text{H H} \\ | \ \ | & | \ \ | \\ \text{H--C=C--H} + Br_2 \rightarrow & \text{H--C--C--H} \\ & | \ \ | \\ & \text{Br Br} \end{array}$$

Ethylene   Ethylene dibromide
(Unsaturated)   (Saturated)

Where the hydrocarbon is more highly unsaturated, as in the case of acetylene, the addition reaction involves two steps.

$$H-C\equiv C-H + Br_2 \rightarrow H-\overset{\overset{\displaystyle Br}{|}}{C}=\overset{\overset{\displaystyle Br}{|}}{C}-H$$

Acetylene dibromide

$$H-\overset{\overset{\displaystyle Br}{|}}{C}=\overset{\overset{\displaystyle Br}{|}}{C}-H + Br_2 \rightarrow H-\overset{\overset{\displaystyle Br}{|}}{\underset{\underset{\displaystyle Br}{|}}{C}}-\overset{\overset{\displaystyle Br}{|}}{\underset{\underset{\displaystyle Br}{|}}{C}}-H$$

Tetrabromoethane

SUBSTITUTION:

$$H-\overset{\overset{\displaystyle H}{|}}{\underset{\underset{\displaystyle H}{|}}{C}}-H + X_2 \rightarrow H-\overset{\overset{\displaystyle H}{|}}{\underset{\underset{\displaystyle H}{|}}{C}}-X + HX$$

ADDITION:

$$H-\overset{\overset{\displaystyle H}{|}}{C}=\overset{\overset{\displaystyle H}{|}}{C}-H + X_2 \rightarrow H-\overset{\overset{\displaystyle H}{|}}{C}-\overset{\overset{\displaystyle H}{|}}{\underset{\underset{\displaystyle X}{|}}{C}}-H$$

15. HALOGEN SUBSTITUTION PRODUCTS

As we have seen, substitution products are obtained by replacing one or more of the hydrogen atoms in organic compounds with one or more different atoms or groups of atoms. If the hydrogen atoms are replaced by halogen atoms, halogen substitution products are formed.

Analysis of the structural formulas of the halogen substitution products reveals that these products are derived from the corresponding hydrocarbons.

a. **Methyl chloride** (CH_3Cl) is formed by substituting one atom of chlorine for one atom of hydrogen in the methane molecule. It is, therefore, also called monochloromethane.

$$H-\overset{\overset{\displaystyle H}{|}}{\underset{\underset{\displaystyle H}{|}}{C}}-H \qquad\qquad H-\overset{\overset{\displaystyle H}{|}}{\underset{\underset{\displaystyle H}{|}}{C}}-Cl$$

Methane   **Methyl chloride**

Methyl chloride is an extremely volatile liquid, producing intense cold upon the surface from which it evaporates. It is therefore used as a local anesthetic.

b. **Chloroform** ($CHCl_3$), sometimes called trichloromethane, is produced by substituting three atoms of chlorine for three atoms of hydrogen in the methane molecule.

<pre>
      H   H
      | |
  H—C—H   Cl—C—Cl
      | |
      H   Cl
  Methane   Chloroform
</pre>

Chloroform is a heavy, colorless liquid having a pleasant odor and a sweet taste. Chloroform is commonly used as a solvent and as a general anesthetic.

c. **Iodoform** (CHI_3) contains three atoms of iodine which have replaced three atoms of hydrogen in the methane molecule. Iodoform, therefore, is similar in structure to chloroform.

<pre>
      H   H
      | |
  Cl—C—Cl   I—C—I
      | |
      Cl   I
  Chloroform   Iodoform
</pre>

Iodoform, a yellow solid with a characteristic odor, is commonly used as an antiseptic.

d. **Carbon tetrachloride** (CCl_4) is formed by substituting four chlorine atoms for four hydrogen atoms in the methane molecule.

<pre>
      Cl
      |
  Cl—C—Cl
      |
      Cl
</pre>

Commonly marketed as Carbona, carbon tetrachloride is a volatile, noncombustible liquid which does not conduct an electric current. Because of these properties, it is used in the Pyrene type of fire extinguisher. The heavy vapor of carbon tetrachloride smothers the fire.

Carbon tetrachloride is also used as a solvent for removing certain stains. Because it is nonflammable, it is much safer than such solvents as kerosene, benzene, or gasoline. However, *the vapors of carbon tetra-*

chloride are poisonous, and care should be taken not to inhale excessive amounts. When used in the home, proper ventilation should be provided.

e. Freon, or dichlorodifluoromethane, resembles carbon tetrachloride structurally. Two fluorine atoms, however, have been substituted for two of the four chlorine atoms.

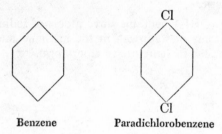

Carbon tetrachloride   Freon

Freon has replaced sulfur dioxide and ammonia as refrigerants.

f. Paradichlorobenzene ($C_6H_4Cl_2$) is a halogen substitution product of benzene used as a mothproofing agent.

Benzene   Paradichlorobenzene

ALCOHOLS, R—OH

16. WHAT ARE ALCOHOLS?

Alcohols represent another large group of organic compounds in which the alcohol group, called the hydroxyl (OH) group or radical, has been substituted for one or more hydrogen atoms in a hydrocarbon. Alcohols may thus be considered as being derived from corresponding hydrocarbons.

HYDROCARBON	ALCOHOL
CH_4	CH_3OH
C_2H_6	C_2H_5OH
C_3H_8	C_3H_7OH

Like hydrocarbons, the complete combustion of alcohols yields carbon dioxide and water. Despite their structural resemblance to bases, alcohols are typical organic compounds and hence do not ionize in water to form hydroxyl ions.

17. METHYL ALCOHOL

Methyl alcohol (CH_3OH), also known as wood alcohol or methanol, is obtained from the fractional distillation of wood tar (pyroligneous acid). Wood tar is the liquid product obtained from the destructive distillation of wood. Methyl alcohol is also made synthetically from the reaction between carbon monoxide and hydrogen. Methyl alcohol may be considered a hydroxyl substitution product of methane.

$$
\begin{array}{cc}
\text{H} & \text{H} \\
| & | \\
\text{H—C—H} & \text{H—C—OH} \\
| & | \\
\text{H} & \text{H} \\
\text{Methane} & \text{Methyl alcohol}
\end{array}
$$

Methyl alcohol is extremely poisonous. It is used as a solvent in making paints and lacquers, as an antifreeze in automobiles, and as a fuel in small alcohol stoves. It is sometimes added to grain alcohol to make the latter unfit for drinking. This mixture is called *denatured alcohol* and is used for industrial purposes.

18. ETHYL ALCOHOL

Ethyl alcohol (C_2H_5OH), called grain alcohol or ethanol, is a hydroxyl substitution product of ethane.

$$
\begin{array}{cc}
\text{H H} & \text{H H} \\
| | & | | \\
\text{H—C—C—H} & \text{H—C—C—OH} \\
| | & | | \\
\text{H H} & \text{H H} \\
\text{Ethane} & \text{Ethyl alcohol}
\end{array}
$$

The OH group may be attached to any carbon atom in any position without changing the properties of the alcohol. This means that ethyl alcohol can have no isomers.

a. **Preparation from Glucose or Fructose.** Ethyl alcohol is obtained by the alcoholic fermentation of glucose (grape sugar) or fructose (fruit sugar) by yeast. *Fermentation is a chemical action brought about by enzymes secreted by living organisms.* Yeast contains several enzymes, one of which, zymase, brings about the fermentation.

$$
\underset{\text{glucose}}{C_6H_{12}O_6} \xrightarrow{\text{zymase}} \underset{\text{alcohol}}{2\ C_2H_5OH} + 2\ CO_2 \uparrow
$$

Continued fermentation may change the alcohol to acetic acid.

b. Preparation from Cane or Beet Sugar. Cane or beet sugar is a complex sugar and is not directly fermentable. Yeast, however, contains an additional enzyme, invertase, which can convert cane sugar into a mixture of glucose and fructose called invert sugar. This process is known as *inversion*.

$$C_{12}H_{22}O_{11} + H_2O \xrightarrow[\text{invertase}]{} \underbrace{\underset{\text{glucose}}{C_6H_{12}O_6} + \underset{\text{fructose}}{C_6H_{12}O_6}}_{\text{invert sugar}}$$

The zymase then brings about the alcoholic fermentation of the components of the invert sugar. The inversion of cane sugar can also be brought about by boiling the sugar with water in the presence of a little hydrochloric acid as a catalytic agent.

As shown in Fig. 18b, ethyl alcohol can be prepared in the laboratory by adding yeast to a saturated molasses (or sugar) solution and keeping the mixture in a warm place for several days. This permits alcoholic fermentation to take place. The formation of carbon dioxide can be shown by allowing the evolved gas to bubble through limewater.

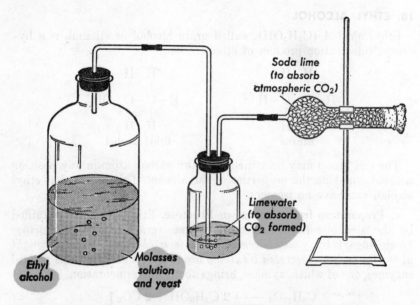

Soda lime
(to absorb
atmospheric CO₂)

Limewater
(to absorb
CO₂ formed)

Ethyl
alcohol

Molasses
solution
and yeast

Fig. 18b. Laboratory Preparation of Ethyl Alcohol

The alcohol is separated from the fermented mixture by fractional distillation. To obtain pure (absolute) alcohol, this distillate may be mixed with quicklime and redistilled.

c. Preparation from Starch. Starch can be converted into glucose by boiling with water containing a little hydrochloric acid as a catalyst.

$$C_6H_{10}O_5 + H_2O \xrightarrow[\text{HCl}]{} C_6H_{12}O_6$$
$$\text{starch} \qquad\qquad\qquad \text{glucose}$$

The glucose is then converted into ethyl alcohol by fermenting with yeast.

d. Uses of Ethyl Alcohol. Ethyl alcohol is used in alcoholic beverages. In small quantities, it acts as a stimulant and fuel in the body; but in large quantities, it is harmful.

Ethyl alcohol used industrially is first denatured so that it may be sold without government tax. Denatured alcohol is rendered unfit for drinking by adding small quantities of poisonous and bad tasting substances, such as methyl alcohol. The specific denaturant, however, depends upon the intended use of the alcohol. Thus, ethyl alcohol is denatured with isopropyl alcohol in the preparation of rubbing alcohol.

Ethyl alcohol, like wood alcohol, is used as a fuel and in the manufacture of dyes, drugs, perfumes, insecticides, and cosmetics. It is also used in the synthesis of ether, chloroform, and iodoform. It is an important solvent, forming alcoholic solutions called tinctures.

19. PROPYL AND ISOPROPYL ALCOHOLS

Propyl alcohol, also called propanol, is a hydroxyl substitution product of propane (C_3H_8). The position of the OH group on the hydrocarbon chain determines the properties of the alcohol. There are only two different positions possible for this group. The OH group may be attached to either of the end carbons or to the middle carbon.

Propane   Propyl alcohol   Isopropyl alcohol

The two varieties of propyl alcohol are called isomers. As described previously, isomers have the same composition but different structural formulas. Propyl alcohol is used as a solvent while isopropyl alcohol is used as a rubbing alcohol.

20. GLYCERINE

Glycerine, $C_3H_5(OH)_3$, also called glycerol, is obtained as a by-product in the manufacture of soap. It is an alcohol which may be considered a substitution product of propane, in which three of the hydrogen atoms have been replaced by hydroxyl groups. Glycerine is therefore also known as trihydroxypropane.

$$
\begin{array}{ccc}
\text{H} & \text{H} & \text{H} \\
| & | & | \\
\text{H}-\text{C}-\text{C}-\text{C}-\text{H} \\
| & | & | \\
\text{H} & \text{H} & \text{H}
\end{array}
\qquad
\begin{array}{ccc}
\text{H} & \text{H} & \text{H} \\
| & | & | \\
\text{H}-\text{C}-\text{C}-\text{C}-\text{H} \\
| & | & | \\
\text{OH} & \text{OH} & \text{OH}
\end{array}
$$

Propane   Glycerine

Glycerine is a colorless, odorless, syrupy liquid with a sweet taste, and is soluble in water. Because it is hygroscopic, it is used as a moistening agent. It is also used in the manufacture of nitroglycerine, cosmetics, and medicines.

21. PHENOL

Phenol (C_6H_5OH) is a hydroxyl substitution product of benzene.

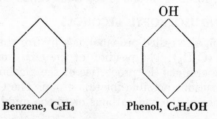

Benzene, C_6H_6 Phenol, C_6H_5OH

Sometimes called carbolic acid, phenol is derived from coal tar. It is an extremely important organic raw material used in the preparation of many dyes, drugs, and plastics.

ALCOHOLS, R—OH

CH_3OH	Hydroxymethane (Methyl alcohol)
C_2H_5OH	Hydroxyethane (Ethyl alcohol)
C_3H_7OH	Hydroxypropane (Propyl alcohol)
$C_3H_5(OH)_3$	Trihydroxypropane (Glycerine)
C_6H_5OH	Hydroxybenzene (Phenol)

22. ALDEHYDES, R—CHO

An aldehyde may be considered as a hydrocarbon in which a hydrogen atom has been replaced by a —CHO group. The —CHO group is written structurally as

$$-C-H$$
$$\|$$
$$O$$

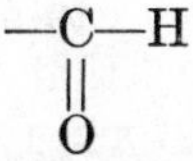

The —CHO group acts as an unsaturated group, indicating that addition reactions may occur at the double bond. Aldehydes are prepared by mild oxidation of an alcohol.

Formaldehyde (HCHO), which is the simplest aldehyde, is written structurally as

$$H-C-H$$
$$\|$$
$$O$$

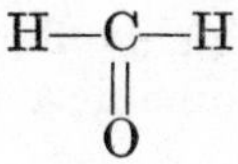

It is prepared by passing a mixture of methanol vapor and air over heated copper gauze, causing the methanol to be mildly oxidized. Formaldehyde is a gas with an irritating odor. Both as a gas and in water solution, formaldehyde is used as a disinfectant. Formalin, a common preservative, is a 40% water solution of formaldehyde. Formaldehyde reacts with urea or phenol in the manufacture of certain types of plastics.

Acetaldehyde (CH_3CHO) is used as a starting material in the manufacture of many organic compounds.

23. KETONES $\frac{R}{R'} > CO$

The ketones are a class of organic compounds which contain the carbonyl group. The carbonyl group is written structurally as

$$\diagdown \atop \diagup C=O$$

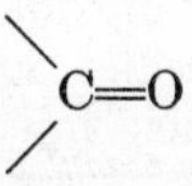

Ketones may also be produced by the mild oxidation of certain alcohols. Acetone (CH_3COCH_3), a common ketone, may be prepared by the oxidation of isopropyl alcohol. Acetone is a volatile, combustible liquid. It is used commercially as an organic solvent to remove nail polish, paint, and lacquer. Acetone is also an important raw material in the manufacture of chloroform and iodoform.

24. ETHERS $\dfrac{R}{R'}\!\!>\!\!O$

An ether consists of an oxygen atom to which two hydrocarbon radicals are attached. Ethers are therefore organic oxides. Ordinary ether, or diethyl ether, is also known as diethyl oxide. The formula for diethyl ether is $(C_2H_5)_2O$, which can also be written $C_2H_5—O—C_2H_5$. From the latter formula, we see that an ether may be considered an alcohol in which the hydrogen atom of the OH group has been replaced by a hydrocarbon radical. Diethyl ether may be prepared by dehydrating two molecules of ethyl alcohol (C_2H_5OH) with concentrated H_2SO_4.

$$\begin{array}{c} C_2H_5O\;\;\boxed{H} \\ C_2H_5\;\;\boxed{OH} \end{array} \xrightarrow[\text{H}_2\text{SO}_4]{} C_2H_5—O—C_2H_5 + H_2O$$

Ethyl ether is a volatile, highly flammable liquid with a characteristic odor. It is used as an organic solvent and as an anesthetic.

ORGANIC ACIDS, R—COOH

25. WHAT ARE ORGANIC ACIDS?

Organic acids are organic compounds containing the carboxyl (COOH) group. A study of the structure of organic acids reveals that they too are derived from corresponding hydrocarbons. They may be considered to be hydrocarbons in which one or more of the hydrogen atoms is replaced by acid (COOH) groups.

26. FORMIC ACID

Formic acid (HCOOH), the simplest organic acid, consists of the carboxyl group attached to one hydrogen atom. It is a colorless liquid with an odor resembling sulfur dioxide. Formic acid occurs in nature in ants, stinging nettles, pine needles, and bees. The irritation of a bee sting results from the formic acid injected into the skin.

27. ACETIC ACID

Acetic acid ($HC_2H_3O_2$ or CH_3COOH) is obtained commercially by the fractional distillation of wood tar or by the oxidation of ethyl alcohol. When sweet cider sours on continued exposure to air, two fermentations take place. The first is the alcoholic fermentation of the sugar in the cider by yeast plants present in the air.

$$C_6H_{12}O_6 \rightarrow 2\ C_2H_5OH + 2\ CO_2 \uparrow$$

The second is the fermentation of the alcohol to acetic acid by acetic acid bacteria also present in the air.

$$C_2H_5OH + O_2 \xrightarrow[\substack{\text{acetic} \\ \text{acid} \\ \text{bacteria}}]{} HC_2H_3O_2 + H_2O$$

The product, a dilute solution of acetic acid, is called vinegar.

Besides its use in vinegar, acetic acid is used as a solvent and in the manufacture of cellulose acetate, an important synthetic fiber.

28. OTHER ORGANIC ACIDS

ACID	FORMULA	OCCURRENCE IN NATURE	USES
Benzoic	C_6H_5COOH	Tree resins Certain berries	Medicines Dyes Food preservative
Oxalic	$(COOH)_2$	In certain plants—in the form of potassium acid oxalate	Bleaching straw Dyes Cleaning metals
Tartaric	$(CHOH)_2(COOH)_2$	Grapes—in the form of potassium acid tartrate	Medicines Baking powder
Citric	$(CH_2)_2COH(COOH)_3$	Citrus fruits Berries	Medicines Flavoring of soft drinks Manufacture of blueprint paper

ESTERS, R—COOR'

29. WHAT ARE ESTERS?

An ester is an organic compound formed by the reaction between an alcohol and an acid. All esters, therefore, contain an acid radical and an organic group. Some common organic radicals are the: methyl (CH_3), ethyl (C_2H_5), glyceryl (C_3H_5), amyl (C_5H_{11}), and phenyl (C_6H_5). The presence of an organic radical instead of a metal or metallic radical distinguishes an ester from a salt. In addition, esters do not ionize in water solution, while salts do.

30. ESTERIFICATION

The reaction between an alcohol and an acid to form an ester is called *esterification*.

GENERAL METHOD OF PREPARATION

$$R—O\ H\ +\ R'CO\ OH\ \rightarrow RCOOR' + H_2O$$

Esterification and neutralization are somewhat similar.

ESTERIFICATION: Alcohol + Acid ⇌ An Ester + Water

NEUTRALIZATION: Base + Acid → A Salt + Water

Neutralizations, however, go to completion, while esterifications are reversible. Concentrated sulfuric acid is frequently used as a catalyst to cause the esterification to go more nearly to completion. The acid used to produce an ester may be either organic or inorganic.

Esterification Reactions:

(1) The ester *ethyl acetate* can be prepared by warming a mixture of ethyl alcohol and acetic acid in the presence of sulfuric acid.

$$C_2H_5O\ H\ +\ CH_3CO\ OH\ \xrightarrow[H_2SO_4]{}\ \underset{\text{ethyl acetate}}{CH_3COOC_2H_5} + H_2O$$

(2) The ester *nitroglycerine* (glyceryl trinitrate) is prepared by treating glycerine with nitric acid in the presence of sulfuric acid.

$$C_3H_5(OH)_3 + 3\ HNO_3 \xrightarrow[H_2SO_4]{} \underset{\text{nitroglycerine}}{C_3H_5(NO_3)_3} + 3\ H_2O$$

(3) The ester *methyl salicylate* (oil of wintergreen) can be prepared by heating a mixture of methyl alcohol and salicylic acid in the presence of sulfuric acid.

$$CH_3O\overline{|H} + C_6H_4OHCO\overline{|OH|} \xrightarrow[H_2SO_4]{} C_6H_4OHCOOCH_3 + H_2O$$

salicylic acid   methyl salicylate

(4) The ester *methyl chloride* may be prepared by treating methyl alcohol with hydrochloric acid in the presence of sulfuric acid.

$$CH_3OH + HCl \xrightarrow[H_2SO_4]{} CH_3Cl + H_2O$$

methyl chloride

Because esters are responsible for the flavors of fruits and the odors of flowers, they are called ethereal salts. Vegetable oils, such as olive and cottonseed oils, are mixtures of esters. Butter is such a mixture. Animal fats are glyceryl esters of organic acids, of which stearic acid ($C_{17}H_{35}COOH$) is the most common. Hence, substances such as stearic acid are known as *fatty acids*.

SOAPS

31. WHAT ARE SOAPS?

A soap is a metallic salt of a fatty acid. Some of the fatty acids used in soapmaking are stearic acid, oleic acid, and palmitic acid. A few typical soaps are sodium stearate, potassium oleate, and sodium palmitate. In the presence of hard waters, insoluble derivatives of the fatty acids are formed. (See **9a,** page 250, for the equations involved.)

32. MANUFACTURE OF SOAP

Soap is made by boiling a vegetable oil or animal fat with a strong base such as sodium or potassium hydroxide. The reaction that takes place, called *saponification,* always results in the formation of a soap and glycerine.

| Fat | + Base → | Soap | + Glycerine |

$$C_3H_5(C_{18}H_{35}O_2)_3 + 3\ NaOH \rightarrow 3\ NaC_{18}H_{35}O_2 + C_3H_5(OH)_3$$

glyceryl stearate   sodium hydroxide   sodium stearate   glycerine

When the saponification is complete, common salt is added to separate the soap from the glycerine, which is a by-product. Since soap is generally colloidal, it is electrically charged. The addition of salt neutralizes this charge, precipitating the soap. Different substances are added to the soap before it solidifies in order to produce the many commercial varieties.

33. CLEANSING ACTION OF SOAP

The surface film on water, also called *surface tension,* is sufficiently tough to prevent oil and grease molecules from penetrating it.

The cleansing action of soap is due to its ability to lower the surface tension of water.

The decrease in surface tension permits the formation of a permanent lather, a fine suspension of soap in water. The lather presents a considerable surface area, permitting the adsorption of dirt particles so that they are loosened and wash out. The lather also emulsifies oils and greases, thus completing the cleansing process.

The ability of soap to emulsify is explained by the fact that structurally soap consists of a long chain hydrocarbon (Fig. 33), one end of which contains oil-soluble organic groups, while the other end contains water-soluble ionic groups. When oil or grease is added to soap solutions, the soap molecule rearranges itself so that the oil-

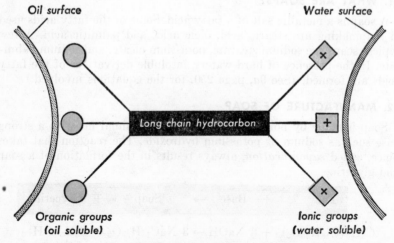

Oil surface

Water surface

Long chain hydrocarbon

Organic groups
(oil soluble)

Ionic groups
(water soluble)

Fig. 33. Cleansing Action of Soap

soluble groups attach themselves to the oil, while the ionic groups remain in the water. Upon thorough shaking, an emulsion is formed.

34. KINDS OF SOAP

Hard soaps are made from sodium hydroxide, while soft soaps are made from potassium hydroxide. Floating soaps are filled with air bubbles. Transparent soaps contain glycerine, while hard water soaps contain borax or sodium carbonate. Soap powders also contain sodium carbonate in addition to soap. Scouring powders contain an abrasive such as powdered pumice.

35. DETERGENTS

Detergents are also classified as cleansing agents. During recent years, a variety of soapless detergents has been manufactured. Detergents are *wetting agents* which can lower the surface tension of water. Detergents contain sodium lauryl sulfate, which, like ordinary soap, is also a long chain molecule containing oil-soluble groups at one end and water-soluble groups at the other end. Because the calcium and magnesium derivatives of detergents are soluble, they may be used efficiently in hard waters. As many detergents are made from non-fatty materials, fats may be conserved.

CARBOHYDRATES, $C_n(H_2O)$,

36. WHAT ARE CARBOHYDRATES?

Carbohydrates are compounds of carbon, hydrogen, and oxygen in which the ratio of hydrogen to oxygen is 2:1, the same as in water. This class of compounds is a most important source of energy, and a source of clothing and shelter. Common carbohydrates are sugars, starch, and cellulose.

37. SUGARS

a. **Glucose** $(C_6H_{12}O_6)$, also known as dextrose or grape sugar, is the simple sugar present in grapes and fruits. Commercially, it is produced by the hydrolysis of starch, that is, boiling starch with water containing a little dilute hydrochloric acid.

$$C_6H_{10}O_5 + H_2O \xrightarrow[\text{HCl}]{} C_6H_{12}O_6$$
$$\text{starch} \qquad\qquad\qquad \text{glucose}$$

Glucose is used for making candy and syrups. By a process of fermentation, glucose may be converted into grain alcohol. Glucose is known as a reducing sugar, because of its action on alkaline solutions of copper sulfate such as Fehling's or Benedict's solution. A brick-red precipitate of cuprous oxide obtained by warming an unknown with either of these reagents indicates the presence of glucose or some other reducing sugar.

b. **Sucrose** ($C_{12}H_{22}O_{11}$), or saccharose, is our ordinary cane sugar. It should not be confused with *saccharin,* the artificial sweetening agent, which is an aromatic compound containing sulfur and nitrogen.

Sucrose is obtained commercially from sugar cane and sugar beet. The sucrose is first extracted by crushing and dissolving. Impurities are then precipitated. The raw sugar is obtained by evaporation under reduced pressure to prevent charring. Refining consists of (1) redissolving the sugar, (2) filtering through boneblack in order to decolorize it, (3) evaporation in vacuum pans, (4) crystallization, (5) separation of the crystals of sugar in centrifuges.

Sucrose, which is a nonreducing sugar, will not produce a brick-red precipitate upon being warmed with Fehling's or Benedict's solution. In the presence of hydrochloric acid as a catalyst, sucrose combines with water to form a mixture of glucose and fructose called invert sugar.

$$C_{12}H_{22}O_{11} + H_2O \xrightarrow[\text{HCl}]{} \underbrace{\underset{\text{glucose}}{C_6H_{12}O_6} + \underset{\text{fructose}}{C_6H_{12}O_6}}_{\text{invert sugar}}$$

38. STARCH

Starch $(C_6H_{10}O_5)_x$ is manufactured by green plants in the process of photosynthesis, a discussion of which appears under *f*, page 225.

$$6\ CO_2 + 5\ H_2O \rightarrow \underset{\text{starch}}{C_6H_{10}O_5} + 6\ O_2 \uparrow$$

The formula $C_6H_{10}O_5$ merely suggests the proportion of elements present (empirical formula). The correct formula for starch is $(C_6H_{10}O_5)_x$. The value of x depends on the molecular weight of starch, which is undetermined because of its complexity. Estimates place the molecular weight at several hundred thousand.

Starch is insoluble in cold water, but is somewhat soluble in hot water. Addition of dilute iodine solution to starch results in a blue-black coloration.

Starch is obtained from potatoes and grains such as wheat and corn. In addition to its importance as food, starch is used for laundering, in adhesives, and in the preparation of grain alcohol and glucose.

39. CELLULOSE

Cellulose $(C_6H_{10}O_5)_y$ has the same empirical formula as starch. Because its molecular weight differs from that of starch, the subscript y is used. Cellulose is found in the walls of plant cells, in wood, and in cotton. Cellulose has varied uses. Paper, rayon, plastics, photographic film, celluloid, and guncotton are all made from cellulose.

CARBOHYDRATES, $C_n(H_2O)_x$

$C_6H_{12}O_6$	Glucose
$C_{12}H_{22}O_{11}$	Sucrose
$(C_6H_{10}O_5)_x$	Starch
$(C_6H_{10}O_5)_y$	Cellulose

1. *a.* What is meant by the vital force doctrine?
   b. This doctrine was overthrown by (1) Lavoisier (2) Einstein (3) Wöhler (4) Moissan.
   c. Organic chemistry is the study of all the compounds of _____.
2. List five important sources of organic compounds.
3. *a.* From its position in the periodic table, carbon should be an _____ (active, inactive) element.
   b. Carbon compounds are generally (1) ionic (2) electrovalent (3) covalent (4) ionic and electrovalent.
   c. By means of electronic formulas, show how:
      (1) a single carbon atom can complete its outer ring in the presence of four hydrogen atoms
      (2) two carbon atoms can complete their outer rings in the presence of six hydrogen atoms
   d. Compounds that have the same composition but a different arrangement of the atoms are called *isotopes*. [True or false? If false, correct the italicized term.]
   e. Using graphic formulas, show how the atoms in the compound C_5H_{12} can be arranged in three different ways.

4. *a.* For any given compound, a structural formula does not indicate the (1) number of atoms (2) kind of atoms (3) arrangement of atoms (4) activity of the compound.

    b. In a structural formula, a single valence bond represents *one pair* of shared electrons. [True or false? If false, correct the italicized term.]

    c. Write structural formulas for (1) CH_4 (2) C_2H_6 (3) C_3H_8.

5. *a.* From the following list of properties, select those that are restricted specifically to organic compounds:

    (1) soluble in ether

    (2) high melting point

    (3) very stable

    (4) combustible

    (5) exhibit isomerism

    (6) high density

    b. Why do reactions between organic compounds proceed more slowly than do reactions between inorganic compounds?

6.**a.* Why do carbon compounds tend to exhibit covalent rather than electrovalent bonding?

    b. Saturated organic compounds contain carbon atoms bonded by _____ of shared electrons.

    c. As the number of valence bonds between carbon atoms increases, the degree of saturation _____ (decreases, increases, remains the same).

    d. By means of structural formulas, give two illustrations each of saturated and unsaturated compounds.

    e. As organic compounds become more unsaturated, their chemical activity generally _____ (decreases, increases, remains the same).

    f. Of the following, the most active compound is (1) methane (2) butane (3) ethylene (4) propane.

7. *a.* Straight-chain carbon compounds are called _____, while ring compounds are called _____.

    b. Why are organic compounds subdivided into classes?

    c. List nine classes of organic compounds.

8. *a.* Many organic compounds are actually or theoretically derived from *carbohydrates*. [True or false? If false, correct the italicized term.]

    b. An example of an homologous series is (1) CH_4, C_2H_2, C_3H_8 (2) CH_4, C_2H_6, C_3H_6 (3) CH_4, C_2H_4, C_3H_6 (4) C_2H_2, C_3H_4, C_4H_6.

9. *a.* A hydrocarbon that is not a member of the paraffin series is (1) CH_4 (2) C_2H_2 (3) C_3H_8 (4) C_8H_{18}.

    b. All the members of an homologous series have the same (1) physical state (2) odor (3) boiling and freezing points (4) general formula.

10. *a.* The common name for methane is (1) choke damp (2) marsh gas (3) natural gas (4) water gas.

    b. List three sources of methane.

    c. The combustion of any hydrocarbon always yields *carbon dioxide*. [True or false? If false, correct the italicized term.]

    d. Write a balanced equation for each of the following reactions:

        (1) complete combustion of ethane (C_2H_6)

        (2) incomplete combustion of acetylene (C_2H_2) to yield carbon monoxide

        (3) incomplete combustion of octane (C_8H_{18}) to yield carbon

11. *a.* An important naturally occurring source of many hydrocarbons is _____.

    b. Kerosene is a mixture of (1) alcohols (2) carbohydrates (3) esters (4) hydrocarbons.

    c. Gasoline contains hydrocarbons of the _____ series.

12. *a.* What is meant by "cracking" processes?

    b. How do cracking processes increase the yield of gasoline from petroleum?

    c. Gasoline may be manufactured from coal by a process which involves (1) destructive distillation (2) polymerization (3) fermentation (4) hydrogenation.

    d. Heavy molecules may be obtained from light molecules by a process called _____.

    e. Octane rating expresses the tendency of a sample of gasoline to _____.

    f. How is the octane rating of a specific grade of gasoline measured?

    g. As the octane rating of a sample of gasoline decreases, the tendency to produce knocking _____ (decreases, increases, remains the same).

    h. Why must care be exercised in handling and storing gasoline?

13. *a.* The general formula of the ethylene series is _____.

    b. Write the structural formula of the member of the ethylene series which contains three carbon atoms.

    c. Unsaturated hydrocarbons react by (1) addition (2) substitution (3) oxidation (4) reduction.

    d. List two uses of ethylene.

14. *a.* In the acetylene series, adjacent carbon atoms are bonded by *two pairs* of shared electrons. [True or false? If false, correct the italicized term.]

    b. Ethylene is always more active than (1) methane (2) acetylene (3) butylene (4) propylene.

    c. State two uses of acetylene and for each use indicate the property which makes the use possible.

15. *a.* Benzene is a hydrocarbon which is (1) saturated and aromatic (2) unsaturated and aromatic (3) saturated and aliphatic (4) unsaturated and aliphatic.

   *b. In the structural formula for benzene, is the position of the double bonds fixed? Explain.

    c. Benzene is derived from (1) coal (2) wood (3) petroleum (4) gasoline.

    d. Contrasted with fractional distillation, destructive distillation (1) uses heat (2) destroys matter (3) is employed on a commercial scale only (4) produces a chemical change.

    e. A substance that is not a product of the fractional distillation of coal tar is (1) acetic acid (2) benzene (3) phenol (4) toluene.

   *f. In the laboratory, how can benzine be distinguished from benzene?

    g. Two members of the benzene series are _____ and _____.

16. *a.* Benzene is related to benzine in the same way that naphthalene is related to _____.

    b. Naphthalene, as a moth repellent, is being replaced by _____.

17. *a.* By means of equations, and employing structural formulas wherever possible, give two examples of:

       (1) substitution reactions

       (2) addition reactions

    b. Substitution reactions take place _____ (more, less) readily than addition reactions.

18. *a.* Methyl chloride is a (an) _____ (substitution, addition) product of methane.

b. Fill in the blanks in the following chart of organic compounds:

MOLECULAR FORMULA	STRUCTURAL FORMULA	IMPORTANT PROPERTIES	USE
$C_6H_4Cl_2$		XXX	
			Local anesthetic
CHI_3			
		Volatile, very dense, and non-combustible liquid	
	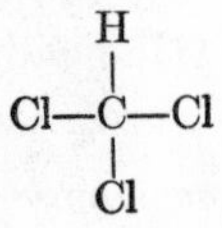 $\begin{array}{c} H \\ \| \\ Cl-C-Cl \\ \| \\ Cl \end{array}$		
			Refrigerant

19. *a.* Alcohols may be considered hydroxyl *addition* products of hydrocarbons. [True or false? If false, correct the italicized term.]

    b. An alcohol is represented by the formula (1) $Ba(OH)_2$ (2) $HCHO$ (3) $C_6H_{12}O_6$ (4) $C_5H_{11}OH$.

    c. In the laboratory, how can an alcohol be distinguished from a base?

    d. Methyl alcohol may be prepared from (1) coal tar (2) carbon monoxide (3) hydrogen (4) wood tar.

    e. The complete combustion of methyl alcohol yields (1) carbon and water (2) carbon dioxide and hydrogen (3) carbon dioxide and water (4) chloroform and water.

    f. List two uses of methyl alcohol and for each use indicate the property which makes the use possible.

20. *a.* By means of structural formulas, show the difference between methyl and ethyl alcohol.

    *b. Can either of these alcohols have isomers? Explain.

    c. Ethyl alcohol is obtained from glucose by the process of ―――――――.

    d. Using balanced equations, show how ethyl alcohol may be prepared from cane sugar.

    e. Make a labeled diagram to show how ethyl alcohol can be prepared in the laboratory.

    f. How is the alcohol collected?

    g. What is meant by denatured alcohol? What determines the selection of the denaturing agent?

    h. Ethyl alcohol is not used in the manufacture of (1) glucose (2) ether (3) iodoform (4) dyes.

21. *a.* Write the structural formulas of the two isomers of propyl alcohol.
   b. Write a balanced equation to illustrate the complete combustion of propyl alcohol.
   c. The hydrocarbon which is most closely related to glycerine is _____.
   d. State an important use of glycerine and indicate the property which makes this use possible.
   e. By means of a structural formula, indicate whether phenol is an aliphatic or aromatic compound.
   f. Phenol is derived from (1) coal tar (2) wood (3) sea water (4) petroleum.

22. *a.* The group or structure present in all aldehydes is _____.
   b. Formaldehyde is used (1) as an anesthetic (2) as an antiseptic (3) in the manufacture of plastics (4) in the manufacture of ethyl alcohol.
   c. An example of a ketone is (1) CH_3CHO (2) CH_3COCH_3 (3) CH_3OH (4) CH_3OCH_3.
   d. State an important use of acetone and indicate the property which makes this use possible.
   e. An example of an ether is (1) $CHCl_3$ (2) $CH_3OC_2H_5$ (3) CH_3OH (4) $C_2H_5COC_2H_5$.
   f. Why is ordinary hospital ether sometimes called sulfuric ether?
   g. List two uses of ethyl ether.

23. *a.* The group present in all organic acids is (1) CH_3 (2) OH (3) COOH (4) CHO.
   b. The formula for the simplest organic acid is _____.

24. *a.* The structural formula of acetic acid is _____.
   b. By means of a balanced equation, show how acetic acid can be prepared from ethyl alcohol.
   c. List three important uses of acetic acid.
   d. An organic acid used to manufacture a common food preservative is _____.
   e. The structural formula of oxalic acid is _____.
   f. Write two possible structural formulas for tartaric acid.
   g. What type of isomerism is exhibited in *f?*

25. *a.* The reaction between an alcohol and an acid yields _____ and _____.
   b. Of the following, the one which is not an example of an organic radical is (1) C_3H_5 (2) C_2H_6 (3) C_3H_7 (4) C_6H_5.
   c. Describe two important differences between neutralization and esterification.
   d. Write a balanced equation to show how each of the following reactions takes place in the presence of a little concentrated sulfuric acid.
   (1) $CH_3OH + CH_3COOH \rightarrow$
   (2) $C_3H_5(OH)_3 + HNO_3 \rightarrow$
   (3) $C_2H_5OH + HCl \rightarrow$
   (4) $C_3H_5(OH)_3 + C_{17}H_{35}COOH \rightarrow$

26. *a.* In composition, soaps most closely resemble (1) fats (2) esters (3) salts (4) fatty acids.
   b. Two examples of fatty acids are _____ and _____.
   c. Describe a commercial process for making soap, including:
   (1) the balanced equation for the reaction
   (2) the name and one use of an important by-product
   (3) the reason for the use of sodium chloride in the process

    d. The cleansing action of soap is due to its ability to _____ (lower, raise) the surface tension of water.

    e. How does the formation of lather aid in the cleansing process?

    f. By means of a labeled diagram, explain how soap acts as an emulsifying agent.

    g. State the composition of three different types of soaps or soap products.

    h. Why do detergents behave as cleansing agents?

    i. List two advantages of detergents over soaps.

27. *a.* The ratio of oxygen to hydrogen in carbohydrates is _____.

    b. Three common types of carbohydrates are sugars, starch, and *aldehydes.* [True or false? If false, correct the italicized term.]

28. *a.* What is meant by a simple sugar?

    b. Describe the chemical changes that occur in using Fehling's or Benedict's reagent.

    c. The formula for sucrose is _____.

    d. An artificial sweetening agent commonly confused with sucrose is called _____.

    e. List the important steps in the process of extracting sucrose from sugar cane.

    **f.* Why will sucrose alone fail to respond to the Fehling's or Benedict's test, while an acidified sucrose solution will respond?

29. *a.* Two possible carbohydrate products of photosynthesis are _____ and _____.

    b. What is meant by an empirical formula?

    c. Why is the molecular formula of starch unknown?

    d. List two uses of starch and for each use indicate the property which makes the use possible.

    **e.* What significance lies in the fact that starch and cellulose have similar empirical formulas?

    f. Cellulose is not found in (1) mineral matter (2) plant cells (3) wood (4) cotton.

    g. Cellulose esters are used in the manufacture of *rayon.* [True or false? If false, correct the italicized term.]

 **APPLIED ORGANIC CHEMISTRY**

NATURAL AND SYNTHETIC PRODUCTS

An increasing emphasis upon research has enabled the organic chemist to develop a variety of synthetic materials. The use of synthetic materials has provided the consumer with cheaper and frequently superior substitutes, resulting in greater conservation of natural resources.

1. FIBERS

Up to the beginning of the 20th century, man had been dependent upon nature for the fibers used in the manufacture of woven textiles.

The most important **natural fibers** are cotton and linen, which are of plant origin; and silk and wool, which are of animal origin.

Today, the textile industry uses synthetic fibers that the chemist has learned to make from common, simple materials. The textiles woven from synthetic fibers are superior in many ways to those made from natural fibers.

Examples of some **synthetic fibers** are rayon, nylon, dacron, orlon, acrilan, and vicara.

NATURAL FIBERS

FIBER	STRUCTURE	COMPOSITION	PROPERTIES	USES
Cotton (cotton plant)	Flat, twisted ribbon	Cellulose $(C_6H_{10}O_5)_y$	Leaves little ash on burning. Unaffected by acids. Treatment with NaOH produces a stronger, more lustrous cotton called mercerized cotton.	Textiles and thread Manufacture of guncotton

FIBER	STRUCTURE	COMPOSITION	PROPERTIES	USES
Linen (flax plant)	Long, jointed, cylindrical segments	Cellulose $(C_6H_{10}O_5)_y$	Good conductor of heat, highly absorbent (hygroscopic), strong, and durable. Resembles cotton chemically.	Textiles for wearing apparel, handkerchiefs, tablecloths, dish towels, and bed linen
Silk (silkworm)	Long, thin, tubular, with projecting nodules	Protein material, but lacking in sulfur	Has a very high luster and is the strongest of the natural fibers. Soluble in concentrated HCl, concentrated HNO_3, and in warm, dilute NaOH.	Textiles and thread
Wool (sheep, goat, llama)	Notched, overlapping segments	Protein material containing sulfur	Poor conductor of heat, and hygroscopic. Soluble in concentrated NaOH. Turns yellow in presence of HNO_3 (test for wool).	Textiles Wool grease (source of lanolin)

SYNTHETIC FIBERS

FIBER	COMPOSITION	PROPERTIES	USES
Rayon	Regenerated cellulose Viscose type: sodium cellulose xanthate Acetate type: cellulose acetate	Since it is nearly pure cellulose, its properties resemble those of cotton.	Textiles Upholstery fabrics Automobile tires Manufacture of cellophane
Nylon	Synthetic protein called a polyamide (made from adipic acid and hexamethylene diamine)	Strong, tough, elastic, mothproof, absorbs little water, and does not burn. Dissolves in concentrated acids.	Textiles Hosiery Cord for tires Brushes

FIBER	COMPOSITION	PROPERTIES	USES
Dacron	Polyester fiber made from the reaction between dimethyl terephthalate and ethylene glycol	Resists water penetration and is thus quick drying. High resilience and thus does not crease easily. Resists mildew and moths.	Textiles With nylon and orlon, in manufacturing synthetic paper Shirts and other wearing apparel
Orlon	Polyacrylonitrile fiber	Same as dacron	Same as dacron
Acrilan	Similar to orlon	Light, resilient, pleasant to touch.	Manufacture of sweaters and sport shirts
Vicara	Protein-like material made from corn kernels	Poor conductor of heat.	Wool substitutes
Fiberglas	Fine glass filaments	Lightweight and non-flammable.	Textiles Lamp shades, curtains, and drapes

The production of synthetic fibers may someday present serious economic problems. The increased use of nylon has already begun to affect the Japanese export of silk. However, the total production of all synthetic fibers is still only a small percentage of all the cotton, wool, and silk in use today.

2. RUBBER

The term rubber is used to describe any natural or synthetic organic substance which possesses to a considerable degree the properties of toughness, resilience, and elasticity.

Rubber-like substances are known as **elastomers.**

Both synthetic and natural rubber consist chemically of giant molecules built up from simpler units. *The combination of unit molecules (called monomers) to form larger, more complex units (polymers) is called polymerization.* When different monomers are first combined and the product is polymerized, the process is called *co-polymerization.*

Natural rubber molecules are thought to contain several thousand units of the monomer, isoprene (C_5H_8).

a. **Natural Rubber.** Natural rubber is obtained from the latex of rubber trees. The rubber in the latex, a milky liquid, is usually coagulated by the addition of acetic acid.

Raw rubber is not a very strong substance and is readily affected by extreme temperatures. By heating it with sulfur, a process called *vulcanization,* the rubber becomes tougher and stronger, and is not seriously affected by changes in temperature. The addition of carbon black also strengthens and toughens rubber, making it more resistant to wear.

b. **Synthetic Rubber.** The need for synthetic rubber was brought sharply into focus during World War II when we were cut off from our source of natural rubber. Today, large quantities of synthetic rubber are manufactured annually.

Synthetic rubber is more resistant to the deteriorating action of oil and gasoline than is natural rubber. Synthetic rubber can be made from petroleum, natural gas, coal, or grain. Hydrocarbon molecules derived from these substances are polymerized and co-polymerized to form long chains.

Some well-known synthetic rubbers are *Buna N* and *Buna S*. These are known as Government Rubber N (GR-N) and Government Rubber S (GR-S). Buna N is made from butadiene and acrylonitrile; Buna S is obtained from butadiene and styrene, and is the chief synthetic rubber in use today. Other common synthetic rubbers are butyl rubber, which is made from isobutylene and butadiene; and Thiokol, Koroseal, and Neoprene, which are made from chlorinated hydrocarbons.

3. PLASTICS

Plastics are synthetic organic materials which can be molded.

Plastics are classified according to their response to heat treatment. Those plastics which become permanently hard as a result of their first heat treatment are called *thermosetting* plastics. If a plastic can be repeatedly softened by heating, it is said to be *thermoplastic.*

Some examples of plastics are as follows:

a. **Cellulose plastics** are made from cellulose and nitric acid. One of the earliest plastics, celluloid, is made from cellulose nitrate, camphor, and alcohol. A nonflammable type of celluloid, used to make "safety" film, is produced from cellulose acetate, camphor, and alcohol.

b. **Phenolic plastics** are made from phenol (carbolic acid) and other organic substances. Bakelite, another early plastic, is made from phenol and formaldehyde, and has many uses.

c. **Urea plastics** are made from urea and formaldehyde. They take colors well and are used to make tableware, radio cabinets, buttons, umbrella handles, etc.

d. **Methacrylate plastics** are made from methyl methacrylate. These plastics, which are transparent and flexible, found many wartime applications, especially in airplanes. Plexiglas and lucite are the best-known methacrylate plastics.

e. **Casein plastics** are made from casein and formaldehyde. Casein is the curd, or clot, of curdled milk. These plastics are used in the manufacture of small articles such as buttons and belt buckles.

f. **Silicone plastics** are long chain compounds formed by polymerization. Structurally, they are composed of alternate silicon and oxygen atoms with hydrocarbon branches linked to the silicon atoms. *Silicones,* as they are commonly called, are used in making special kinds of rubber which remain unaffected by ordinary solvents. Silicones are also good insulators and can withstand high temperatures, making them useful in electric motors. Silicone oils are generally more stable than hydrocarbon oils and can be used for high temperature lubrication.

Some of the reasons for the increased use of plastics are:

(1) They do not corrode or mildew.
(2) They are excellent heat and electrical insulators.
(3) They may be easily fabricated to specific uses.
(4) Their sources are generally more abundant than the naturally occurring materials they are replacing.

4. INSECTICIDES

The sharp increase in population following World War II has made increased demands on our food supply. Protection and conservation of the food supply depend on many factors, one of which is adequate insect control. The development of new insecticides has done much to insure a maximum crop production. Insecticides are substances used to kill insects. Some of these insecticides are listed below.

a. **DDT** is used in the control of the tent caterpillar, coddling moth, and corn borer.

b. **Chlordane** is effective against grasshoppers and plant aphids.

c. **2, 4D** is used in weed control.

5. DRUGS

Organic chemistry has come to the aid of the sick and disabled. With the help of specific chemical compounds, many of which are synthetic, considerable progress has been made in the diagnosis and treatment of disease.

The use of specific chemical compounds for the destruction of disease-producing bacteria is known as **chemotherapy.**

Salvarsan, an arsenic compound discovered by Paul Ehrlich and used in the treatment of syphilis, is an example of an early chemo-therapeutic agent. The more recent sulfa drugs, which are complex sulfur compounds, are also chemotherapeutic agents. When such chemicals are naturally produced by living organisms, they are called *antibiotics.*

a. **Sulfa Drugs.** The first sulfa drug, sulfanilamide, was discovered by Gerhard Domagk. During World War II, it was dusted into wounds to prevent infection. Sulfanilamide and sulfapyridine have been used successfully in combatting pneumonia, meningitis, and streptococcus infections. Sulfaguanidine is used in the tropics to treat dysentery. Sulfadiazine, in the form of an ointment, is used in the treatment of burns and skin infections.

b. **Antibiotics.** The best known of the antibiotics are penicillin, strep-tomycin, and aureomycin. Penicillin, discovered by Sir Alexander Fleming in England in 1929, is obtained from a certain type of mold. It is even more effective than the sulfa drugs against certain diseases. Streptomycin has been successfully used in treating infections which do not respond to sulfa or penicillin.

Other effective antibiotic agents in use today are terramycin, bacitracin, and chloromycetin.

6. DYES

Up to the middle of the 19th century, the dyeing of textiles was restricted to dyes obtained from naturally occurring substances. Certain plants furnished indigo blue and Turkey red, while certain insects supplied cochineal red. The synthetic dye industry was born in 1856. Perkin, an English chemist, while attempting to synthesize the drug quinine from aniline, a coal tar derivative, accidentally produced the purple dye, mauve. Perkin and other chemists continued their research on coal tar and succeeded in synthesizing a large number of aniline dyes. Today, thousands of synthetic dyes are available.

Both natural and synthetic dyes may be classified according to the way in which they react with the fabric to be dyed.

a. **Direct dyes** are those that react with fibers directly in the absence of any intermediary substance. Direct dyes such as Congo red and picric acid are used largely on cotton and rayon fabrics. These dyes are called fast dyes because they do not wash out.

b. **Vat dyes** are formed in fibers as a result of some chemical action. For example, a textile to be dyed is soaked in a colorless solution of a derivative of indigo. Upon drying, air oxidation of the derivative occurs, resulting in the formation of an indigo-blue dye. Vat dyes are usually fast dyes and are commonly used for cotton and, to a lesser extent, for linen and rayon.

c. **Mordant dyes** require the use of an intermediary substance called a *mordant* to prevent the dye from washing out. By chemical action, the mordant precipitates a material within the fiber which is capable of adsorbing the dye. In practice, the cloth to be dyed is soaked in a mordant solution, such as alum, and is then rolled into a tank containing ammonium hydroxide. The reaction between the alum and the base precipitates aluminum hydroxide within the fibers of the cloth. In the next step, the cloth containing the mordant is rolled into the dye vat, where the dye is adsorbed by the mordant, forming an insoluble material called a *lake*. Alizarin, a mordant dye, is frequently used on cotton goods.

The techniques utilized in dyeing processes depend largely upon the nature of the fiber to be dyed.

FOODS AND VITAMINS

7. WHAT IS NUTRITION?

Nutrition is the science that deals with the composition of foods and their utilization by the body.

Foods contain substances required by the body for the release of energy and for the growth and repair of cells.

8. WHAT ARE NUTRIENTS?

Nutrients are specific chemical compounds found in foods. A balanced diet includes a variety of these nutrients in proper amounts to supply all the needs of the body. The following table summarizes the sources, composition, and tests for the different nutrients:

NUTRIENT	SOURCE	COMPOSITION	TEST
Carbohydrates a. Sugars	Cane sugar and beet sugar, fruits, honey	Sucrose, $C_{12}H_{22}O_{11}$ Fruit sugar (glucose), $C_6H_{12}O_6$	Glucose produces a brick-red precipitate upon being warmed with Fehling's or Benedict's solution. If sucrose is first acidified, it behaves in the same manner.
b. Starch	Potatoes, grain, rice	$(C_6H_{10}O_5)_x$	Boil food in water. Allow to cool and add a few drops of dilute iodine solution. The formation of a blue-black color indicates the presence of starch.
Fats and Oils	Meat, fish, nuts, cooking oil	Esters of fatty acids	Rub food on unglazed paper. A translucent spot is obtained.
Proteins	Meat, fish, eggs	Complex structure of very high molecular weight derived from amino acids, which are organic acids containing nitrogen. Contain C, H, O, N and frequently S and P.	The addition of concentrated nitric acid to foods produces a yellow color (xanthoproteic acid) if protein is present. The yellow color will turn to orange if the food is washed and ammonium hydroxide is added.
Minerals	Milk, eggs, fruits, vegetables	Compounds of Na, Ca, K, P, Fe, I, Mg, Cl, and traces of Cu, Zn, Mn.	Burn the food completely until all organic matter is consumed. A gray ash remains to indicate the presence of mineral matter.

9. WHAT ARE VITAMINS?

Vitamins are complex organic compounds required by the body in very small concentrations. They appear to act as catalytic agents in the regulation of specific body functions. The absence of these vitamins from the diet produces a number of diseases, called *vitamin-deficiency diseases*, such as scurvy and rickets.

VITAMIN	SOURCE	FUNCTION
A	Liver, carrots, butter, green leafy vegetables	Helps to manufacture a substance called visual purple, which enables the eye to see in the dark; helps the body to resist infections; aids in the growth of cells.
B-Complex *a.* B₁ (thiamine)	Dried beans, peas, peanuts, wheat germ	Aids in proper functioning of the nervous system; reduces fatigue; stimulates appetite; aids digestion.
b. B₂ (riboflavin)	Meat, eggs, milk, green vegetables	Controls growth processes; needed for oxidation of food; prevents eye, mouth, and skin disorders.
c. Niacin (nicotinic acid)	Meat, eggs, fowl, whole wheat	Prevents certain skin and nervous disorders; prevents pellagra.
C (ascorbic acid)	Citrus fruits, tomatoes, green vegetables	Aids in formation of teeth and bone; promotes the healing of wounds; prevents scurvy.
D	Exposure of skin to sunlight; dairy products; fish and fish liver oils	Insures strong teeth and bones; prevents rickets.
E	Wheat germ, butter, vegetables	Needed by certain animals for reproduction.
K	Leafy vegetables such as cabbage, spinach, and cauliflower	Promotes normal clotting of blood.

In addition to the vitamins previously listed, there are others that are still undergoing investigation. Some of these are members of the B-complex group, such as biotin, folic acid, and pantothenic acid.

10. FOODS AND ENERGY

The oxidation of food supplies the body with the energy necessary to maintain normal life processes. This energy, in the form of heat, is measured in a unit called the calorie. *A calorie is the amount of heat required to raise the temperature of one gram of water one degree centigrade.* Since this unit is frequently too small to be used to express the energy value of a food, the large Calorie (capitalized) is used. The large Calorie is equal to 1,000 calories. On an equal weight basis, fat supplies more calories than any other nutrient. For an individual, the average daily caloric requirement varies considerably. It depends largely upon the age, sex, and activity of the individual.

1. Indicate whether each of the following fibers is of plant, animal, or synthetic origin: vicara, linen, dacron, rayon, silk, orlon, wool, nylon, and cotton.
2. *a.* A natural fiber which becomes stronger and more lustrous when treated with sodium hydroxide is _____.
   b. A natural fiber which consists of long, jointed, cylindrical segments is (1) cotton (2) linen (3) silk (4) wool.
   c. Two natural fibers that have similar composition are (1) cotton and linen (2) cotton and wool (3) silk and wool (4) silk and linen.
   d. The strongest natural fiber is *cotton*. [True or false? If false, correct the italicized term.]
   e. An animal that does not supply wool is the (1) sheep (2) mink (3) llama (4) goat.
   f. A natural fiber which is a very poor conductor of heat is _____.
   *g. By means of chemical tests, how can the presence of each of the four natural fibers in a textile be established?

3. Fill in the blanks in the following chart of synthetic fibers:

FIBER	COMPOSITION	PROPERTIES	USE
	Regenerated cellulose		
Fiberglas			
Vicara			
	Synthetic polyamide protein		
		Quick-drying and does not crease	

4. *a.* Another name for rubber or rubber-like materials is (1) monomer (2) elastomer (3) isomer (4) isotope.

    b. The giant molecules present in synthetic and natural rubber are formed by a process called _____.

   c. How does the chemist know that natural rubber is a polymer of isoprene?

    d. The process of heating raw rubber with sulfur is called _____.

    e. A rubber additive which increases the resistance of rubber to wear is (1) carbon (2) silicon (3) chromium (4) phosphorus.

    f. List two advantages of synthetic rubber over natural rubber.

  g. Using structural formulas, describe the preparation of a synthetic rubber by polymerization and by co-polymerization.

5. *a.* What is meant by a plastic?

    b. Distinguish between thermoplastic and thermosetting plastics.

    c. Cellulose acetate plastics are used in the manufacture of film because these plastics (1) have high tensile strength (2) are nonflammable (3) do not corrode (4) do not mildew.

    d. Bakelite is an example of *a urea* plastic. [True or false? If false, correct the italicized term.]

    e. Plastics manufactured from milk are called _____ plastics.

    f. Describe the composition and special uses of silicones.

    g. List four reasons for the increased use of plastics.

6. *a.* What is meant by an insecticide?

    b. Adequate insect control conserves our food supply. Explain.

    c. List three specific insecticides and indicate their uses.

7. *a.* The destruction of disease-producing bacteria by specific chemicals is known as _____.

    b. An arsenic compound once used in the treatment of syphilis is (1) penicillin (2) chloromycetin (3) terramycin (4) salvarsan.

    c. Two examples of sulfa drugs are _____ and _____.

    d. Antibiotics are chemotherapeutic agents produced by _____.

    e. Three examples of antibiotics are _____, _____, and _____.

8. *a.* An English chemist who founded the synthetic dye industry was (1) Priestley (2) Davy (3) Faraday (4) Perkin.

    b. Dyes not requiring an intermediary substance are called _____ dyes.

    c. Dyes formed in fibers by chemical action are called _____ dyes.

    d. An intermediary substance required in dyeing is called *a lake.* [True or false? If false, correct the italicized term.]

    e. Describe how a mordant is used in dyeing.

    f. Classify each of the following as direct, vat, or mordant dyes: Congo red, indigo, picric acid, and alizarin.

9. *a.* Nutrition deals with the _____ of foods and how the body _____ foods.

    b. Why do living things require food?

    c. Specific compounds present in foods are called _____.

    d. What is meant by a balanced diet?

10. *a.* Benedict's solution will give a positive test with (1) sucrose (2) starch (3) cellulose (4) glucose.

    *b. Describe the important chemical reactions that take place when using either Fehling's or Benedict's solution.

    c. Iodine is used in the test for (1) protein (2) fat (3) starch (4) sucrose.

    d. Fats belong to a class of organic compounds called (1) ethers (2) esters (3) soaps (4) acids.

    *e. How are proteins related to amino acids?

    f. In the presence of protein, nitric acid produces *a brown ring.* [True or false? If false, correct the italicized term.]

    g. Why must foods be burned to test for the presence of mineral matter?

11. *a.* Vitamins are required by the body in _____ concentrations.

    b. In the regulation of body functions, vitamins seem to act as _____.

    c. What is meant by a vitamin-deficiency disease?

    d. Fill in the blanks in the following chart of vitamins:

VITAMIN	SOURCE	FUNCTION
	Fish and fish liver oils	
		Helps to control night blindness
B_1		
	Citrus fruits	
		Promotes normal blood clotting
		Prevents pellagra
B_2		

    e. The *nutrients* required for life processes result from the oxidation of food. [True or false? If false, correct the italicized term.]

    f. One calorie will raise the temperature of 1 g. of water _____°C.

    g. A large Calorie equals (1) 10 (2) 100 (3) 1,000 (4) 10,000 calories.

    h. The nutrient that has the highest caloric value is (1) starch (2) sugar (3) protein (4) fat.

23 NUCLEAR ENERGY

1. NUCLEONICS, OR NUCLEAR SCIENCE

Within the short span of about half a century, man has discovered and developed one of the most interesting and important new fields of science, called *nucleonics,* or *nuclear science.*

Nucleonics is the study of the composition and transformation of atomic nuclei.

Nucleonics has revealed a tremendous source of energy, the energy stored in atomic nuclei and known as nuclear energy. Man has successfully utilized this energy in atomic bombs. He is also learning how to put nuclear energy to work to provide him with electric power and to drive ships and submarines. Another important application of this science is in the production of new elements, some of which are being used in industry, agriculture, medicine, and research.

2. RADIOACTIVITY

a. **Stability of Nuclei.** The nuclei of elements such as iron and cobalt are very stable, and do not undergo change in ordinary chemical reactions. On the other hand, the nuclei of elements such as radium and polonium are unstable.

Elements which have unstable nuclei undergo spontaneous disintegration and are said to be **radioactive.**

Radioactive elements are very dense and have large atomic weights. Other examples of such elements are found in the actinide series of the periodic table.

Radioactivity is the spontaneous disintegration of an element accompanied by the emission of radiation. The disintegration proceeds at a constant rate for a given radioactive substance and is unaffected by external conditions.

b. Natural Radioactivity. Natural radioactivity was first discovered by Henri Becquerel in 1896, while he was studying uranium ores. The phenomenon of radioactivity was further investigated by the Curies. In 1898, Pierre and Marie Curie, while working with an ore called pitchblende, discovered the radioactive elements radium and polonium. At the same time, they discovered that radioactivity is accompanied by the emission of certain radiations which can be readily detected and distinguished from each other.

c. Kinds of Radioactive Emanations. Radioactive substances emit three kinds of radiations or emanations: (1) *alpha particles or rays,* (2) *beta particles or rays,* and (3) *gamma rays.*

Radioactive emanations differ from each other in mass, electrical charge, penetrating power, and ionizing power.

The complex nature of these radiations suggests that they behave both as particles and as waves (rays); hence both terms are used.

(1) *Alpha Rays.* Alpha (α) particles are high-speed, positively charged helium nuclei. They have a mass number (atomic weight) of 4 and a nuclear charge (atomic number) of 2. They are usually represented by the symbol $_2He^4$. Alpha particles, with a mass four times that of a proton, are much heavier than beta particles. Alpha particles move with a speed of from 10,000 to 20,000 miles per second, and are less penetrating than either beta or gamma rays. Alpha particles can be readily absorbed or screened out by thin aluminum foil or a thin sheet of paper.

(2) *Beta Rays.* Beta (β) particles are high-speed electrons moving with velocities approaching the speed of light (186,000 miles per second). They are negatively charged, and are assigned a mass number of 0 because their actual mass is exceedingly small. Beta particles are usually represented by the symbol $_{-1}e^0$. Beta particles have a much smaller mass than alpha particles; but, because of greater velocity, their penetrating power is 100 times as great. Beta rays can be absorbed or screened out by sheet aluminum.

(3) *Gamma Rays.* Gamma (γ) rays are high-energy X-rays of very short wave length traveling with the speed of light. Because they have no electric charge, gamma rays are not deflected by electric or magnetic fields. They are the most penetrating of the radiations emitted by radioactive elements. Even four inches of lead do not shield a body completely from gamma rays.

It is possible to separate the three types of radiations. (See figure below.) If we direct the radiation from a radioactive substance, such as radium, through an electric or magnetic field, the positively charged alpha rays are deflected in one direction and are screened out by aluminum foil. The negatively charged beta rays are deflected in the opposite direction and are screened out by aluminum sheet. The uncharged gamma rays are not deflected and are not screened out.

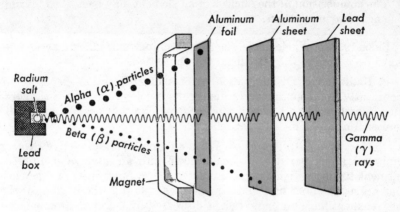

Fig. 2c. Separating Alpha, Beta, and Gamma Rays

d. Artificial Radioactivity. Artificial radioactivity was first demonstrated in 1919 by Ernest Rutherford, the father of nuclear physics.

Rutherford produced the first nuclear disintegration by bombarding nitrogen with alpha particles given off by the disintegration of radium.

The reaction that took place can be expressed in the form of a nuclear equation:

$$\underset{\text{nitrogen}}{_{7}N^{14}} + \underset{\substack{\text{alpha}\\\text{particle}}}{_{2}He^{4}} \rightarrow \underset{\substack{\text{oxygen}\\\text{isotope}}}{_{8}O^{17}} + \underset{\text{proton}}{_{1}H^{1}}$$

e. Nuclear Equations. Since in a nuclear reaction only the nuclei of atoms are involved, only nuclei are represented in the nuclear equation. The equation contains subscripts written to the left of the symbols and superscripts written to the right of the symbols. The subscripts represent atomic numbers, and the superscripts denote atomic weights. Note that in the above equation, the sum of the subscripts (atomic numbers) on the left side of the equation, 9, is equal to the sum of the subscripts on the right side. The same is true for the sum of the superscripts, 18, on both sides of the equation.

f. **Transmuting Elements.** By bombarding nitrogen with alpha particles, Rutherford succeeded in artificially converting nitrogen into oxygen. *The process of converting one element into another element is known as transmutation.*

The composition of the nucleus of an element may be altered by adding or removing protons.

Since 1919, other elements, such as plutonium, curium, and berkelium, have been produced by artificial transmutation.

g. **Radioactive Disintegration.** Atoms of radioactive elements are constantly and spontaneously undergoing nuclear decay or disintegration. There are two kinds of nuclear disintegration resulting from the emission of alpha or beta particles.

(1) *Alpha Disintegration.* When an atom of a radioactive element emits an alpha particle, it breaks down into an atom of a different element having a lighter and simpler nucleus. Since an alpha particle has a mass number of 4 and a nuclear charge of 2, the nucleus of the new element has an atomic weight decreased by 4 and an atomic number decreased by 2. The decay of radium-226 to radon-222 is an example of alpha emission.

$$_{88}\text{Ra}^{226} \rightarrow {}_{86}\text{Rn}^{222} + {}_2\text{He}^4$$
radium   radon   alpha
                         particle

(2) *Beta Disintegration.* When the nucleus of an atom emits a beta particle, the atomic number increases by 1. Since the weight of a beta particle is extremely small, the weight of the nucleus remains unchanged. The beta particle is probably formed from the breakdown of a neutron, which is believed to consist of a proton and an electron. Hence, during beta decay, the atomic weight does not change, but the atomic number increases by 1 unit. The decay of thorium-234 to protoactinium-234 is an example of beta emission.

$$_{90}\text{Th}^{234} \rightarrow {}_{91}\text{Pa}^{234} + {}_{-1}e^0$$
thorium   protoactinium   beta
                                  particle

The disintegration of uranium-238 takes place by the emission of both alpha and beta particles. The process involves fifteen transformations before it terminates in the formation of a nonradioactive isotope of lead, Pb-206.

PROPERTIES OF PRODUCTS OF NUCLEAR DISINTEGRATION

TYPE OF DISINTEGRATION	ATOMIC NUMBER	ATOMIC WEIGHT
Alpha	Decreased by 2	Decreased by 4
Beta	Increased by 1	No change

3. RATE OF DECAY

We have just seen that radioactive disintegration is accompanied by the emission of alpha, beta, and gamma radiations.

The rate of decay for a given radioactive element is uniform and cannot be controlled by either chemical or physical means.

The rate of decay, however, differs greatly for different radioactive elements and is expressed as the half-life of the element. The *half-life of a radioactive element is the time it takes for half the atoms of a given sample of a radioactive element to disintegrate into simpler atoms.* Radium, with a half-life of approximately 1,600 years, will decrease in mass from one gram to one-half gram in this period of time. The half-lives of some radioactive elements are given below:

ELEMENT	SYMBOL	HALF-LIFE
Uranium-238	$_{92}U^{238}$	4.55×10^9 years, or 4.5 billion years
Protoactinium-234	$_{91}Pa^{234}$	1.14 minutes
Radium-226	$_{88}Ra^{226}$	1,590 years
Polonium-214	$_{84}Po^{214}$	1.5×10^{-4} second, or 0.00015 second
Polonium-210	$_{84}Po^{210}$	140 days

4. DETECTING AND MEASURING RADIOACTIVITY

Radioactivity may be detected by means of its fluorescent, photographic, and ionizing effects.

Some of the instruments used to detect and measure the rate of radioactive disintegration and intensity of radiation are:

a. **Scintillation Counter.** The operation of the scintillation counter, also called a *spinthariscope,* is based upon the fact that when alpha particles strike a fluorescent zinc sulfide screen, they produce flashes of light called scintillations. These scintillations can be detected and amplified by an electron-multiplier tube.

b. **Cloud Chamber.** The cloud chamber, invented by C. T. R. Wilson in 1911, is a device which makes visible the paths or cloud tracks of charged particles from radium.

This instrument consists of an air chamber saturated with water vapor (or alcohol vapor) and fitted with a movable piston. When the piston is suddenly withdrawn, there is an instantaneous increase in the volume of the chamber, which causes a decrease in both the pressure and temperature. As a result, the air becomes supersaturated with vapor. Charged particles moving through this supersaturated air contain ions on which the vapor condenses, forming paths or tracks. These tracks can be photographed.

c. **Geiger Counter.** When radiations, such as alpha, beta, or gamma rays, collide with gas molecules, they remove electrons from these molecules, causing them to ionize and become conductors of electricity. This ionizing effect is used in the operation of the Geiger counter.

A Geiger counter is essentially a sealed chamber housing two electrodes in the presence of argon gas at low pressure. Voltage applied to the tube makes the tungsten electrode positive and the brass electrode negative. No current will flow through the tube, however, because the gas is normally nonconducting. In the presence of radiation, the gas becomes ionized and permits the momentary flow of current. The current may be amplified and allowed to operate a counter or a clicking device.

d. **Electroscope.** Another device which makes use of the ionizing effects of charged particles is the electroscope. The electroscope consists of a flask through which a metal knob projects. The metal knob is connected through an insulated conductor to a pair of gold leaves. When the electroscope is charged, the leaves acquire the same charge, causing them to repel each other and diverge. A sample of radioactive material placed near the electroscope causes the air around it to ionize and become a good conductor. The ionized air conducts the electric charge away from the knob. This causes a charged electroscope to become partially or completely discharged, as indicated by the collapse of the leaves. The extent to which the leaves collapse and the rate of convergence are an indication of the amount of radioactivity.

5. PRODUCTION OF ARTIFICIALLY RADIOACTIVE ELEMENTS

a. **Bombarding the Nucleus.** Many stable elements can be made artificially radioactive by intense nuclear bombardment. The problem is essentially for certain particles (subatomic bullets) to pass through the shells of electrons and penetrate the positively charged nucleus.

> The nuclear capture or ejection of electrons, protons, neutrons, deuterons (heavy hydrogen nuclei) results in transmutation of the element.

The nucleus formed by transmutation may become unstable and emit radiation. Particles that can be used as subatomic bullets are illustrated below.

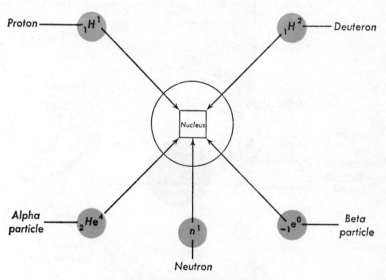

Fig. 5a. Subatomic Bullets

The mass and velocity of the subatomic particles will determine the extent to which the nucleus will be penetrated. These particles may be activated to very high energies by various types of machines called accelerators.

b. **Charged-particle Accelerators.** These machines accelerate various charged particles in such a way as to smash the atom and bring about transmutation. Accelerators make it possible to control the energy, intensity, and direction of the charged particles to be used as projectiles. The particles most commonly accelerated are protons, deuterons, alpha particles, and electrons. Neutrons, because they are uncharged, cannot be accelerated. (Actually, when neutrons are used, they are frequently slowed down to make them effective.)

There are two types of accelerators, linear and circular. Linear accelerators produce particles of relatively low energy; circular accelerators, such as the *cyclotron,* produce high-speed particles of tremendous energy.

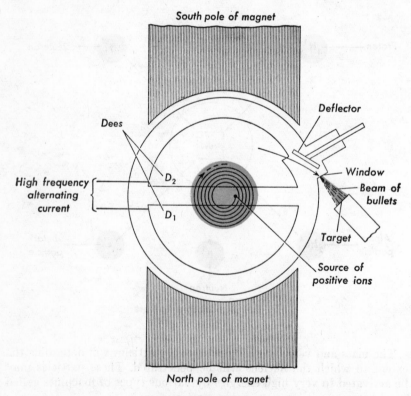

Fig. 5b. The Cyclotron

The unit used to describe the amount of energy possessed by accelerated charged particles is the *electron volt*. One electron volt is the energy acquired by an electron in passing through a potential difference of one volt. Since the electron volt is a relatively small unit of energy, larger units, the *Mev* and *Bev*, are used.

Mev = Million electron volts
Bev = Billion electron volts

The cyclotron, devised by E. O. Lawrence, an American scientist, consists of a flat, metal box from which the air has been exhausted. (See Fig. 5b.) Inside the box are two semicircular, D-shaped, hollow electrodes called dees, which are separated by a gap. The dees are surrounded by the poles of a powerful electromagnet and serve as electrodes for a high frequency alternating current. A heated filament at the center of the dees causes the incoming gas to form positive ions. The charged particles, by alternate attraction and repulsion, properly timed, move in an ever-widening spiral path. When the particles have attained tremendous speeds, they are allowed to escape and are deflected toward the target. In this way, these particles acquire ever-increasing velocities until their energies are sufficient to make them effective atom smashers.

A typical cyclotron accelerates particles and develops energies as shown below:

Protons . . . .   8 Mev
Deuterons . . . . 16 Mev
Alpha particles . . . . 32 Mev

Other types of accelerators, together with the particles they accelerate and the energies attained by the particles, are listed below:

ACCELERATOR	PARTICLE	ENERGY
Synchrotron	Electron	70 Mev
Betatron	Electron	100 Mev
Cosmotron	Proton	3 Bev
Bevatron	Proton	7 Bev

6. MASS AND ENERGY

It had been known for a long time that matter could be neither created nor destroyed, but could readily be changed from one form into another. This, the Law of Conservation of Matter, was first demonstrated by Lavoisier in 1774, when he disproved the phlogiston theory. It was also found that energy, like matter, could be neither created nor destroyed, but could also be changed from one form to another. This fundamental law of science is known as the Law of Conservation of Energy. It remained for Albert Einstein, in 1905, to propose the idea that matter (mass) and energy are interrelated, that is, matter can be converted into energy and energy can be converted into matter. The fundamental laws of mass and energy have been combined into the *Law of Conservation of Mass-Energy:*

The total amount of mass and energy in the universe cannot be changed but is interconvertible.

This law suggested for the first time the possibility of releasing atomic or nuclear energy.

The formula proposed by Einstein

$$E = mc^2$$

can be used to calculate the amount of energy released from a given amount of matter. In this formula, E represents energy, expressed in units called ergs; m represents the amount of matter (mass) in grams; and c stands for the velocity of light expressed in centimeters/sec. To calculate properly the energy derived, correct units must be used. The energy (in ergs) obtained from one gram of mass may be determined by multiplying one gram by the square of the velocity of light $(3 \times 10^{10}$ cm/sec) expressed in metric units.

$E = mc^2$

$E = 1$ gram $\times (3 \times 10^{10}$ cm/sec$)^2$

$E = 9 \times 10^{20}$ ergs of energy, which is equivalent to 25 million kilowatt-hours

Thus, one gram of mass will yield 25 million kilowatt-hours of energy. One pound (454 grams) of matter will yield 11.4 billion kilowatt-hours of energy ($454 \times 25{,}000{,}000$), whereas the liberation of an equal amount of energy would require burning almost two million tons of coal. The reason for the production of such tremendous quantities of energy from relatively little mass can be readily seen from the Einstein equation, in which mass is multiplied by the square of the velocity of light (a very large number).

When a uranium-235 atom is split (undergoes fission), only one-tenth of one per cent of its mass is transformed into energy. Therefore, one pound of U-235 produces 0.001×11.4 billion or 11.4 million kilowatt-hours of energy.

7. MASS DEFECT AND BINDING ENERGY

Where does the nucleus of an atom get its energy? We have learned that all nuclei (except hydrogen) contain protons and neutrons. It has been estimated that the force of repulsion between the similarly charged protons in the nucleus is enormous. Yet, since most nuclei are stable, there must be energy present in the nucleus sufficiently large to counteract this force of repulsion. The source of this energy can be generally explained by the Einstein equation.

The combination of protons and neutrons to form a stable atomic nucleus always results in the loss of mass.

Note that the actual mass of the nucleus is always slightly less than the total calculated mass of the nuclear particles (nucleons) which make up the nucleus.

According to the Einstein equation, the mass difference, which is known as the *mass defect*, results in the formation of tremendous energy. This energy, called *binding energy*, represents the force counteracting the repulsive force in the nucleus, thereby holding the nucleons together. In order to split (fission) an atom, this binding energy must be overcome.

To illustrate mass defect, let us consider the helium nucleus. A helium nucleus consists of two neutrons and two protons. The mass number (sum of the protons and neutrons) of helium is therefore 4 and its atomic number is 2. Since the calculated mass of a proton is 1.00758, while the calculated mass of a neutron is 1.00893, it follows that the total mass of the helium nucleus is

$$(2 \times 1.00758) + (2 \times 1.00893) \text{ or } 4.03302$$

The actual mass of the helium nucleus has been found to be 4.003, or approximately 0.030 mass unit less than the 4.033 calculated above for the separate particles. The difference or mass defect of 0.030 mass unit represents the binding energy of the nucleons in the helium nucleus. This means that energy corresponding to 0.030 mass unit must be added to the helium nucleus to separate it into its nucleons (fission).

The mass defect is also applicable to the reverse situation (fusion). Thus, when nuclei are formed from their component particles, enormous amounts of energy are released equivalent to the mass defect or binding energy of the nuclei. The energy of the sun is believed to be largely due to the fusion of hydrogen nuclei to form helium nuclei. How energy is derived from this change will be considered later.

8. HOW ATOMS MAY ACHIEVE MAXIMUM STABILITY

The tremendous energy released in nuclear reactions is the result of atomic fission or atomic fusion.

Fission is the splitting of an atom, or, more accurately, an atomic nucleus.

Fusion is the building up of heavier nuclei from lighter nuclei.

In Fig. 8, binding energy (stability) is related graphically to mass number. Note that maximum binding energy occurs at about mass number 60. This means that the nuclei of atoms about mass number 60 are most stable. To achieve maximum stability, lighter nuclei such as hydrogen must fuse, while heavier nuclei such as uranium must fission.

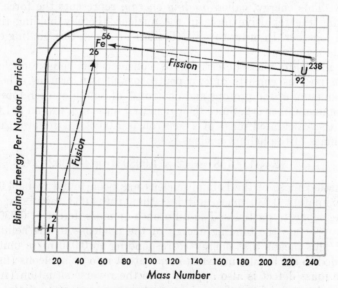

Fig. 8. Binding Energy Curve

9. ATOMIC FISSION

a. **Splitting the Atom.** Fission is brought about by bombarding fissionable atoms with neutrons. The products are fission fragments (particles containing atoms of lower atomic weight), large amounts of energy, and additional neutrons. Below, a uranium nucleus (U-235) is shown being bombarded with slow neutrons.

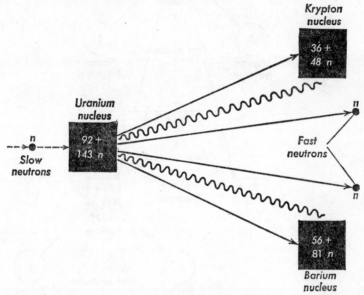

Fig. 9a. Atomic Fission

The combined mass of the fission fragments (Ba-137 + Kr-84 = 221) is less than the original mass of the material undergoing fission (U-235). This mass difference is accounted for by the ejected neutrons and the conversion of some mass into energy in accordance with the Einstein equation. It is the ejected neutrons, however, that are responsible for a self-sustaining source of energy.

b. **Chain Reactions.** Let us consider what happens when a neutron source is directed at a fissionable atom, such as U-235. As shown in Fig. 9b, a U-235 nucleus captures a single neutron and splits into fragments, usually consisting of barium (*A* on figure), krypton (*B*), and three new neutrons. If one of these three ejected neutrons is captured by another U-235 atom, a second fission occurs. The products of this second fission liberate more neutrons, which can produce a third fission, and so on.

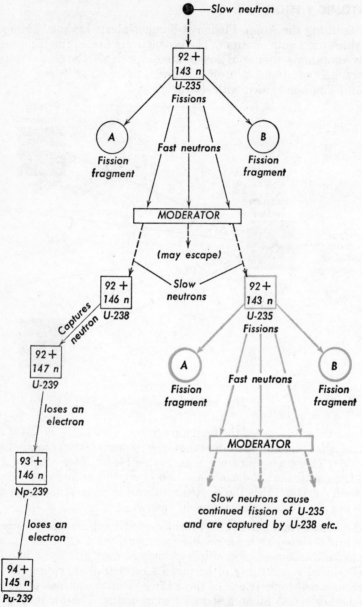

Fig. 9b. Chain Reaction

A series of successive fissions is called a **chain reaction.**

(Nuclear equations for a series of fissions appear on page 364.)

The size or mass of the U-235 is critical in the formation of a chain reaction. The number of neutrons that escape depends on the surface area of fissionable material present, while the number of neutrons captured depends upon the volume. As the mass of the fissionable material increases, the volume increases faster than the surface area. The critical size is that size of fissionable material at which the number of neutrons captured exceeds the number which escape. This is the same as saying that critical mass is that mass of material just large enough to maintain a chain reaction. Thus, when the critical mass of U-235 is used, U-235 nuclei capture neutrons as fast as they are produced, and instantaneous fission occurs, resulting in a violent explosion. If the emitted neutrons are slowed down sufficiently, controlled fission occurs in place of an instantaneous explosion; and the energy developed is released in the form of heat. Controlled fission is utilized in the nuclear reactor and will be discussed later.

Fissionable U-235, which is an isotope of the more abundant U-238, can be separated from it with great difficulty by physical methods, such as gaseous diffusion (see **6,** page 130) and electromagnetic separation. However, the separation processes were found so difficult that chemists were forced to seek other fissionable materials. As a result, plutonium (Pu-239) was manufactured from U-238. The separation of fissionable Pu-239 from U-238 is essentially a chemical problem because it involves two elements with different chemical properties.

10. ATOMIC FUSION

Atoms of lightweight elements may undergo fusion to form elements of increased atomic weight. Such a process is called atomic fusion and can be readily illustrated by nuclear reactions involving hydrogen or isotopes of hydrogen. In these reactions, the product formed weighs less than the combined weight of the atoms which undergo fusion. The loss of weight or mass accounts for the tremendous amounts of energy resulting from fusion reactions, despite the fact that energy must be supplied to bring about the fusion. A simple illustration of atomic fusion is shown in the following equation:

$$_1H^1 + {}_1H^1 + {}_1H^1 + {}_1H^1 \rightarrow \quad {}_2He^4 \quad + \text{energy}$$

$$\underbrace{\phantom{_1H^1 + {}_1H^1 + {}_1H^1 + {}_1H^1}}$$

4 hydrogen atoms
Total atomic weight =
$4 \times 1.00758 = 4.03032$

1 helium atom
Atomic weight = 4.003

In this reaction it can be seen that four atoms of hydrogen have combined to form one atom of helium with a loss of 0.030 unit of mass. The conversion of hydrogen into helium always results in the loss of mass.

Another example of a fusion reaction is:

$$_1H^2 \; + \; _1H^3 \; \rightarrow \; _2He^4 + \; _0n^1 \; + \text{energy}$$

deuterium   tritium   helium   neutron

Solar energy may be the result of the fusion of hydrogen atoms to form helium. Although the entire process is probably more complex, it is believed that four hydrogen nuclei or the nuclei of four hydrogen isotopes unite to form a helium nucleus, liberating energy on the order of 30 million electron volts. Since reactions involving the fusion of atoms occur at solar temperatures of several million degrees, they are also known as *thermonuclear reactions*.

11. FISSION AND FUSION BOMBS

a. **Fission Bomb.** The atomic bomb is a nuclear fission bomb containing a critical mass of fissionable material. In order to control the explosion of the atomic bomb, the fissionable material is divided into two portions, each below the critical mass. The total of the two portions, however, is just above the critical mass. When these portions are suddenly brought together, the critical mass is exceeded and the bomb explodes. The explosion is the result of a chain reaction in which the number of neutrons multiplies indefinitely. In a nonexplosive chain reaction, the number of neutrons builds up to a certain controlled level and then remains constant.

b. **Fusion Bomb.** The hydrogen bomb is a fusion bomb. It is called a thermonuclear bomb because extremely high temperatures are required to initiate the fusion process, which itself liberates even greater quantities of heat. Hydrogen bombs are therefore probably triggered by atomic bombs. As has already been explained, the fusion of hydrogen or hydrogen isotopes into helium results in a loss of mass. This mass defect, according to the Einstein equation, accounts for the tremendous energy liberated. The advantage of a fusion bomb over a fission bomb is that the amount of material used in the fusion bomb is not limited by any critical size. Since a hydrogen bomb can be built to any specification and dimension, its destructive power is unlimited.

Atomic bomb—Nuclear fission bomb
Hydrogen bomb—Nuclear fusion bomb

---

12. NUCLEAR REACTORS

The nuclear reactor, or atomic pile, is a device for producing nuclear energy by the controlled fission of a radioactive fuel, such as U-238. The atomic pile also may be used to produce artificial elements, such as neptunium and plutonium. Radioactive isotopes, or radioisotopes, useful in medicine, science, and industry, are also products of the atomic pile.

The **atomic pile** is nothing more than an atomic bomb so designed that a controlled, instead of an explosive chain reaction, will occur.

The earliest nuclear reactors were built in Oak Ridge, Tennessee, in 1943. This type of reactor, shown in Fig. 12, consists essentially of:

a. **A Fuel That Is a Fissionable Material.** The fuel is usually naturally occurring uranium, which consists of 99.3% U-238, 0.7% U-235, and a trace of U-234. The fuel may be enriched by the addition of U-235. The amount of uranium used is sufficient to sustain a chain reaction. The uranium is sealed in aluminum cans, which are inserted into the reactor.

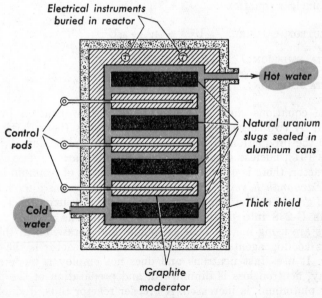

Fig. 12. A Nuclear Reactor

b. **A Moderator.** The moderator, which makes up most of the reactor, usually consists of carbon in the form of graphite. The moderator slows down the neutrons so that they may either bring about a controlled fission or be captured by U-238 to produce plutonium.

c. **A Neutron Control.** Control rods of cadmium or boron steel, both of which are good neutron absorbers, are inserted into the pile to provide additional control of the speed, energy, and activity of the neutrons.

d. **A Protective Shield.** A thick shield of concrete or steel is necessary to provide protection against the dangerous radiations emitted during operation of the pile. Because of its high density, lead can also be used as an effective shield.

e. **A Cooling Agent (Coolant).** Water is circulated through the reactor to absorb the tremendous amount of heat generated. The reactor may also be air-cooled. The heat produced during operation of the reactor can be converted into mechanical power or electricity.

A number of reactions occur in this reactor. Neutrons initially cause some U-235 to fission. Other neutrons strike U-238 and in a series of steps produce plutonium. These steps may be summarized by the following nuclear equations:

NEUTRON CAPTURE: $_{92}U^{238} + _{0}n^1 \rightarrow _{92}U^{239}$

BETA EMISSION: $_{92}U^{239} \rightarrow _{93}Np^{239} + _{-1}e^0$

BETA EMISSION: $_{93}Np^{239} \rightarrow _{94}Pu^{239} + _{-1}e^0$

These equations show that capture of a slow neutron by $_{92}U^{238}$ followed by two successive emissions of electrons (beta particles) results in the production of fissionable man-made plutonium, $_{94}Pu^{239}$.

Since 1943, nuclear engineers have devised a variety of reactors. In each reactor, there is essentially controlled fission of uranium isotopes. In the *Savannah River reactor*, heavy water is used as a moderator in place of graphite. The *Hanford reactor* is a slow-neutron reactor which converts U-238 into plutonium and uses water as a coolant. Other reactors are using metals such as sodium and potassium in the liquid state as cooling agents. An example of such a reactor is the *breeder reactor*. It uses fast neutrons and does not employ a moderator. In this way, neutron loss is diminished, and preparation of the product, usually plutonium, is increased. A breeder reactor thus produces more fissionable material than it consumes.

13. RADIOISOTOPES

Numerous radioactive isotopes (radioisotopes) are produced in the nuclear reactor as a result of neutron bombardment or atomic fission. Radioisotopes disintegrate spontaneously, emitting radiation. Because the radiation can be detected, these isotopes are called tracer isotopes or "tagged atoms."

Tracer isotopes are used to study chemical processes in plants and animals. Several radioisotopes are also being used in place of radium for the treatment of cancer. Cobalt-60 is used in the treatment of certain forms of cancer. Iodine-131 is used in treating cancer of the thyroid, and phosphorus-27 is used in treating bone cancer.

14. THE NUCLEAR AGE

The birth of the atomic age was marked by the explosion of the first atomic bomb in 1945. The destructive force of the atomic bomb, originally equivalent to 20,000 tons of TNT, has been supplemented by the hydrogen bomb, with an explosive force one thousand times as great. Explosions produced by atomic bombs are accompanied by severe shock waves, temperatures near 5,000°C, and deadly radiation. Explosions of hydrogen bombs, in addition, send a cloud of radioactive particles miles into the sky. These particles eventually settle in the form of a dust, called *radioactive fallout*. Fallout contaminates water and food supplies, and causes severe body injury. Some scientists believe that fallout may alter the genetic structure of the body in future generations. Recognizing the dangers of fallout, scientists are endeavoring to develop a "clean bomb," that is, one that will minimize the harmful effects of fallout.

15. NUCLEAR ENERGY—DESTRUCTIVE WEAPON OR SERVANT OF MAN?

Since the dropping of the first atomic bomb, nuclear energy has been regarded with horror as an instrument of war. It is believed that man's survival is possible only by some system of international control under the sponsorship of the United Nations. Toward this end, the nations of the world have been holding conferences to reach agreement.

The bomb is said by some observers to be an instrument of peace rather than war, since it acts as a deterrent to any would-be aggressors. Furthermore, research has uncovered many peacetime uses for this new and vital force. It may soon rival petroleum and coal as a source of energy. Atomic engines have already been designed and some are in use in ships and submarines. An atomic submarine has already made a successful trip around the world, utilizing a minute quantity of nuclear fuel. Nuclear power plants are presently being constructed which will generate tremendous quantities of electricity economically. Although chemical fuels are still more practical for rockets, space travel will be eased considerably with engines powered by atomic energy.

The impact of this mighty force has just begun to be felt. All signs point to the discovery of nuclear energy as one of the foremost scientific achievements of all time.

1. *a.* Nuclear science deals with the _____ and _____ of atomic nuclei.
   b. List three important applications of nucleonics.
2. *a.* An example of an element that has an unstable nucleus is (1) polonium (2) nickel (3) iron (4) cobalt.
   b. Radioactive elements undergo _____ disintegration accompanied by the emission of _____.
   c. Natural radioactivity was first discovered by (1) Madame Curie (2) Becquerel (3) Einstein (4) Rutherford.
   d. An example of a radium ore is (1) sphalerite (2) pitchblende (3) cassiterite (4) cinnabar.
3. *a.* The following is a list of some of the comparative properties of alpha, beta, and gamma particles. After each property, indicate the correct particle.
   (1) represented by the symbol $_{-1}e^0$
   (2) have a nuclear charge of 2
   (3) are X-rays of very short wave length
   (4) have highest density
   (5) are most penetrating
   (6) have lowest speed
   b. By means of a labeled diagram, show how the three types of radioactive emanations can be separated.
4. *a.* The first artificial nuclear disintegration was carried out by *Rutherford*. [True or false? If false, correct the italicized term.]
   b. State the two important steps required to balance a nuclear equation.
   c. Complete and balance each of the following nuclear equations:
   (1) $_7N^{14} + _2He^4 \rightarrow _1H^1 +$ _____
   (2) $_{90}Th^{234} \rightarrow _{91}Pa^{234} +$ _____
   (3) $_{93}Np^{239} \rightarrow _{-1}e^0 +$ _____
   (4) $_5B^{11} + _2He^4 \rightarrow _0n^1 +$ _____
   (5) $_{27}Co^{59} + _1H^3 \rightarrow _{27}Co^{61} +$ _____

d. What is meant by transmutation?

e. The addition or removal of _____ from the nucleus of an element results in transmutation.

5. a. The emission of alpha or beta particles causes the nucleus to _____.

b. When an atom emits an alpha particle, its atomic number (1) increases by one (2) remains unchanged (3) decreases by two (4) decreases by four.

c. When an atom emits a beta particle, its atomic weight (1) increases by one (2) remains unchanged (3) decreases by two (4) decreases by four.

d. Since the nucleus of an atom does not contain electrons, how does beta disintegration occur?

e. Complete and balance each of the following nuclear equations:
   (1) $_{94}Pu^{239} \rightarrow {}_2He^4 +$ _____
   (2) $_{92}U^{238} \rightarrow {}_{90}Th^{234} +$ _____
   (3) $_{15}P^{32} \rightarrow {}_{16}S^{32} +$ _____

*f. Using nuclear equations, show how lead-206 is formed from uranium-238 by alpha and beta disintegration.

6. a. As the temperature is increased, the rate of decay for a given radioactive element _____ (decreases, increases, remains the same).

b. The half-life of polonium-210 is 140 days. In 70 days, one gram of polonium-210 will decrease in mass to (1) one-half (2) one-quarter (3) three-fourths (4) one-eighth gram.

*c. How is the half-life of radioactive elements utilized in estimating the age of the earth?

7. a. Describe a device which detects radiation by its fluorescent effect.

b. Describe the construction and operation of a Wilson cloud chamber.

c. Make a labeled diagram of a Geiger counter.

d. How does the Geiger counter detect and measure radiation?

e. An electroscope detects radiation by utilizing its _____ effects.

8. a. Intense nuclear bombardment may result in *transmutation* of an element. [True or false? If false, correct the italicized term.]

b. List four commonly used subatomic bullets.

c. The extent to which a nucleus can be penetrated depends upon the (1) mass (2) velocity (3) force (4) mass and velocity of the projectiles used.

9. a. What is the function of a particle accelerator?

b. Distinguish between linear and circular accelerators.

c. Describe the principle of operation of the cyclotron.

d. Accelerated charged particles possess energy measured in _____ units.

e. List four types of accelerators and indicate the particle accelerated by each.

10. a. The Law of Conservation of Matter states that _____.

b. The interrelation between matter and energy was first proposed by (1) Lavoisier (2) Newton (3) Einstein (4) the Curies.

c. The Law of Conservation of Mass-Energy states that _____.

d. As the amount of mass increases, the amount of energy that it will yield from the equation $E = mc^2$ _____ (decreases, increases, remains the same).

e. Using Einstein's equation, explain why tremendous quantities of energy may be obtained from relatively small quantities of matter.

11. a. When neutrons and protons combine to form a stable nucleus, the actual mass of the nucleus is (1) slightly less than (2) slightly more than (3)

either slightly less or slightly more than (4) the same as   the calculated mass of the nucleons.

b. The energy which counteracts the forces of repulsion in the nucleus is called _____.

c. Using the lithium nucleus, illustrate what is meant by mass defect.

d. The separation of a nucleus into its nucleons is called (1) fission (2) fusion (3) transmutation (4) decomposition.

e. Solar energy is thought to result from the *fission* of hydrogen nuclei. [True or false? If false, correct the italicized term.]

12.*a. Why do light nuclei tend to fuse, while heavy nuclei tend to fission?

b. As the stability of nuclei increases, their binding energies _____ (increase, decrease).

13. a. When an atom is split, the fission fragments weigh _____ (more, less) than the fissionable atom.

b. The products of fission include _____, without which there can be no self-sustaining source of energy.

c. When a neutron fissions a U-235 nucleus, _____ new neutrons are ejected.

d. A series of successive fissions is called *a chain reaction*. [True or false? If false, correct the italicized term.]

e. The size of fissionable material at which the number of neutrons captured exceeds the number that escapes is known as _____.

f. How does controlled fission differ from instantaneous fission?

g. How are each of the fission processes mentioned in f used?

h. The uranium isotopes can be separated by (1) electrolysis (2) selective precipitation (3) dialysis (4) gaseous diffusion.

i. Why is the separation process mentioned in h so difficult?

j. A fissionable material that can be manufactured from U-238 is _____.

14. a. The formation of atoms of increased atomic weight from atoms of lesser atomic weight is called (1) transformation (2) transmutation (3) fission (4) fusion.

b. In the nuclear reaction $4\ _1H^1 \rightarrow\ _2He^4$, account for the liberation of energy.

c. What is meant by a thermonuclear reaction?

15. a. The atomic bomb is a (1) fission bomb (2) fusion bomb (3) thermonuclear bomb (4) high-explosive bomb of unlimited size.

b. In an atomic bomb, the total fissionable material (1) equals (2) is less than (3) is greater than (4) is sometimes greater and sometimes less than   the critical size.

c. In an explosive chain reaction, the number of neutrons produced _____.

d. In a nonexplosive chain reaction, the number of neutrons (1) decreases (2) increases (3) remains the same (4) increases at first and then remains constant.

e. Why are hydrogen bombs called thermonuclear bombs?

f. The size of a fusion bomb is _____ (limited, unlimited).

16. a. Nuclear energy from a (an) _____ (explosive, nonexplosive) chain reaction is obtained in nuclear reactors.

b. An artificial element produced in the atomic pile is _____.

c. The atomic pile produces _____ for use in medicine.

d. Using a labeled diagram, show the important parts of a nuclear reactor.

e. Indicate a specific use for each of the parts shown in d.

f. By means of nuclear equations, show how $_{94}Pu^{239}$ is made in a nuclear reactor.

g. A reactor which uses heavy water as a moderator is called _____.

h. The coolant in the Hanford reactor is (1) liquid sodium (2) liquid potassium (3) heavy water (4) water.

i. The reactor which does not employ a moderator and uses fast neutrons is the (1) Savannah River (2) Hanford (3) breeder (4) Oak Ridge reactor.

17. *a.* Why are radioisotopes sometimes called "tagged atoms"?

b. Two radioisotopes used in the treatment of disease are _____ and _____.

c. In tabular form, compare the destructive force of atomic and hydrogen bombs under the following headings:

(1) explosive force

(2) temperatures and pressures created

(3) radiation hazard

APPENDIX

1. FINAL REVIEW QUESTIONS

Multiple-Choice Questions

Write the number preceding the term that best completes the statement or answers the question.

1. A substance classified as a compound is (1) argon (2) plutonium (3) sugar (4) water gas.
2. The symbol for lead is (1) P (2) Pb (3) Po (4) Pt.
3. The products of the combustion of coal gas weigh (1) less than (2) more than (3) the same as (4) exactly half as much as the original weight of the gas.
4. Liquid air is an important source of (1) argon (2) carbon dioxide (3) chlorine (4) hydrogen.
5. In order to produce two liters of ozone, how many liters of oxygen must be completely converted? (1) 1 (2) 2 (3) 3 (4) 4.
6. The number of atoms in the ozone molecule is (1) 1 (2) 2 (3) 3 (4) 4.
7. Hydrogen gas may be dried by running it through a tube filled with calcium (1) carbonate (2) chloride (3) fluoride (4) hydroxide.
8. A thistle tube is standard equipment in the laboratory preparation of (1) hydrogen (2) nitric acid (3) iodine (4) slaked lime.
9. When sodium reacts with water and the resulting solution is evaporated, the residue is (1) hydrogen (2) sodium chloride (3) sodium hydroxide (4) water.
10. Hydrogen may be prepared by the reaction between iron and (1) dilute HNO_3 (2) concentrated HNO_3 (3) dilute H_2SO_4 (4) concentrated H_2SO_4.
11. Which metal requires the highest temperature in order to liberate hydrogen from water? (1) iron (2) lithium (3) potassium (4) sodium.
12. When water is added to anhydrous copper sulfate, the solution formed is (1) black (2) blue (3) white (4) yellow.
13. The presence of water of crystallization in washing soda may be detected by (1) dissolving (2) heating (3) precipitating (4) touching the washing soda.
14. Water may be decomposed into hydrogen and oxygen by (1) electrolysis (2) hydrolysis (3) osmosis (4) synthesis.
15. The term "heavy water" refers to (1) deuterium oxide (2) ice (3) redistilled water (4) water at 4°C.
16. After salt water has been distilled, the salt is found in the (1) condenser (2) cooling water (3) distilling flask (4) receiver.
17. Large quantities of drinking water are usually prepared from impure water by (1) ion exchange (2) distillation (3) boiling (4) aeration.
18. It is possible to make a concentrated solution of (1) barium nitrate (2) calcium hydroxide (3) lead chloride (4) silver sulfate.

19. The ratio of hydrogen to oxygen in water, by weight, is (1) 1:2 (2) 1:8 (3) 2:1 (4) 8:1.

20. The correct way to represent the chloride ion is (1) Cl^0 (2) Cl^- (3) Cl_2^0 (4) Cl^{+7}.

21. The element of atomic number 9 is closest in chemical properties to the element of atomic number (1) 8 (2) 10 (3) 17 (4) 19.

22. The charge on the nucleus of an atom is due to an excess of (1) electrons (2) ions (3) neutrons (4) protons.

23. Lithium atoms will combine with atoms of the element having the atomic number (1) 10 (2) 2 (3) 13 (4) 17.

24. The number of electrons in the innermost orbit of any element other than hydrogen is (1) 1 (2) 2 (3) 8 (4) 18.

25. Isotopes of the same element have different numbers of (1) atoms (2) electrons (3) neutrons (4) protons.

26. The number of electrons in the outermost orbit of any inert gas other than helium is (1) 6 (2) 2 (3) 8 (4) 18.

27. The formula SO_4 represents (1) an acid (2) a compound (3) a radical (4) a salt.

28. The neutrons in an atom (1) determine the atomic number (2) equal the number of electrons (3) revolve around the nucleus (4) contribute no charge to the atom.

29. Deuterium has an atomic number of (1) 1 (2) 2 (3) 3 (4) 4.

30. A difference between a molecule of ammonia and an ammonium ion is one (1) electron (2) neutron (3) positron (4) proton.

31. Oxidation occurs in a chemical reaction only when there is also (1) filtration (2) precipitation (3) reduction (4) sublimation.

32. When sulfur dioxide decolorizes potassium permanganate, a product is manganous sulfate. The valence number of manganese has changed from (1) $+7$ to $+2$ (2) $+6$ to $+4$ (3) -7 to -2 (4) $+4$ to $+2$.

33. If two containers of different gases under the same conditions have the same number of molecules, the gases must have (1) an equal number of atoms (2) equal molecular weights (3) equal volumes (4) equal weights.

34. The ratio of the weight of water to the weight of hydrogen it contains is (1) 8 to 1 (2) 2 to 1 (3) 9 to 1 (4) 18 to 1.

35. Potassium chlorate is a salt of (1) chlorous acid (2) chloric acid (3) hydrochloric acid (4) hypochlorous acid.

36. The compound $K_2Cr_2O_7$ should act as (1) a reducing agent (2) an oxidizing agent (3) an anhydride (4) an organic acid.

37. The missing term, x, in the equation $x + H_2SO_4 \rightarrow CaSO_4 + 2\ H_2O$ is (1) CaH_2 (2) CaO (3) $Ca(OH)_2$ (4) CaS.

38. An acid that forms sulfide salts is (1) hydrosulfuric (2) persulfuric (3) sulfuric (4) sulfurous.

39. The number of molecules of sulfuric acid that will be neutralized by two molecules of potassium hydroxide is (1) 1 (2) 2 (3) 3 (4) 4.

40. An example of oxidation is (1) $Cl^- - e \rightarrow Cl^0$ (2) $Na^+ + e \rightarrow Na^0$ (3) $Fe^{+3} + e \rightarrow Fe^{+2}$ (4) $Br^0 + e \rightarrow Br^-$.

41. The weight of 22.4 liters of carbon monoxide is (1) 22.4 (2) 28 (3) 44 (4) 56 grams.

42. In the formula $Al_2(SO_4)_3$, the total number of atoms represented is (1) 5 (2) 6 (3) 14 (4) 17.

43. The number of atoms in a molecule of $Na_2CO_3 \cdot 10\ H_2O$ is (1) 16 (2) 26 (3) 36 (4) 42.

44. A compound containing 50% oxygen by weight is (1) CO_2 (2) FeO (3) H_2O (4) SO_2.

45. Molecular weights may be determined by the use of a principle developed by (1) Avogadro (2) Cavendish (3) Gay-Lussac (4) Priestley.

46. The weight of one liter of hydrogen in grams is approximately (1) 1 (2) 2 (3) 0.09 (4) 22.4.

47. Approximately equal volumes of gas are represented by hydrogen weighing 2 grams and oxygen weighing (1) 8 (2) 16 (3) 32 (4) 48   grams.

48. Under standard conditions of temperature and pressure, the number of molecules in equal volumes of oxygen and ozone are in the ratio of (1) 1:1 (2) 1:2 (3) 1:3 (4) 2:3.

49. If a mixture of 8 ml of oxygen and 4 ml of hydrogen is exploded, there is left uncombined (1) 2.0 ml of hydrogen (2) 3.0 ml of hydrogen (3) 6.0 ml of oxygen (4) 7.5 ml of oxygen.

50. In balanced equations, both sides always represent the same number of (1) atoms (2) coefficients (3) ions (4) molecules.

51. To compare the densities of gaseous compounds, compare their (1) atomic weights (2) molecular weights (3) odors (4) solubilities.

52. During the electrolysis of water, 0.5 gram of hydrogen and 4 grams of oxygen were produced. The quantity of water decomposed was (1) 4.5 (2) 2 (3) 5 (4) 18   grams.

53. The ratio of the combining volumes of nitrogen and ammonia in the equation $N_2 + 3\ H_2 \rightarrow 2\ NH_3$ is (1) 1:2 (2) 2:2 (3) 1:3 (4) 2:8.

54. The total number of atoms of carbon in the formula $K_3Fe(CN)_6$ is (1) 1 (2) 3 (3) 6 (4) 12.

55. The amount of mercury that can be obtained from 5 grams of mercuric oxide is (1) more than 5 grams (2) less than 5 grams (3) exactly 5 grams (4) exactly 5.1 grams.

56. The ratio by weight of sulfur to oxygen in sulfur dioxide is (1) 1:2 (2) 2:1 (3) 1:1 (4) 1:3.

57. Bromine may be prepared from sodium bromide by treating the salt with (1) chlorine (2) iodine (3) hydrochloric acid (4) potassium chloride.

58. Three substances produced by the electrolysis of brine are chlorine, hydrogen, and (1) NaOH (2) HCl (3) KOH (4) $CaCl_2$.

59. Bleaching powder has the formula (1) $CaOCl_2$ (2) $Ca(ClO_3)_2$ (3) $Ca(ClO_2)_2$ (4) $Ca(OCl)_2$.

60. Chlorine chemically resembles oxygen because it (1) acts as a reducing agent (2) has a valence of one (3) is lighter than air (4) acts as an oxidizing agent.

61. The formula Cl_2 represents one (1) atom (2) ion (3) molecule (4) radical.

62. A powdered substance that bursts into flame when dropped into chlorine may be (1) antimony (2) carbon (3) silicon (4) sulfur.

63. A product formed when a hydrocarbon burns in chlorine is (1) CCl_4 (2) CO_2 (3) HCl (4) HClO.

64. In the preparation of chlorine by treating hydrochloric acid with manganese dioxide, the number of electrons gained by each manganese particle in manganese dioxide is (1) 1 (2) 2 (3) 3 (4) 4.

65. Iodine can be separated from a mixture of sand and iodine by (1) adding bromine water (2) adding chlorine water (3) adding MnO_2 and H_2SO_4 (4) heating.

66. The halogen acid most likely to decompose is (1) HBr (2) HCl (3) HF (4) HI.

67. Hydrochloric acid is (1) aqua fortis (2) aqua regia (3) liquid hydrogen chloride (4) a water solution of hydrogen chloride.

68. The reactions between water and nonmetallic oxides yield (1) acids (2) acid anhydrides (3) bases (4) salts.

69. The ionic equation $H^+ + OH^- \rightarrow H_2O$ represents (1) hydrolysis (2) neutralization (3) oxidation (4) reduction.

70. 44.8 liters of ozone under standard conditions of temperature and pressure weigh (1) 2.86 (2) 32 (3) 64 (4) 96 grams.

71. An acid can be produced from one of its salts by the use of an acid of (1) higher boiling point (2) higher density (3) lower boiling point (4) lower density.

72. An acid may have a pH of (1) 7 (2) 2 (3) 8 (4) 10.

73. A neutral salt is formed when sulfuric acid reacts completely with (1) zinc hydroxide (2) sodium hydroxide (3) ammonium hydroxide (4) copper hydroxide.

74. A lead-lined container should not be used to store solutions of (1) Na_2SO_4 (2) $FeSO_4$ (3) $AgNO_3$ (4) $ZnCl_2$.

75. A reaction will go to completion if one of the products formed is (1) K_2SO_4 (2) NaCl (3) NH_4NO_3 (4) PbS.

76. Of the following, the pair that contains two metals most similar to each other in chemical activity is (1) aluminum and gold (2) aluminum and potassium (3) calcium and iron (4) copper and silver.

77. Which reaction does not go to completion? (1) HCl and $Ba(OH)_2$ (2) H_2SO_4 and Na_2CO_3 (3) K_2CO_3 and $Pb(NO_3)_2$ (4) KNO_3 and NaCl.

78. When a strip of copper is placed in a solution of zinc nitrate, (1) each copper atom gains two electrons (2) each copper atom loses two electrons (3) the zinc ion is reduced (4) there is no reaction.

79. A yellow precipitate is formed when hydrogen sulfide is passed into a solution of (1) $Cd(NO_3)_2$ (2) $AgNO_3$ (3) $Pb(NO_3)_2$ (4) $Zn(NO_3)_2$.

80. Heating concentrated H_2SO_4 produces water and (1) SO_2 (2) SO_3 (3) O_2 (4) H_2S.

81. A sulfur compound that will readily dissolve roll sulfur is (1) H_2SO_4 (2) SO_2 (3) CS_2 (4) H_2S.

82. The reaction of a bisulfite with an acid usually yields (1) hydrogen (2) hydrogen sulfide (3) oxygen (4) sulfur dioxide.

83. If a bottle of concentrated sulfuric acid is allowed to stand open to the air, the level (1) rises (2) falls (3) remains the same (4) first rises, then falls.

84. The products formed in the incomplete combustion of hydrogen sulfide are (1) hydrogen and sulfur (2) hydrogen and sulfur dioxide (3) water and sulfur (4) water and sulfur dioxide.

85. Sulfur dioxide unites with oxygen in the presence of a catalyst to produce an oxide known as sulfur (1) dioxide (2) monoxide (3) tetroxide (4) trioxide.

86. The commercial form of sulfur produced by cooling sulfur vapor is (1) roll (2) flowers of (3) milk of (4) rhombic sulfur.

87. The most stable form of sulfur at room temperature is (1) amorphous (2) monoclinic (3) prismatic (4) rhombic.

88. A gas that is collected by the displacement of water in the laboratory is (1) ammonia (2) chlorine (3) nitric oxide (4) sulfur dioxide.

89. The gas produced when ammonium nitrite decomposes is (1) hydrogen (2) nitric oxide (3) nitrogen (4) nitrous oxide.

90. Legumes, such as clover, restore to the soil compounds of (1) nitrogen (2) phosphorus (3) potassium (4) sulfur.

91. A white deposit frequently found on the outside of laboratory glassware is formed by the reaction between ammonia gas and (1) $Ca(OH)_2$ (2) HCl (3) H_2O (4) H_2SO_4.

92. It is thought that lightning supplies the energy for the formation, from the air, of a considerable quantity of compounds of oxygen and (1) argon (2) carbon (3) hydrogen (4) nitrogen.

93. Nitric oxide has the formula (1) NO (2) N_2O (3) NO_2 (4) N_2O_4.

94. The weight of nitrogen compared with an equal volume of air is approximately (1) one-half as great (2) the same (3) twice as great (4) fourteen times as great.

95. Air is a mixture because it (1) is colorless (2) is odorless (3) does not have a uniform composition (4) may be liquefied.

96. Fixation of atmospheric nitrogen is accomplished by (1) electrolysis (2) fractional distillation (3) the contact process (4) the Haber process.

97. An acid-producing substance present in some baking powders is (1) baking soda (2) carbon dioxide (3) cream of tartar (4) sodium carbonate.

98. Of the following, the one that is not prepared in the electric furnace is (1) acetylene (2) carborundum (3) carbon disulfide (4) calcium carbide.

99. Large-scale water softening is accomplished by a process involving the use of (1) heat (2) distillation (3) ion exchange resins (4) washing soda.

100. A carbon compound used to make synthetic wood alcohol is (1) CO_2 (2) $CHCl_3$ (3) CO (4) H_2CO_3.

101. A diamond strongly heated in an excess of oxygen will (1) form only carbon dioxide (2) merely melt (3) not react with the oxygen (4) produce ozone.

102. A constituent of certain gaseous fuels is (1) CO_2 (2) O_2 (3) CO (4) H_2O.

103. Calcium carbide is formed by the reaction of (1) CaO and coke (2) Ca and coke (3) $Ca(OH)_2$ and CO_2 (4) $CaCO_3$ and HCl.

104. The dehydration of formic acid may be used as a laboratory source of (1) CO_2 (2) C_2H_2 (3) CO (4) CH_4.

105. Destructive distillation of soft coal yields (1) ammonia and coke (2) coal gas and acetic acid (3) coal tar and charcoal (4) methanol and benzene.

106. Carbon monoxide is (1) colorless and an oxidizing agent (2) combustible and a reducing agent (3) odorless and much denser than air (4) tasteless and very soluble in water.

107. A crystalline form of carbon is (1) boneblack (2) graphite (3) hard coal (4) lampblack.

108. An isotope of carbon has the atomic number (1) 6 (2) 11 (3) 12 (4) 13.

109. Sulfuric acid reacts with an unknown substance. A gas is produced. The unknown substance (1) is a chloride (2) is a carbonate (3) may be a carbonate (4) cannot be a carbonate.

110. An unknown gas burns with a pale-blue flame. After it has burned, the resulting compound causes limewater to become cloudy. The unknown gas is (1) carbon dioxide (2) nitrogen (3) carbon monoxide (4) hydrogen.

111. Uncombined hydrogen is found in (1) soda water (2) acids (3) hydrogen peroxide (4) water gas.

112. When coke and sand are heated in an electric furnace, a product obtained is (1) CaC_2 (2) SiF_4 (3) SiC (4) H_2CO_3.

113. Sodium carbonate is obtained by heating (1) NaCl (2) NaClO₃ (3) NaHCO₃ (4) NaHSO₄.

114. Sodium should be stored in (1) alcohol (2) kerosene (3) sawdust (4) water.

115. Potassium salts are important in the manufacture of (1) carborundum (2) fertilizers (3) plastics (4) washing soda.

116. In the electrolysis of fused sodium chloride, the substance liberated at the anode is (1) Cl₂ (2) H₂ (3) Na (4) NaOH.

117. The formula of a compound found in soda water is (1) C₆H₁₀O₅ (2) H₂CO₃ (3) Na₂CO₃ (4) NaOH.

118. An abundant raw material used in the commercial preparation of sodium hydroxide, hydrogen, and sodium is (1) NaCl (2) NaClO (3) NaHCO₃ (4) NaNO₃.

119. Water is said to be permanently hard if it contains dissolved (1) CaCl₂ (2) Ca(HCO₃)₂ (3) NaCl (4) Na₂CO₃.

120. If temporary hard water is boiled, a substance which will be formed is (1) CaCl₂ (2) CaCO₃ (3) Ca(HCO₃)₂ (4) CaSO₄.

121. Slaked lime is added to soil mainly to (1) adjust the pH (2) provide oxygen for plant growth (3) remove carbonates (4) hold moisture near the surface.

122. Bleaching powder is effective as a disinfectant because it (1) contains calcium (2) releases chlorine (3) is strongly acid (4) has a strong odor.

123. The formula for magnesium bicarbonate is (1) MgCO₃ (2) Mg(CO₃)₂ (3) MgHCO₃ (4) Mg(HCO₃)₂.

124. The compound CaOCl₂ is generally used (1) as a catalyst (2) as a fertilizer (3) to bleach cotton (4) to melt ice.

125. Phosphorus is obtained commercially from (1) P₄S₃ (2) P₂O₅ (3) H₃PO₄ (4) Ca₃(PO₄)₂.

126. The mechanical removal of impurities from ores is accomplished by a process which uses (1) coke (2) carbon monoxide (3) oil and air (4) coke and sand.

127. The reaction of a sulfide with oxygen is called (1) amalgamation (2) electrolysis (3) flotation (4) roasting.

128. Amalgamation requires the use of (1) gold (2) mercury (3) silver (4) platinum.

129. The limestone in some iron ores is removed by using (1) carbon filters (2) compressed air (3) sand (4) sulfuric acid.

130. Sterling silver is an alloy of silver and (1) copper (2) gold (3) tin (4) platinum.

131. In the extraction of aluminum from its oxide ore, the ore is dissolved in (1) bauxite (2) cryolite (3) sulfuric acid (4) water.

132. An example of an alloy is (1) duralumin (2) mercury (3) mortar (4) silver paint.

133. A metal that is found uncombined in nature is (1) zinc (2) aluminum (3) lead (4) gold.

134. Methyl salicylate is (1) a salt (2) a base (3) an ester (4) an acid.

135. The process by which benzene may be obtained from soft coal is (1) destructive distillation (2) fractional distillation (3) flotation (4) electrolysis.

136. Producer gas is a mixture of (1) acetylene and hydrogen (2) carbon monoxide and hydrogen (3) methane and oxygen (4) nitrogen and carbon monoxide.

137. Petroleum is chiefly a mixture of (1) alcohols (2) esters (3) hydrocarbons (4) oxides.

138. Using high temperatures and pressures to split petroleum molecules is called (1) cracking (2) destructive distillation (3) fission (4) fractional distillation.

139. In carbohydrates, the ratio of the number of hydrogen atoms to the number of oxygen atoms is (1) 1:1 (2) 1:2 (3) 2:1 (4) 2:2.

140. Natural gas is chiefly (1) carbon monoxide (2) ethane (3) hydrogen (4) methane.

141. The process of fermentation that produces ethyl alcohol from glucose also produces (1) CO_2 (2) H_2 (3) H_2O (4) O_2.

142. The action of concentrated sulfuric acid on carbohydrates is known as (1) dehydration (2) esterification (3) hydrolysis (4) oxidation.

143. Large amounts of sodium hydroxide are used in the manufacture of (1) soap (2) glass (3) washing soda (4) sodium chloride.

144. Rubber is a mixture of (1) carbohydrates (2) esters (3) alcohols (4) hydrocarbons.

145. The general formula for the members of the methane series of hydrocarbons is (1) C_nH_n (2) C_nH_{2n-2} (3) C_nH_{2n} (4) C_nH_{2n+2}.

146. Soap forms an insoluble compound when it reacts with a solution of (1) Na_2CO_3 (2) $KHCO_3$ (3) $MgSO_4$ (4) NH_4Cl.

147. The complete combustion of ethyl alcohol yields (1) ethylene glycol (2) carbon monoxide and hydrogen (3) chloroform (4) carbon dioxide and water.

148. The most recently discovered of the following elements is (1) argon (2) plutonium (3) silicon (4) uranium.

149. Of the following, neutrons are best absorbed in an atomic pile by rods of (1) cadmium (2) calcium (3) copper (4) zinc.

150. The metal that forms both a soluble carbonate and a soluble sulfate is (1) barium (2) lead (3) magnesium (4) sodium.

Completion Questions

Write the term that, when inserted in the blank, will make the statement true.

1. Heat is absorbed when a substance changes from a liquid to a _____.
2. According to the Law of _____, analysis of the same compound will always give the same results.
3. Ozone has a molecular weight of _____.
4. The fractional distillation of liquid air yields _____, which is used in welding.
5. When two elements combine with sufficient rapidity to produce heat and light, the process is ordinarily called _____.
6. The allotropic form of oxygen is called _____.
7. The reaction between acetic acid and aluminum yields hydrogen and _____.
8. When steam reacts with hot carbon, the element formed is _____.
9. When calcium liberates hydrogen from water, a solution of _____ remains.
10. In the reaction between hydrogen and ferric oxide, the _____ acts as the oxidizing agent.

11. Water is formed when a compound containing the element _____ burns in air.
12. Washing soda loses weight upon standing because _____ is given off.
13. In the compound $MgSO_4 \cdot 7\ H_2O$, the 7 H_2O is known as _____.
14. A solution that contains all the solute it can dissolve at a given temperature is called a (an) _____ solution.
15. When the hydrogen peroxide in a bottle decomposes and becomes ineffective, the compound left in the bottle is _____.
16. In a mixture, liquids that have different boiling points may be separated by the process of _____.
17. Water is most rapidly decomposed by _____.
18. Heating usually _____ the ability of water to dissolve solids.
19. Water containing dissolved solids can be purified by _____.
20. A chlorine atom has an atomic weight of 35. Another chlorine atom has an atomic weight of 37. The two kinds of chlorine atoms are called _____.
21. An element having atomic number 6 would have a valence number of _____.
22. The element with atomic number 5 has _____ electrons in its innermost ring.
23. "Heavy" water is so called because it contains _____.
24. When oxygen reacts with copper, the oxygen _____ (gains, loses, shares) electrons.
25. When a sodium atom loses an electron, an ion that has a _____ charge is formed.
26. Positively charged particles in the nuclei of atoms are called _____.
27. $S^{-2} - 2\ e$ yields _____.
28. The total number of atoms in a molecule of $Zn(NO_3)_2$ is _____.
29. $Cu^0 - 1\ e$ yields _____.
30. A metallic ion and an acid radical combine to form a substance called a (an) _____.
31. The gram-molecular volume of any gas at standard conditions is approximately equal to _____ liters.
32. If TiO_2 is the correct formula for titanium oxide, the formula for titanium chloride is _____.
33. The valence number of phosphorus in the compound phosphorus pentoxide (P_2O_5) is _____.
34. Salts of hydrochloric acid are called _____.
35. The formulas of two different oxides of antimony are Sb_2O_3 and _____.
36. A molecule of nitrogen is represented by the formula _____.
37. The salts of phosphoric acid are called _____.
38. If a gas whose density is 1.782 grams per liter doubles in volume, the new density of the gas is _____ grams per liter.
39. Under standard conditions, the weight of 11.2 liters of oxygen is _____ grams.
40. Under standard conditions, 22.4 liters of ozone weigh _____ grams.
41. "Equal volumes of gases measured under the same conditions of temperature and pressure contain the same number of molecules" is a statement credited to _____.
42. One liter of nitrogen reacts with three liters of hydrogen to form _____ liters of ammonia.

43. At standard conditions, the volume of one gram-molecular weight of ethane is _____ liters.
44. The formula that represents rubidium (Rb) carbonate is _____.
45. Bromine will replace _____ from its compounds.
46. Tincture of iodine consists principally of iodine dissolved in _____.
47. MnO_2 used in the preparation of _____ acts as an oxidizing agent.
48. Bleaching powder purifies water because it yields _____.
49. A solid element that gives off a violet vapor when heated is probably _____.
50. The formula of a halogen acid that will etch glass is _____.
51. Zinc was treated with hydrochloric acid. The compound formed was heated with sulfuric acid. The second reaction produced the gas _____.
52. Fluorine collects at the _____ electrode during the electrolysis of molten potassium fluoride.
53. Salts of hydrobromic acid are called _____.
54. The electrolysis of sodium chloride solution yields the gases chlorine and _____.
55. The gaseous elements oxygen and _____ support combustion.
56. A water solution of pH 5 has a higher concentration of _____ ions than a water solution of pH 10.
57. Calcium oxide is the anhydride of _____.
58. A solution with a pH of 4 will turn litmus _____.
59. A metallic ion and a hydroxyl ion combine to form a substance called a (an) _____.
60. Soda water does not taste as sour as lemon juice because the concentration of _____ ions in the soda water is lower.
61. An element common to all acids and bases is _____.
62. Litmus paper moistened with a solution containing OH ions will become _____.
63. An acid _____ is an oxide that unites with water to form an acid.
64. It is believed that if an electric current passes through a solution, there are _____ present in the solution.
65. An acid plus a base yields _____ and undissociated water.
66. Acetic acid is called a (an) _____ acid because it ionizes slightly when in solution.
67. Sodium acetate solution turns litmus _____.
68. Metallic ions generally plate out on the _____ electrode.
69. Sulfites are salts of _____ acid.
70. Sulfur trioxide is the anhydride of _____ acid.
71. Compounds that contain the SO_3 radical are called _____.
72. The compound formed when zinc dust combines with sulfur is called _____.
73. The formula of a selenium compound related to sulfuric acid is _____.
74. A compound of carbon and sulfur burns completely. The products formed are carbon dioxide and _____.
75. Salts of hydrosulfuric acid are called _____.
76. The presence in air of compounds of _____ causes silverware to tarnish.
77. H_2SO_4 is classified as a (an) _____ acid because it is highly ionized.
78. _____ sulfur is made by pouring boiling sulfur into water.
79. The element _____ is used in vulcanizing rubber.

80. A nitrogen compound obtained commercially by the destructive distillation of soft coal is _____.

81. Moist red litmus paper turns blue in the presence of _____ gas.

82. The most abundant element in the air is _____.

83. The "brown ring" test is used to determine the presence of the _____ ion.

84. After oxygen and carbon dioxide have been removed from air, _____ is one of the gases remaining that will unite under certain conditions with hydrogen.

85. The direct union of nitrogen and hydrogen is accomplished commercially by a process called the _____ process.

86. In the reaction between concentrated nitric acid and copper, copper behaves as a (an) _____ agent.

87. Ammonia passed into a water solution of hydrochloric acid forms a compound called _____.

88. _____ is a salt used with sulfuric acid to prepare nitric acid.

89. Aqua regia is a mixture of _____ and _____.

90. The source of CO_2 in baking powders is _____.

91. A compound of carbon that may be used to sharpen tools is _____.

92. The destructive distillation of soft coal yields a solid product called _____.

93. Acetylene is prepared by the reaction between calcium carbide and _____.

94. Carbon is used as a (an) _____ agent in obtaining metals from oxide ores.

95. The reaction between calcium oxide and carbon yields carbon monoxide and _____.

96. Diamonds are a crystalline form of _____.

97. An acid reacts with a bicarbonate to yield the gas _____.

98. When carbon and oxygen combine and the product of the reaction is dissolved in water, the formula of the final product is _____.

99. Lampblack, diamond, and _____ are _____ forms of carbon.

100. The gas that escapes when a bottle of soda water is opened is _____.

101. Carborundum and ordinary sand contain the element _____.

102. Sodium carbonate will yield _____ (more, less) CO_2 than an equal weight of sodium bicarbonate.

103. In fractional distillation, the ingredients of a mixture of liquids are separated according to their different _____.

104. A poisonous gas that combines chemically with the hemoglobin of the blood is _____.

105. The chemical type of fire extinguisher generates _____ gas under pressure.

106. A precipitate of _____ is formed when limewater is exposed to air.

107. Water that contains carbon dioxide dissolves magnesium carbonate, forming the compound _____.

108. Carnallite is a source of _____.

109. A sodium compound heated in a Bunsen flame will impart a (an) _____ color to the flame.

110. The electrolysis of a solution of _____ yields hydrogen, chlorine, and potassium hydroxide.

111. When plaster of Paris hardens, it combines with _____.

112. The most common compound of phosphorus found in nature is _____.
113. The formula of a compound found in temporary hard water is _____.
114. The compound _____ results when gypsum is heated.
115. Metals most often occur combined in nature as sulfides, carbonates, and _____.
116. The impure calcium silicate produced in the blast furnace is known as _____.
117. "Tin" cans are composed mostly of the metal _____ coated with tin.
118. Impure copper is made the _____ electrode in the electrolytic refining of copper.
119. Zinc carbonate, when roasted, yields the compound zinc _____.
120. The mineral galena is a source of the metal _____.
121. An alloy of tin and lead is called _____.
122. The electrolytic method of extracting aluminum from bauxite was invented by a young American named _____.
123. The purest commercial copper is produced by the process of _____.
124. Photography is made possible because certain _____ compounds are sensitive to _____.
125. In the thermite process, the metal _____ is used as a reducing agent to obtain iron from iron oxide.
126. Water dripping from the exhaust of an automobile on a cold day indicates that gasoline is a mixture of compounds containing _____.
127. An acid formed during the fermentation of glucose is _____.
128. The incomplete combustion of gasoline may produce the element _____.
129. Methane is 75% carbon. The other 25% is _____.
130. If water collects on a cold plate held above a flame, the element _____ is present in the fuel.
131. Methane and benzene belong to a class of organic compounds called _____.
132. Waste animal fat is often used in making _____.
133. The part of an atom not affected by chemical change is called the _____.
134. A mixture of sulfuric acid and _____ acid is used in making some explosives.

True-False Questions

In some of the following statements, the italicized term makes the statement incorrect. For each incorrect statement, write the term that must be substituted for the italicized term to make the statement correct. For each correct statement, write the word *true*.

1. A physical change is a change in the *composition* of matter.
2. Every compound has a definite composition by *weight*.
3. The incomplete combustion of a hydrocarbon always produces *carbon*.
4. The reaction between active metals and water produces hydrogen and *a basic anhydride*.
5. In the reaction between zinc and dilute sulfuric acid, the sulfuric acid behaves as *an oxidizing agent*.
6. The percentage of water in the atmosphere is *fixed*.
7. *Destructive* distillation represents a physical change.

8. Water is a very *stable* compound.
9. Under proper conditions, *8 cc* of oxygen will combine with 1 cc of hydrogen.
10. A saturated solution of calcium hydroxide is *dilute*.
11. As the pressure is increased and the temperature is decreased, *more* CO_2 will dissolve in water.
12. *Sodium chloride* crystals contain water of crystallization.
13. The particles of *a colloidal dispersion* are larger than molecules but smaller than suspended particles.
14. *Volatile* impurities may be separated from water by distillation.
15. The compound H_2O_2 illustrates the Law of *Multiple* Proportions.
16. According to the Dalton theory, the smallest particle of matter is the *electron*.
17. The *molecular* weight of a given substance never changes.
18. All elements in the same group in the periodic table have *identical* properties.
19. Isotopes of an element differ in the number of *neutrons*.
20. Atoms having complete outer shells are *inactive*.
21. Compounds formed by the sharing of electrons are called *covalent* compounds.
22. The valence number of manganese in MnO_2 is *+2*.
23. When chlorine gas acts as an oxidizing agent, it *gains* electrons.
24. Equal volumes of all gases measured under the same temperature and pressure contain the same number of *molecules*.
25. Strong acids contain *more* hydrogen ions than weak acids.
26. All electrovalent compounds have a *positive* charge.
27. Neutralization is the reverse of *decomposition*.
28. A *molar* solution contains one gram-molecular weight in 1,000 grams of solvent.
29. A reaction will go to completion if one of the products formed is *an electrolyte*.
30. Sodium chloride, in the *solid* state, contains ions.
31. *Sodium acetate* is a salt of a weak acid and a weak base.
32. All the halogens contain *2 electrons* in the shell nearest the nucleus.
33. A free halogen may be obtained by the *oxidation* of the corresponding halide ion.
34. The *heaviest* halogen is a solid.
35. *Sodium chloride* is the source of most sodium compounds.
36. Chemically, sulfur most closely resembles the element *chlorine*.
37. The reaction between sulfites and acids generally produces *sulfuric acid*.
38. Ammonia may be prepared commercially by the *contact* process.
39. Because HNO_3 is a volatile liquid, it is collected by the process of *sublimation*.
40. Nitric acid reacts with metals to form different *oxides* of nitrogen.
41. In the nitrogen cycle, bacteria convert atmospheric nitrogen into *ammonia*.
42. Like *chlorine*, carbon occurs in several allotropic forms.
43. The continued passage of CO_2 into limewater results in the formation of *calcium carbonate*.
44. The soda-acid fire extinguisher liberates *carbon dioxide*, which puts out the fire.
45. To extract a metal from its ore, the ore must be *roasted*.
46. The impurities present in an ore may be removed by *fractional distillation*.

47. The refining of iron in the manufacture of steel results in *an increase* in carbon content.
48. Large numbers of organic compounds are due to the presence of *isotopes*.
49. Nuclear fission results in the formation of particles of *higher* atomic weight than the fissioned material.
50. There is no limit to the size of *a hydrogen* bomb.

Decreases, Increases, Remains the Same Questions

Write the term (*decreases, increases, remains the same*) that, when inserted in the blank, will make the statement true.

1. When metals are heated in air, their weight _____.
2. As mercuric oxide is heated, its weight _____.
3. As the surface area of reacting substances is made smaller, the reaction rate _____.
4. As the temperature of water is raised above 4°C, its volume _____.
5. Closing the air holes of a Bunsen burner causes the temperature of the flame to _____.
6. As the temperature of water is lowered, the percentage of hydrogen present in the water _____.
7. As the volume of solvent increases, the concentration of a solution _____.
8. As the temperature of a solution of a gas in water is lowered, the solubility of the gas _____.
9. As the temperature of a hydrate is raised, the weight of the hydrate _____.
10. At constant temperature, as the pressure of a gas increases, its volume _____.
11. As the atomic weights of rare gases increase, their chemical activity _____.
12. As the number of electron shells in atoms increases, the atomic number _____.
13. As the number of protons in atoms increases, the number of neutrons _____.
14. As organic compounds increase in molecular weight, the number of possible isomers _____.
15. As the atomic number of halogens increases, their chemical activity _____.
16. As sodium bicarbonate is added to a solution, the pH of the solution _____.
17. As the temperature of a solution of hydrochloric acid is raised, the pH of the solution _____.
18. As more water is added to a sugar solution, the conductivity of the solution _____.
19. As a salt solution is made more concentrated, the freezing point of the solution _____.
20. As the temperature of a metal is increased, the number of neutrons in its nucleus _____.

21. As the temperature of a gas is increased, the gram-molecular volume of the gas _____.
22. As the atomic radius of metals increases, the activity of the metals generally _____.
23. As the per cent of carbon in steel increases, the hardness of the steel _____.
24. As more solute is added to a saturated solution, the concentration of the solution _____.
25. As the atomic weight of radioactive elements increases, the half-life of these elements _____.
26. As the acidity of a solution increases, the pH value of the solution _____.
27. As ferric chloride changes to ferrous chloride, the charge on the chloride ion _____.
28. As the molecular weight of gases increases, the number of molecules in 22.4 liters at standard conditions _____.
29. As the number of ions in a solution decreases, the boiling point _____.
30. As the size of fissionable material is increased, the number of slow neutrons produced _____.

Matching Questions

Match the items in column *A* with those in column *B*.

GROUP I

Column A	*Column B*
1. arc process	*a.* refrigerant
2. contact process	*b.* cane sugar
3. Haber process	*c.* steel
4. open-hearth process	*d.* ammonia
5. Hall process	*e.* glycerine
6. green plants	*f.* solvent for grease
7. $C_{12}H_{22}O_{11}$	*g.* removal of carbon dioxide from the air
8. $C_3H_5(OH)_3$	*h.* nitric acid
9. carbon tetrachloride	*i.* sulfuric acid
10. CCl_2F_2	*j.* aluminum

GROUP II

Column A	*Column B*
1. Curie	*a.* oxyacetylene torch
2. Lavoisier	*b.* produces carbon dioxide
3. chlorine	*c.* a liquid element
4. bromine	*d.* theory of burning
5. nitric oxide	*e.* radium
6. hydrogen sulfide	*f.* strong oxidizing agent
7. animals	*g.* produces SO_2 and H_2O on burning
8. glucose	*h.* turns brown when exposed to air
9. dilute acetic acid	*i.* reacts with Fehling's solution
10. cutting metals	*j.* vinegar

GROUP III

Column A	*Column B*
1. cracking process	a. Dalton
2. bauxite	b. galvanizing
3. fertilizer	c. low kindling temperature
4. detergent	d. increased yield of gasoline
5. moth-proofing	e. soap substitute
6. zinc	f. stainless steel
7. phosphorus	g. ammonium sulfate
8. CO_2 and H_2O	h. photosynthesis
9. atomic theory	i. Hall process
10. chromium	j. naphthalene

GROUP IV

Column A	*Column B*
1. alum	a. plaster of Paris
2. copper and aluminum	b. electric signs
3. carbon monoxide	c. welding of steel
4. benzene	d. hard water
5. galena	e. rayon
6. gypsum	f. aluminum bronze
7. $Ca(HCO_3)_2$	g. banked coal fires
8. acetylene	h. organic solvent
9. neon	i. water purification
10. cellulose	j. ore

GROUP V

Column A	*Column B*
1. amalgam	a. alloy
2. bauxite	b. anesthetic
3. calcium oxide	c. basic anhydride
4. glucose	d. bleaching agent
5. helium	e. carbohydrate
6. hydrogen peroxide	f. fuel gas
7. methane	g. inert element
8. vital force	h. metallic element
9. nitrous oxide	i. Wöhler
10. vanadium	j. ore

Selection Questions

Four of the substances in each of the following groups contain the *same* element. A fifth substance *does not contain* that element. Write the *number* of the substance that does not contain the element common to the other four substances.

1. (1) potassium chlorate (2) grain alcohol (3) barium oxide (4) hydrogen fluoride (5) sulfurous acid
2. (1) charcoal (2) diamond (3) carbon tetrachloride (4) calcium carbonate (5) calcium oxide

3. (1) water (2) mercuric oxide (3) sodium hydroxide (4) ammonia (5) hydrochloric acid

4. (1) air (2) aluminum sulfate (3) ammonia (4) sodium nitrate (5) magnesium nitride

5. (1) table salt (2) bauxite (3) borax (4) baking soda (5) sodium sulfide

6. (1) aluminum oxide (2) sodium chloride (3) acetic acid (4) zinc carbonate (5) sodium nitrate

7. (1) methane (2) ammonia (3) acetylene (4) calcium hydroxide (5) calcium carbide

8. (1) gypsum (2) blue vitriol (3) Epsom salts (4) smithsonite (5) galena

9. (1) ether (2) charcoal (3) chloroform (4) ethylene (5) oil of vitriol

10. (1) dry ice (2) starch (3) calcium nitrate (4) calcium carbide (5) lead oxide .

11. (1) aqua regia (2) vinegar (3) hydrochloric acid (4) calcium hydroxide (5) silver chloride

12. (1) baking soda (2) limestone (3) Chile saltpeter (4) table salt (5) sodium bromide

13. (1) glucose (2) potassium carbonate (3) ethane (4) methyl alcohol (5) potassium chloride

14. (1) laughing gas (2) nitric acid (3) nitroglycerine (4) calcium cyanamid (5) carbon monoxide

15. (1) bleaching powder (2) calcium chloride (3) rock salt (4) marble (5) plaster of Paris

16. (1) benzene (2) sand (3) zinc oxide (4) gypsum (5) glycerine

17. (1) chloroform (2) gold amalgam (3) mercury bichloride (4) potassium chlorate (5) table salt

18. (1) baking soda (2) cane sugar (3) carbon disulfide (4) methane (5) zinc sulfate

19. (1) calcium carbide (2) calcium cyanamid (3) nitric acid (4) nitroglycerine (5) potassium nitrate

20. (1) methyl alcohol (2) potassium hydroxide (3) methane (4) nitric acid (5) sulfuric acid

2. USING THE REGENTS REFERENCE TABLES

The Regents reference tables contain a variety of data which, if properly used, will provide the answers to many questions relating to the properties of elements and compounds. Some of the data are especially useful in solving chemical problems involving mathematical calculations.

PERIODIC TABLE OF THE ELEMENTS

The periodic table provides us with much valuable information about the elements, as shown below.

1. Symbol, Atomic Weight, Atomic Number, Atomic Radius, Electron Structure, and Oxidation State. For example, consider the element carbon, which appears in the table in Group IV A and Period 2.

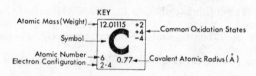

The atomic weight (12.01115) is given in the upper left-hand corner above the symbol (C). The atomic number (6) is shown in the lower left-hand corner below the symbol. The electronic structure of the element (2-4) is indicated below the atomic number. The number below the symbol (0.77) is the covalent atomic radius expressed in Angstrom units (Å). One Angstrom unit equals 10^{-8} cm. The atomic radius describes the size of the atom. The oxidation number(s) appears in the upper right-hand corner. For many metals and nonmetals, the oxidation numbers are the same as the valence numbers. If the oxidation numbers are crisscrossed and the signs are dropped, these numbers can be used to write a formula. For example, the oxidation number of sodium is $+1$, and the oxidation number of chlorine is -1. The formula of sodium chloride is therefore NaCl. The oxidation states of radicals are discussed in Table C.

2. Important Relationships Among the Properties of the Elements. By referring to the position of an element in the table, we can predict the properties of the element. For example, all the elements in Group II A of the table contain two electrons in their outermost energy level. As a result, when these atoms enter into a chemical reaction, they tend to lose these two electrons, forming ions which have a charge of $+2$.

The relationships among the properties of the elements provide us with even more information. For example, we have already learned that as the atomic radius of metals increases, the activity of the metals generally increases. Applying this concept, we see that in Group II A the metal barium is more active than the metal calcium. In turn, calcium is more active than magnesium.

3. Atomic Weights for Problem Solving. In most cases, the atomic weights are given to four, five, or six significant figures. However, in solving problems, atomic weights may be rounded off to the nearest whole number. Thus, the atomic weight of hydrogen becomes 1, while the atomic weight of boron becomes 11.

Question 1. The number of electrons in the outer energy level of the elements in Group II A of the periodic table is (1) 1 (2) 2 (3) 3 (4) 4.

Answer. By referring to the table, we see that the number of electrons in the outer energy level for elements in Group II A is 2 (choice 2).

Question 2. The element with atomic number 7 is likely to have properties similar to the element whose atomic number is (1) 2 (2) 11 (3) 15 (4) 17.

Answer. The table shows that the element with atomic number 7 has 5 electrons in its outer energy level. Of the suggested answers, only the element with atomic number 15 has 5 electrons in its outer energy level. The table also shows that both of these elements are in the same group, namely, V A. Therefore, the outer energy level structures of these elements and their properties must be similar. Choice (3) is the correct answer.

Question 3. A possible sulfide of antimony has the formula (1) SbS (2) SbS$_3$ (3) Sb$_2$S$_5$ (4) Sb$_5$S$_2$.

Answer. By referring to the table, we note that antimony has two positive oxidation states, $+3$ and $+5$. Sulfur has one negative oxidation state, -2. Two possible sulfides of antimony are, therefore, Sb$_2$S$_3$ or Sb$_2$S$_5$. Of the choices given, only Sb$_2$S$_5$ appears. Choice (3) is correct.

Question 4. Within a period of the periodic table, as the atomic numbers increase, the atomic radii (1) tend to increase (2) remain the same (3) tend to decrease (4) show no definite pattern.

Answer. Examination of the table shows that the atomic radii tend to decrease as the atomic numbers increase. This can be predicted from the fact that the increasing nuclear charge exerts a greater attractive force on the inner electrons, tending to shrink the atom. Thus, choice (3) is correct.

TABLE A. DENSITY AND SOLUBILITY OF SOME COMMON GASES

This table provides us with the following information:

1. Density of Gases. The density of a number of gases is expressed in grams/liter at standard conditions of temperature and pressure (0°C and 760 mm). *A study of the molecular weights of these gases reveals that the density of the gas is proportional to its molecular weight.*

2. Solubility of Gases. The solubility of these gases at 0°C and 760 mm pressure (sea level) is also tabulated. Using the information provided by the density and solubility columns of the table, we are able to predict the method of collection of the listed gases. Thus, chlorine, which is moderately soluble in water and denser than air, is collected by displacement of air. Hydrogen, which is slightly soluble in water and less dense than air, is collected by displacement of water or by displacement of air.

Question 1. The least dense gas is (1) hydrogen (2) ammonia (3) carbon monoxide (4) oxygen.

Answer. The table clearly indicates that the answer to this question is hydrogen, choice (1).

NAME	DENSITY grams/liter 0° C 760 mm.	SOLUBILITY*
Air	1.29	—
Ammonia	0.77	89.5
Carbon dioxide	1.98	0.3346
Carbon monoxide	1.25	0.0044
Chlorine	3.21	0.9972†
Nitrogen monoxide	1.34	0.0098
Hydrogen	0.09	0.0002
Hydrogen chloride	1.64	82.3
Hydrogen sulfide	1.54	0.7066
Nitrogen	1.25	0.0029
Oxygen	1.43	0.0069
Sulfur dioxide	2.93	22.83

* Weight of gas in grams dissolved in 100 grams of water at 0° C
  and 760 mm. † at 10° C

Table A

Question 2. A gas that is collected by displacement of either water or air is (1) carbon dioxide (2) hydrogen chloride (3) ammonia (4) sulfur dioxide.
Answer. The solubility table shows that of the given gases only carbon dioxide is moderately soluble in water. Hence, it can be collected by either air or water displacement. The correct answer, therefore, is choice (1).

Question 3. The weight of hydrogen sulfide that will dissolve in 1000 grams of water at STP is (1) 0.7066 gram (2) 0.07066 gram (3) 1.7066 grams (4) 7.066 grams.
Answer. The solubility of hydrogen sulfide is 0.7066 gram in 100 grams of water at STP. This means that 10×0.7066 gram of hydrogen sulfide will dissolve in 10×100 grams of water. Thus, 7.066 grams (choice 4) is correct.

TABLE B. SOLUBILITY CURVES

1. Solubilities of Solids. This table presents the solubility of a number of solids in the form of a graph in which the number of grams of solid dissolving in 100 ml of water has been plotted against the temperature in degrees centigrade. Where the curve does not rise sharply, as in the case of sodium chloride, the solubility of the solid does not change appreciably with an increase in temperature. Where the curve rises sharply, as in the case of potassium nitrate, the solubility of the solid increases markedly with a rise in temperature. Where the curve falls, as in the case of cerium (III) sulfate, the solubility of the solid decreases with a rise in temperature. *Thus, the shape of the curve indicates the effect of changes in temperature on the solubility of the solid.* The eight curves that appear in the graph immediately reveal the comparative solubilities of each of the eight solids.

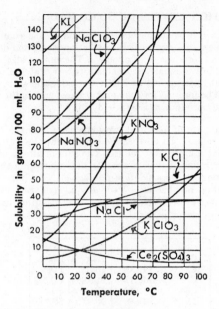

Table B

2. Approximate Concentrations of Solutions. The solubility curves also reveal the approximate concentrations of the saturated solutions of the solids. Thus, at 20°C, a saturated solution of potassium chlorate is dilute because only about 9 grams of solute have dissolved in 100 ml of water. On the other hand, at this same temperature, 88 grams of sodium nitrate have dissolved in the same volume of water. A saturated solution of sodium nitrate is therefore concentrated.

Question 1. At 100°C, the least soluble salt is (1) cerium (III) sulfate (2) sodium nitrate (3) potassium chlorate (4) sodium chloride.

Answer. The graph reveals that at 100°C only 4 grams of cerium (III) sulfate will dissolve in 100 ml of water. This is the smallest quantity of solute of the four suggested answers, and thus choice (1) is the correct answer.

Question 2. With which of the following substances is it most difficult to make a saturated solution at 70°C? (1) sodium nitrate (2) potassium nitrate (3) potassium chlorate (4) potassium chloride.

Answer. Referring to the graph, we see that at 70°C the solubilities of the solids in 100 ml of water are approximately as follows: 33 grams of potassium chlorate, 48 grams of potassium chloride, 130 grams of potassium nitrate, and 133 grams of sodium nitrate. Since it is most difficult to saturate a given volume of water with the largest quantity of solute, the correct answer is sodium nitrate, choice (1).

TABLE C. OXIDATION STATES OF SOME RADICALS

This table indicates the oxidation states of some of the common radicals. By crisscrossing the numbers that represent the oxidation states and dropping the signs, we can write the correct formulas of compounds. The sum of all the oxidation numbers in a compound always equals zero. Thus, we see that the oxidation state of the ammonium radical (NH_4) is $+1$ and that the oxidation state of the phosphate radical (PO_4) is -3. The formula for ammonium phosphate is therefore $(NH_4)_3PO_4$. The sum of the oxidation numbers is $+3 - 3 = 0$.

From the oxidation state of a radical, we may determine the oxidation number of an element in the radical. To do this, we must know the oxidation numbers of the other elements that comprise the radical. The sum of all the oxidation numbers of the elements in the radical equals a number that represents the oxidation state of the radical. To determine the oxidation number of N in NH_4^+, we assume that each H has an oxidation number of $+1$ for a total oxidation number of $+4$. In order for the oxidation state of NH_4 to be $+1$, the oxidation number of N must be equal to -3, that is, $+4 - 3 = +1$.

CH_3COO^-	ClO_4^-	$H_2PO_4^-$	NO_3^-
CO_3^-	$Cr_2O_7^-$	H_3O^+	OH^-
$C_2O_4^-$	HCO_3^-	Hg_2^{++}	PO_3^-
ClO^-	HPO_4^-	MnO_4^-	PO_4^-
ClO_2^-	HSO_3^-	NH_4^+	SO_3^-
ClO_3^-	HSO_4^-	NO_2^-	SO_4^-

Table C

Question 1. The correct formula for zinc hydroxide is (1) ZnO (2) ZnO_2 (3) ZnOH (4) $Zn(OH)_2$.

Answer. From the periodic table, we see that the oxidation state of zinc is $+2$. Since the total oxidation number of the molecule must be zero, the hydroxide (OH) radical must have a total oxidation number of -2. From the table of oxidation states, we see that the hydroxyl radical has an oxidation state of -1. Therefore, two hydroxyl radicals with a total oxidation number of -2 must be present. Choice (4), $Zn(OH)_2$, is the correct answer.

Question 2. The oxidation number of chlorine in potassium chlorate is (1) -1 (2) $+1$ (3) $+5$ (4) $+7$.

Answer. Reference to the table indicates that the oxidation state of the chlorate radical (ClO_3) is -1. Since the oxidation number of oxygen is -2, the total oxidation number of the oxygen in the ClO_3 radical is -6. If the oxidation state of ClO_3 is -1, the chlorine must therefore have an oxidation number of $+5$, that is, $+5 - 6 = -1$. Choice (3) is the correct answer.

TABLE D. SOLUBILITIES IN WATER

1. Degree of Solubility. This table lists the solubilities of a large number of compounds in water. The degree of solubility is indicated by five separate categories: *i*—nearly insoluble, *ss*—slightly soluble, *s*—soluble, *d*—decomposes, and *n*—not isolated. Thus, calcium carbonate is nearly insoluble in water, while calcium hydroxide is slightly soluble. Calcium chloride is soluble in water, while calcium sulfide decomposes in water to form calcium hydroxide and hydrogen sulfide. Iron (III) carbonate has not been isolated.

i—nearly insoluble ss—slightly soluble s—soluble d—decomposes n—not isolated	acetate	bromide	carbonate	chloride	hydroxide	iodide	nitrate	oxide	phosphate	sulfate	sulfide
Aluminum	s	s	n	s	i	s	s	i	i	s	d
Ammonium	s	s	s	s	s	s	s	n	s	s	s
Barium	s	s	i	s	s	s	s	s	i	i	d
Calcium	s	s	i	s	ss	s	s	ss	i	ss	d
Copper II	s	s	i	s	i	d	s	i	i	s	i
Iron II	s	s	i	s	i	s	s	i	i	s	i
Iron III	s	s	n	s	i	s	s	i	i	ss	d
Lead	s	ss	i	ss	i	ss	s	i	i	i	i
Magnesium	s	s	i	s	i	s	s	i	i	s	d
Mercury I	ss	i	i	i	n	i	s	i	i	ss	i
Mercury II	s	ss	i	s	i	i	s	i	i	d	i
Potassium	s	s	s	s	s	s	s	s	s	s	s
Silver	ss	i	i	i	n	i	s	i	i	ss	i
Sodium	s	s	s	s	s	s	s	d	s	s	s
Zinc	s	s	i	s	i	s	s	i	i	s	i

Table D

2. Concentrations of Solutions. Table D can be used to predict the concentrations of saturated solutions. Thus, calcium hydroxide, which is slightly soluble, forms a saturated solution that is dilute; while calcium chloride, which is more soluble than calcium hydroxide, forms a saturated solution that is concentrated.

3. Completion of Reactions. To predict whether a double replacement reaction will go to completion due to the formation of an insoluble substance, we need merely to consult this table. For example, the reaction between sodium hydroxide and copper (II) sulfate will go to completion because of the formation of insoluble copper (II) hydroxide.

Question 1. A water solution of one of the following substances will be dilute when saturated: (1) lead acetate (2) magnesium sulfide (3) lead iodide (4) magnesium nitrate.

Answer. Of the suggested answers, only lead iodide is slightly soluble. Since lead iodide is the only saturated solution that is dilute, the correct answer is choice (3).

Question 2. Which one of the following reactions goes to completion due to the formation of a precipitate? (1) aluminum chloride + sodium nitrate (2) barium chloride + sodium phosphate (3) calcium acetate + sodium nitrate (4) potassium chloride + sodium phosphate.

Answer. The only combination that produces a precipitate is (2). This reaction goes to completion, forming sodium chloride and insoluble barium phosphate.

TABLE E. SYMBOLS OF SOME PARTICLES

This table lists the symbols for some atomic particles and is useful in writing equations for nuclear reactions. Each symbol contains a superscript that indicates mass and a subscript that indicates charge. For example, the nuclear equation for the bombardment of nitrogen by alpha particles may be written:

electron	$_{-1}e^0$
neutron	$_0n^1$
proton	$_1H^1$
deuteron	$_1H^2$
triton	$_1H^3$
alpha particle	$_2He^4$

Table E

$$_7N^{14} + _2He^4 \rightarrow _8O^{17} + _1H^1$$

nitrogen   alpha   oxygen   proton
       particle   isotope

Note that the sum of the superscripts on the left equals the sum of the superscripts on the right. The same is true for the subscripts.

Question 1. The equation for the decay of radium-226 to radon-222 is

$$_{88}Ra^{226} \rightarrow _{86}Rn^{222} + (1) \ _1H^1 \ (2) \ _{-1}e^0 \ (3) \ _1H^2 \ (4) \ _2He^4.$$

Answer. When a radioactive element breaks down into an atom of an element having a lighter nucleus, an alpha particle may be emitted. Hence, the correct answer is $_2He^4$, choice (4). Note, also, that choice (4) balances both the superscripts ($226 = 222 + 4$) and the subscripts ($88 = 86 + 2$).

TABLE F. HEAT AND FREE ENERGY OF FORMATION OF COMPOUNDS

The heat of formation of a compound is the heat liberated or absorbed when one mole of a compound is formed from its elements. Negative heats of formation indicate that the reaction is *exothermic* (liberates heat), whereas positive heats of formation indicate that the reaction is *endothermic* (absorbs heat). Exothermic reactions generally tend to occur spontaneously with little energy input. Since some endothermic reactions also proceed spontaneously, the heat change during a reaction is only a partial measure of the tendency of the reaction to occur. The free energy change in a reaction indicates the total driving force of a reaction. In addition to the heat change, the free energy change includes another factor called the *probability change* (the entropy). In many reactions, however, the probability change is small, so that the heat change alone is sufficient to reveal the driving force of the reaction. In Table F, note that, for a specific compound, the value for the heat of formation and the value for the free energy of formation are fairly close. Both the heat of formation and the free energy of formation are expressed in kilocalories per mole (kcal/mole).

COMPOUND	HEAT OF FORMATION kcal/mole (ΔH)*	FREE ENERGY OF FORMATION kcal/mole (ΔF)*
Aluminum oxide (s)	−399.09	−376.77
Ammonia (g)	−11.04	−3.98
Barium sulfate (s)	−350.2	−323.4
Calcium hydroxide (s)	−235.80	−214.33
Carbon dioxide (g)	−94.39	−94.26
Copper (II) sulfate (s)	−184.00	−158.2
Dinitrogen monoxide (g)	19.49	24.76
Ethyne (acetylene) (g)	54.19	50.00
Hydrogen fluoride (g)	−63.99	—
Hydrogen iodide (g)	5.93	—
Hydrogen oxide (ℓ)	−68.32	−56.69
Iron (II, III) oxide (s)	−267.0	−242.4
Lead monoxide (s)	−52.40	−45.25
Magnesium oxide (s)	−143.84	−136.13
Mercury (II) oxide (s)	−21.68	−13.99
Nitrogen monoxide (g)	21.60	20.72
Potassium chloride (s)	−104.18	−97.59
Sodium chloride (s)	−98.23	−91.79
Sulfur dioxide (g)	−70.96	−71.79
Zinc oxide (s)	−83.17	−76.05

(s) = solid   (ℓ) = liquid   (g) = gas
* Minus sign indicates an exothermic reaction.

Table F

Question 1. The sign of ΔH for the formation of carbon dioxide (g) indicates that (1) energy is released in its formation (2) energy is absorbed in its formation (3) carbon dioxide molecules have high energy (4) the bonds in carbon dioxide are less numerous than in carbon and oxygen.

Answer. According to the table, the signs for ΔH and ΔF indicate whether the reaction is exothermic or endothermic. Reference to the table shows that ΔH for carbon dioxide is −94.39. Since the minus sign indicates an exothermic reaction, choice (1), energy is released in its formation, is the correct answer.

Question 2. The free energy of formation of copper (II) sulfate is (1) −184.00 (2) −158.2 (3) −342.20 (4) +158.2.

Answer. According to the table, ΔF for copper (II) sulfate is −158.2. Thus, choice (2) is correct.

Question 3. Of the following, the most stable compound is (1) calcium hydroxide (2) sodium chloride (3) dinitrogen monoxide (4) nitrogen monoxide.

Answer. The greater the heat of formation, the more stable is the compound. Thus, calcium hydroxide, with a heat of formation of −235.80, is the most stable compound of those listed. Choice (1) is therefore correct.

TABLE G. HALF-LIVES OF SOME RADIOISOTOPES

Half-life has been defined as the time required for one-half a given mass of radioactive material to disintegrate. The table of half-lives, therefore, indicates the relative stability of some radioactive isotopes. The most stable isotope appearing in the table is chlorine-36 (^{36}Cl) with a half-life of 4×10^5 years, while the least stable isotope is potassium-42 (^{42}K), with a half-life of 12.4 hours.

^{14}C	5,700 years
^{45}Ca	152 days
^{36}Cl	4×10^5 years
^{60}Co	5.3 years
^{137}Cs	33 years
^{131}I	8 days
^{42}K	12.4 hours
^{32}P	14.3 days
^{90}Sr	20 years

Table G

Question 1. Of the following, the most stable radioisotope is (1) calcium-45 (2) cobalt-60 (3) iodine-131 (4) phosphorus-32.

Answer. From the table, we note that cobalt-60 has a half-life of 5.3 years. Of the elements listed, this is the longest half-life and thus represents the most stable radioisotope. Choice (2) is the correct answer.

Question 2. If you started with 32 grams of I-131, at the end of 32 days, how many grams of the radioisotope would remain? (1) 1 (2) 2 (3) 8 (4) 16.

Answer. Since the half-life of I-131 is 8 days, at the end of 8 days, 16 grams would remain. Eight days later (total of 16 days), half of that quantity, or 8 grams, would remain. Eight days later (total of 24 days), 4 grams would remain. Eight days after that (total of 32 days), 2 grams would remain. Choice (2) is the correct answer.

TABLE H. ACID-BASE CHART

According to the Bronsted theory, an acid is a substance that donates protons, whereas a base is a substance that accepts protons. The conjugate base of an acid is formed by the loss of a proton (hydrogen ion) from the acid. The conjugate acid of a base is formed by the addition of a proton (hydrogen ion) to the base.

$$\underbrace{Acid_1 + \overbrace{Base_2 = Acid_2}^{\text{conjugate pair}} + Base_1}_{\text{conjugate pair}}$$

$$\underbrace{HCl + \overbrace{H_2O = H_3O^+}^{} + Cl^-}_{}$$

Some common conjugate acid-base pairs are shown in the table.

CONJUGATE ACID	CONJUGATE BASE
HCl	Cl⁻
HNO₃	NO₃⁻
H₂SO₄	HSO₄⁻
H₃O⁺	H₂O
HSO₄⁻	SO₄⁻
Al(H₂O)₆⁺⁺⁺	Al(H₂O)₅(OH)⁺⁺
NH₄⁺	NH₃
H₂O	OH⁻
NH₃	NH₂⁻

Left margin: acid strength decreases (↓)
Right margin: base strength decreases (↑)

Table H

The conjugate of a strong acid is a weak base, whereas the conjugate of a weak acid is a strong base. The table also lists the acids in order of decreasing strength, and the bases in order of increasing strength.

From the chart, we can see that the loss of a proton from hydrochloric acid (strong acid) will result in the formation of its conjugate base Cl⁻ (weak base). The reverse reaction, with the addition of the hydrogen ion (proton) to Cl⁻ will produce the conjugate acid, HCl.

Some substances, such as water, are amphiprotic; that is, they can act either as acids or as bases. When water reacts with hydrochloric acid, water acts as a base and accepts protons to form H_3O^+ ions.

$$HCl + H_2O = H_3O^+ + Cl^-$$

In reacting with ammonia, water acts as an acid by donating a proton to form OH^- ions.

$$H_2O + NH_3 = NH_4^+ + OH^-$$

Question 1. At a given concentration and temperature, which acid will react most rapidly with iron to liberate hydrogen? (1) H_3O^+ (2) H_2O (3) HSO_4^- (4) NH_4^+.
Answer. The strongest acid is the one that donates protons most readily. The strongest acid will react most rapidly with iron. The table shows that the acids decrease in strength from HCl, at the top of the chart, to NH₃, at the bottom of the chart. Of the acids listed, H_3O^+ will donate protons most readily. Choice (1) is therefore the correct answer.

Question 2. When NH₃ reacts with water, the two acids involved in the reaction are (1) NH_4^+ and H_2O (2) NH_4^+ and OH^- (3) NH₃ and H_2O (4) NH₃ and OH^-.
Answer. In the reaction $NH_3 + H_2O = NH_4^+ + OH^-$, H_2O, a stronger acid than NH₃, donates a proton to NH₃ (which accepts the proton and acts as a base). In the reverse reaction, the proton donor is NH_4^+ (acid), and the OH^- accepts the proton (base). Therefore, choice (1), NH_4^+ and H_2O, is the correct answer. (Since NH_4^+ is a stronger acid than NH₃, the reaction goes to the left.)

Question 3. When HCl reacts with water, the two bases involved in the reaction are (1) HCl and H_3O^+ (2) Cl⁻ and H_2O (3) H_3O^+ and Cl⁻ (4) Cl⁻ and HCl.
Answer. In the reaction $HCl + H_2O = H_3O^+ + Cl^-$, HCl, a stronger acid than H_2O, donates a proton to the H_2O (which accepts the proton and acts as a base).

In the reverse reaction, the proton donor is the H_3O^+ (acid), and the Cl^- accepts the proton (base). Therefore, choice (2), Cl^- and H_2O, is the correct answer. (Since HCl is a stronger acid than H_3O^+, the reaction goes to the right.)

TABLE I. HEATS OF REACTION

This table lists a number of heats of reaction in kilocalories per mole (kcal/mole) of product formed. (Since each reaction forms only a single product, these heats of reaction are also the heats of formation of the product formed.) As in Table F, the sign preceding the heat of reaction for a particular reaction indicates whether heat is released or absorbed in the reaction. For instance, when one mole of H_2SO_4 is formed from hydrogen, sulfur, and oxygen, 194.0 kcal of heat are released. When one mole of NO_2 is formed from nitrogen and oxygen, 8.1 kcal of heat are absorbed.

t = 25° C p = 1 atm.	kcal/mole*
H_2 (g) $+ \frac{1}{2} O_2$ (g) $= H_2O$ (g)	-57.8
H_2 (g) $+ \frac{1}{2} O_2$ (g) $= H_2O$ (ℓ)	-68.3
S (s) $+ O_2$ (g) $= SO_2$ (g)	-71.0
H_2 (g) $+ S$ (s) $+ 2 O_2$ (g) $= H_2SO_4$ (ℓ)	-194.0
$\frac{1}{2} N_2$ (g) $+ \frac{1}{2} O_2$ (g) $= NO$ (g)	21.6
$\frac{1}{2} N_2$ (g) $+ O_2$ (g) $= NO_2$ (g)	8.1
$\frac{1}{2} N_2$ (g) $+ \frac{3}{2} H_2$ (g) $= NH_3$ (g)	-11.0
C (s) $+ \frac{1}{2} O_2$ (g) $= CO$ (g)	-26.4
C (s) $+ O_2$ (g) $= CO_2$ (g)	-94.0
$2 C$ (s) $+ 3 H_2$ (g) $= C_2H_6$ (g)	-20.2
* of the product formed	
(Minus sign indicates an exothermic reaction.)	

Table I

Question 1. If two moles of NO_2 are formed from one mole of N_2 and two moles of O_2, the heat of reaction in kilocalories is (1) -8.1 (2) $+8.1$ (3) -16.2 (4) $+16.2$.
Answer. Since the table shows that 8.1 kcal of heat are absorbed in the formation of one mole of NO_2, then twice as much heat, or 16.2 kcal, must be absorbed in the formation of two moles. Since the heat is absorbed, choice (4) is the correct answer.

Question 2. The condensation of water involves the (1) absorption of 68.3 kcal/mole (2) release of 57.8 kcal/mole (3) absorption of 10.5 kcal/mole (4) release of 10.5 kcal/mole.
Answer. The heat of reaction for the formation of H_2O (l) is -68.3 kcal/mole, and the heat of reaction for the formation of H_2O (g) is -57.8 kcal/mole. The difference between the two values represents the amount of heat released in the condensation.

$$-68.3 \text{ kcal/mole} - (-57.8 \text{ kcal/mole}) = -10.5 \text{ kcal/mole}$$

Hence, choice (4) is the correct answer.

TABLE J. REPRESENTATIVE ELEMENTS

This table lists the ionization energies, sometimes referred to as ionization potentials (in electron volts) and electronegativities (in arbitrary units), for selected elements.

I A	II A	III A	IV A	V A	VI A	VII A
13.5 **H** 2.1 ◄──Ionization Energy* ──Electronegativity**						
5.4 **Li** 1.0	9.3 **Be** 1.5	8.3 **B** 2.0	11.2 **C** 2.5	14.5 **N** 3.0	13.6 **O** 3.5	17.3 **F** 4.0
5.1 **Na** 0.9	7.6 **Mg** 1.2	6.0 **Al** 1.5	8.1 **Si** 1.8	10.9 **P** 2.1	10.3 **S** 2.5	13.0 **Cl** 3.0
4.3 **K** 0.8	6.1 **Ca** 1.0	6.0 **Ga** 1.6	8.1 **Ge** 1.8	10.5 **As** 2.0	9.7 **Se** 2.4	11.8 **Br** 2.8
4.2 **Rb** 0.8	5.7 **Sr** 1.0	5.8 **In** 1.7	7.3 **Sn** 1.8	8.5 **Sb** 1.9	9.0 **Te** 2.1	10.6 **I** 2.5
3.9 **Cs** 0.7	5.2 **Ba** 0.9	6.1 **Tl** 1.8	7.4 **Pb** 1.8	8.0 **Bi** 1.9	**Po** 2.0	**At** 2.2
Fr 0.7	5.3 **Ra** 0.7	* 1st ionization energy in e.v. ** Arbitrary scale				

Table J

Ionization energy refers to the amount of energy required to remove the least tightly bound electron from an isolated (gaseous) atom.

$$Na^0 + 5.1 \text{ e.v.} = Na^+ + e$$
$$\underset{\substack{\text{ionization} \\ \text{energy}}}{}$$

Metals generally have low ionization energies while a great deal of energy is required to remove an electron from a nonmetallic element.

The magnitude of the ionization energy depends generally upon three factors:

1. The distance between the nucleus and the outer electron energy level (atomic size).

2. The charge on the nucleus.

3. The screening effect of inner electron energy levels.

Within a given group (column) of elements in the periodic table, the ionization energies generally decrease with increasing atomic number. Although the charge on the nucleus increases considerably as the atomic numbers of the members of a group increase, the attractive force exerted by the nucleus is diminished (screened) by the presence of inner energy levels. In addition, the atomic size is increasing and therefore the net effect is to lessen the energy required to remove the most loosely held electron.

Within a given period (row) of elements in the periodic table, the ionization energies generally increase with increasing atomic number. As we proceed across a period, the effect of increasing nuclear charge is to shrink the atom while the number of energy levels remains constant. Thus, the energy required to remove the most loosely bound electron generally increases with increasing nuclear charge.

Electronegativity refers to the tendency of an atom in a covalently bonded molecule to attract the shared electrons holding that atom to another one. Atoms with high electronegativity tend to attract shared electrons. Atoms with low electronegativity attract shared electrons weakly. The displacement of electron pairs produces a charge separation, resulting in the formation of polar species.

The electronegativity scale arbitrarily varies from 0.7 for cesium to 4.0 for fluorine. Metals tend to have low electronegativity values. The lower the electronegativity value the more apparent are the metallic characteristics. The lowest electronegativities are found in the lower left-hand area of the periodic table.

Nonmetals are highly electronegative. Elements possessing the highest electronegativity values are found in the upper right-hand area of the periodic table. (Inert gases do not bond under usual conditions and are not assigned electronegativity values.) Fluorine is the most electronegative element, with oxygen second.

Electronegativity values tend to decrease with increasing atomic number within a group (column). Electronegativity values tend to increase as we go from left to right across a period (row) of the periodic table.

Question 1. Of the following, the element that has the greatest tendency to form a positive ion is (1) Na (2) Mg (3) F (4) Cs.

Answer. Cesium (4) has an ionization energy of 3.9 e.v. Of the elements listed, this is the lowest amount of energy required to remove the most loosely bound electron. Thus, choice (4) is the correct answer.

Question 2. Of the following elements, the most difficult to ionize is (1) strontium (2) lead (3) fluorine (4) aluminum.

Answer. Since, of the elements listed, fluorine has the highest electronegativity value, fluorine has the greatest tendency to attract electrons. This means that fluorine should have the lowest tendency to lose an electron, a fact borne out by its high ionization energy. Thus, fluorine (choice 3) is the most difficult to ionize.

Question 3. The electronegativity value of nitrogen is (1) equal to that of chlorine (2) equal to that of aluminum (3) greater than that of chlorine (4) less than that of aluminum.

Answer. The table reveals that the electronegativity value of nitrogen is 3.0, which is identical to that of chlorine. Therefore, the correct answer is choice (1).

Question 4. High electronegativity is characteristic of the (1) metals (2) inert gases (3) nonmetals (4) transitional elements.

Answer. The table reveals that the highest electronegativity value is assigned to fluorine, and that, in general, the nonmetals have higher electronegativities than any other kind of element. Thus, choice (3), nonmetals, is the correct answer.

Question 5. The electronegativity difference for the bonds in CO_2 is (1) 4.5 (2) 6.0 (3) 9.5 (4) 1.0.

Answer. Since we are seeking the electronegativity difference between carbon and oxygen, we subtract the electronegativity value of carbon (2.5) from that of oxygen (3.5). Choice (4), 1.0, is the correct answer.

TABLE K. pH VALUES FOR EQUIVALENT (0.1 N) SOLUTIONS

The table of pH values gives a measure of the relative acidity and alkalinity of various solutions of equal concentration (0.1 N).

Hydrochloric acid	1.1	Alum	3.2
Sulfuric acid	1.2	Boric acid	5.2
Phosphoric acid	1.5	Pure water	7.0
Citric acid	2.2	Sodium bicarbonate	8.4
Acetic acid	2.9	Borax	9.2

Ammonium hydroxide	11.1
Sodium carbonate	11.6
Trisodium phosphate	12.0
Sodium hydroxide	13.0
Potassium hydroxide	13.0

Table K

A pH value of 7 is neutral. As the pH value decreases, the acidity increases; and as the pH value increases, the alkalinity increases. This means that a solution of pH 2 is more acidic than a solution of pH 6, while a solution of pH 12 is more alkaline than a solution of pH 8. In the table, the most acidic substance (least alkaline) is hydrochloric acid, while the most alkaline (least acidic) is potassium hydroxide or sodium hydroxide.

Question 1. Citric acid is more acidic than (1) sulfuric acid (2) acetic acid (3) phosphoric acid (4) hydrochloric acid.

Answer. The pH table shows that of the choices given in the question, only the pH value of acetic acid (2.9) is greater than the pH value of citric acid (2.2). Since the greater the pH value the weaker the acid, the correct answer is choice (2), acetic acid.

Question 2. A base may have a pH of (1) 1 (2) 3 (3) 7 (4) 14.

Answer. Since only a substance with a pH value above 7 is basic, the correct answer is choice (4), a pH of 14.

TABLE L. STANDARD OXIDATION POTENTIALS

This table lists a series of half-reactions in which atoms, molecules, or ions tend to lose electrons. This tendency is measured against the tendency of a standard half-cell ($H_2 = 2 H^+ + 2 e^-$) to lose electrons and is expressed as the E^0 in volts. All concentrations are measured at 1 molal at 25°C. The position of the atoms, molecules, or ions in the table indicates the relative ease with which these particles lose electrons. In a broad sense, the table lists the comparative activities of metals and nonmetals. The higher in the table, the more active is the metal (more powerful reducing agent). The lower in the table, the more active is the nonmetal (more powerful oxidizing agent).

IONIC CONCENTRATIONS 1 MOLAL IN WATER AT 25° C	
HALF-CELL REACTION	E^0 (volts)
$Li = Li^+ + e^-$	3.05
$Rb = Rb^+ + e^-$	2.93
$K = K^+ + e^-$	2.93
$Cs = Cs^+ + e^-$	2.92
$Ba = Ba^{++} + 2 e^-$	2.90
$Sr = Sr^{++} + 2 e^-$	2.89
$Ca = Ca^{++} + 2 e^-$	2.87
$Na = Na^+ + e^-$	2.71
$Mg = Mg^{++} + 2 e^-$	2.37
$Be = Be^{++} + 2 e^-$	1.85
$Al = Al^{+++} + 3 e^-$	1.66
$Mn = Mn^{++} + 2 e^-$	1.18
$Zn = Zn^{++} + 2 e^-$	0.76
$Cr = Cr^{+++} + 3 e^-$	0.74
$Fe = Fe^{++} + 2 e^-$	0.44
$Cd = Cd^{++} + 2 e^-$	0.40
$Co = Co^{++} + 2 e^-$	0.28
$Ni = Ni^{++} + 2 e^-$	0.25
$Sn = Sn^{++} + 2 e^-$	0.14
$Pb = Pb^{++} + 2 e^-$	0.13
$H_2 = 2 H^+ + 2 e^-$	0.00
$Sn^{++} = Sn^{++++} + 2 e^-$	−0.15
$Cu^+ = Cu^{++} + e^-$	−0.15
$Cu = Cu^{++} + 2 e^-$	−0.34
$2 I^- = I_2 + 2 e^-$	−0.53
$Fe^{++} = Fe^{+++} + e^-$	−0.77
$2 Hg = Hg_2^{++} + 2 e^-$	−0.79
$Ag = Ag^+ + e^-$	−0.80
$Hg_2^{++} = 2 Hg^{++} + 2 e^-$	−0.92
$NO + 2 H_2O = NO_3^- + 4 H^+ + 3 e^-$	−0.96
$2 Br^- = Br_2 (l) + 2 e^-$	−1.07
$2 H_2O = O_2 + 4 H^+ + 4 e^-$	−1.23
$2 Cr^{+++} + 7 H_2O = Cr_2O_7^{--} + 14 H^+ + 6 e^-$	−1.33
$2 Cl^- = Cl_2 + 2 e^-$	−1.36
$Au = Au^{+++} + 3 e^-$	−1.50
$Mn^{++} + 4 H_2O = MnO_4^- + 8 H^+ + 5 e^-$	−1.51
$2 F^- = F_2 + 2 e^-$	−2.87

Table L

1. Metals

a. Replacement of Hydrogen from Acids. All metals above hydrogen in the series will replace hydrogen from most acids. Because of this, hydrogen may be prepared by the reaction of zinc or iron with hydrochloric or dilute sulfuric acid.

b. Replacement of Hydrogen from Water. The most active metals, such as potassium, calcium, and sodium, are sufficiently active to replace hydrogen from cold water. In each of these chemical actions, the metal reacts with the water to form hydrogen and a base. Metals like magnesium and aluminum are not sufficiently active to replace hydrogen from cold water. However, as the temperature of the water is increased, the ability of the metal to replace the hydrogen from the water also increases.

c. Replacement of Metals. Any metal listed in the series will replace any other metal below it in the series from a salt solution of the less active metal. Thus, a strip of iron immersed in a copper (II) sulfate solution will replace the copper, forming free copper and iron (II) sulfate. Lead, which is less active than zinc and below it in the table, will not react with a zinc chloride solution.

d. Reducing Agents. The degree of activity of a metal depends upon the ease with which the metal loses electrons. The more active a metal, the more powerful a reducing agent it is. Thus, aluminum is a more powerful reducing agent than iron. Aluminum will react with (reduce) iron (III) oxide to form free iron and aluminum oxide (thermite reaction).

e. Stability of Compounds. Active metals form stable compounds. Thus, potassium chloride is a more stable compound than zinc chloride. The stability of the compound is also related to its heat of formation.

2. Nonmetals

a. Replacement Power of the Halogens. The tendency to gain electrons is inversely related to the tendency to lose electrons. Thus, in Table L, fluorine has the greatest tendency to gain electrons. This means that the order of activity (replacement) of the halogens is fluorine, chlorine, bromine, and iodine.

b. Oxidizing Agents. The degree of activity of a nonmetal depends upon the ease with which the nonmetal gains electrons. The more active a nonmetal is, the more powerful an oxidizing agent it is. Thus, fluorine is the most powerful oxidizing agent in the halogen family.

c. Stability of Compounds. Combined with the same metal, active nonmetals form more stable compounds than less active nonmetals. Thus, potassium fluoride is a more stable compound than potassium bromide.

Question 1. Sodium may be obtained from sodium chloride by a process of (1) electrolysis (2) hydrolysis (3) reduction with aluminum (4) reduction with carbon. *Answer.* Since sodium is near the top of the table, it is a powerful reducing agent. It can be extracted from its compounds either byjusing a more active metal or by electrochemical reduction. Since the answers do not list a more active metal, the correct choice is (1).

Question 2. Lead will replace the metallic ion in a solution of (1) $CaCl_2$ (2) $Cu(NO_3)_2$ (3) KI (4) $ZnCl_2$.

Answer. Of the four metals suggested, the only one below lead in the table is copper. Since lead can replace copper (II) ions, the correct answer is choice (2).

Question 3. Of the following, the least stable compound is (1) HF (2) HBr (3) HCl (4) HI.

Answer. Since iodine is the least active of the halogens, its hydrogen compound will be the least stable. Thus, the correct answer is choice (4).

Question 4. Of the following, the strongest reducing agent is (1) Au (2) Na (3) Pb (4) H_2O.

Answer. Since a substance that is easily oxidized is a strong reducing agent, the table indicates that the relative reducing strength increases progressively from F^- to Li. Thus, of those listed, choice (2), Na, is the strongest reducing agent.

Question 5. Assume that chemists have replaced the present standard oxidation potentials with the following:

$$Ag = Ag^+ + e^- \qquad E^0 = 0.0 \text{ volts}$$

If the assumed new reference standard is used, then the E^0 for $Li = Li^+ + e^-$ becomes (1) 2.25 (2) -2.25 (3) 3.85 (4) -3.85 volts.

Answer. Using the present table of oxidation potentials, $H_2 = 2 H^+ + 2 e^-$ ($E^0 = 0.0$ volts), we note that the E^0 of $Li = Li^+ + e^-$ is 3.85 volts greater than that of $Ag = Ag^+ + e^-$ [$3.05 - (-0.80) = 3.85$]. Therefore, using the new standard, E^0 of $Li = Li^+ + e^-$ would become 3.85 volts, choice (3).

TABLE M. IONIZATION CONSTANTS OF ACIDS AND BASES

1. Ionization. The ionization constant, derived from the Law of Mass Action, is a quantitative measure of the ability of a given substance to ionize. The table of constants predicts the relative activity of acids and bases at 25°C in terms of their ability to ionize, the strongest ionizing completely and the weakest ionizing only slightly. The larger the value of the ionization constant, the stronger is the acid or base. Since strong acids and strong bases are completely ionized in water, their ionization constants are infinitely large. Hence, hydrochloric acid, which ionizes completely or nearly completely, is a stronger acid than phosphoric acid, which ionizes only moderately. Reference to the table also shows that phosphoric acid, with an ionization constant of 7.5×10^{-3}, is a stronger acid than acetic acid, with an ionization constant of 1.8×10^{-5}. Similarly, potassium hydroxide is a stronger base than ammonium hydroxide.

The ionization constants of weak acids and weak bases are determined in the same manner as are equilibrium constants. For example, the ionization constant for acetic acid may be determined as follows:

$$CH_3COOH = H^+ + CH_3COO^-$$

$$K_i = \frac{[H^+][CH_3COO^-]}{[CH_3COOH]} = 1.8 \times 10^{-5}$$

The weaker the acid or base, the larger is the denominator and the smaller is the value for the ionization constant.

Acetic acid	1.8×10^{-5}
Boric acid	5.8×10^{-10}
Carbonic acid	4.3×10^{-7}
Hypochlorous acid	3.5×10^{-8}
Phosphoric acid	7.5×10^{-3}
Ammonium hydroxide	1.8×10^{-5}
Lead hydroxide	9.6×10^{-4}

Some acids and bases which are completely or nearly completely ionized in dilute solutions at 25° C are:

ACIDS	BASES
Hydrochloric	Potassium hydroxide
Nitric	Sodium hydroxide
Sulfuric	

Table M

2. Hydrolysis. The information in Table M also enables us to predict the effect on litmus when a salt solution hydrolyzes. The products of hydrolysis are either an acid or a base. Since the table indicates the comparative strength of the acid and the base, we are able to predict the action of the hydrolyzed salt solution on litmus. For example, a solution of sodium carbonate turns red litmus blue because the products of hydrolysis are sodium hydroxide, a strong base, and carbonic acid, a weak acid. A solution of ammonium nitrate turns blue litmus red because the products of hydrolysis are nitric acid, a strong acid, and ammonium hydroxide, a weak base.

Question 1. A strong acid differs from a weak acid in the (1) amount of dissolved hydrogen (2) number of replaceable hydrogen atoms (3) number of hydrogen ions produced (4) ability to combine with oxygen.

Answer. The table indicates that the strong acids (hydrochloric, nitric, and sulfuric) ionize completely or nearly completely, while weak acids ionize only partially. Since the greater ionization of strong acids produces a greater number of hydrogen ions, the answer to the question is choice (3).

Question 2. A strong base is (1) CH_3COOH (2) KOH (3) NH_4OH (4) C_2H_5OH.

Answer. Of the suggested answers, only KOH and NH_4OH are bases. The table shows that KOH ionizes more completely than NH_4OH; KOH is therefore the stronger base. Choice (2) is the correct answer.

Question 3. Lead nitrate will hydrolyze in water solution to form (1) a strong acid and a strong base (2) a strong acid and a weak base (3) a strong base and a weak acid (4) a weak acid and a weak base.

Answer. When a solution of lead nitrate hydrolyzes, lead hydroxide and nitric acid are formed. Since the table indicates that lead hydroxide is only slightly ionized, it is a weak base. Nitric acid, on the other hand, is highly ionized and is therefore a strong acid. The correct answer is (2).

Question 4. The weakest of the following acids is (1) acetic (2) boric (3) carbonic (4) phosphoric.

Answer. The table shows that boric acid has the lowest ionization constant (5.8×10^{-10}). Thus, boric acid is the weakest acid because it releases the smallest number of hydrogen ions when undergoing ionization. The correct answer is (2).

TABLE N. EQUILIBRIUM CONSTANTS

This table lists some examples of equilibrium constants at 25°C. At constant temperature, a system in equilibrium, at any given moment, has a constant composition. Using the Law of Mass Action, the constant (K) can be determined by dividing the product of the equilibrium concentrations in moles/liter of the substances formed by the product of the equilibrium concentrations in moles/liter of the reacting substances. The concentration of each substance is raised to a power equal to the number of moles of the substance in the chemical equation. At equilibrium, a large constant indicates a relatively high concentration of products, while a low constant indicates a relatively small concentration of products. Thus, the equilibrium constant for the dissociation of acetic acid molecules in water, $CH_3COOH = H^+ + CH_3COO^-$, is derived from the relationship

$$K_i = \frac{[H^+][CH_3COO^-]}{[CH_3COOH]} = 1.8 \times 10^{-5}$$

Since the K value for this reaction is low (1.8×10^{-5}), only small amounts of H^+ and CH_3COO^- ions are present at equilibrium.

When AgCl dissolves in water, a relatively small amount of Ag^+ and Cl^- ions forms. The equilibrium constant (K) is 1.7×10^{-10} and is derived from the relationship

$$K = [Ag^+][Cl^-] = 1.7 \times 10^{-10}$$

(This K should be more accurately called the *solubility product constant*.)

In the reaction between copper metal Cu (s) and silver ions in solution (Ag^+), the amount of Cu^{+2} ions at equilibrium is large as compared to Ag^+ ions. ($K = 2 \times 10^{15}$, a large number.)

$$Cu \text{ (s)} + 2 Ag^+ = Cu^{+2} + 2 Ag \text{ (s)}$$

$$K = \frac{[Cu^{+2}]}{[Ag^+]^2} = 2 \times 10^{15}$$

(The concentrations of solids in moles/liter at equilibrium are constant. These concentrations are fixed by the densities of the solids and do not appear in the equilibrium expression.)

Cu (s) + 2 Ag$^+$ (aq) = Cu^{+2} (aq) + 2 Ag (s)	2×10^{15}
CH$_3$COOH (aq) = H$^+$ (aq) + CH$_3$COO$^-$ (aq)	1.8×10^{-5}
AgCl (s) = Ag$^+$ (aq) + Cl$^-$ (aq)	1.7×10^{-10}

Table N

Question 1. In the reaction $3 Fe + 4 H_2O = Fe_3O_4 + 4 H_2$, the equilibrium constant, K, is equal to:

(1) $\dfrac{[Fe][H_2O]}{[Fe_3O_4][H_2]}$

(2) $\dfrac{[Fe]^3[H_2O]^4}{[Fe_3O_4][H_2]^4}$

(3) $\dfrac{[Fe_3O_4][H_2]^4}{[Fe]^3[H_2O]^4}$

(4) $[Fe]^3[H_2O]^4[Fe_3O_4][H_2]^4$

Answer. Since the equilibrium constant is equal to the product of the concentrations of the resultants raised to the power represented by their coefficients, divided by the product of the concentrations of the reactants raised to the power represented by their coefficients, choice (3) is correct.

Question 2. In the reaction $AgCl = Ag^+ + Cl^-$, in a one-liter closed system, 1.0 moles of Ag^+ are present at equilibrium. How many moles of Cl^- are present in the system? (1) 2 (2) 6 (3) 1.7×10^{-10} (4) 3.4×10^{-10}.

Answer. From the table, the value for K is 1.7×10^{-10}. Since the equilibrium concentration for Ag^+ ion is 1.0 moles/liter, then

$$K = [Ag^+][Cl^-]$$

$$1.7 \times 10^{-10} = [1.0][Cl^-]$$

$$Cl^- = 1.7 \times 10^{-10} \text{ moles/l}$$

Choice (3) is the correct answer.

TABLE O. PRESSURE OF WATER VAPOR IN MILLIMETERS OF MERCURY

This table lists the pressures of water vapor at different temperatures and is useful in determining the partial pressures of gases. Water tends to evaporate at all temperatures. Thus, whenever a gas is collected over water, some water vapor will be present with the collected gas. The pressure exerted by the water vapor increases with increasing temperature. Assuming that the water inside and outside the collecting apparatus is adjusted to the same level, the sum of the partial pressures of the water vapor and of the gas collected is then equal to the atmospheric pressure. Each gas in a mixture of gases exerts its pressure independently of the other gases in the mixture. Thus, the pressure exerted by each gas is directly proportional to the number of molecules (or moles) of each gas. To determine the partial pressure of the gas collected, one must then subtract the partial pressure of the water vapor (as shown in the table) from the atmospheric pressure.

° C	mm.	° C	mm.	° C	mm.	° C	mm.
0.0	4.6	17.0	14.5	21.0	18.7	25.0	23.8
5.0	6.5	18.0	15.5	22.0	19.8	26.0	25.2
10.0	9.2	19.0	16.5	23.0	21.1	27.0	26.7
15.0	12.8	20.0	17.5	24.0	22.4	28.0	28.3

Table O

Question 1. Oxygen is collected over water, with the water levels inside and outside the apparatus equalized. The atmospheric pressure is 755 mm of Hg and the temperature is 22°C. In mm of Hg, the partial pressure of the oxygen is (1) 774.8 (2) 777 (3) 733 (4) 735.2.

Answer. From the table we can see that, at 22°C, the pressure of water vapor is 19.8 mm of Hg. Subtracting this from the atmospheric pressure (755 mm − 19.8 mm), we find that the partial pressure of the oxygen is 735.2 mm of Hg, choice (4).

Question 2. 20.0 ml of nitrogen are collected by water displacement. Assume inside and outside water levels to be equal. The temperature is 20°C and the barometric pressure is 750 mm. What would be the volume of the dry nitrogen at STP? (1) 17.9 ml (2) 20.5 ml (3) 19.3 ml (4) 22.3 ml.

Answer. The partial pressure of the nitrogen is determined by subtracting the pressure of the water vapor at 20°C from the atmospheric pressure (750 mm − 17.5 mm = 732.5 mm). The problem now involves the conversion of 20.0 ml of nitrogen measured at 20°C and 732.5 mm to a new volume at 0°C and 760 mm (STP). According to Charles' Law, at constant pressure, the volume of a gas varies directly with the absolute (Kelvin) temperature. Thus, the volume change due to the change in temperature is

$$20.0 \text{ ml} \times \frac{0°C + 273}{20°C + 273}$$

According to Boyle's Law, at constant temperature, the volume of a gas varies inversely with pressure. Thus, the volume change due to the change in pressure is

$$20.0 \text{ ml} \times \frac{732.5 \text{ mm}}{760 \text{ mm}}$$

Combining both changes, the new volume is

$$20.0 \text{ ml} \times \frac{273° \text{ K}}{293° \text{ K}} \times \frac{732.5 \text{ mm}}{760 \text{ mm}} = 17.9 \text{ ml}$$

Choice (1) is the correct answer.

TABLE P. PHYSICAL CONSTANTS

This table lists some of the common physical constants used in numerical calculations in chemistry.

NAME	SYMBOL	VALUE
Speed of light	c	3.00×10^{10} cm/sec.
Avogadro's number	N_0	6.02×10^{23}
Universal gas constant	R	0.0821 liter-atm/mole-°K
Planck's constant	h	6.63×10^{-34} joule-sec.
Charge of electron	e	1.60×10^{-19} coulomb
Mass of an electron	m_e	9.11×10^{-28} gm.
Mass of a proton	m_p	1.67×10^{-24} gm.
Mass of a neutron	m_n	1.67×10^{-24} gm.

Table P

The speed of light is used to calculate the energy evolved during the transformation of mass into energy. The energy evolved from 1 gram of matter can be calculated from Einstein's equation, $E = mc^2$, as follows:

$$E = mc^2$$
$$E = 1 \text{ gram} \times (3.00 \times 10^{10} \text{ cm/sec})^2$$
$$E = 9 \times 10^{20} \text{ gram cm}^2/\text{sec}^2$$
$$E = 9 \times 10^{20} \text{ ergs of energy}$$

Question. The number of coulombs in 1 faraday is approximately (1) 1 (2) 22.4 (3) 96,500 (4) 6.02×10^{23}.

Answer. One faraday is the quantity of electricity required to discharge Avogadro's number of singly charged ions. Since 1 electron is required to discharge 1 singly charged ion, Avogadro's number of electrons is required to discharge Avogadro's number of singly charged ions. From the table, we note that the charge on a single electron is 1.60×10^{-19} coulomb, and Avogadro's number is 6.02×10^{23}. The number of coulombs in

$$1 \text{ faraday} = e \times N_0$$
$$= (1.60 \times 10^{-19} \text{ coulomb}) \times (6.02 \times 10^{23}) = 9.6320 \times 10^4$$
$$= 96,320 \text{ coulombs}$$

Choice (3) is the correct answer.

3. A SUMMARY OF IMPORTANT CHEMICAL PRINCIPLES

1. FUNDAMENTAL IDEAS

a. States of Matter

1. Matter exists in three physical states: gas, liquid, and solid. The relationship between the states of matter in terms of heat can be expressed as follows:

$$\text{Gas} \underset{-\text{ heat}}{\overset{+\text{ heat}}{\rightleftarrows}} \text{Liquid} \underset{-\text{ heat}}{\overset{+\text{ heat}}{\rightleftarrows}} \text{Solid}$$

b. Chemical Equation

2. An equation represents a fundamental weight relationship between the starting substances (reactants) and the products (resultants) of a chemical reaction. The sum of the weights of all the reactants equals the sum of the weights of all the resultants. By using the proper density factors, the weights may be converted into the corresponding volumes.

c. Atoms

3. All atoms consist of a positively charged nucleus surrounded by shells of negatively charged electrons. The electrical charge on the nucleus is equal to the atomic number. The atomic number also represents the total number of electrons in the shells. Atoms are therefore electrically neutral. Differences between atoms of various elements are due to differences in the number and arrangement of particles in these atoms.

d. Valence Number

4. The valence number of an atom is equal to the number of electrons that the atom can lend, borrow, or share in a chemical change.

e. Ions

5. An ion is an electrically charged particle having the same nuclear structure as the atom or group of atoms from which the particle was derived. The charge on the ion depends on the number of electrons lost or gained by the atom or group of atoms during a chemical change.

f. Organization of the Periodic Table

6. Electropositive elements generally occupy the left side of the table, while electronegative elements generally occupy the right side. Elements which form amphoteric compounds are usually found near the center of the table.

g. Activity of Elements

7. The activity of a metal depends upon the ease with which its atoms lose electrons. The activity of a nonmetal depends upon the ease with which its atoms gain electrons.

8. In any given family of metals, the activity of the metal generally increases as the atomic number (atomic radius) of the metal increases. In any given family of nonmetals, the activity of the nonmetal generally decreases with an increase in atomic number.

h. Oxidation-Reduction

9. Oxidation is a process in which a particle loses electrons. As a result of the loss of electrons, there is an increase in positive valence number or a decrease in negative valence number.

10. Reduction is a process in which a particle (atom or ion) gains electrons. As a result of the gain of electrons, there is a decrease in positive valence number or an increase in negative valence number.

11. In a reaction where there is oxidation, there must be corresponding reduction.

12. An oxidizing agent is any substance containing a particle which can gain electrons.

13. A reducing agent is any substance containing a particle which can lose electrons.

14. In electrolysis, oxidation always takes place at the anode, while corresponding reduction always takes place at the cathode.

i. Extraction of Elements from Compounds

15. The extraction of a metallic element from its compound requires the restoration of electrons (reduction) to the metal ion. This reduction may be accomplished by:
(a) The use of suitable reducing agents for moderately active metals.
(b) Electrolysis of fused compounds for active metals.

16. The extraction of a nonmetallic element from its compound requires the removal of electrons (oxidation) from the nonmetallic ion. This oxidation may be accomplished by:
(a) The use of suitable oxidizing agents for moderately active nonmetals.
(b) Electrolysis of fused compounds for active nonmetals.

j. Electrolytes

17. Solutions of acids, bases, and salts that conduct an electric current are called electrolytes. An electric current passing through an electrolyte produces an oxidation-reduction reaction which causes the electrolyte to decompose.

2. LABORATORY PREPARATIONS

a. Oxygen

18. Oxygen may be prepared in the laboratory by the decomposition of metallic oxides or compounds ending in the suffix *-ate*.
    a. Metallic oxide → metal + oxygen
    b. Metal *-ate* → metal *-ide* + oxygen

b. Hydrogen

19. Hydrogen may be prepared in the laboratory by either of the following general methods:
    a. Moderately active metal + non-oxidizing acid → hydrogen + a salt of the metal.
    b. Active metal + water → hydrogen + a base.

c. Acids

20. The general method for preparing an acid (HX) in the laboratory is to react a salt of the acid to be prepared with H_2SO_4.

$$2\ NaX + H_2SO_4 \rightarrow 2\ HX + Na_2SO_4$$

d. Bases

21. The general method for preparing a base depends on the solubility of the base in water.

a. Soluble Base

Reaction of an active metal (M) with water:

$$2\ M + 2\ H_2O \rightarrow 2\ \underset{\substack{\text{soluble} \\ \text{base}}}{MOH} + H_2 \uparrow$$

Reaction of a soluble metal oxide (M_2O) with water:

$$M_2O + H_2O \rightarrow 2\ \underset{\substack{\text{soluble} \\ \text{base}}}{MOH}$$

b. Insoluble Base

Reaction between a soluble base and a soluble salt of the desired insoluble base:

$$2\ NaOH + CuSO_4 \rightarrow Na_2SO_4 + Cu(OH)_2 \downarrow$$

e. Salts

22. Salts may be prepared in the following ways. The salt prepared has the general formula MCl (soluble salt of univalent metal M).

a. Neutralization

$$MOH + HCl \rightarrow MCl + H_2O$$

b. Direct Combination or Synthesis

$$2\ M + Cl_2 \rightarrow 2\ MCl$$

c. Single Replacement

$$2\ M + 2\ HCl \rightarrow 2\ MCl + H_2 \uparrow$$

d. Action of an Acid on a Metallic Oxide

$$M_2O + 2\ HCl \rightarrow 2\ MCl + H_2O$$

e. Double Replacement Due to Volatility

$$M_2S + 2\ HCl \rightarrow 2\ MCl + H_2S \uparrow$$

f. Double Replacement Due to Insolubility

$$M_2SO_4 + BaCl_2 \rightarrow 2\ MCl + BaSO_4 \downarrow$$

f. Preparation of Acid Anhydrides

23. Acid anhydrides are prepared by the decomposition of their respective acids.

$$H_2CO_3 \rightarrow H_2O + CO_2 \uparrow$$
$$H_2SO_3 \rightarrow H_2O + SO_2 \uparrow$$

The acids are prepared as outlined generally in **20**, page 397.

$$CO_3^{-2} + 2\ H^+ \rightarrow H_2CO_3 \rightarrow H_2O + CO_2 \uparrow$$
$$HCO_3^- + \ \ H^+ \rightarrow H_2CO_3 \rightarrow H_2O + CO_2 \uparrow$$
$$SO_3^{-2} + 2\ H^+ \rightarrow H_2SO_3 \rightarrow H_2O + SO_2 \uparrow$$
$$HSO_3^- + \ \ H^+ \rightarrow H_2SO_3 \rightarrow H_2O + SO_2 \uparrow$$

g. Preparation of Ammonia

24. Ammonia is prepared by the decomposition of ammonium hydroxide.

$$NH_4OH \rightarrow H_2O + NH_3 \uparrow$$

In order to prepare ammonium hydroxide, any ammonium compound (NH_4^+) may be treated with any soluble base (OH^-). The general equation is:

$$NH_4^+ + OH^- \rightarrow NH_4OH \rightarrow H_2O + NH_3 \uparrow$$

3. PREDICTION OF REACTIONS

25. The rate of reaction is generally increased by an increase in temperature, surface area, or concentration of the reactants. An increase in pressure generally favors the reaction between gases.

26. Certain reactions, such as the combination of elements, the decomposition of compounds, and single replacement, involve oxidation-reduction. The rate at which such reactions take place is in direct proportion to the ease with which the elements involved in these reactions lose or gain electrons.

27. Double replacement reactions go to completion if one of the products formed is a weak electrolyte.

28. In a given reaction, when the speed of formation of the products is equal to the speed of re-formation of the original substances, equilibrium has been attained.

29. Hydrolysis reactions are the reverse of neutralization. In a neutralization reaction, an acid and a base react to form water and a salt. In a hydrolysis reaction, certain salts react with water to liberate an acid and a base. The extent of hydrolysis and the action on litmus depend on the relative strengths of the acid and base produced.

4. ORGANIC CHEMISTRY

a. Why Carbon Forms So Many Compounds

30. Carbon forms covalent linkages with many atoms, including other carbon atoms.

31. Organic compounds exhibit isomerism. As the molecular weights of these compounds increase, the number of possible isomers also increases.

b. Classification

32. Organic compounds are actually or theoretically derived from hydrocarbons.

33. An organic radical (R) may be derived by removing one or more hydrogen atoms from the corresponding hydrocarbon. The radical may be used to express the general group formula. Thus, R—H represents the hydrocarbon family.

34. Organic compounds may be classed as chain (aliphatic) compounds or ring (aromatic) compounds. Each of these groups may contain saturated or unsaturated linkages.

c. Reactions

35. Saturated compounds may react by substitution, while unsaturated compounds may react by addition.

36. Because of the absence of ions, organic reactions are generally slower than inorganic reactions.

5. NUCLEAR CHEMISTRY

a. Disintegration of Radioactive Elements

37. The nuclear capture and/or ejection of electrons, protons, neutrons, and alpha particles results in transmutation.
38. The emission of an alpha particle from the nucleus of an atom decreases the atomic weight by 4 units and the atomic number by 2 units.
39. The emission of a beta particle from the nucleus of an atom leaves the atomic weight unchanged, but increases the atomic number by 1 unit.
40. Light atoms achieve nuclear stability by fusion, while heavy atoms achieve nuclear stability by fission.

b. Nuclear Equations

41. The sum of all the subscripts (atomic numbers) on the left side of a nuclear equation equals the sum of all the subscripts on the right side of the equation. Similarly, the sum of all the superscripts (atomic weights) on the left side of a nuclear equation equals the sum of all the superscripts on the right side of the equation.

4. A REVIEW OF CHEMICAL PRINCIPLES THROUGH EQUATIONS

I. OXYGEN

Laboratory Preparation

1. $2 \; KClO_3 \rightarrow 2 \; KCl + 3 \; O_2\uparrow$
2. $2 \; NaClO_3 \rightarrow 2 \; NaCl + 3 \; O_2\uparrow$
3. $2 \; HgO \rightarrow 2 \; Hg + O_2\uparrow$
4. $2 \; H_2O_2 \rightarrow 2 \; H_2O + O_2\uparrow$
5. $2 \; Na_2O_2 + 2 \; H_2O \rightarrow 4 \; NaOH + O_2\uparrow$

Commercial Preparation

6. $2 \; H_2O \xrightarrow{\text{electrolysis}} 2 \; H_2\uparrow + O_2\uparrow$

Chemical Properties (Formation of Oxides)

7. $C + O_2 \rightarrow CO_2\uparrow$
8. $S + O_2 \rightarrow SO_2\uparrow$
9. $4 \; P + 5 \; O_2 \rightarrow 2 \; P_2O_5$
10. $4 \; Fe + 3 \; O_2 \rightarrow 2 \; Fe_2O_3$
11. $2 \; Mg + O_2 \rightarrow 2 \; MgO$

Preparation of Ozone

12. $3 \; O_2 \rightarrow 2 \; O_3\uparrow$

Action of Ozone on Metals

13. $2 \; Ag + O_3 \rightarrow Ag_2O + O_2\uparrow$

II. HYDROGEN

Laboratory Preparation

   a. From Acids

   14. $Zn + 2\ HCl \rightarrow ZnCl_2 + H_2 \uparrow$
   15. $Mg + H_2SO_4 \rightarrow MgSO_4 + H_2 \uparrow$

   b. From Water

   16. $2\ Na + 2\ H_2O \rightarrow 2\ NaOH + H_2 \uparrow$
   17. $Ca + 2\ H_2O \rightarrow Ca(OH)_2 + H_2 \uparrow$

Commercial Preparation

   18. $4\ H_2O + 3\ Fe \rightarrow Fe_3O_4 + 4\ H_2 \uparrow$
   19. $H_2O\ \ \ + C\ \rightarrow CO \uparrow + H_2 \uparrow$
   20. $2\ H_2O \xrightarrow{\text{electrolysis}} 2\ H_2 \uparrow + O_2 \uparrow$

Chemical Properties

   a. Combustibility

   21. $2\ H_2 + O_2 \rightarrow 2\ H_2O$
   22. $H_2 + Cl_2 \rightarrow 2\ HCl \uparrow$

   b. Reducing Agent

   23. $CuO + H_2 \rightarrow H_2O + Cu$

III. WATER

Preparation

   a. Direct Combination

   24. $2\ H_2 + O_2 \rightarrow 2\ H_2O$

   b. Oxidation of Hydrogen Compounds

   25. $2\ H_2S + 3\ O_2 \rightarrow 2\ H_2O + 2\ SO_2 \uparrow$
   26. $CH_4 + 2\ O_2 \rightarrow 2\ H_2O + CO_2 \uparrow$

   c. From the Reducing Action of Hydrogen

   27. $CuO + H_2 \rightarrow H_2O + Cu$

   d. Partial Decomposition of Hydrates

   28. $CuSO_4 \cdot 5\ H_2O \rightarrow CuSO_4 + 5\ H_2O$

   e. Neutralization Reactions

   29. $Ca(OH)_2 + 2\ HCl \rightarrow 2\ H_2O + CaCl_2$

Properties

   a. Reaction with Active Metals

   30. $2\ K + 2\ H_2O \rightarrow 2\ KOH + H_2 \uparrow$
   31. $Mg + 2\ H_2O \rightarrow Mg(OH)_2 + H_2 \uparrow$

b. Reaction with Acid Anhydrides

    32. $CO_2 + H_2O \rightarrow H_2CO_3$

    33. $N_2O_5 + H_2O \rightarrow 2\ HNO_3$

c. Reaction with Basic Anhydrides

    34. $Na_2O + H_2O \rightarrow 2\ NaOH$

    35. $BaO + H_2O \rightarrow Ba(OH)_2$

d. Hydration

    36. $Na_2CO_3 + 10\ H_2O \rightarrow Na_2CO_3 \cdot 10\ H_2O$

    37. $HCl + H_2O \rightarrow\ H_3O^+\ + Cl^-$

IV. HYDROGEN PEROXIDE

Preparation

    38. $BaO_2 + H_2SO_4 \rightarrow H_2O_2 + BaSO_4 \downarrow$

Chemical Properties

a. Decomposition

    39. $2\ H_2O_2 \rightarrow 2\ H_2O + O_2 \uparrow$

b. Oxidizing Agent

    40. $H_2S + H_2O_2 \rightarrow 2\ H_2O + S$

V. IONIZATION

Ionization of Acids

    41. $HCl + H_2O \rightarrow H_3O^+ + Cl^-$

    42. $H_2SO_4 + 2\ H_2O \rightarrow 2\ H_3O^+ + SO_4^{-2}$

    43. $HNO_3 + H_2O \rightarrow H_3O^+ + NO_3^-$

Ionization of Bases

    44. $NaOH \rightarrow Na^+ + OH^-$

    45. $Ca(OH)_2 \rightarrow Ca^{+2} + 2\ OH^-$

    46. $NH_4OH \underset{\longrightarrow}{\longleftarrow} NH_4^+ + OH^-$

Ionization of Salts

    47. $NaCl \rightarrow Na^+ + Cl^-$

    48. $CaBr_2 \rightarrow Ca^{+2} + 2\ Br^-$

    49. $Al_2(SO_4)_3 \rightarrow 2\ Al^{+3} + 3\ SO_4^{-2}$

Preparation of Acids, Bases, and Salts

ACIDS

a. From the Reaction Between Sulfuric Acid and a Salt Containing the Desired Acid Radical

    50. $2\ NaCl + H_2SO_4 \rightarrow Na_2SO_4 + 2\ HCl$

    51. $2\ NaNO_3 + H_2SO_4 \rightarrow Na_2SO_4 + 2\ HNO_3$

b. From the Corresponding Acid Anhydride

    52. $SO_2 + H_2O \rightarrow H_2SO_3$

    53. $CO_2 + H_2O \rightarrow H_2CO_3$

c. Direct Union of the Elements

 54. $H_2 + Cl_2 \rightarrow 2\ HCl$

BASES

a. Reaction Between Water and an Active Metal

 55. $2\ Na + 2\ H_2O \rightarrow 2\ NaOH + H_2\uparrow$
 56. $Ca + 2\ H_2O \rightarrow Ca(OH)_2 + H_2\uparrow$

b. From the Corresponding Basic Anhydride

 57. $Na_2O + H_2O \rightarrow 2\ NaOH$
 58. $BaO + H_2O \rightarrow Ba(OH)_2$

SALTS

a. Neutralization Reactions

 59. $NaOH + HCl \rightarrow NaCl + H_2O$
 60. $Ca(OH)_2 + 2\ HNO_3 \rightarrow Ca(NO_3)_2 + 2\ H_2O$

b. Direct Union of the Elements

 61. $2\ K + Cl_2 \rightarrow 2\ KCl$
 62. $2\ Li + Br_2 \rightarrow 2\ LiBr$

c. Single Replacement Reactions

 63. $Fe + H_2SO_4 \rightarrow FeSO_4 + H_2\uparrow$
 64. $Fe + CuSO_4 \rightarrow FeSO_4 + Cu$

d. Double Replacement Reactions

 65. $Na_2SO_4 + BaCl_2 \rightarrow 2\ NaCl + BaSO_4\downarrow$
 66. $Na_2S + 2\ HCl \rightarrow 2\ NaCl + H_2S\uparrow$

e. Reaction Between an Acid and a Basic Anhydride (Metallic Oxide)

 67. $2\ HCl + K_2O \rightarrow 2\ KCl + H_2O$
 68. $2\ HCl + BaO \rightarrow BaCl_2 + H_2O$

f. Reaction Between a Base and an Acid Anhydride (Nonmetallic Oxide)

 69. $2\ KOH + SO_2 \rightarrow K_2SO_3 + H_2O$
 70. $2\ KOH + CO_2 \rightarrow K_2CO_3 + H_2O$

VI. HALOGENS

A. FLUORINE

Preparation

 71. $2\ KHF_2 \xrightarrow{\text{electrolysis}} K_2F_2 + H_2\uparrow + F_2\uparrow$

Chemical Properties (Powerful Oxidizing Agent)

 72. $Cu + F_2 \rightarrow CuF_2$
 73. $3\ H_2O + 3\ F_2 \rightarrow 6\ HF\uparrow + O_3\uparrow$

B. CHLORINE

Laboratory Preparation

a. From HCl

74. $MnO_2 + 4\ HCl \rightarrow MnCl_2 + 2\ H_2O + Cl_2 \uparrow$

b. From a Metal Chloride

75. $MnO_2 + 2\ NaCl + 2\ H_2SO_4 \rightarrow MnSO_4 + Na_2SO_4 + 2\ H_2O + Cl_2 \uparrow$

Commercial Preparation

76. $2\ NaCl + 2\ H_2O \xrightarrow{\text{electrolysis}} 2\ NaOH + H_2 \uparrow + Cl_2 \uparrow$

77. $CaOCl_2 + H_2SO_4 \rightarrow CaSO_4 + H_2O + Cl_2 \uparrow$

Chemical Properties

a. Oxidizing Agent

78. $2\ Na + Cl_2 \rightarrow 2\ NaCl$
79. $2\ Sb + 3\ Cl_2 \rightarrow 2\ SbCl_3$
80. $H_2 + Cl_2 \rightarrow 2\ HCl \uparrow$

b. Reaction with Water

81. $Cl_2 + H_2O \rightarrow HCl + HOCl$
82. $2\ HOCl \rightarrow 2\ HCl + O_2 \uparrow$

c. Reaction with Hydrocarbons

83. $8\ Cl_2 + \underset{\text{turpentine}}{C_{10}H_{16}} \rightarrow 16\ HCl + 10\ C$

Test for Chloride Ions

84. $NaCl + AgNO_3 \rightarrow NaNO_3 + \underset{\substack{\text{insoluble} \\ \text{in } HNO_3}}{AgCl \downarrow} \text{(white)}$

C. BROMINE

Laboratory Preparation

85. $MnO_2 + 2\ KBr + 2\ H_2SO_4 \rightarrow MnSO_4 + K_2SO_4 + 2\ H_2O + Br_2 \uparrow$

Commercial Preparation (From Sea Water)

86. $MgBr_2 + Cl_2 \rightarrow MgCl_2 + Br_2 \uparrow$

Chemical Properties

a. Oxidizing Agent

87. $2\ Na + Br_2 \rightarrow 2\ NaBr$
88. $H_2 + Br_2 \rightarrow 2\ HBr$

b. Reaction with Water

89. $2\ Br_2 + 2\ H_2O \rightarrow 4\ HBr + O_2 \uparrow$

Test for Bromide Ions

90. $2\ KBr + Cl_2 \rightarrow 2\ KCl + \underset{\substack{\text{turns orange} \\ \text{in } CS_2 \text{ or } CCl_4}}{Br_2}$

D. IODINE

Laboratory Preparation

91. $MnO_2 + 2\ NaI + 2\ H_2SO_4 \rightarrow MnSO_4 + Na_2SO_4 + 2\ H_2O + I_2\uparrow$

Commercial Preparation

92. $2\ KI + Cl_2 \rightarrow 2\ KCl + I_2$

Chemical Properties (Weak Oxidizing Agent)

93. $2\ K + I_2 \rightarrow 2\ KI$

Test for Iodide Ions

94. $2\ KI + Cl_2 \rightarrow 2\ KCl +$ $\underset{\substack{\text{turns violet} \\ \text{in } CS_2 \text{ or } CCl_4}}{I_2}$

95. $2\ KI + Br_2 \rightarrow 2\ KBr +$ $\underset{\substack{\text{turns violet} \\ \text{in } CS_2 \text{ or } CCl_4}}{I_2}$

E. RELATIVE REPLACEMENT POWER OF HALOGENS

96. $F_2 + 2\ NaCl \rightarrow 2\ NaF + Cl_2\uparrow$
97. $F_2 + 2\ NaBr \rightarrow 2\ NaF + Br_2$
98. $F_2 + 2\ NaI \rightarrow 2\ NaF + I_2$
99. $Cl_2 + 2\ NaBr \rightarrow 2\ NaCl + Br_2$
100. $Cl_2 + 2\ NaI \rightarrow 2\ NaCl + I_2$
101. $Br_2 + 2\ NaI \rightarrow 2\ NaBr + I_2$

VII. HYDROGEN HALIDES

A. HYDROGEN CHLORIDE

Laboratory Preparation

102. $2\ NaCl + H_2SO_4 \rightarrow Na_2SO_4 + 2\ HCl\uparrow$

Chemical Properties of Hydrochloric Acid (Reaction with Metals)

103. $Zn + 2\ HCl \rightarrow ZnCl_2 + H_2\uparrow$
104. $2\ Al + 6\ HCl \rightarrow 2\ AlCl_3 + 3\ H_2\uparrow$

B. HYDROGEN FLUORIDE

Laboratory Preparation

105. $CaF_2 + H_2SO_4 \rightarrow CaSO_4 + 2\ HF\uparrow$

Chemical Properties (Reaction with Glass)

106. $SiO_2 + 4\ HF \rightarrow 2\ H_2O + SiF_4\uparrow$

C. HYDROGEN BROMIDE AND HYDROGEN IODIDE

Laboratory Preparation

107. $PBr_3 + 3\ H_2O \rightarrow H_3PO_3 + 3\ HBr\uparrow$
108. $PI_3 + 3\ H_2O \rightarrow H_3PO_3 + 3\ HI\uparrow$

VIII. EFFECTS OF IONIZATION

A. REACTIONS THAT GO TO COMPLETION BECAUSE OF:

Formation of a Volatile Substance

109. MOLECULAR: $2 NH_4Cl + Ca(OH)_2 \rightarrow CaCl_2 + 2 H_2O + 2 NH_3 \uparrow$
IONIC: $2 NH_4^+ + 2 Cl^- + Ca^{+2} + 2 OH^- \rightarrow$
$Ca^{+2} + 2 Cl^- + 2 H_2O + 2 NH_3$

110. MOLECULAR: $Na_2CO_3 + 2 HCl \rightarrow 2 NaCl + H_2O + CO_2 \uparrow$
IONIC: $2 Na^+ + CO_3^{-2} + 2 H^+ + 2 Cl^- \rightarrow$
$2 Na^+ + 2 Cl^- + H_2O + CO_2$

Formation of an Insoluble Substance

111. MOLECULAR: $CuSO_4 + H_2S \rightarrow H_2SO_4 + CuS \downarrow$
IONIC: $Cu^{+2} + SO_4^{-2} + 2 H^+ + S^{-2} \rightarrow 2 H^+ + SO_4^{-2} + CuS$

112. MOLECULAR: $CaCl_2 + 2 AgNO_3 \rightarrow Ca(NO_3)_2 + 2 AgCl \downarrow$
IONIC: $Ca^{+2} + 2 Cl^- + 2 Ag^+ + 2 NO_3^- \rightarrow Ca^{+2} + 2 NO_3^- + 2 AgCl$

Formation of Undissociated Water (Neutralization)

113. MOLECULAR: $2 KOH + H_2SO_4 \rightarrow K_2SO_4 + \underline{2\ H_2O}$
IONIC: $2 K^+ + 2 OH^- + 2 H^+ + SO_4^{-2} \rightarrow 2 K^+ + SO_4^{-2} + \underline{2\ H_2O}$

114. MOLECULAR: $3 NaOH + H_3PO_4 \rightarrow Na_3PO_4 + \underline{3\ H_2O}$
IONIC: $3 Na^+ + 3 OH^- + 3 H^+ + PO_4^{-3} \rightarrow 3 Na^+ + PO_4^{-3} + \underline{3\ H_2O}$

B. HYDROLYSIS

115. MOLECULAR: $CuSO_4 + 2 H_2O \rightarrow H_2SO_4 + Cu(OH)_2$
IONIC: $Cu^{+2} + SO_4^{-2} + 2 H^+ + 2 OH^- \rightarrow 2 H^+ + SO_4^{-2} + Cu(OH)_2$

116. MOLECULAR: $K_2CO_3 + 2 H_2O \rightarrow 2 KOH + H_2CO_3$
IONIC: $2 K^+ + CO_3^{-2} + 2 H^+ + 2 OH^- \rightarrow 2 K^+ + 2 OH^- + H_2CO_3$

C. ELECTROLYSIS

Electrolysis of HCl

117. IONIZATION: $HCl \rightarrow H^+ + Cl^-$ or $HCl + H_2O \rightarrow H_3O^+ + Cl^-$
CATHODE REACTION: $2 H^+ + 2 e \rightarrow H_2^0$
ANODE REACTION: $2 Cl^- - 2 e \rightarrow Cl_2^0$
TOTAL REACTION: $2 HCl \rightarrow H_2 \uparrow + Cl_2 \uparrow$

Electrolysis of ZnCl₂

118. IONIZATION: $ZnCl_2 \rightarrow Zn^{+2} + 2 Cl^-$
CATHODE REACTION: $Zn^{+2} + 2 e \rightarrow Zn^0$
ANODE REACTION: $2 Cl^- - 2 e \rightarrow Cl_2^0$
TOTAL REACTION: $ZnCl_2 \rightarrow Zn^0 + Cl_2$

D. REVERSIBLE REACTIONS

119. MOLECULAR: $2 NaNO_3 + K_2SO_4 \rightleftarrows Na_2SO_4 + 2 KNO_3$
IONIC: $2 Na^+ + 2 NO_3^- + 2 K^+ + SO_4^{-2} \rightleftarrows$
$2 Na^+ + SO_4^{-2} + 2 K^+ + 2 NO_3^-$

120. $N_2 + 3 H_2 \rightleftarrows 2 NH_3$

IX. SULFUR AND ITS COMPOUNDS

A. SULFUR

Chemical Properties

a. Combustibility

121. $S + O_2 \rightarrow SO_2 \uparrow$

b. Formation of Sulfides (Oxidizing Agent)

122. $Fe + S \rightarrow FeS$

123. $2 Al + 3 S \rightarrow Al_2S_3$

B. HYDROGEN SULFIDE

Laboratory Preparation

124. $FeS + 2 HCl \rightarrow FeCl_2 + H_2S \uparrow$

Chemical Properties

a. Incomplete Combustion

125. $2 H_2S + O_2 \rightarrow 2 H_2O + 2 S$

b. Complete Combustion

126. $2 H_2S + 3 O_2 \rightarrow 2 H_2O + 2 SO_2 \uparrow$

c. Tarnishing

127. $2 Ag + H_2S \rightarrow Ag_2S + H_2 \uparrow$

d. Reactions with Salt Solutions

128. $Pb(NO_3)_2 + H_2S \rightarrow 2 HNO_3 + PbS \downarrow$

129. $CdCl_2 + H_2S \rightarrow 2 HCl + CdS \downarrow$

130. $ZnSO_4 + H_2S \rightarrow H_2SO_4 + ZnS \downarrow$

e. Reducing Agent

131. $H_2S + H_2O_2 \rightarrow 2 H_2O + S \downarrow$

Test for Sulfide Ions

132. $\underset{\text{lead acetate}}{Pb(C_2H_3O_2)_2} + H_2S \rightarrow \underset{\text{acetic acid}}{2 HC_2H_3O_2} + \underset{\text{black}}{PbS} \downarrow$

C. SULFUR DIOXIDE

Laboratory Preparation

133. $Na_2SO_3 + 2 HCl \rightarrow 2 NaCl + H_2O + SO_2 \uparrow$

134. $2 NaHSO_3 + H_2SO_4 \rightarrow Na_2SO_4 + 2 H_2O + 2 SO_2 \uparrow$

135. $Cu + 2 H_2SO_4 \rightarrow CuSO_4 + 2 H_2O + SO_2 \uparrow$

Commercial Preparation

136. $S + O_2 \rightarrow SO_2 \uparrow$

137. $4 FeS_2 + 11 O_2 \rightarrow 2 Fe_2O_3 + 8 SO_2 \uparrow$

Chemical Properties

a. Acid Anhydride

138. $SO_2 + H_2O \rightarrow H_2SO_3$

b. Combination with Oxygen Catalytically

139. $2 SO_2 + O_2 \rightarrow 2 SO_3$

c. Reducing Agent (H_2SO_3)

140. $H_2SO_3 + H_2O_2 \rightarrow H_2SO_4 + H_2O$

Test for Sulfite Ions

141. $K_2SO_3 + 2 HCl \rightarrow 2 KCl + H_2O +$ $SO_2 \uparrow$
bleaches purple
permanganate
solutions

D. SULFURIC ACID

Preparation (Contact Process)

142.
$$S + O_2 \rightarrow SO_2 \uparrow$$
$$2 SO_2 + O_2 \rightarrow 2 SO_3$$
$$SO_3 + H_2SO_4 \rightarrow H_2SO_4 \cdot SO_3$$
$$H_2SO_4 \cdot SO_3 + H_2O \rightarrow 2 H_2SO_4$$

Chemical Properties

a. Action on Metals (Dilute H_2SO_4)

143. $Mg + H_2SO_4 \rightarrow MgSO_4 + H_2 \uparrow$
144. $Fe + H_2SO_4 \rightarrow FeSO_4 + H_2 \uparrow$

b. Action on Metals (Concentrated H_2SO_4)

145. $Cu + 2 H_2SO_4 \rightarrow CuSO_4 + 2 H_2O + SO_2 \uparrow$
146. $4 Zn + 5 H_2SO_4 \rightarrow 4 ZnSO_4 + 4 H_2O + H_2S \uparrow$

c. Dehydrating Action (Concentrated H_2SO_4)

147. $C_{12}H_{22}O_{11} \xrightarrow[\text{conc.}]{H_2SO_4} 12 C + 11 H_2O$
sugar

Test for Sulfate Ions

148. $Na_2SO_4 + BaCl_2 \rightarrow 2 NaCl + BaSO_4 \downarrow$
white,
insoluble
in HCl

X. NITROGEN AND ITS COMPOUNDS

A. NITROGEN

Laboratory Preparation

149. $NH_4NO_2 \rightarrow 2 H_2O + N_2 \uparrow$

Chemical Properties

a. Formation of Ammonia Catalytically (Haber Process)

150. $N_2 + 3 H_2 \rightarrow 2 NH_3 \uparrow$

b. Formation of Nitric Oxide Under Special Conditions

   151. $N_2 + O_2 \rightarrow 2 \ NO \uparrow$

c. Reaction with Active Metals

   152. $3 \ Mg + N_2 \rightarrow Mg_3N_2$

   153. $2 \ Al + N_2 \rightarrow 2 \ AlN$

d. Reaction with Hot Calcium Carbide

   154. $CaC_2 + N_2 \rightarrow CaCN_2 + C$

B. AMMONIA

Laboratory Preparation

   155. $2 \ NH_4Cl + Ca(OH)_2 \rightarrow CaCl_2 + 2 \ H_2O + 2 \ NH_3 \uparrow$

   156. $(NH_4)_2SO_4 + 2 \ NaOH \rightarrow Na_2SO_4 + 2 \ H_2O + 2 \ NH_3 \uparrow$

Commercial Preparation

a. Haber Process

   157. $N_2 + 3 \ H_2 \xrightarrow[\text{conditions}]{\text{special}} 2 \ NH_3 \uparrow$

b. Cyanamid Process

   158. $\quad CaC_2 + N_2 \rightarrow CaCN_2 + C$

   $CaCN_2 + 3 \ H_2O \rightarrow CaCO_3 + 2 \ NH_3 \uparrow$

Chemical Properties

a. Reaction with Water

   159. $NH_3 + H_2O \rightarrow NH_4OH$

b. Reaction with Acids

   160. $NH_3 + HCl \rightarrow NH_4Cl$

   161. $2 \ NH_3 + H_2SO_4 \rightarrow (NH_4)_2SO_4$

c. Catalytic Oxidation (Ostwald Process)

   162. $4 \ NH_3 + 5 \ O_2 \rightarrow 6 \ H_2O + 4 \ NO \uparrow$

d. Reactions with Metals at High Temperatures

   163. $2 \ NH_3 + 3 \ Mg \rightarrow Mg_3N_2 + 3 \ H_2 \uparrow$

   164. $2 \ NH_3 + 2 \ Na \rightarrow 2 \ NaNH_2 + H_2 \uparrow$

C. NITRIC ACID

Laboratory Preparation

   165. $2 \ NaNO_3 + H_2SO_4 \rightarrow Na_2SO_4 + 2 \ HNO_3 \uparrow$

Commercial Preparation (Ostwald Process)

   166. $\quad 4 \ NH_3 + 5 \ O_2 \rightarrow 6 \ H_2O + 4 \ NO \uparrow$

   $4 \ NO + 3 \ O_2 + 2 \ H_2O \rightarrow 4 \ HNO_3 \uparrow$

Chemical Properties

a. Ionization

   167. $HNO_3 + H_2O \rightarrow H_3O^+ + NO_3^-$

b. Oxidizing Agent

  168. $3 Cu + 8 HNO_3 \rightarrow 3 Cu(NO_3)_2 + 4 H_2O + 2 NO \uparrow$
            dilute

  169. $Cu + 4 HNO_3 \rightarrow Cu(NO_3)_2 + 2 H_2O + 2 NO_2 \uparrow$
            conc.

  170. $4 Zn + 10 HNO_3 \rightarrow 4 Zn(NO_3)_2 + 3 H_2O + NH_4NO_3$
            dilute

c. Decomposition

  171. $4 HNO_3 \rightarrow 2 H_2O + O_2 \uparrow + 4 NO_2 \uparrow$

D. OXIDES OF NITROGEN

Preparation of N_2O (Nitrous Oxide)

  172. $NH_4NO_3 \rightarrow 2 H_2O + N_2O \uparrow$

Preparation of NO (Nitric Oxide)

  173. $3 Cu + 8 HNO_3 \rightarrow 3 Cu(NO_3)_2 + 4 H_2O + 2 NO \uparrow$
            dilute

Preparation of NO_2 (Nitrogen Dioxide)

  174. $Cu + 4 HNO_3 \rightarrow Cu(NO_3)_2 + 2 H_2O + 2 NO_2 \uparrow$
            conc.

Preparation of N_2O_4 (Nitrogen Tetroxide)

  175. $2 NO_2 \xrightarrow{\text{cool}} N_2O_4 \uparrow$

Preparation of Nitrous Acid from Its Anhydride (N_2O_3)

  176. $N_2O_3 + H_2O \rightarrow 2 HNO_2$

Preparation of Nitric Acid from Its Anhydride (N_2O_5)

  177. $N_2O_5 + H_2O \rightarrow 2 HNO_3$

XI. CARBON AND ITS OXIDES

A. CARBON

Chemical Properties

a. Combustibility

  178. $C + O_2 \rightarrow CO_2 \uparrow$

b. Reducing Agent

  179. $2 CuO + C \rightarrow 2 Cu + CO_2 \uparrow$

c. Electric Furnace Reactions

  180. $SiO_2 + 3 C \rightarrow SiC + 2 CO \uparrow$
  181. $CaO + 3 C \rightarrow CaC_2 + CO \uparrow$
  182. $C + 2 S \rightarrow CS_2$

B. CARBON DIOXIDE

Laboratory Preparation

    183. $CaCO_3 + 2\ HCl \rightarrow CaCl_2 + H_2O + CO_2 \uparrow$

    184. $2\ NaHCO_3 + H_2SO_4 \rightarrow Na_2SO_4 + 2\ H_2O + 2\ CO_2 \uparrow$

Commercial Preparation

  a. From Carbon

    185. $C + O_2 \rightarrow CO_2 \uparrow$

  b. From Calcium Carbonate

    186. $CaCO_3 \rightarrow CaO + CO_2 \uparrow$

  c. From Fruit Sugar

    187. $C_6H_{12}O_6 \xrightarrow{\text{fermentation}} 2\ C_2H_5OH + 2\ CO_2 \uparrow$

Chemical Properties

  a. Reaction with Water

    188. $CO_2 + H_2O \rightarrow H_2CO_3$

  b. Reaction with Limewater

    189. $CO_2 + Ca(OH)_2 \rightarrow H_2O + CaCO_3 \downarrow$
            $CaCO_3 + H_2O + CO_2 \rightarrow Ca(HCO_3)_2$

  c. Reactions at High Temperatures

    190. $CO_2 + 2\ Mg \rightarrow 2\ MgO + C$

    191. $CO_2 + C \rightarrow 2\ CO \uparrow$

Uses

  a. Soda-acid Fire Extinguisher

    192. $2\ NaHCO_3 + H_2SO_4 \rightarrow Na_2SO_4 + 2\ H_2O + 2\ CO_2 \uparrow$

  b. Photosynthesis

    193. $6\ CO_2 + 5\ H_2O \rightarrow C_6H_{10}O_5 + 6\ O_2 \uparrow$

  c. Cream of Tartar Baking Powder

    194. $NaHCO_3 + KHC_4H_4O_6 \rightarrow KNaC_4H_4O_6 + H_2O + CO_2 \uparrow$

Test for Carbonate Ions

    195. $Na_2CO_3 + 2\ HCl \rightarrow 2\ NaCl + H_2O + CO_2 \uparrow$
            $CO_2 + Ca(OH)_2 \rightarrow H_2O + CaCO_3 \downarrow$

C. CARBON MONOXIDE

Sources

    196. $2\ C + O_2 \rightarrow 2\ CO \uparrow$ (incomplete combustion)

    197. $CO_2 + C \rightarrow 2\ CO \uparrow$

Laboratory Preparation

198. $HCOOH \xrightarrow[\text{conc.}]{H_2SO_4} H_2O + CO \uparrow$

Chemical Properties

a. *Combustibility*

199. $2 CO + O_2 \rightarrow 2 CO_2 \uparrow$

b. *Reducing Agent*

200. $Fe_2O_3 + 3 CO \rightarrow 2 Fe + 3 CO_2 \uparrow$

c. *Formation of Carbonyls*

201. $Ni + 4 CO \rightarrow Ni(CO)_4$

d. *Formation of Wood Alcohol Catalytically*

202. $CO + 2 H_2 \rightarrow CH_3OH$

XII. SODIUM AND ITS COMPOUNDS

A. SODIUM

Commercial Preparation

203. $2 NaCl \xrightarrow[\text{fused \quad electrolysis}]{} 2 Na + Cl_2 \uparrow$

204. $2 NaOH \rightarrow 2 Na + O_2 \uparrow + H_2 \uparrow$

Chemical Properties

a. *Combustibility*

205. $2 Na + O_2 \rightarrow Na_2O_2$

b. *Reaction with Water*

206. $2 Na + 2 H_2O \rightarrow 2 NaOH + H_2 \uparrow$

c. *Reaction with Nonmetals*

207. $2 Na + Cl_2 \rightarrow 2 NaCl$

B. SODIUM HYDROXIDE

Commercial Preparation

a. *Electrolysis of Brine*

208. $2 NaCl + 2 H_2O \rightarrow 2 NaOH + H_2 \uparrow + Cl_2 \uparrow$

b. *Lye Process*

209. $Na_2CO_3 + Ca(OH)_2 \rightarrow 2 NaOH + CaCO_3 \downarrow$

C. SODIUM BICARBONATE AND SODIUM CARBONATE

Commercial Preparation (Solvay Process)

210. $NaCl + H_2O + NH_3 + CO_2 \rightarrow NH_4Cl + NaHCO_3 \downarrow$
$2 NaHCO_3 \rightarrow Na_2CO_3 + H_2O + CO_2 \uparrow$

XIII. CALCIUM AND ITS COMPOUNDS

A. CALCIUM

Commercial Preparation

    211. $CaCl_2 \xrightarrow[\text{fused \quad electrolysis}]{} Ca + Cl_2 \uparrow$

Chemical Properties

    a. Combustibility

       212. $2\ Ca + O_2 \rightarrow 2\ CaO$

    b. Reaction with Water

       213. $Ca + 2\ H_2O \rightarrow Ca(OH)_2 + H_2 \uparrow$

B. CALCIUM CARBONATE

Chemical Properties

    a. Decomposition

       214. $CaCO_3 \rightarrow CaO + CO_2 \uparrow$

    b. Reaction with Acids

       215. $CaCO_3 + 2\ HCl \rightarrow CaCl_2 + H_2O + CO_2 \uparrow$

    c. Solution in Soil Water Containing CO_2 (Stalactites and Stalagmites)

       216. $CaCO_3 + H_2O + CO_2 \rightarrow Ca(HCO_3)_2$
              $Ca(HCO_3)_2 \rightarrow CaCO_3 \downarrow + H_2O + CO_2 \uparrow$

C. CALCIUM OXIDE

Commercial Preparation (Reaction in the Lime Kiln)

    217. $CaCO_3 \rightarrow CaO + CO_2 \uparrow$

Chemical Properties

    218. $CaO + H_2O \rightarrow Ca(OH)_2$

D. CALCIUM HYDROXIDE

Preparation

    219. $CaO + H_2O \rightarrow Ca(OH)_2$

Chemical Properties

    a. Reaction with Carbon Dioxide

       220. $Ca(OH)_2 + CO_2 \rightarrow H_2O + CaCO_3 \downarrow$

    b. Reaction with Chlorine

       221. $Ca(OH)_2 + Cl_2 \rightarrow \underset{\substack{\text{bleaching} \\ \text{powder}}}{CaOCl_2} + H_2O$

E. CALCIUM SULFATE

Preparation of Plaster of Paris

    222. $2 \; CaSO_4 \cdot 2 \; H_2O \rightarrow (CaSO_4)_2 \cdot H_2O + 3 \; H_2O$
            gypsum   plaster of
                           Paris

Hardening (Setting of Plaster of Paris)

    223. $(CaSO_4)_2 \cdot H_2O + 3 \; H_2O \rightarrow 2 \; CaSO_4 \cdot 2 \; H_2O$

F. HARD WATERS

Action of Soap on Hard Water

    224. $2 \; NaC_{17}H_{35}CO_2 \; + \quad CaSO_4 \quad \rightarrow Na_2SO_4 + Ca(C_{17}H_{35}CO_2)_2 \downarrow$
              soap   present in   insoluble
     [sodium stearate]   hard water   calcium stearate

Softening Hard Water

  a. Temporary Hard Water

    225. $Ca(HCO_3)_2 \rightarrow CaCO_3 \downarrow + H_2O + CO_2 \uparrow$
    226. $Mg(HCO_3)_2 \rightarrow MgCO_3 \downarrow + H_2O + CO_2 \uparrow$
    227. $Ca(HCO_3)_2 + Ca(OH)_2 \rightarrow 2 \; H_2O + 2 \; CaCO_3 \downarrow$

  b. Permanent Hard Water

    228. $CaSO_4 + Na_2CO_3 \rightarrow Na_2SO_4 + CaCO_3 \downarrow$
    229. $MgCl_2 + Na_2CO_3 \rightarrow 2 \; NaCl + MgCO_3 \downarrow$
    230. $CaSO_4 + 2 \; Na \; (zeolite) \rightarrow Ca \; (zeolite)_2 \downarrow + Na_2SO_4$

XIV. METALS AND METALLURGY

A. EXTRACTION OF IMPORTANT METALS

Iron

    231. $3 \; Fe_2O_3 + CO \rightarrow 2 \; Fe_3O_4 + CO_2 \uparrow$
          $Fe_3O_4 + CO \rightarrow 3 \; FeO + CO_2 \uparrow$
          $FeO + CO \rightarrow Fe + CO_2 \uparrow$

Zinc

    232. $ZnO + C \rightarrow Zn + CO \uparrow$
    233. $\quad ZnCO_3 \rightarrow ZnO + CO_2 \uparrow$
          $ZnO + C \rightarrow Zn + CO \uparrow$
    234. $2 \; ZnS + 3 \; O_2 \rightarrow 2 \; ZnO + 2 \; SO_2 \uparrow$
          $ZnO + C \rightarrow Zn + CO \uparrow$

Lead

    235. $2 \; PbS + 3 \; O_2 \rightarrow 2 \; PbO + 2 \; SO_2 \uparrow$
          $PbO + C \rightarrow Pb + CO \uparrow$

Tin

    236. $SnO_2 + 2 \; C \rightarrow Sn + 2 \; CO \uparrow$

Mercury

    237. $HgS + O_2 \rightarrow Hg + SO_2 \uparrow$

Aluminum

238. $2 Al_2O_3 \xrightarrow[\text{electrolysis}]{} 4 Al + 3 O_2 \uparrow$

Copper (Electrolytic Refining)

239. ANODE REACTION: $Cu^0 - 2 e \rightarrow Cu^{+2}$
CATHODE REACTION: $Cu^{+2} + 2 e \rightarrow Cu^0$

Magnesium

240. $2 MgO \xrightarrow[\text{electrolysis}]{} 2 Mg + O_2 \uparrow$

B. PROPERTIES OF IMPORTANT METALS

Iron

   a. Oxidation of Ferrous Compounds

   241. $2 FeCl_2 + Cl_2 \rightarrow 2 FeCl_3$

   b. Reduction of Ferric Compounds

   242. $2 FeCl_3 + H_2 \rightarrow 2 FeCl_2 + 2 HCl$

   c. Test for Ferrous Salts

   243. $2 K_3Fe(CN)_6 + 3 FeCl_2 \rightarrow 6 KCl + Fe_3[Fe(CN)_6]_2 \downarrow$
                                              Turnbull's blue

   d. Test for Ferric Salts

   244. $3 K_4Fe(CN)_6 + 4 FeCl_3 \rightarrow 12 KCl + Fe_4[Fe(CN)_6]_3 \downarrow$
                                              Prussian blue

Zinc

   a. Reaction with Nonmetals (Reducing Agent)

   245. $2 Zn + O_2 \rightarrow 2 ZnO$
   246. $Zn + S \rightarrow ZnS$

   b. Reaction with Dilute Acids

   247. $Zn + 2 HCl \rightarrow ZnCl_2 + H_2 \uparrow$
   248. $Zn + H_2SO_4 \rightarrow ZnSO_4 + H_2 \uparrow$

   c. Reaction with a Base

   249. $Zn + 2 NaOH \rightarrow Na_2ZnO_2 + H_2 \uparrow$

   d. Amphoteric Nature of Zinc Hydroxide

   250. $Zn(OH)_2 + 2 HCl \rightarrow ZnCl_2 + 2 H_2O$
        $Zn(OH)_2 + 2 NaOH \rightarrow Na_2ZnO_2 + 2 H_2O$

Aluminum

   a. Reaction with Dilute Acids

   251. $2 Al + 6 HCl \rightarrow 2 AlCl_3 + 3 H_2 \uparrow$
        $2 Al + 3 H_2SO_4 \rightarrow Al_2(SO_4)_3 + 3 H_2 \uparrow$

   b. Reaction with a Base

   252. $2 Al + 6 NaOH \rightarrow 2 Na_3AlO_3 + 3 H_2 \uparrow$

c. Reducing Agent (Thermite Reaction)

253. $Fe_2O_3 + 2\ Al \rightarrow Al_2O_3 + 2\ Fe$
254. $Cr_2O_3 + 2\ Al \rightarrow Al_2O_3 + 2\ Cr$

d. Amphoteric Nature of Aluminum Hydroxide

255. $Al(OH)_3 + 3\ HCl \rightarrow AlCl_3 + 3\ H_2O$
$Al(OH)_3 + 3\ NaOH \rightarrow Na_3AlO_3 + 3\ H_2O$

XV. ORGANIC CHEMISTRY

Complete Combustion of a Hydrocarbon

256. $2\ C_2H_2 + 5\ O_2 \rightarrow 4\ CO_2 \uparrow + 2\ H_2O$

Incomplete Combustion of a Hydrocarbon

257. $2\ C_2H_2 + 3\ O_2 \rightarrow 4\ CO \uparrow + 2\ H_2O$
$2\ C_2H_2 + O_2 \rightarrow 4\ C + 2\ H_2O$

Substitution Reactions

258. $C_2H_6 + Cl_2 \rightarrow C_2H_5Cl + HCl$
259. $CH_4 + Br_2 \rightarrow CH_3Br + HBr$

Addition Reactions

260. $C_2H_4 + Cl_2 \rightarrow C_2H_4Cl_2$
261. $C_2H_4 + Br_2 \rightarrow C_2H_4Br_2$

Fermentation of Sugar (Alcoholic)

262. $C_6H_{12}O_6 \xrightarrow{\text{zymase}} 2\ C_2H_5OH + 2\ CO_2 \uparrow$

Inversion of Cane Sugar (Sucrose)

263. $\underset{\text{sucrose}}{C_{12}H_{22}O_{11}} + H_2O \xrightarrow{\text{invertase}} \underset{\underbrace{\text{glucose}\quad\text{fructose}}_{\text{invert sugar}}}{C_6H_{12}O_6 + C_6H_{12}O_6}$

Hydrolysis of Starch

264. $C_6H_{10}O_5 + H_2O \xrightarrow{\text{HCl}} C_6H_{12}O_6$

Fermentation of Alcohol

265. $C_2H_5OH + O_2 \xrightarrow{\substack{\text{acetic acid} \\ \text{bacteria}}} HC_2H_3O_2 + H_2O$

Esterification Reactions

266. $C_2H_5OH + HC_2H_3O_2 \xrightarrow{H_2SO_4} C_2H_5 \cdot C_2H_3O_2 + H_2O$

267. $C_3H_5(OH)_3 + 3\ HNO_3 \xrightarrow{H_2SO_4} C_3H_5(NO_3)_3 + 3\ H_2O$

268. $CH_3OH + HC_7H_5O_3 \xrightarrow{H_2SO_4} CH_3C_7H_5O_3 + H_2O$

269. $CH_3OH + HCl \xrightarrow{H_2SO_4} CH_3Cl + H_2O$

Preparation of Soap

270. $C_3H_5(C_{18}H_{35}O_2)_3 + 3\ NaOH \rightarrow 3\ NaC_{18}H_{35}O_2 + C_3H_5(OH)_3$

XVI. NUCLEAR CHEMISTRY

Production of Artificial Radioactivity

271. $\underset{\text{nitrogen}}{_7N^{14}} + \underset{\substack{\text{alpha}\\\text{particle}}}{_2He^4} \rightarrow \underset{\substack{\text{oxygen}\\\text{isotope}}}{_8O^{17}} + \underset{\text{proton}}{_1H^1}$

Alpha Disintegration

272. $\underset{\text{radium}}{_{88}Ra^{226}} \rightarrow \underset{\text{radon}}{_{86}Rn^{222}} + \underset{\substack{\text{alpha}\\\text{particle}}}{_2He^4}$

Beta Disintegration

273. $\underset{\text{thorium}}{_{90}Th^{234}} \rightarrow \underset{\text{protoactinium}}{_{91}Pa^{234}} + \underset{\substack{\text{beta}\\\text{particle}}}{_{-1}e^0}$

Atomic Fusion

274. $_1H^3 + _1H^2 \rightarrow _2He^4 + _0n^1 + \text{energy}$

Nuclear Changes in the Uranium Reactor

275. $_{92}U^{238} + _0n^1 \rightarrow _{92}U^{239}$
$\quad\quad _{92}U^{239} \rightarrow _{93}Np^{239} + _{-1}e^0$
$\quad\quad _{93}Np^{239} \rightarrow _{94}Pu^{239} + _{-1}e^0$

5. ADDITIONAL CHEMICAL CALCULATIONS

1. DETERMINING THE SIMPLEST FORMULA OF A COMPOUND FROM ITS PERCENTAGE COMPOSITION

In this type of problem, we are required to find the simplest (the *empirical*) formula of a compound when the percentage composition of each of the elements in the compound is known. This problem is the reverse of the type of problem in which we know the formula of a compound and are required to find the percentage composition of each of the elements.

METHOD

a. Determine the relative number of atoms present in a compound by dividing the percentage composition of each element by the atomic weight of the element. The ratio of these quotients, known as the *atomic ratio,* is the ratio of the number of atoms in the compound.

b. Since a compound can consist of only whole numbers of atoms, the atomic ratio must be reduced to small whole numbers. This is done by dividing each of the relative number of atoms by their highest common factor. If the quotients obtained from this division are not whole numbers, the quotients should be rounded off to the nearest whole number. Each whole number represents the number of atoms of each element in the simplest formula of the compound. The simplest formula, however, is not necessarily the true formula of the compound. Frequently, the simplest formula indicates only the ratio of the atoms in a compound but does not indicate their actual numbers. *The exact numbers of atoms, or the true formula of a compound, can be determined only when the molecular weight is known.*

TYPE PROBLEMS

1. Determine the simplest formula of a compound containing 2.04% hydrogen, 32.65% sulfur, and 65.31% oxygen.

$$\text{Relative number of atoms of H} = \frac{\% \text{ H}}{\text{atomic weight of H}} = \frac{2.04}{1} = 2.04$$

$$\text{Relative number of atoms of S} = \frac{\% \text{ S}}{\text{atomic weight of S}} = \frac{32.65}{32} = 1.02$$

$$\text{Relative number of atoms of O} = \frac{\% \text{ O}}{\text{atomic weight of O}} = \frac{65.31}{16} = 4.08$$

The atomic ratio is therefore $H_{2.04} S_{1.02} O_{4.08}$.

The highest common factor is 1.02. The empirical formula is therefore

$$H_{\frac{2.04}{1.02}} = 2 \quad S_{\frac{1.02}{1.02}} = 1 \quad O_{\frac{4.08}{1.02}} = 4 \text{ or } H_2SO_4.$$

Since the molecular weight of this compound was not given, the formula H_2SO_4 represents the simplest formula of the compound. The true formula could be $H_4S_2O_8$, $H_8S_4O_{16}$, or any other formula containing 2 parts H, 1 part S, and 4 parts O by weight. However, if we are given 98 as the molecular weight, the only formula possible with the above composition is H_2SO_4.

2. Determine the simplest formula of a substance composed of 92.3% carbon and 7.7% hydrogen.

$$\text{Relative number of atoms of C} = \frac{92.3}{12} = 7.7$$

$$\text{Relative number of atoms of H} = \frac{7.7}{1} = 7.7$$

The atomic ratio is therefore $C_{7.7} H_{7.7}$. Dividing by 7.7, the highest common factor, gives us the simplest formula of this substance, C_1H_1. Since such a substance does not actually exist, the molecular weight must be known to determine the true formula of the compound. For example, both C_2H_2 and C_6H_6 have the same empirical formula, C_1H_1. Given a molecular weight of 26, the true formula of the above compound becomes C_2H_2. Similarly, given a molecular weight of 78, the true formula of the above compound becomes C_6H_6.

3. Determine the simplest formula of a compound composed of 70% iron and 30% oxygen.

$$\text{Relative number of atoms of Fe} = \frac{70}{56} = 1.25$$

$$\text{Relative number of atoms of O} = \frac{30}{16} = 1.88$$

The atomic ratio is therefore $Fe_{1.25} O_{1.88}$.

The highest common factor is approximately 0.625.

The simplest formula is therefore $Fe_{\underset{0.625}{1.25}} O_{\underset{0.625}{1.88}}$ or Fe_2O_3.

2. PROBLEMS INVOLVING THE GAS LAWS

a. Properties of Gases. A gas consists of tiny particles, called molecules, moving about in random fashion. The volume occupied by the molecules themselves is only a small fraction of the total volume of the gas. Thus, a gas consists largely of empty space.

Because the molecules in a gas are in constant motion, the volume of an unconfined gas is indefinite. The volume of a confined gas, however, is determined by its container. The impact of gas molecules against the walls of the container constitutes the pressure of the gas. If the volume of the container is decreased, the number of impacts per unit area (pressure) becomes greater (Boyle's Law). As the temperature increases, the molecules of gas move more rapidly. This makes the gas expand, increasing its volume (Charles' Law).

The volume of a gas therefore depends upon its pressure and temperature. In the laboratory, it is often necessary to change a given volume of gas at existing conditions of temperature and pressure to a new volume at different conditions. For example, the gram-molecular volume (GMV) is equal to approximately 22.4 liters at standard conditions of temperature and pressure (sometimes abbreviated STP). In problems where the GMV is to be used, all gas volumes must be changed to standard conditions. The laws of Boyle and Charles can be used to do this.

b. The Gas Laws

(1) *Boyle's Law.* The volume of a gas (dry) varies inversely as the pressure exerted on it, provided the temperature does not change. Boyle's Law may be expressed mathematically as follows:

$$V = \frac{K}{P} \quad \text{or} \quad PV = K$$

where $V =$ volume, $P =$ pressure, and $K =$ constant.

METHOD

If a volume of gas is subjected to a change in pressure only, the new volume may be calculated by applying Boyle's Law. The new volume equals the old volume multiplied by the correction factor due to a pressure change. *The correction factor due to Boyle's Law is always equal to the original pressure divided by the new pressure.* This can be stated mathematically as:

$$\text{New volume} = \text{Old volume} \times \text{Correction factor}$$

$$\text{Correction factor} = \frac{\text{Original pressure}}{\text{New pressure}}$$

Since an increase in pressure must result in a decrease in volume, the new larger pressure is in the denominator of the fraction, yielding a quotient that is less than one. Conversely, since a decrease in pressure will result in an increase in volume, the new smaller pressure is now in the denominator of the fraction, yielding a quotient that is greater than one.

TYPE PROBLEMS

1. The volume of a gas is 500 cm³ at 740 mm pressure. Calculate the new volume at 370 mm pressure.

For a change in pressure:

$$\text{New volume} = \text{Old volume} \times \frac{\text{Original pressure}}{\text{New pressure}}$$

$$\text{New volume} = 500 \text{ cm}^3 \times \frac{740}{370}$$

$$\text{New volume} = 1000 \text{ cm}^3$$

2. The volume of a gas is 10 liters at 500 mm pressure. Calculate the new volume at 700 mm pressure.

For a change in pressure:

$$\text{New volume} = \text{Old volume} \times \frac{\text{Original pressure}}{\text{New pressure}}$$

$$\text{New volume} = 10 \text{ liters} \times \frac{500}{700}$$

$$\text{New volume} = 7.2 \text{ liters}$$

(2) *Charles' Law.* The volume of a gas varies directly as the absolute temperature, provided the pressure remains constant. Absolute temperature equals centigrade temperature plus 273 degrees. Charles' Law may be expressed mathematically as follows:

$$V = KT$$

where V = volume, T = absolute temperature, and K = constant.

METHOD

If a volume of gas is subjected to a change in temperature only, the new volume may be calculated by applying Charles' Law. As in the case of a change in pressure, the new volume equals the old volume multiplied by a correction factor. In this case, the correction factor is due to a temperature change (Charles' Law). From Boyle's Law, we have learned that there is an inverse relationship between the volume and pressure of a gas. According to Charles' Law, there is a direct relationship between the volume and absolute temperature of a gas. Therefore, the correction factor for a change in temperature is the reverse of the correction factor for a change in pressure. *The correction factor for a change in temperature is the new temperature in degrees absolute divided by the original temperature in degrees absolute.* This can be stated mathematically as:

$$\text{New volume} = \text{Old volume} \times \text{Correction factor}$$

$$\text{Correction factor} = \frac{\text{New temperature in }°A}{\text{Original temperature in }°A}$$

According to Charles' Law, an increase in temperature causes an increase in volume; thus, the new larger temperature is in the numerator of the fraction, yielding a quotient that is greater than one. Conversely, since a decrease in temperature will result in a smaller volume, the new smaller temperature is in the numerator of the fraction, yielding a quotient that is less than one.

TYPE PROBLEMS

1. The volume of a gas is 250 cm³ at 20°C. Calculate the new volume at 100°C.

For change in temperature:

$$\text{New volume} = \text{Old volume} \times \frac{\text{New temperature in }°A}{\text{Original temperature in }°A}$$

$$\text{New volume} = 250 \text{ cm}^3 \times \frac{100 + 273}{20 + 273}$$

$$\text{New volume} = 318.3 \text{ cm}^3$$

2. The volume of a gas is 100 liters at 273°C. Calculate the new volume at 0°C.

For change in temperature:

$$\text{New volume} = \text{Old volume} \times \frac{\text{New temperature in }°A}{\text{Original temperature in }°A}$$

$$\text{New volume} = 100 \text{ liters} \times \frac{0 + 273}{273 + 273}$$

$$\text{New volume} = 50 \text{ liters}$$

(3) *Boyle's and Charles' Laws Combined.* To determine the effect on the volume of a gas caused by a change in both temperature and pressure, the laws of Boyle and Charles are combined and may be expressed mathematically as follows:

$$\frac{PV}{T} = K$$

where P = pressure, V = volume, T = absolute temperature, and K = constant.

METHOD

When a gas is being subjected simultaneously to a change in both temperature and pressure, the new volume may be calculated by combining both correction factors. Thus, for a change in pressure and temperature:

$$\text{New volume} = \text{Old volume} \times \overbrace{\frac{\text{Original pressure}}{\text{New pressure}}}^{\substack{\text{Correction factor due to} \\ \text{Boyle's Law}}} \times \overbrace{\frac{\text{New temperature in °A}}{\text{Original temperature in °A}}}^{\substack{\text{Correction factor due to} \\ \text{Charles' Law}}}$$

TYPE PROBLEMS

1. The volume of a gas is 100 cm³ at a temperature of 30°C and 770 mm pressure. Calculate the new volume at 10°C and 740 mm.

For change in pressure and temperature:

$$\text{New volume} = \text{Old volume} \times \overbrace{\frac{\text{Original pressure}}{\text{New pressure}}}^{\substack{\text{Pressure} \\ \text{correction}}} \times \overbrace{\frac{\text{New temperature in °A}}{\text{Original temperature in °A}}}^{\substack{\text{Temperature} \\ \text{correction}}}$$

New volume = $100 \text{ cm}^3 \times \dfrac{770}{740} \times \dfrac{10 + 273}{30 + 273}$

New volume = 97.2 cm³

2. 50 cm³ of oxygen were collected dry at a temperature of 20°C and 750 mm pressure. Find the volume the oxygen will occupy at standard conditions (0°C and 760 mm).

For change in pressure and temperature:

$$\text{New volume} = \text{Old volume} \times \overbrace{\frac{\text{Original pressure}}{\text{New pressure}}}^{\substack{\text{Pressure} \\ \text{correction}}} \times \overbrace{\frac{\text{New temperature in °A}}{\text{Original temperature in °A}}}^{\substack{\text{Temperature} \\ \text{correction}}}$$

New volume = $50 \text{ cm}^3 \times \dfrac{750}{760} \times \dfrac{0 + 273}{20 + 273}$

New volume = 45.97 cm³

c. Determining the Molecular Weight of a Gas. The molecular weight of a gas whose formula is not known can be found in a number of ways, depending on the given information. One method involves the use of the gram-molecular volume. A second method utilizes the vapor density of the gas.

(1) *From the Gram-Molecular Volume.* We have already learned that at standard conditions of temperature and pressure, the gram-molecular weight of any gas occupies approximately 22.4 liters. Therefore, if the weight of one liter of a gas at standard conditions is known, the molecular weight of the gas equals the weight of one liter multiplied by 22.4. If conditions are not standard, corrections in volume are made for pressure and temperature according to the laws of Boyle and Charles.

(2) *From the Vapor Density.* The vapor density of a gas is the ratio of the weight of a given volume of gas to the weight of an equal volume of hydrogen measured under the same conditions of temperature and pressure. The vapor density of a gas can also be expressed as the ratio of the density of the gas to the density of hydrogen. As the density of a gas is proportional to its molecular weight and as the molecular weight of hydrogen is 2, the molecular weight of any gas is equal to its vapor density multiplied by 2.

METHOD

To find the molecular weight of a gas:

(*a*) Multiply the weight of one liter at standard conditions by 22.4, *or*
(*b*) Multiply the vapor density of the gas by 2.

TYPE PROBLEMS—METHOD (*a*)

1. The weight of one liter of a gas at standard conditions is 1.34 grams. Calculate its molecular weight.

$$\text{Molecular weight} = 1.34 \times 22.4 = 30$$

2. The weight of 500 cm³ of a gas at standard conditions is 1.58 grams. Calculate its molecular weight.

Since 500 cm³ = 0.5 liter, the weight of one liter of this gas = 3.16 grams.

$$\text{Molecular weight} = 3.16 \times 22.4 = 71$$

TYPE PROBLEMS—METHOD (*b*)

1. The vapor density of a gas is 23. Determine the molecular weight of the gas.

$$\text{Molecular weight} = \text{Vapor density} \times 2$$
$$\text{Molecular weight} = 23 \times 2 = 46$$

2. A gas has a vapor density of 49.5. Determine its molecular weight.

$$\text{Molecular weight} = \text{Vapor density} \times 2$$
$$\text{Molecular weight} = 49.5 \times 2 = 99$$

6. ADDITIONAL METHODS FOR EXPRESSING
SOLUTION CONCENTRATION

1. PERCENTAGE

The concentration of a solution may be expressed in parts of solute per 100 parts of total solution. A 5% salt solution would therefore contain 5 grams of salt dissolved in 95 grams of water.

2. MOLARITY

A *molar* solution contains one gram-molecular weight of solute to which sufficient solvent has been added to make a total of one liter of solution. Thus, a 2 molar sodium chloride solution (abbreviated 2 M) is made by dissolving two gram-molecular weights of NaCl (117 grams) in enough water to make one liter of total solution.

3. MOLALITY

A *molal* solution contains one gram-molecular weight of solute dissolved in 1,000 grams of solvent. Thus, in order to prepare a 2 molal sodium chloride solution (2 m), 117 grams (2 GMW's) are dissolved in 1,000 grams of water.

4. NORMALITY

A *normal* solution contains one gram-equivalent weight of solute to which sufficient solvent has been added to make a total of one liter of solution. The *equivalent weight* is taken as the gram-molecular weight of the substance divided by the total positive valence number. Where the valence number is equal to one, the gram-equivalent weight and the gram-molecular weight are identical, and for such solutes a normal and a molar solution have the same concentration. A one normal (1 N) sodium chloride solution contains 58.5 grams of sodium chloride dissolved in a liter of total solution. A one molar sodium chloride solution has the same concentration.

A one normal magnesium chloride solution contains the gram-molecular weight of $MgCl_2$, 95 grams, divided by 2 (total positive valence number), or 47.5 grams of solute dissolved in a liter of total solution.

7. EMINENT SCIENTISTS

Acheson, Edward (1856-1931). American. Developed a process for making carborundum and artificial graphite in the electric furnace.

Anderson, Carl D. (1905 —). American. Discovered a new nuclear particle, the positron, in 1932.

Arrhenius, Svante A. (1859-1927). Swedish. First proposed the *Theory of Electrolytic Dissociation* to explain the properties of electrolytes and nonelectrolytes.

Aston, Francis W. (1877-1945). English. Devised an instrument called the mass spectrograph to detect the presence and quantity of isotopes of different elements.

Avogadro, Amadeo (1776-1856). Italian. Stated that equal volumes of all gases at the same temperature and pressure contain the same number of molecules (Avogadro's Law).

Becquerel, Henri (1852-1908). French. Observing that certain uranium salts disintegrate spontaneously, he thus discovered the phenomenon of radioactivity.

Bohr, Niels (1885-1962). Danish. Proposed an atomic theory to account for the spectra of certain elements. He pictured the atom as a miniature solar system.

Boyle, Robert (1627-1691). English. Determined the relationship between the volume of a gas and the pressure exerted on it (Boyle's Law).

Bunsen, Robert W. (1811-1899). German. Constructed the Bunsen burner. With Kirchhoff, he designed a spectroscope with which they were able to discover cesium and rubidium.

Cavendish, Henry (1731-1810). English. Discovered hydrogen.

Chadwick, James (1891 —). English. Discovered the uncharged nuclear particle, the neutron, in 1932.

Charles, Jacques A. (1746-1823). French. Determined the relationship between the volume of a gas and its temperature (Charles' Law).

Curie, Marie (1867-1934). Polish. With her husband, Pierre Curie, she did considerable research in radioactivity, resulting in the extraction of radium and polonium from pitchblende.

Dalton, John (1766-1844). English. Best known for his atomic theory and the laws of definite and multiple proportions.

Davy, Sir Humphry (1778-1829). English. Invented the miner's safety lamp. He isolated many metals, including sodium and potassium, by electrolysis of their fused compounds.

Einstein, Albert (1879-1955). German-American. Best known for his *Theory of Relativity* and for the *Law of Conservation of Mass-Energy*. The latter defined the relationship between mass and energy by the equation $E = mc^2$.

Faraday, Michael (1791-1867). English. Discovered the principle of electromagnetic induction, the laws of electrolysis, and methods for the liquefaction of gases.

Fermi, Enrico (1901-1954). Italian-American. Helped develop the first successful atomic pile by utilizing moderators for slowing down fast neutrons.

Frasch, Herman (1852-1914). American. Developed a method for the extraction of sulfur from underground deposits.

Gay-Lussac, Joseph L. (1778-1850). French. Stated that, in a reaction involving gases only, the volumes of the combining gases may be expressed in ratios of small whole numbers (Gay-Lussac's Law).

Graham, Thomas (1805-1869). Scottish. Founded the science of colloid chemistry. He also showed the relationship between the ability of a gas to diffuse and its density or molecular weight.

Haber, Fritz (1868-1934). German. Devised a method of nitrogen-fixation in which ammonia was synthesized from hydrogen and atmospheric nitrogen.

Hall, Charles M. (1863-1914). American. Invented a process for the electrochemical extraction of aluminum from bauxite.

Joliot-Curie, Irene (1897-1956) and **Frederic** (1900-1958). French. Produced radioactive elements by nuclear bombardment.

Langmuir, Irving (1881-1957). American. In collaboration with Gilbert D. N. Lewis, developed an electron theory to explain the variations in the properties of the elements. Invented the atomic hydrogen torch and gas-filled electric light bulbs.

Lavoisier, Antoine L. (1743-1794). French. The first to introduce quantitative methods in the study of chemistry. These methods enabled him to determine the true nature of burning, which led to the disproof of the phlogiston theory.

Lawrence, Ernest O. (1901-1958). American. Devised the cyclotron, an instrument for accelerating particles in nuclear bombardment (smashing the atom).

Meitner, Lise (1878 —). German. Among the first scientists to study uranium fission. She concluded that the splitting of uranium into lighter fragments would release tremendous amounts of energy.

Mendeléef, Dmitri I. (1834-1907). Russian. Stated that the properties of the elements were periodic functions of their atomic weights. As a result, he devised the first periodic table arranging the elements in order of increasing atomic weight.

Millikan, Robert A. (1868-1953). American. Determined the mass of the electron and the amount of charge upon it. He also did intensive research on cosmic rays.

Moissan, Henri (1852-1907). French. Succeeded in isolating fluorine by electrolysis of its fused compound.

Moseley, Henry G. J. (1887-1915). English. From studies of X-ray spectra, determined the atomic numbers of the elements.

Nobel, Alfred (1833-1896). Swedish. Invented dynamite. Also set up a fund for granting annual awards (Nobel Prizes) in the arts, sciences, and the humanities.

Ostwald, Wilhelm (1853-1932). German. The first to make nitric acid by the catalytic oxidation of ammonia.

Perkin, William H. (1838-1907). English. By synthesizing aniline from coal tar, he founded the aniline dye industry.

Priestley, Joseph (1733-1804). English. Discovered the element oxygen when he decomposed mercuric oxide.

Ramsay, Sir William (1852-1916). English. In collaboration with another English scientist, Lord Rayleigh, he discovered argon. Aided by other scientists, he discovered other rare gases in the atmosphere, such as neon, krypton, and xenon.

Richards, Theodore W. (1868-1928). American. Known for his accurate determinations of atomic weights.

Rutherford, Ernest (1871-1937). English. In 1911 he discovered the proton, which led to his exposition of the nuclear structure of the atom. He developed theories of transmutation and, with the English scientist Frederick Soddy, evolved the theory of radioactive decay.

Scheele, Karl (1742-1786). Swedish. Discovered chlorine and isolated a variety of substances such as glycerine, tungsten, and molybdenum.

Seaborg, Glenn (1912 —). American. Discovered and prepared many of the trans-uranic elements such as plutonium, americium, and curium.

Solvay, Ernest (1832-1922). Belgian. Developed a process for manufacturing both sodium carbonate and sodium bicarbonate from brine.

Thomson, J. J. (1856-1940). English. Discovered the electron in 1897.

Urey, Harold (1893 —). American. Discovered the hydrogen isotopes and prepared heavy water.

Wöhler, Friedrich (1800-1882). German. In synthesizing urea, an organic substance, from ammonium cyanate, an inorganic substance, he succeeded in overthrowing the "vital force" theory. This theory, that organic substances could be produced only from other organic substances, had dominated organic chemistry for many years.

8. COMMON SUBSTANCES

COMMON NAME	CHEMICAL NAME	FORMULA
Acetylene	Acetylene	C_2H_2
Alcohol, grain	Ethyl alcohol or ethanol	C_2H_5OH
Alcohol, wood	Methyl alcohol or methanol	CH_3OH
Ammonia water	Ammonium hydroxide solution	NH_4OH
Aqua fortis	Concentrated nitric acid	HNO_3
Aqua regia	Mixture of concentrated nitric and hydrochloric acids	$HNO_3 + 3\ HCl$
Baking powder	Mixture of bicarbonate of soda, acid-producing substance, and starch	———
Baking soda	Sodium bicarbonate	$NaHCO_3$
Bauxite	Impure aluminum oxide	Al_2O_3
Benzol	Benzene	C_6H_6
Bleaching powder	Calcium oxychloride or chloride of lime	$CaOCl_2$
Blue vitriol	Copper sulfate, crystals	$CuSO_4 \cdot 5\ H_2O$
Borax	Sodium tetraborate, crystals	$Na_2B_4O_7 \cdot 10\ H_2O$
Brine	Sodium chloride solution	$NaCl$
Calomel	Mercurous chloride	Hg_2Cl_2
Cane sugar	Sucrose	$C_{12}H_{22}O_{11}$
Carbolic acid	Phenol	C_6H_5OH
Carbona	Carbon tetrachloride	CCl_4
Carborundum	Silicon carbide	SiC
Caustic potash	Potassium hydroxide	KOH
Caustic soda	Sodium hydroxide	$NaOH$
Chalk	Calcium carbonate	$CaCO_3$
Chile saltpeter	Sodium nitrate	$NaNO_3$
Chloroform	Trichloromethane	$CHCl_3$
Cinnabar	Impure mercuric sulfide	HgS
Corrosive sublimate	Mercuric chloride	$HgCl_2$

COMMON NAME	CHEMICAL NAME	FORMULA
Cream of tartar	Potassium bitartrate	$KHC_4H_4O_6$
Dry ice	Solid carbon dioxide	CO_2
Epsom salts	Magnesium sulfate, crystals	$MgSO_4 \cdot 7\ H_2O$
Ether	Di-ethyl oxide	$(C_2H_5)_2O$
Fire damp	Methane mixed with air	CH_4
Freon	Dichlorodifluoromethane	CCl_2F_2
Galena	Impure lead sulfide	PbS
Glycerine	Glycerol or trihydroxypropane	$C_3H_5(OH)_3$
Gypsum	Hydrated calcium sulfate	$CaSO_4 \cdot 2\ H_2O$
Hematite	Impure ferric oxide	Fe_2O_3
Hypo	Sodium thiosulfate	$Na_2S_2O_3$
Iodoform	Tri-iodomethane	CHI_3
Laughing gas	Nitrous oxide	N_2O
Limestone	Calcium carbonate	$CaCO_3$
Limewater	Calcium hydroxide solution	$Ca(OH)_2$
Lunar caustic	Silver nitrate	$AgNO_3$
Lye	Sodium hydroxide	$NaOH$
Marsh gas	Methane	CH_4
Muriatic acid	Impure hydrochloric acid	HCl
Nitroglycerine	Glyceryl nitrate or glyceryl trinitrate	$C_3H_5(NO_3)_3$
Oil of vitriol	Concentrated sulfuric acid	H_2SO_4
Plaster of Paris	Hydrated calcium sulfate	$(CaSO_4)_2 \cdot H_2O$
Potash	Potassium carbonate (Other potassium compounds are also called potash.)	K_2CO_3
Prussian blue	Ferric ferrocyanide	$Fe_4[Fe(CN)_6]_3$
Quicksilver	Mercury	Hg
Rochelle salts	Sodium potassium tartrate	$NaKC_4H_4O_6$
Sal ammoniac	Ammonium chloride	NH_4Cl
Salt, table	Sodium chloride	$NaCl$
Saltpeter	Potassium nitrate	KNO_3
Sand	Silicon dioxide	SiO_2
Slaked lime	Calcium hydroxide	$Ca(OH)_2$
Smithsonite	Impure zinc carbonate	$ZnCO_3$
Turnbull's blue	Ferrous ferricyanide	$Fe_3[Fe(CN)_6]_2$
Vinegar	Dilute acetic acid	$HC_2H_3O_2$
Washing soda	Sodium carbonate, crystals	$Na_2CO_3 \cdot 10\ H_2O$
Water glass	Sodium silicate	Na_2SiO_3
White lead	Basic lead carbonate	$Pb(OH)_2 \cdot 2\ PbCO_3$
Zinc blende	Impure zinc sulfide	ZnS

9. THE COLLEGE BOARD ACHIEVEMENT TEST IN CHEMISTRY

1. WHAT ARE COLLEGE BOARD TESTS?

Students seeking admission to certain colleges may be required to take a special aptitude test, called the scholastic aptitude test (S.A.T.), and a maximum of three achievement tests. These examinations are prepared by the College Entrance Examination Board (C.E.E.B.). The examination in chemistry is one of fourteen achievement tests prepared by the Board. All achievement tests have a maximum time allowance of one hour. In the past, all the questions have been of the multiple-choice variety.

2. HOW ARE COLLEGE BOARD TESTS USED?

Scores on college board examinations are not rated as passing or failing. A numerical score ranging from a low of 200 to a high of 800 is reported to the college of the applicant's choice. It has been found that students who do well on college board tests generally do well in college. Performance on college board tests, however, is only *one* of a number of criteria used to determine admission to college.

3. SCOPE OF THE CHEMISTRY TEST

The scope of the chemistry test is limited to the subject matter commonly taught in the high school. The questions are designed to test the following skills:

a. Acquisition of subject matter.

b. The ability to associate scientific statements with their explanations.

c. Understanding of "big ideas," commonly called concepts, and their applications.

d. Understanding and applying quantitative relationships.

e. Application of what the student has learned in the laboratory, especially the interpretation of experimental data.

4. HOW TO PREPARE FOR THE CHEMISTRY TEST

To prepare for the achievement test in chemistry, the following procedures will be helpful:

a. Restudy the content of *Review Text in Chemistry*, emphasizing the review of equations and fundamental principles found in the Appendix.

b. Review the answers to the asterisked questions in the Study Guide following each chapter. These questions, designed for the more enthusiastic student, afford content coverage somewhat above the usual high school course.

c. Use the questions (pages 443-451) and the answers (pages 452-455) as a self-test to indicate areas that need further study. Do not memorize these questions or the answers, since the same material will not appear on the college board test you will take.

5. A SAMPLE OF COLLEGE BOARD TYPE QUESTIONS IN CHEMISTRY

The following questions have been designed to acquaint you with the scope of the test and the types of questions that have appeared. These questions are grouped according to the areas indicated under Scope of the Chemistry Test.

a. Acquisition of Subject Matter

By letter, select the word or phrase which best completes each of the following statements:

1. The acid found in sour milk is (A) citric (B) oxalic (C) tartaric (D) lactic (E) acetic.
2. A cubic meter is a unit of (A) length (B) density (C) volume (D) weight (E) area.
3. One liter exactly equals (A) one quart (B) 1000 cubic centimeters (C) 1000 cubic liters (D) 1000 milliliters (E) four quarts.
4. As a rule, metals (A) gain electrons only (B) lose electrons only (C) gain and lose electrons (D) neither gain nor lose electrons (E) share electrons.
5. The test for carbon dioxide resembles the test for (A) carbon monoxide (B) sulfur dioxide (C) sulfur trioxide (D) ammonia (E) oxygen.
6. An element which is a liquid at ordinary temperatures is (A) lithium (B) cesium (C) water (D) radium (E) ether.
7. A pair of substances which illustrates amphoterism is (A) O_2 and O_3 (B) $Zn(OH)_2$ and H_2ZnO_2 (C) NaOH and NaH (D) F_2 and Cl_2 (E) He and Ne.
8. Hydrogen cannot be obtained from (A) acids (B) bases (C) water (D) water gas (E) the reaction between hydrogen peroxide and manganese dioxide.
9. The Law of Conservation of Matter was established by (A) Priestley (B) Einstein (C) Davy (D) Lavoisier (E) Boyle.
10. A substance which, at its melting point, will probably liberate oxygen is (A) $Ca(ClO_3)_2$ (B) $C_6H_{12}O_6$ (C) NaOH (D) H_2O (E) Wood's metal.
11. Sodium peroxide reacts with water to form oxygen and (A) sodium oxide (B) sodium hydroxide (C) hydrogen (D) sodium metal (E) sodium hydride.
12. The reaction between metals and ozone produces (A) an oxide (B) an ozonide (C) a carbonate (D) an hydroxide (E) a carbide.
13. In the reaction between zinc and hydrochloric acid, the hydrochloric acid acts as (A) a reducing agent (B) an oxidizing agent (C) neither an oxidizing nor a reducing agent (D) an oxidizing and a reducing agent (E) a catalytic agent.
14. Of the following, the element that reacts with water least readily is (A) lithium (B) sodium (C) potassium (D) fluorine (E) chlorine.
15. In the reaction between iron and steam, iron (A) gains electrons (B) is reduced (C) is the oxidizing agent (D) loses electrons (E) is neither oxidized nor reduced.
16. The pH of a weak acid is approximately (A) 1 (B) 2 (C) 6 (D) 8 (E) 14.
17. A substance which is usually not hydrated is (A) ammonium chloride (B) washing soda (C) borax (D) Epsom salts (E) alum.

18. The reaction between a metallic oxide and an acid produces (A) another acid (B) a base (C) a salt (D) oxygen (E) hydrogen.

19. The halogen which loses electrons least readily is (A) fluorine (B) chlorine (C) bromine (D) iodine (E) astatine.

20. Of the following acids, the most stable is (A) HF (B) HCl (C) HBr (D) HI (E) HNO_3.

21. In the electrolysis of brine, the ion that is reduced at the cathode is (A) sodium (B) hydrogen (C) chlorine (D) hydroxide (E) oxygen.

22. Of the following, the most electronegative element is (A) chlorine (B) sulfur (C) oxygen (D) fluorine (E) nitrogen.

23. In the gaseous diffusion process for separating the uranium isotopes, uranium is first converted into (A) UF (B) U_2F_2 (C) UF_2 (D) UF_4 (E) UF_6.

24. When chlorine is dissolved in water, the bleaching agent produced has the formula (A) Cl_2 (B) Cl (C) O (D) $CaOCl_2$ (E) HOCl.

25. Element Z has an atomic number of 15 while element Q has an atomic number of 20. The formula of a possible compound containing these elements is (A) Z_3Q_2 (B) Q_3Z_2 (C) ZQ (D) ZQ_3 (E) QZ_2.

26. Of the following, the pair of elements most commonly extracted by electrolysis is (A) sodium and copper (B) fluorine and iron (C) aluminum and magnesium (D) chlorine and bromine (E) sodium and bromine.

27. A commercial process that does not require a catalyst is the (A) Haber (B) contact (C) Ostwald (D) cracking (E) Frasch   process.

28. The correct formula for manganous oxide is (A) MnO_2 (B) MnO (C) Mn_2O_3 (D) MnO_4 (E) Mn_2O_7.

29. When hydrochloric acid reacts with manganese dioxide, the hydrochloric acid acts as (A) an oxidizing agent (B) a reducing agent (C) a dehydrating agent (D) a catalytic agent (E) neither of these.

30. A property not true of zinc is that it (A) is more active than iron (B) is used to make brass (C) has a relatively low melting point (D) loses electrons more readily than aluminum (E) forms amphoteric compounds.

31. An element that is not man-made is (A) nobelium (B) fermium (C) plutonium (D) thorium (E) neptunium.

32. The reaction between hydronium ions and hydroxyl ions to form water is called (A) hydrolysis (B) neutralization (C) combination (D) hydrogenation (E) addition.

33. All bases contain (A) hydronium (B) sodium (C) metallic (D) hydroxyl (E) calcium   ions.

34. The valence number of chromium in $K_2Cr_2O_7$ is (A) -3 (B) $+2$ (C) $+4$ (D) $+6$ (E) $+7$.

35. The formula of a salt whose water solution has a pH above 7 is (A) NaCl (B) NH_4Cl (C) $ZnCl_2$ (D) $NaHSO_4$ (E) $NaHCO_3$.

36. A substance when placed in water liberates ammonia gas. It may be concluded that the substance
   (A) is an ammonium compound.
   (B) is ammonium chloride.
   (C) is a mixture of an ammonium compound and a base.
   (D) may be a nitrate.
   (E) may be a nitride.

37. The addition of silver nitrate to an unknown solution results in the formation of a white precipitate which dissolves in nitric acid. It may be concluded that the solution
    (A) contains chloride ions.
    (B) may contain chloride ions.
    (C) does not contain chloride ions.
    (D) contains fluoride ions.
    (E) may contain fluoride ions.

38. A student prepares carbon dioxide, bubbles the gas into a sample of limewater, and does not get a white precipitate. Instead, the solution remains colorless. The most likely explanation of this difficulty is that the student
    (A) did not prepare enough CO_2.
    (B) prepared too much CO_2.
    (C) used the wrong acid in the preparation.
    (D) did not heat the reacting substances.
    (E) used a sample of limewater that was too concentrated.

In each of the following unbalanced equations (39-48), one formula is underlined. For this formula, select the letter which indicates the correct coefficient needed to balance the equation:

(A) 1 (B) 2 (C) 3 (D) 4 (E) 5

39. $Ca + \underline{H_2O} \rightarrow Ca(OH)_2 + H_2$
40. $B + \underline{O_2} \rightarrow B_2O_3$
41. $NH_3 + O_2 \rightarrow \underline{NO} + H_2O$
42. $H_2SO_4 + Na\underline{HSO_3} \rightarrow \underline{H_2O} + Na_2SO_4 + SO_2$
43. $H_2S + \underline{O_2} \rightarrow H_2O + SO_2$
44. $P + \underline{O_2} \rightarrow P_2O_5$
45. $Al + \underline{H_2SO_4} \rightarrow Al_2(SO_4)_3 + H_2$
46. $CO + \underline{H_2} \rightarrow CH_3OH$
47. $Cu + HNO_3 \rightarrow Cu(NO_3)_2 + \underline{H_2O} + NO$
48. $Sb + \underline{Cl_2} \rightarrow SbCl_3$

For each of the following statements (49-55), select the letter which indicates the correct process involved.

    (A) electrolysis
    (B) vacuum distillation
    (C) destructive distillation
    (D) polymerization
    (E) oxidation

49. The commercial extraction of magnesium
50. The refining of sugar
51. The manufacture of synthetic rubber
52. The action of drying oils in paints
53. The preparation of boneblack
54. The refining of copper
55. Commercial preparation of lye

b. Associating Scientific Statements with Their Proper Explanations

Each of the questions below (56-65) consists of a statement and an explanation. Select the correct answer by letter from the following choices:

(A) Both the statement and explanation are true, and the explanation is related to the statement.
(B) Both the statement and explanation are true, but the explanation is *not* related to the statement.
(C) The statement is true, but the explanation is false.
(D) The statement is false, but the explanation is true.
(E) Both the statement and explanation are false.

	SUMMARY OF DIRECTIONS		
	STATEMENT	EXPLANATION	
(A)	True	True	Explanation is *related* to statement.
(B)	True	True	Explanation is *unrelated* to statement.
(C)	True	False	
(D)	False	True	
(E)	False	False	

STATEMENT	EXPLANATION
56. Hydrogen gas is generally a reducing agent	*because* it is the lightest element.
57. Dilute sulfuric acid is an oxidizing agent	*because* it reacts with zinc to form zinc sulfate and hydrogen.
58. Sodium chloride is a covalent compound	*because* covalent bonds are produced by electron transfer.
59. All compounds are formed by the transfer of electrons	*because* oppositely charged ions attract one another.
60. Carbon forms large numbers of compounds	*because* carbon can share electrons with other carbon atoms.
61. The total weight of the products of a reaction is slightly greater than the weight of the starting substances	*because* in a chemical reaction, matter can be neither created nor destroyed.
62. The production of synthetic rubber is decreasing	*because* it is inferior to natural rubber in many of its uses.
63. Unsaturated organic compounds are highly reactive	*because* structurally, they contain only one pair of shared electrons.
64. Sulfur dioxide is collected by air displacement	*because* it is denser than air.
65. Fluorine is a powerful oxidizing agent	*because* it has a marked affinity for electrons.

c. Understanding Concepts and Their Applications

66. Potassium reacts more vigorously with water than does sodium because
 (A) potassium is denser than sodium.
 (B) sodium loses electrons more readily than does potassium.
 (C) potassium is a more powerful oxidizing agent.
 (D) sodium is covered by a layer of kerosene in which it has been stored.
 (E) potassium is a more powerful reducing agent.

67. A statement that is not true is that the Mendeléef periodic table
 (A) predicted many new elements.
 (B) arranged the atoms in order of increasing atomic weight.
 (C) explained why some atoms did not react.
 (D) was based on the Dalton concept of the atom.
 (E) was proposed about 1869.

68. In electrolysis, oxidation always takes place at the anode because the anode has
 (A) a deficiency of protons.
 (B) a deficiency of electrons.
 (C) an excess of electrons.
 (D) an equal number of protons and electrons.
 (E) an attraction for positive ions.

In each of the following incomplete statements (69-77), *one* of the lettered items may be used to complete the statement correctly. Select

  (A) if only 1 is correct.
  (B) if 1 and 2 are correct.
  (C) if only 3 and 4 are correct.
  (D) if only 2, 3, and 4 are correct.
  (E) if another answer or combination of answers is correct.

69. Electrovalent compounds
 1. do not contain molecules.
 2. are electrically charged.
 3. are formed by the sharing of electrons.
 4. are formed by the transfer of electrons.

70. When reversible reactions reach equilibrium at a given temperature,
 1. the concentrations of the starting substances and the products are equal.
 2. the velocities of the opposing reactions are equal.
 3. the Law of Mass Action can be applied.
 4. changes in concentration will shift the equilibrium point.

71. To more effectively bombard the nucleus of an atom, certain particles are accelerated in devices such as the
 1. cosmotron.
 2. synchrotron.
 3. betatron.
 4. cyclotron.

72. Naturally occurring radioactive elements such as radium, thorium, and polonium disintegrate by the emission of
    1. neutrons.
    2. gamma rays.
    3. alpha particles.
    4. beta particles.

73. In the periodic table, elements which form amphoteric compounds are found
    1. nearer the center.
    2. in main groups only.
    3. on the left side.
    4. on the right side.

74. Oxidation-reduction always takes place in reactions involving
    1. double replacement.
    2. decomposition.
    3. single replacement.
    4. combination of elements.

75. The rate of solution of a gas in a liquid solvent may be increased by
    1. increasing the pressure of the gas.
    2. decreasing the temperature of the solvent.
    3. decreasing the pressure of the gas.
    4. increasing the temperature of the solvent.

76. Sulfur, like nitrogen, exhibits many different valence numbers. It may therefore be concluded that
    1. sulfur forms many compounds.
    2. nitrogen forms many compounds.
    3. sulfur and nitrogen may undergo oxidation-reduction.
    4. sulfur and nitrogen can form electrovalent compounds only.

77. The pH scale was developed by Sorenson and is equal to the logarithm of the reciprocal of the hydrogen ion concentration. It therefore follows that
    1. some solutions can have a pH value of zero.
    2. some solutions can have negative pH values.
    3. the higher the hydrogen ion concentration, the lower the pH value.
    4. the lower the hydrogen ion concentration, the higher the pH value.

The symbols T, Q, X, Y, and Z represent five different elements. Assuming the atomic numbers are T = 5, Q = 9, X = 14, Y = 18, and Z = 19, answer questions 78-80.

78. The most powerful oxidizing agent is (A) T (B) Q (C) X (D) Y (E) Z.

79. The element with the lowest atomic weight that can form amphoteric compounds is (A) T (B) Q (C) X (D) Y (E) Z.

80. The formula of a possible compound is (A) TZ_3 (B) XY (C) TQ_3 (D) ZQ_3 (E) T_3X_4.

d. Understanding and Applying Quantitative Relationships

The decomposition of sodium chlorate yields sodium chloride and oxygen:

$$2 \ NaClO_3 \rightarrow 2 \ NaCl + 3 \ O_2$$

Using the above equation, answer questions 81-83.

81. The volume of oxygen that can be obtained from one mole (106 grams) of sodium chlorate at standard conditions is (A) 1.5 (B) 3 (C) 22.4 (D) 33.6 (E) 67.2 liters.

82. The weight of oxygen that can be obtained from two moles (212 grams) of sodium chlorate is (A) 3 (B) 6 (C) 32 (D) 48 (E) 96 grams.

83. The weight of oxygen liberated (A) depends upon the weight of catalyst used (B) depends upon the temperature only (C) depends upon the pressure only (D) is always less than the weight of sodium chloride produced (E) is always greater than the weight of sodium chloride produced.

84. If 0.5 g. of hydrogen are exploded in air, the weight of water formed (A) equals 4 grams (B) equals 4.5 grams (C) equals 0.25 gram (D) equals 0.75 gram (E) cannot be calculated from the data given.

85. A certain hydrocarbon has the following composition: hydrogen, 16%; carbon, 84%. The molecular formula of this compound is (A) CH_4 (B) C_2H_6 (C) C_7H_{16} (D) $C_{14}H_{32}$ (E) cannot be determined from the data given.

86. If one liter of a gas, at standard conditions, weighs 11.2 grams, the approximate gram-molecular weight of the gas is (A) 11.2 (B) 22.4 (C) 44.8 (D) 224 (E) 251.

87. X and Z are elemental gases that react to form XZ_2, which is also gaseous. The equation is as follows: $X_2 + 2 \ Z_2 \rightarrow 2 \ XZ_2$. From one liter of X, it will be possible to form (A) ½ (B) 1 (C) 2 (D) 3 (E) 4 liter(s) of XZ_2.

e. Applications of What the Student Has Learned in the Laboratory

88. In the laboratory, a student heats a crystal to determine its percentage of water of hydration. Upon completing the experiment, he gets a value of 31%. The correct value is 15%. The most likely source of error made by the student is that he
    (A) used too large a sample of hydrate.
    (B) used too small a sample of hydrate.
    (C) did not drive off enough water.
    (D) drove off too much water.
    (E) decomposed the anhydrous material.

89. In the electrolysis of 100 ml. of water, a student finds that he has prepared 30 ml. of hydrogen and only 5 ml. of oxygen. A likely source of error to account for the deficiency of oxygen is that the student
    (A) used too little H_2SO_4.
    (B) used too much H_2SO_4.
    (C) failed to take into account the solubility of oxygen.
    (D) failed to take into account the solubility of hydrogen.
    (E) did not check to see that the apparatus was airtight.

90. When two solids are heated, a gas is evolved. The gas is extremely soluble in water and denser than air. In the preparation and collection of this gas, a piece of equipment that is not necessary is a
(A) gas collecting bottle.
(B) thistle tube.
(C) Bunsen burner.
(D) one-hole rubber stopper.
(E) delivery tube.

Indicated by letter are the diagrams of five pieces of equipment commonly used in the chemical laboratory.

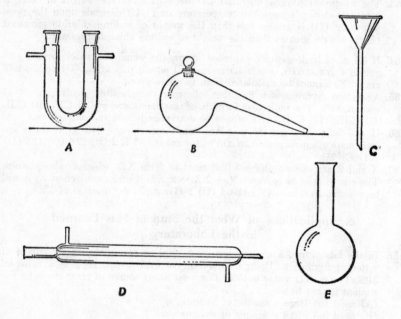

Select the one piece of equipment that should be used for each laboratory procedure (91-96) below.

91. To demonstrate the extreme solubility of gases in water.
92. To prepare volatile liquids.
93. To show that a definite weight of water is formed in certain reactions.
94. To show that the catalyst remains unchanged in the preparation of oxygen.
95. To separate a mixture of liquids of different boiling points.
96. To allow organic reactions to continue indefinitely with minimum loss of any volatile components.

The following diagrams illustrate **three different types of gas generators commonly** used in the laboratory:

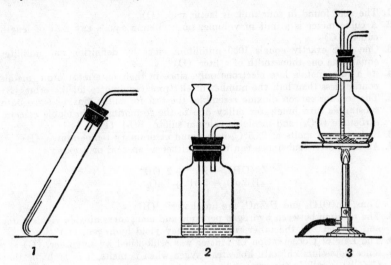

1   2   3

97. Generator 1 is most commonly used to prepare **(A)** carbon dioxide **(B)** sulfur dioxide **(C)** chlorine **(D)** oxygen **(E)** hydrogen.

98. Generator 2 is most commonly used to prepare **(A)** carbon monoxide **(B)** carbon dioxide **(C)** nitrous oxide **(D)** oxygen **(E)** ammonia.

99. Generator 3 is most commonly used to prepare **(A)** carbon monoxide **(B)** chlorine **(C)** ammonia **(D)** hydrogen sulfide **(E)** hydrogen.

100. Generators 1, 2, and 3 are not commonly used to prepare **(A)** nitrogen dioxide **(B)** hydrogen fluoride **(C)** nitric oxide **(D)** hydrogen chloride **(E)** acetylene.

Answers to Questions

1. The acid found in sour milk is lactic acid. (D)

2. A cubic meter is a unit of volume, since volume equals any unit of length cubed. (C)

3. One liter exactly equals 1000 milliliters, since by definition one milliliter equals one one-thousandth of a liter. (D)

4. As a rule, metals lose electrons only, since in their outermost orbit, metals contain less than half the number of electrons required to fill the orbit. (B)

5. The test for carbon dioxide resembles the test for sulfur dioxide, since both substances turn limewater milky due to the formation of insoluble calcium carbonate (CO_2) and insoluble calcium sulfite (SO_2). (B)

6. Since cesium melts at $28.5°C$, it is liquid at ordinary temperatures. (B)

7. An amphoteric substance can behave either as an acid or a base:

$$Zn(OH)_2 \rightarrow Zn^{+2} + 2\ OH^-$$
$$H_2ZnO_2 \rightarrow 2\ H^+ + ZnO_2^-$$

Thus, $Zn(OH)_2$ and H_2ZnO_2 are amphoteric. (B)

8. The reaction between hydrogen peroxide and manganese dioxide yields water and oxygen. All the other substances may yield hydrogen. (E)

9. The Law of Conservation of Matter was established by Lavoisier. (D)

10. Since potassium chlorate liberates oxygen when it melts, it is probable that $Ca(ClO_3)_2$ will do the same. (A)

11. Sodium peroxide reacts with water to form oxygen and sodium hyroxide. (B)

12. The reaction between metals and ozone produces a metallic oxide. (A)

13. Since hydrochloric acid contains a reducible particle ($2\ H^+ + 2\ e \rightarrow H_2$), it behaves as an oxidizing agent when it reacts with zinc. (B)

14. Since chlorine is the least active element in the suggested answers, it reacts with water least readily. (E)

15. When iron reacts with steam, hydrogen is formed ($2\ H^+ + 2\ e \rightarrow H_2$). Thus, iron must lose the necessary electrons required to reduce $2\ H^+$. (D).

16. By definition, the pH of a weak acid is a little less than 7. Hence, the correct answer is pH 6. (C)

17. Of the suggested answers, all are hydrates except ammonium chloride. (A)

18. Since metallic oxides are base forming (basic anhydrides), the reaction between such oxides and acids involves neutralization. Thus, a salt is formed. (C)

19. The most active halogen, fluorine, gains electrons most readily. Hence, fluorine loses electrons least readily. (A)

20. The most stable acid in the group is HF. (A)

21. Since the cathode has an excess of electrons, it attracts those ions that have a deficiency of electrons. Of the suggested answers, sodium ions and hydrogen ions have a deficiency of electrons. However, since hydrogen is less active than sodium, it is the hydrogen ions that are more easily reduced. (B).

22. The periodic table reveals that, of the suggested elements, the most electronegative is fluorine. (D)

23. In the gaseous diffusion process, uranium is first converted into UF_6. (E)

24. The bleaching agent produced is HOCl. (E)

$$Cl_2 + H_2O \rightarrow HCl + HOCl$$

25. Element Z, atomic number 15, has a valence number of -3. Element Q, atomic number 20, has a valence number of $+2$. The formula of a possible compound is Q_3Z_2. (B)

26. Of the suggested answers, aluminum and magnesium are most commonly extracted by electrolysis. (C)

27. The Frasch process does not require a catalyst. (E)

28. Since manganous manganese has a valence number of $+2$, the formula of manganous oxide is MnO. (B)

29. Since HCl contains Cl^-, and since in this reaction Cl^- is oxidized to chlorine gas, HCl behaves as a reducing agent. (B)

30. Of the suggested properties, zinc does not lose electrons more readily than aluminum, since zinc is less active than aluminum. (D)

31. Thorium is one of the 92 naturally occurring elements. (D)

32. The reaction $H_3O^+ + OH^- \rightarrow 2\ H_2O$ is called neutralization. (B)

33. All bases contain hydroxyl ions. (D)

34. The valence number of chromium is $+6$, since $2\ K = +2$ and $7\ O = -14$. (D)

35. Of the salts listed, only $NaHCO_3$ is alkaline in water solution, resulting in a pH above 7. (E)

36. The substance *may* be either a mixture of an ammonium compound and a base, or a nitride. From the wording of the question, the correct answer is (E).

37. Since silver fluoride is soluble, of the suggested answers, only a chloride forms a white precipitate with silver nitrate. However, silver chloride does not dissolve in nitric acid. Thus, the solution cannot contain chloride ions. (C)

38. An excess of CO_2 causes the white precipitate of $CaCO_3$ to dissolve to form soluble $Ca(HCO_3)_2$. (B)

39. $Ca + \underline{2\ H_2O} \rightarrow Ca(OH)_2 + H_2$ (B)

40. $4\ B + \underline{3\ O_2} \rightarrow 2\ B_2O_3$ (C)

41. $4\ NH_3 + 5\ O_2 \rightarrow \underline{4\ NO} + 6\ H_2O$ (D)

42. $H_2SO_4 + 2\ NaHSO_3 \rightarrow \underline{2\ H_2O} + Na_2SO_4 + 2\ SO_2$ (B)

43. $2\ H_2S + \underline{3\ O_2} \rightarrow 2\ H_2O + 2\ SO_2$ (C)

44. $4\ P + 5\ \underline{O_2} \rightarrow 2\ P_2O_5$ (E)

45. $2\ Al + \underline{3\ H_2SO_4} \rightarrow Al_2(SO_4)_3 + 3\ H_2$ (C)

46. $CO + 2\ \underline{H_2} \rightarrow CH_3OH$ (A)

47. $3\ Cu + 8\ HNO_3 \rightarrow 3\ Cu(NO_3)_2 + \underline{4\ H_2O} + 2\ NO$ (D)

48. $2\ Sb + \underline{3\ Cl_2} \rightarrow 2\ SbCl_3$ (C)

49. The activity of magnesium requires that it be extracted from its ores by electrolysis. (A)

50. Since sugar decomposes at temperatures near the boiling point of water, it cannot be separated from water by distillation at atmospheric pressure. As the pressure is lowered, water will boil at a lower temperature. (B)

51. The manufacture of synthetic rubber requires the polymerization of simpler units (monomers). (D)

52. The action of drying oils, such as linseed oil, in paints is due to oxidation. (E)

53. Boneblack is prepared by the destructive distillation of bones. (C)

54. Copper is refined electrolytically. (A)

55. Lye is prepared commercially by the electrolysis of brine. **(A)**

56. Both the statement and the explanation are true, but the explanation is unrelated to the statement. Hydrogen gas is generally a reducing agent because hydrogen atoms tend to lose electrons. (B)

57. When zinc reacts with dilute sulfuric acid, the H^+ of the acid oxidizes the zinc to form zinc sulfate and hydrogen. (A)

58. Sodium chloride is an electrovalent compound containing ionic bonds, resulting from electron transfer. (E)

59. Only electrovalent compounds are formed by electron transfer. (D)

60. The statement and the explanation are true and related. (A)

61. The total weight of the products of a reaction can never be greater than the weight of the starting substances since, in a reaction, matter can be neither created nor destroyed. (D)

62. The production of synthetic rubber is increasing, and it is superior to natural rubber in many of its uses. (E)

63. Unsaturated organic compounds are highly reactive because structurally they contain more than one pair of shared electrons. (C)

64. Both the statement and the explanation are true, but the explanation is unrelated to the statement. Sulfur dioxide is collected by air displacement because it is soluble in water. (B)

65. The statement and the explanation are true and related. (A)

66. Since potassium and sodium are both in Group I A, and since potassium has the larger atomic radius, it is more active (a more powerful reducing agent) than sodium. (E)

67. Since the Mendeléef table preceded the promulgation of the electron theory, the table did not adequately explain the nature of chemical change. (C)

68. Since oxidation involves a loss of electrons, this loss occurs at the terminal which has a deficiency of electrons, namely, the anode. (B)

69. (1) and (4) are correct. (E)

70. (2), (3), and (4) are correct. (D)

71. All four choices are correct. (E)

72. (2), (3), and (4) are correct. (D)

73. (1) is correct. (A)

74. Only double replacement does not involve oxidation-reduction. (D)

75. (1) and (2) are correct. (B)

76. (1), (2), and (3) are correct. (E)

77. Since $pH = \log \dfrac{1}{[H^+]}$, when $[H^+]$ equals 1 M, pH equals zero; when $[H^+] =$ 10 M, pH equals −1. As $[H^+]$ increases, pH decreases. Thus, (1), (2), (3), and (4) are correct. (E)

78. Oxidizing agents contain reducible particles (particles that can gain electrons). Structure of Q is 2-7. (B)

79. Elements T and X are near the center of the periodic table and thus form amphoteric compounds. Because T has a lower atomic number, it has a lower atomic weight. (A)

80. Element T has a valence number of +3 and will combine with electronegative elements such as Q, which has a valence number of −1, to form compound TQ_3. (C)

81. One mole of NaClO₃ produces 1.5 moles of O₂. The volume of this gas would be 33.6 liters. (D)

82. Since two moles of $NaClO_3$ produce 3 moles of O_2, the weight of this gas is 96 grams. (E)

83. Since the formula weight of 2 NaCl equals 116, while the formula weight of 3 O_2 equals 96, the weight of oxygen produced is always less than the weight of sodium chloride produced. (D)

84. From the weight composition of water, 0.5 gram of hydrogen will combine with 4 grams of oxygen. Hence, 4.5 grams of water will be formed. (B)

85. Since the molecular weight is not given, the molecular formula cannot be determined from the data given. (E)

86. The approximate gram-molecular weight equals the weight of 22.4 liters at standard conditions. (E)

87. The equation reveals that one volume of X_2 forms two volumes of XZ_2. Hence, one liter of X_2 forms 2 liters of XZ_2. (C)

88. Of the suggested answers, only the decomposition of the anhydrous material would account for the error. (E)

89. The slight solubility of oxygen in water rules out (C). If the apparatus were not airtight, the loss of 10 ml. of oxygen could be accounted for. (E)

90. Since liquids are not involved in the preparation, a thistle tube is unnecessary. (B)

91. The extreme solubility of gases can be demonstrated by the use of the fountain. Hence, a round bottom flask is required. (E)

92. A retort is used to prepare volatile liquids. (B)

93. A drying tube containing $CaCl_2$ is required to show the formation of water in certain reactions. (A)

94. To show that MnO_2 is a catalyst in the preparation of oxygen, it is necessary to separate the KCl formed from the insoluble MnO_2. Hence, a funnel and filter paper are required. (C)

95. To separate a mixture of liquids of different boiling points, distillation is required. Hence, a condenser is necessary. (D)

96. To minimize loss of organic reactants, a condenser in the vertical (reflux) position is inserted into the flask which contains the reactants. Volatile substances thus drop back into the flask. (D)

97. Since only solids are required to make oxygen, a test tube generator is used. (D)

98. The presence of a thistle tube in the generator suggests the reaction between a solid and a liquid. Carbon dioxide is prepared by the reaction between a solid (limestone) and a liquid (some acid). (B)

99. In addition to the reaction between a liquid and a solid, heat is also required. The preparation of chlorine requires heating a mixture of manganese dioxide and hydrochloric acid. (B)

100. Since hydrogen fluoride attacks glass, a special generator is required. (B)

CHEMISTRY—JUNE 1959 (1)

Part I

Answer all questions in this part.

Directions (1-30): Write on the line at the right of *each* statement or question the *number* preceding the term that, of those given, best completes the statement or answers the question.   [30]

1. Chemically pure water is prepared by (1) distillation   (2) aeration   (3) filtration   (4) chlorination

2. Identical laboratory apparatus may be used to prepare and collect carbon dioxide and (1) ammonia   (2) hydrogen   (3) iodine   (4) nitric acid

3. The maximum number of electrons found in the first (K) shell of atoms is (1) 8   (2) 2   (3) 18   (4) 32

4. The products formed by the complete combustion of hydrogen sulfide gas are (1) $H_2O + S$ (2) $H_2 + SO_2$ (3) $H_2O + SO_2$ (4) $H_2 + S + O_2$

5. A chemical property used to test for hydrogen gas may be its (1) density   (2) solubility   (3) ability to burn   (4) boiling point

6. The formation of a brown ring is often used as a test for a (1) chloride   (2) phosphate   (3) nitrate   (4) sulfate

7. Lead may be replaced from solutions of lead salts by (1) copper   (2) magnesium   (3) mercury   (4) silver

8. Under standard conditions, ten liters of oxygen weighs approximately (1) 10 gm.   (2) 2 gm.   (3) 14 gm.   (4) 32 gm.

9. The probable formula for chloric acid is (1) HClO   (2) $HClO_2$ (3) $HClO_3$ (4) $HClO_4$

10. Sulfur combines directly with the alkali metals to form (1) an acid   (2) a base   (3) an oxide   (4) a salt

11. Helium may be produced by the fusion of isotopes of (1) radium   (2) uranium   (3) plutonium   (4) hydrogen

12. With which of the following will bromine gas react most readily? (1) C_2H_4 (2) C_2H_6 (3) C_3H_8 (4) C_4H_{10}

13. Hematite is an ore of (1) aluminum   (2) titanium   (3) copper   (4) iron

14. Which property of sulfuric acid is illustrated by the reaction $Cu + 2H_2SO_4 \rightarrow CuSO_4 + 2H_2O + SO_2$? (1) strong acid   (2) dehydrating agent   (3) oxidizing agent   (4) high boiling point

15. The valence of the dichromate radical in the compound $K_2Cr_2O_7$ is (1) -2 (2) $+2$ (3) -6 (4) $+6$

16. Polymerization is a process used to increase the yield of (1) methane   (2) soft coal   (3) gasoline   (4) coke

17. One would expect the molecular structure of silicon to be similar to that of (1) zinc   (2) diamond   (3) sulfur   (4) magnesium

18. In the electrolysis of a solution of cupric sulfate, the cupric ions are (1) oxidized at the anode   (2) oxidized at the cathode   (3) reduced at the anode   (4) reduced at the cathode

19. The compounds of calcium and magnesium usually responsible for permanent hard water are (1) bicarbonates (2) nitrates (3) carbonates (4) sulfates

20. Manganese dioxide is frequently used in the laboratory preparation of (1) fluorine (2) hydrogen chloride (3) bromine (4) potassium iodide

21. The chemist classifies iron as a metal because iron (1) is a solid at room temperature (2) dissolves readily in strong bases (3) can be used for structural purposes (4) loses its valence electrons readily

22. Which substance may be used to speed the conversion of sulfur dioxide to sulfur trioxide in the manufacture of sulfuric acid? (1) platinum (2) sodium chloride (3) sodium (4) water

23. A light-sensitive halide frequently used in preparing photographic film is (1) SiF_4 (2) $AgBr$ (3) CCl_4 (4) I_2

24. Element No. 56 forms a stable compound with element No. (1) 9 (2) 19 (3) 54 (4) 55

25. In the reaction $CO_2 + 2\ Mg \rightarrow 2MgO + C$, the oxidation number or valence number of carbon changes from (1) $+4$ to 0 (2) $+2$ to 0 (3) 0 to $+4$ (4) 0 to $+2$

26. The fuel in a nuclear reactor may be (1) carbon (2) uranium (3) radium (4) lead

27. Automobile springs are made of (1) cast iron (2) pig iron (3) wrought iron (4) steel

28. An example of an ester is (1) C_2H_5OH (2) CH_3COOCH_3 (3) $C_{12}H_{22}O_{11}$ (4) CH_3COOH

29. A solution containing both hydrogen ions and hydroxyl ions (1) is a nonelectrolyte (2) is basic (3) may be acidic (4) must be neutral

30. The halogens exhibit similar chemical properties because they (1) are diatomic (2) are gases (3) have variable valences (4) have seven electrons in their outermost shells

Directions (31-40): Write on the line at the right of *each* statement the term that, when inserted in the blank, will correctly complete the statement. [10]

31. An electrically charged atom is a (an) . . . .

32. The name of the solvent in tincture of iodine is . . . .

33. Destructive distillation of wood produces the commercial form of carbon known as . . . .

34. Limestone is principally used in the blast furnace because it acts as a (an) . . . .

35. The name of the acid used to etch calibration marks on thermometer tubes is . . . acid.

36. A solution of sodium acetate in water turns litmus . . . .

37. The process of coating iron with zinc in order to prevent corrosion is called . . . .

38. The name of a poisonous gas which combines readily with the hemoglobin of red blood cells is . . . .

39. Low grade copper sulfide ores are concentrated by the process of . . . .

40. When nonmetallic oxides dissolve in water, they form a class of compounds known as . . . .

Directions (41-50): Write on the line at the right of *each* statement the term (*decreases, increases, remains the same*) that, when inserted in the blank, will correctly complete the statement.   [10]

41. When a bottle of soda water is opened, it fizzes because the solubility of the carbon dioxide . . . .

42. In the ethylene series, as the molecular weights increase, the ratio of hydrogen atoms to the carbon atoms . . . .

43. As the purity of iron increases, its tendency to corrode . . . .

44. As the activity of metals increases, the stability of their compounds usually . . . .

45. As the cadmium (or boron steel) rods are withdrawn from a nuclear reactor, the speed of the reaction . . . .

46. As radium emits alpha particles, the mass of the radium . . . .

47. As the surface area between reacting materials increases, the speed of the reaction . . . .

48. As the temperature rises, the solubility in water of most solids . . . .

49. As the radius of atoms in Group 7 increases, the stability of their compounds usually . . . .

50. Using graphite electrodes, a solution of copper chloride is electrolyzed. During the process, the number of ions in solution . . . .

Part II

Answer five questions from this part. [*Show all numerical work when computation is required.*]

1. Write a correctly balanced equation for each of *five* of the following: [10]
   a. Reaction between calcium sulfate and sodium carbonate
   b. Heating a solution of magnesium bicarbonate
   c. Converting zinc sulfide to an oxide
   d. Complete combustion of heptane (C_7H_{16})
   e. Neutralization of phosphoric acid by sodium hydroxide
   f. Reaction of H_2SO_4 with water to form hydronium ions

2. Answer ALL parts of the following question: [The atomic weights from the *Reference Tables* may be used to the *nearest whole numbers;* e.g., $Cl = 35.46$ becomes 35.]
   a. HCl is oxidized by $KMnO_4$ according to the following equation:
      $$2KMnO_4 + 16HCl \rightarrow 2KCl + 2MnCl_2 + 8H_2O + 5Cl_2$$
      What weight of $KMnO_4$ is required in the above reaction to produce 20 grams of chlorine?   [3]
   b. In the Ostwald process, ammonia is oxidized according to the following equation: $4NH_3 + 5O_2 \rightarrow 4NO + 6H_2O$
      What volume of oxygen is required to oxidize 15 liters of ammonia by this process?   [3]
   c. Find the percentages by weight of copper, sulfur, and oxygen in blue vitriol, $CuSO_4 \cdot 5H_2O$.   [4]

3. *a.* (1) As sulfuric acid is slowly added to a solution of **barium** hydroxide, **the** conductivity of the resulting mixture decreases to a minimum. Explain. [2]

   (2) Upon continued addition of sulfuric acid, the conductivity of the mixture increases. Explain. [1]

   (3) Write the ionic equation for the reaction between barium hydroxide and sulfuric acid. [2]

   b. (1) Methyl orange is red at a pH less than 3, orange at any pH between 3 and 4, and yellow at a pH greater than 4. Phenolphthalein is colorless at a pH less than 8, pink at any pH between 8 and 10, and red at a pH greater than 10. What is the *only conclusion* that can be drawn about the *numerical* pH of a solution in which methyl orange is red and phenolphthalein is colorless? [2]

   (2) On the basis of your answer in *b*(1), is the solution acidic, basic, **or** neutral? [1]

   (3) What is the color of *each* of these indicators in pure water? [1, 1]

4. *a.* Draw a diagram of the complete structure of the *fluoride* ion. [2]

   b. Write an *electronic* equation to show the formation of the stannous **ion** from the stannic ion. [2]

   c. In terms of atomic structure, explain why cesium is more active than potassium. [2]

   d. Show by a *nuclear* equation how U^{239} is converted to Np^{239}. [2]

   e. Explain why isotopes of the same element are separated by physical rather than by chemical means. [2]

5. *a.* Answer the questions below with reference to the following groups **of** metals:

Group *A* .... Fe, Co, Ni	Group *D* .... Cu, Ag, Au	
Group *B* .... V, Cr, Mn	Group *E* .... Hg, Na, Pb	
Group *C* .... Be, Al, Mg		

   Which group contains metals *all of which*
   (1) may be found free in nature? [1]
   (2) are obtained by electrolysis of their fused salts? [1]
   (3) possess magnetic properties? [1]
   (4) are alloyed with iron to make special steels? [1]

   b. The following questions may be answered from the *Reference Tables:*

   (1) A saturated solution of potassium nitrate is prepared in *1,000 ml.* of water at 52° C. What is the weight of potassium nitrate which will probably precipitate if the temperature is lowered to 33° C.? [2]

   (2) Saturated solutions of sodium chloride and potassium chlorate are prepared at 20° C. Compare the concentrations of these solutions at this temperature. Explain your answer. [1, 1]

   (3) Saturated solutions of sodium chloride and potassium chlorate are prepared at 80° C. Compare the concentrations of these solutions at this temperature. Explain your answer. [1, 1]

6. *a.* Draw a labeled diagram of the apparatus used in the laboratory to prepare and collect chlorine gas. [4]
   b. Write a correctly balanced equation for the above reaction. [2]
   c. Describe a test for an iodide. [2]
   d. Hydrogen chloride and hydrochloric acid have different chemical bonding. State *two* differences in properties between these compounds which result from their different bonding. [2]

7. *a.* Explain how you would determine whether a bottle that is marked "Ethanol" contains water. [2]
   b. Describe how you would distinguish between a saturated and a supersaturated solution of hypo (sodium thiosulfate) in water. [2]
   c. Explain why a solution of calcium sulfate may be both saturated and dilute at the same time. [2]
   d. Describe laboratory procedures to distinguish between sodium sulfite and sodium carbonate. [2]
   e. Describe laboratory procedures to distinguish between ammonium chloride and zinc chloride. [2]

8. *a.* Write the *structural* formula for each of *three* of the following: ethyl alcohol (ethanol), dichlorodifluoro methane (Freon), ethylene, propane. [3]
   b. Saponification and fermentation are important commercial processes. Describe *one* of these processes. Include the materials used, the procedure, and the final products. [3]
   c. Hydrogen is usually prepared in the laboratory by the action of an acid on a metal. Briefly explain why *each* of the following materials would *not* be used in the preparation of hydrogen: (1) nitric acid, (2) concentrated sulfuric acid, (3) copper, (4) sodium. [4]

Part I

Answer all questions in this part.

Directions (1–29): Write on the line at the right of *each* statement or question the *number* preceding the word or expression that, of those given, best completes the statement or answers the question. [29]

1. Which substance is usually used as a catalyst in the laboratory preparation of oxygen gas? (1) manganese dioxide (2) nickel (3) platinum (4) potassium chlorate

2. A common laboratory preparation for hydrogen gas involves the action of (1) copper with H_2SO_4 (2) heat upon HCl (3) zinc with HCl (4) zinc with HNO_3

3. Which physical property is common to most metals? (1) low melting point (2) luster (3) reaction with acids (4) yellow color

4. Hydrogenation is a process used to (1) fill weather balloons (2) homogenize fats (3) increase the yield of gasoline (4) reduce an oxide ore

5. A light-sensitive substance used in photographic films has the formula (1) AgBr (2) CaF_2 (3) $CuCl_2$ (4) NaI

6. Oxygen is obtained commercially chiefly from the (1) decomposition of hydrogen peroxide (2) decomposition of mercuric oxide (3) decomposition of potassium chlorate (4) fractional distillation of air

7. The burning of H_2S in air always produces (1) H_2 (2) H_2O (3) S (4) SO_2

8. The volume occupied by 16 grams of oxygen gas at S.T.P. is (1) 1.43 liters (2) 11.2 liters (3) .16 liters (4) 22.4 liters

9. The smallest possible number of atoms in a molecule is (1) one (2) two (3) three (4) four

10. The pH of a solution of sodium chloride is approximately (1) 5 (2) 7 (3) 9 (4) 13

11. Which compound is most likely to make water permanently hard? (1) $MgCl_2$ (2) $MgCO_3$ (3) $Mg(HCO_3)_2$ (4) $Mg_3(PO_4)_2$

12. Which metal will release hydrogen from cold water? (1) Al (2) Fe (3) Ca (4) Mg

13. Soluble salts make good electrolytes because they contain many (1) atoms (2) ions (3) electrons (4) molecules

14. The chief reason for using different methods to collect hydrogen and ammonia in the laboratory is that ammonia is (1) combustible (2) heavier than hydrogen (3) lighter than air (4) very soluble in water

15. An atom containing 9 protons, 10 neutrons, and 9 electrons has a mass number of (1) 9 (2) 18 (3) 19 (4) 28

16. A water solution of hydrogen sulfide is called (1) hydrosulfuric acid (2) persulfuric acid (3) sulfuric acid (4) sulfurous acid

17. A metal used in the manufacture of semiconductors for transistors is (1) germanium (2) iron (3) silver (4) tungsten

18. Which is used in testing for barium ions? (1) sodium bromide (2) sodium chloride (3) sodium nitrate (4) sodium sulfate

19. Which is formed when two miscible liquids are put together? (1) an emulsion (2) a precipitate (3) a solution (4) a suspension

20. Upon analysis, a gas is found to be odorless, tasteless, slightly heavier than air, and slightly soluble in water. This gas is probably (1) chlorine (2) hydrogen (3) nitrogen (4) oxygen

21. An ester may be produced in the presence of concentrated sulfuric acid by the action of (1) an acid on a base (2) an alcohol on an acid (3) an alcohol on a base (4) an alcohol on an alcohol

22. Which gas is given off when sulfurous acid is heated? (1) H_2 (2) H_2S (3) SO_2 (4) SO_3

23. A gaseous compound of fluorine which may be used to separate U-235 from U-238 has the formula (1) CaF_2 (2) H_2F_2 (3) SiF_4 (4) UF_6

24. When hydrogen burns in chlorine, the product is (1) Cl_2O_7 (2) HCl (3) HClO (4) H_2O

25. The element with atomic number 8 is likely to have properties similar to the element with atomic number (1) 12 (2) 16 (3) 3 (4) 18

26. Anhydrous copper sulfate may be used to test for the presence of (1) hydrogen (2) nitrogen (3) oxygen (4) water

27. An example of an organic compound that contains an equal number of carbon and hydrogen atoms is (1) benzene (2) ethylene (3) methane (4) propane

28. All types of steel contain (1) carbon (2) chromium (3) nickel (4) tungsten

29. A mixture of equal amounts of hydrogen chloride and carbon monoxide was passed through a flask of water. The gas coming out of the flask probably contained (1) equal amounts of hydrogen chloride and carbon monoxide (2) more carbon monoxide than hydrogen chloride (3) more hydrogen chloride than carbon monoxide (4) neither carbon monoxide nor hydrogen chloride

Directions (30–40): Write on the line at the right of *each* statement the term that, when inserted in the blank, will correctly complete the statement. [11]

30. When ammonia gas is dissolved in water, the resulting solution turns litmus paper ....

31. The number of atoms represented by the formula $C_3H_5(NO_3)_3$ is ....

32. The valence number of manganese in $KMnO_4$ is ....

33. The name of the gas given off at the negative pole during the electrolysis of brine is ....

34. The name of the nitrogen compound produced in fairly large quantity during the destructive distillation of soft coal is ....

35. Metal oxides may react with nonmetal oxides to form ....

36. Nitrites are salts of ... acid.

37. Strontium-90 has a half-life of 20 years. At the end of 40 years an *original* sample of 8 grams of strontium-90 will weigh ... grams.

38. In a structural formula each dash or line between the atoms represents a pair of ....

39. The gas that is evolved during the fermentation of a sugar solution may be identified by passing it through ....

40. A 2-molar solution of hydrochloric acid would contain ... grams of hydrogen chloride per liter of solution.

Directions (41–50): Write on the line at the right of *each* statement the term (*decreases, increases, remains the same*) that, when inserted in the blank, will correctly complete the statement. [10]

41. As carbon monoxide changes to carbon dioxide, the atomic number of carbon ....

42. A crystal of hypo is dropped into a supersaturated solution of hypo. The concentration of the solution ....

43. In general, as the number of bonds between two adjacent carbon atoms in organic compounds increases, the reactivity of the compounds ....

44. As the atomic weight of each element in period 3 of the Periodic Table increases, the metallic property of the elements ....

45. As concentrated sulfuric acid is added to water, the degree of ionization of the acid first ....

46. As the mercuric ion is reduced to the mercurous ion, the valence number of the ion ....

47. As a neutron is added to a nucleus, the atomic number of the element ....

48. As the atomic number of the halogens increases, the stability of each corresponding binary acid ....

49. As the molecular weight of the hydrocarbons increases, their boiling point ....

50. For all practical purposes, when the pressure is increased on a solution of potassium nitrate in water, the solubility of the potassium nitrate ....

Part II

Answer five questions from this part. [Show all numerical work when computation is required.]

1. On the line at the right of *each* of the following write the *term* that answers each question. [10]

   a. The following is a nuclear equation: $_{13}Al^{27} + _2He^4 \rightarrow _{15}X^{30} + _0Y^1$
      (1) What is the name of the term represented by X?
      (2) What is the name of the term represented by Y?

   b. The following substances are used in a nuclear reactor: aluminum, boron steel, graphite, lead, uranium. What is the name of the substance, *selected from this list,* whose *specific* purpose is to
      (1) act as a radiation shield?
      (2) act as a source of neutrons?
      (3) capture neutrons?
      (4) slow down neutrons?

   c. What is the name of a *metal* produced *commercially* by the process of
      (1) electrolysis of the molten ore?
      (2) reduction by coke?
      (3) separation of the metal from native ores by mechanical means?
      (4) roasting followed by reduction?

2. Write a correctly balanced equation for each of *five* of the following: [10]
   a. Reaction between potassium and water
   b. Reaction between nitric acid and calcium carbonate
   c. Neutralization of sodium hydroxide by phosphoric acid
   d. Reaction between ferrous sulfide and hydrochloric acid
   e. Synthesis of ammonia from nitrogen and hydrogen
   f. Complete combustion of ethane

3. a. Draw a diagram showing the laboratory preparation and collection of nitric acid. [3]
   b. Write the balanced equation for this reaction. [2]
   c. Name the substance which gives the yellowish appearance to many samples of concentrated nitric acid. [1]

d. Name the *two* chemicals often used to test an unknown salt for the nitrate ion. [2]

e. Copper may react with dilute nitric acid to produce $Cu(NO_3)_2$. Is the copper atom oxidized or reduced? Explain. [1, 1]

4. Answer *all* of the following: [The atomic weights from the *Reference Tables* may be used to the *nearest whole number*, e.g., Cl = 35.46 becomes 35.]

a. Sodium bromide reacts with sulfuric acid according to the following equation:

$$2NaBr + 3H_2SO_4 \rightarrow Br_2 + SO_2 + 2NaHSO_4 + 2H_2O$$

What weight of NaBr is required to produce 360 grams of $NaHSO_4$? [3]

b. Ethyl alcohol oxidizes according to the following equation:

$$C_2H_5OH + 3O_2 \rightarrow 2CO_2 + 3H_2O$$

What volume of *oxygen* is required to produce 22 liters of CO_2? [3]

c. (1) Calculate the *weight* of one liter of a gas from the following data: 140 ml. of the gas weighs 0.41 grams at S.T.P. [3]

(2) Referring to the tables of "some common gases" in the *Reference Tables,* name this gas. [1]

5. *a.* A solution of 150 grams of potassium nitrate in 100 ml. of water is heated to 80° C. and then filtered. A second solution of 150 grams of potassium chloride in 100 ml. of water is also heated to 80° C. and then filtered. Answer the following questions by use of the *Reference Tables*:

(1) How many grams of potassium nitrate will pass through the filter? [2]

(2) At 80° C., is the filtrate of potassium nitrate solution unsaturated, saturated, or supersaturated? Explain. [1, 1]

(3) How many grams of potassium chloride will remain on the filter? [2]

b. Explain how you could determine whether a clear liquid contains colloidal particles. [2]

c. State *two* ways by which the solubility of carbon dioxide in water may be increased. [2]

6. *a.* The following substances are available in a chemical laboratory: sodium fluoride, manganese dioxide, chlorine water, sodium sulfate, carbon tetrachloride, sulfuric acid, sodium iodide, acetic acid. From this list of substances select

(1) *two* you would use to prepare a compound which will etch glass [2]

(2) *two* you would use to determine whether a compound is a bromide [2]

(3) *one* you would use to prepare chlorine from hydrochloric acid [1]

(4) *one* you would use in preparing hydrochloric acid, *and* give a reason for your choice [2]

b. Compare the methods of *collecting* bromine and iodine during their laboratory preparations. [2]

c. Name *one* halogen whose compound is considered to prevent tooth decay. [1]

7. *a.* Draw a diagram of the probable structure of the hydrogen *molecule.* [The nucleus may be omitted.] [2]

b. How does the bonding between two hydrogen atoms differ from the bonding between atoms of potassium and chlorine? [2]

c. Draw diagrams of the probable structure of the nuclei of deuterium and tritium. [2]

d. Write the *ionic* equation for the reaction between ammonium chloride and silver nitrate. [2]

e. A water solution of zinc sulfate contains hydronium and hydroxyl ions.
(1) Which of these two ions is present in greater number? [1]
(2) How does this solution affect litmus? [1]

8. *a.* Name *one* hydrocarbon which forms compounds by substitution *and one* compound which forms compounds by addition. [1, 1]

b. Name *one* alcohol produced commercially by fermentation *and one* alcohol produced commercially by saponification. [1, 1]

c. The following are formulas of some organic compounds: $CH_3CH_2CH_3$, $CH_3CHOHCH_3$, CH_3COOH.
(1) Select the formula representing an acid. [1]
(2) Select the formula representing a hydrocarbon. [1]

d. Copper and zinc strips are placed in silver nitrate solutions of the same concentration. After a short time the strips are removed. Which strip has the larger deposit? Explain. [1, 1]

e. The oxide of element *A* decomposes at 2,000° C. The oxide of element *B* decomposes at 426° C. The oxide of element *C* does *not* decompose at its melting point, 2,640° C.
(1) Which of the three elements is *most* active? [1]
(2) Which of the three elements is *least* active? [1]

CHEMISTRY—JUNE 1960 (1)

Part I

Answer all questions in this part.

Directions (1-35): Write on the line at the right of *each* statement or question the *number* preceding the term that, of those given, best completes the statement or answers the question. [35]

1. Hard water may be caused by ions of (1) magnesium (2) potassium (3) sodium (4) lithium

2. When zinc sulfide is completely roasted, the product(s) formed would be (1) Zn only (2) ZnO only (3) $ZnO + S$ (4) $ZnO + SO_2$

3. Which substance is used as a moderator in an atomic pile? (1) uranium (2) concrete (3) graphite (4) cadmium

4. Nitrogen combines directly with the more active metals to produce (1) nitrates (2) nitrites (3) hydrides (4) nitrides

5. How many ions are represented by $Al_2(SO_4)_3$ when it dissociates? (1) 5 (2) 2 (3) 9 (4) 17

6. The general formula for the compounds of the acetylene series is (1) C_nH_n (2) C_nH_{2n} (3) C_nH_{2n+2} (4) C_nH_{2n-2}

7. Hydrogen is often prepared and collected in the laboratory by adding zinc to (1) diluted HCl (2) concentrated H_2SO_4 (3) concentrated HNO_3 (4) diluted HNO_3

8. The atom whose nucleus contains the largest number of neutrons is (1) $_{92}U^{239}$ (2) $_{93}Np^{239}$ (3) $_{93}Np^{237}$ (4) $_{95}Am^{243}$

9. In its reaction with water, chlorine forms an oxidizing and bleaching agent whose formula is (1) HCl (2) HClO (3) $HClO_3$ (4) $HClO_4$

10. When ammonia is passed over hot copper oxide, copper is formed. This indicates that ammonia is a (1) dehydrating agent (2) reducing agent (3) catalytic agent (4) nitrating agent

11. In the contact process, the catalyst is used to accelerate the combination of (1) sulfur and oxygen (2) sulfur trioxide and water (3) sulfur dioxide and oxygen (4) fuming sulfuric acid and water

12. The destructive distillation of soft coal is a commercial source of (1) carbon dioxide (2) ammonia (3) charcoal (4) acetic acid

13. The slag from the blast furnace consists chiefly of (1) Fe_2O_3 (2) SiO_2 (3) $CaCO_3$ (4) $CaSiO_3$

14. An orange precipitate results when H_2S reacts with a soluble metallic salt. The salt was probably (1) $AgNO_3$ (2) $Sb(NO_3)_3$ (3) $Pb(NO_3)_2$ (4) $Cu(NO_3)_2$

15. The solvent used in the extraction of aluminum from its ore is (1) cryolite   (2) bauxite   (3) water   (4) molten sodium chloride

16. The reaction $H_3O+ + OH- \rightarrow 2\ H_2O$ illustrates the principle of (1) hydrolysis   (2) neutralization   (3) electrolysis   (4) ionization

17. A 0.1 N water solution of potassium phosphate has a pH value of   (1) 1.5   (2) 5.9   (3) 7   (4) more than 7

18. Taconite is an ore of   (1) tungsten   (2) titanium   (3) iron (4) copper

19. Covalent linkage is most closely associated with solutions of (1) acids   (2) bases   (3) salts   (4) organic compounds

20. The approximate number of pounds of combined hydrogen in 9 pounds of water is   (1) 1   (2) 4.5   (3) 7   (4) 18

21. Of the following, the best shield for gamma rays would be 2 feet of   (1) concrete   (2) lead   (3) wood   (4) steel

22. Tritium is an isotope of   (1) uranium   (2) plutonium   (3) hydrogen   (4) helium

23. An emulsion is the dispersion of a   (1) liquid in a gas   (2) liquid in a liquid   (3) solid in a liquid   (4) gas in a solid

24. If 8 milliliters of uncombined oxygen remain after exploding oxygen with 4 milliliters of hydrogen, the number of milliliters of oxygen that were originally mixed with the hydrogen was   (1) 12   (2) 2 (3) 10   (4) 4

25. The valence number of chlorine in $HClO_4$ is   (1) −1   (2) +1 (3) −7   (4) +7

26. Carbon monoxide is produced when carbon dioxide is passed over hot   (1) coke   (2) calcium carbonate   (3) calcium carbide (4) silicon dioxide

27. Which group of metals is obtained from their ores by electrolytic reduction?   (1) Pb, Cu   (2) Fe, Zn   (3) Al, Mg   (4) Au, Pt

28. In the reaction $HCl + H_2O \rightarrow H_3O+ + Cl-$, the water molecule serves as   (1) the proton acceptor   (2) the proton donor (3) a strong acid   (4) an electrovalent compound

29. In the preparation of the ester methyl acetate, the substance which prevents a reversible reaction is   (1) methyl alcohol   (2) sodium acetate   (3) acetic acid   (4) sulfuric acid

30. Radioactive strontium has a half life of 20 years. An original sample of strontium weighs 4 pounds. At the end of 40 years, how much of the original strontium will remain?   (1) 1 lb.   (2) 2 lb. (3) 3 lb.   (4) ½ lb.

31. A true solution may be   (1) milky   (2) cloudy   (3) colored (4) opaque

32. A liter of oxygen is mixed with a liter of hydrogen at S.T.P. How

many grams do they weigh together?   (1) 1.52   (2) 3.4   (3) 17   (4) 34

33. A crystal of KNO_3 is dissolved in a concentrated solution of KNO_3. The solution must have been   (1) unsaturated   (2) saturated   (3) supersaturated   (4) dilute

34. Coke is used in metallurgical processes chiefly as the   (1) oxidizing agent   (2) reducing agent   (3) flux   (4) slag

35. If an electric spark were passed through a tube filled with hydrogen,   (1) the hydrogen would explode   (2) the hydrogen would condense   (3) water vapor would form   (4) no chemical reaction would occur

Directions (36-47): Write on the line at the right of *each* statement or question the term that will correctly complete the statement or answer the question.   [12]

36. What is the formula of a calcium compound used as a drying agent?

37. Sodium hydroxide is the only substance formed when .... reacts with water.

38. Silicon is most similar in chemical activity to the element ....

39. The name of the halogen which is a reddish-brown liquid at room temperature is ....

40. The formula for the anhydride of sulfuric acid is ....

41. The reaction between calcium sulfite and hydrochloric acid goes to completion because one of the resulting compounds is a(an) ....

42. The organic radical —COOH characterizes the group of compounds called ....

43. What is the end product of the oxidation of ammonia in the Ostwald process?

44. What is the maximum number of electrons that can be held by the second (L) shell?

45. Two substances with the same empirical formula but different structural formulas are called ....

46. When concentrated sulfuric acid reacts with a carbohydrate to form carbon, it is acting as a(an) .... agent.

47. The particle X in the equation $_4Be^9 + _2He^4 \rightarrow _6C^{12} + X$ is named a(an) ....

Directions (48-60): Write on the line at the right of *each* statement the term (*decreases, increases, remains the same*) that, when inserted in the blank, will correctly complete the statement.   [13]

CHEMISTRY—JUNE 1960 (4)

48. Generally as the concentration of the reacting chemicals in a chemical action increases, the speed of their reaction ....

49. As the size of the particles of a soluble solid decreases, the rate at which the solid dissolves in water ....

50. As the atomic weight of chlorine isotopes increases, the number of protons ....

51. As metals increase in activity, the stability of the metallic compounds formed generally ....

52. As the molecular weight of the hydrocarbons in a series increases, the boiling point ....

53. In general, as one goes from left to right in any period of the *Periodic Table*, the tendency for an element to be oxidized ....

54. In the Haber process, as the pressure on the system is increased, the percentage yield of ammonia ....

55. As the ferrous ion is oxidized to the ferric ion, the valence number of the ion ....

56. As the octane rating of gasoline increases, its tendency to "knock" ....

57. As a known weight of lead and oxygen sealed in a container is heated, the observable weight of the contents ....

58. When a radioactive atom emits a beta particle, its atomic number ....

59. As the amount of bromine water being added to a solution of sodium chloride increases, the number of chlorine ions ....

60. As the molecular weight of binary halogen acids increases, the stability of the acids ....

Part II

Answer four questions from this part. Be sure that you answer all parts of each question selected. [Show all numerical work when computation is required.]

1. A study of the variation of solubility with temperature yielded the following experimental results:

VARIATION OF SOLUBILITY WITH TEMPERATURE
(In grams per 100 grams of water)

Salt	10° C.	20° C.	30° C.	40° C.	50° C.	80° C.
KBr	59.5	65.2	70.6	75.5	80.2	95
K_2SO_4	9.21	11.1	13.0	14.8	16.5	21.4
NaCl	35.8	36.0	36.3	36.6	37	38.4
$NaNO_3$	80	88	96	104.0	114	148
$Ce_2(SO_4)_3$	11	9	4	3.2	2.0	1.9

a. From the data given above, answer *each* of the following in the space provided. [5]

(1) Which salt showed the greatest weight increase in solubility as the temperature rose from 10° C. to 80° C.?

(2) Which salt showed the *least* weight change in solubility as the temperature rose from 10° C. to 80° C.?

(3) Which salt showed a decrease in solubility with an increase in temperature?

(4) A solution containing 100 grams of water and 10 grams of K_2SO_4 was raised to 50° C. How many additional grams of K_2SO_4 must be added to saturate the solution at 50° C.?

(5) A saturated solution of $NaNO_3$ containing 100 grams of water is cooled from 30° C. to form a saturated solution at 10° C. What weight of $NaNO_3$ will be precipitated?

b. Column A contains symbols of elements. Column B contains descriptions associated with some of these elements. Using the *Periodic Table* as a reference, write on the line at the right of *each* description in column B the *number* preceding the element from column A that is most closely related to that description. [5]

Column A   Column B

(1) Ba   (*a*) Element X in the oxide X_2O_3

(2) Si   (*b*) Has a zero valence

(3) Fr   (*c*) Forms an ion by gaining two electrons

(4) Ga   (*d*) Has the electron structure 2-8-18-18-8-2

(5) Se   (*e*) The most active alkali metal

(6) Kr

(7) Na

2. *a.* Cobalt will replace tin from a solution of tin salts but will not replace iron from a solution of iron salts. Each of the chemicals below is placed in an individual test tube with distilled water and shaken. A freshly cleaned strip of cobalt is placed in each test tube.

Referring to the *Reference Tables,* write on the line at the right of *each* substance the *letter* taken from the key below that best describes the situation. [5]

Key

R—Visible Reaction

N—No Visible Reaction

I—Insufficient Information

(1) Hydrochloric acid   (4) Nickel sulfate

(2) Calcium chloride   (5) Lead acetate

(3) Silver nitrate

b. On the line at the right of *each* chemical test in column *B*
write the *number* preceding the ion in column *A* with which
it is most closely associated. [5]

Column A   Column B
(1) $SO_3^=$ (a) Bunsen flame turns yellow-green.
(2) NO_3^- (b) Lead acetate paper turns black.
(3) Ba^{++} (c) Moist red litmus turns blue.
(4) $S^=$ (d) Brown ring appears between two liquids.
(5) $SO_4^=$ (e) Potassium permanganate solution becomes
(6) Ca^{++} colorless.
(7) OH^-

3. *a.* Below is a schematic diagram showing how blister copper is
refined by electrolysis. Answer the following questions on
your answer paper with reference to this diagram.

(1) Pure copper is deposited on
     the .... [1]
(2) A salt frequently used as the
     electrolyte is .... [1]
(3) A metal that is recovered
     from the sludge is ....
     [1]
(4) Reduction occurs at the .... [1]

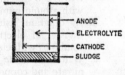

b. Methanol, ethylene, carbon tetrachloride, acetylene, acetic
acid, and benzene are all organic compounds.

(1) Mention *two* compounds from this group which have
     double or triple bonds between carbon atoms. [2]
(2) Draw the *structural* formula of methanol. [2]
(3) Name *two* of the above compounds you would use to make
     an ester. [2]

4. Write a correctly balanced equation for each of *five* of the following: [10]

a. Laboratory preparation of hydrogen chloride gas from sodium
   chloride
b. Neutralization of potassium hydroxide by sulfuric acid
c. Reaction of a solution of potassium iodide and bromine water
d. Reaction of ammonium chloride and sodium hydroxide
e. Heating of zinc carbonate
f. Complete combustion of propane

5. Answer ALL parts of the following question. [The atomic weights
from the *Reference Tables* may be used to the *nearest whole numbers*;
e.g., Cl = 35.46 becomes 35.]

a. Nitric acid reacts with glycerin according to the following equation:
$$3HNO_3 + C_3H_5(OH)_3 \rightarrow C_3H_5(NO_3)_3 + 3H_2O$$
How many pounds of nitroglycerin are formed when nitric acid is added to 207 pounds of glycerin?   [3]

b. Ammonia is oxidized according to the following equation:
$$4NH_3 + 5O_2 \rightarrow 4NO + 6H_2O$$
How many liters of nitric oxide are formed when 90 liters of O_2 react with the ammonia?   [3]

c. Dolomite has the general formula $CaMg(CO_3)_2$.
   (1) What is the percent by weight of calcium in this compound?   [2]
   (2) What weight of calcium could be obtained from 150 pounds of rock that is 80% dolomite?   [2]

6. a. Draw the diagram of the complete structure of the element with atomic number 37.   [2]

b. By diagram, using valence shell electrons only, indicate the transfer of electrons that takes place when element No. 37 combines with element No. 16.   [2]

c. Write the *ionic* equation for the reaction between barium nitrate and copper sulfate in a water solution.   [2]

d. A water solution of ferric chloride turns litmus red. Explain.   [2]

e. In the nuclear reaction involving the formation of helium from hydrogen, the mass of the helium formed is not equal to the total mass of the hydrogen used. State whether there is an increase or a decrease in mass in this reaction. Explain.   [2]

7. a. Draw a labeled diagram of the apparatus used in the laboratory for the preparation and collection of carbon dioxide.   [3]

b. Write a balanced equation for the reaction.   [2]

c. Name *two* gases other than CO_2 that may be *collected* by the same method that you have indicated in answer to *a*.   [2]

d. The gases CO_2, CO and H_2 are stored separately, each gas in its own bottle. Describe briefly a procedure that may be used to identify the contents of each bottle.   [3]

CHEMISTRY—JUNE 1961 (1)

Part I

Answer all questions in this part.

Directions (1-40): Write on the line at the right of *each* statement or question the *number* preceding the term that, of those given, best completes the statement or answers the question. [40]

1. Decomposition of a compound into its elements is called (1) analysis (2) nuclear fission (3) synthesis (4) double replacement

2. The most dangerous method of preparing hydrogen would be by the action of hydrochloric acid and (1) zinc (2) iron (3) potassium (4) aluminum

3. The pH of a solution formed by the neutralization of nitric acid by sodium hydroxide is closest to (1) 1 (2) 10 (3) 7 (4) 4

4. An allotropic form of carbon used in the decolorization of sugar is (1) graphite (2) coke (3) lampblack (4) charcoal

5. Which hydroxide will react with either an acid or a base? (1) potassium hydroxide (2) barium hydroxide (3) aluminum hydroxide (4) calcium hydroxide

6. Which basic solution would leave *no* solid residue upon evaporation? (1) NH_4OH (2) $Ca(OH)_2$ (3) $NaOH$ (4) Na_2CO_3

7. Aluminum is used in the thermite mixture chiefly because of its (1) resistance to corrosion (2) activity (3) lightness (4) silvery color

8. Which hydrocarbon is a member of the methane (paraffin) series? (1) C_2H_2 (2) C_2H_4 (3) C_2H_6 (4) C_6H_6

9. A saturated solution of potassium nitrate may be made unsaturated by (1) raising the temperature (2) raising the pressure (3) adding more solute (4) evaporating some of the water

10. Which has the greatest mass? (1) an electron (2) a proton (3) an alpha particle (4) a neutron

11. The process of fermentation which produces ethanol also yields (1) O_2 (2) H_2 (3) H_2O (4) CO_2

12. There is no oxidation-reduction in a reaction involving (1) single replacement (2) double replacement (3) simple decomposition (4) direct combination of elements

13. In the electrolysis of brine, the element liberated at the cathode is (1) hydrogen (2) oxygen (3) chlorine (4 sodium

14. Low grade sulfide ores are often concentrated by the process of (1) amalgamation (2) roasting (3) reduction (4) flotation

15. The general formula for an organic acid is   (1) RCOOR   (2) ROH   (3) ROR   (4) RCOOH

16. An example of a strong electrolyte is   (1) sugar   (2) calcium chloride   (3) glycerin   (4) boric acid

17. The source of the aluminum obtained in the Hall Process is   (1) hematite   (2) bauxite   (3) cryolite   (4) galena

18. The hydride ion H⁻ has the same number of orbital electrons as an atom of   (1) helium   (2) lithium   (3) beryllium   (4) boron

19. Copper oxide is heated with charcoal. The reaction is an example of   (1) reduction only   (2) oxidation only   (3) both oxidation and reduction   (4) neither oxidation nor reduction

20. Nonmetal oxides, when dissolved in water, tend to form   (1) acids   (2) bases   (3) salts   (4) hydrides

21. Which substance is *not* used to soften hard water?   (1) calcium hydroxide   (2) sodium carbonate   (3) calcium sulfate   (4) permutit

22. The best reducing agent is   (1) mercury   (2) hydrogen   (3) copper   (4) carbon dioxide

23. The bonding of the water molecule is   (1) electrovalent   (2) covalent polar   (3) coordinate covalent   (4) covalent nonpolar

24. The test for a nitrate results in   (1) a precipitate   (2) a red flame   (3) a brown ring   (4) litmus turning blue

25. A solution that contains all the solute it can normally dissolve at a given temperature must be   (1) concentrated   (2) super-saturated   (3) saturated   (4) unsaturated

26. The oxides of barium and sulfur combine to form   (1) a salt   (2) a base   (3) an acid   (4) an anhydride

27. Chlorine gas is obtained commercially chiefly by the   (1) replacement of chlorine from hydrochloric acid by use of a metal   (2) replacement of chlorine by a more active halogen   (3) electrolysis of hydrochloric acid   (4) electrolysis of brine

28. The reason why concentrated H_2SO_4 is used extensively to prepare other acids is that concentrated sulfuric acid   (1) is highly ionized   (2) is an excellent dehydrating agent   (3) has a high specific gravity   (4) has a high boiling point

29. Which two liquids are immiscible?   (1) ethyl alcohol and water   (2) carbon tetrachloride and water   (3) gasoline and kerosene   (4) hydrochloric acid and water

30. The oxidation number of phosphorus in potassium phosphate (K_3PO_4) is   (1) −1   (2) +5   (3) −3   (4) +7

31. When $BaCl_2$ was added to a salt solution, there was formed a white precipitate insoluble in hydrochloric acid. The salt solution

was most likely a   (1) carbonate   (2) nitrate   (3) sulfite   (4) sulfate

32. Reactions involving organic compounds take place more slowly than those involving inorganic compounds mainly because organic compounds   (1) are generally electrovalent   (2) are generally covalent   (3) have high boiling points   (4) have small molecules

33. The most stable of the following atomic nuclei is the nucleus of an atom of   (1) $_{92}U^{239}$ (2) $_{82}Pb^{206}$ (3) $_{94}Pu^{239}$ (4) $_{93}Np^{239}$

34. The greater the chemical activity of a metal, the greater the tendency of its atoms to   (1) gain protons   (2) gain electrons   (3) lose electrons   (4) lose neutrons

35. Which takes place when freshly prepared H_2S is bubbled through a solution of antimony trichloride?   (1) Hydrogen is liberated from the solution.   (2) A yellow precipitate appears.   (3) An orange precipitate appears.   (4) There is no apparent reaction.

36. In general, an atom will form a positive ion most easily if the   (1) size of the atom is large   (2) size of the atom is small   (3) charge on the ion is large   (4) atom appears below hydrogen in the activity series

37. Hydrogen is a product when water is reduced by the action of   (1) chlorine   (2) calcium   (3) sulfur   (4) bromine

38. A yellow-green color is obtained when the flame test is applied to a certain barium salt. The color (radiant energy) is emitted when the   (1) cations are oxidized   (2) electrons are raised to higher energy levels by the heat of the flame   (3) electrons drop back to lower energy levels   (4) electrons in the highest energy levels are given off

39. Which compound is highly covalent?   (1) cesium chloride   (2) carbon bisulfide   (3) potassium bromide   (4) calcium fluoride

40. If positive and negative electrodes are immersed in a solution of cupric chloride, chlorine will be liberated at the anode because the   (1) metals give up electrons to nonmetals   (2) chloride ions were repelled by the copper particles   (3) chloride ions obtained a positive charge from the anode   (4) chloride ions lost electrons to the anode

Directions (41-50): Write on the line at the right of *each* statement the term that will correctly complete the statement.   [10]

41. Vegetable oil can be changed to a solid by the use of a catalyst and the element . . . .

42. The chemical *formula* for the sodium salt of chlorous acid is . . . .

43. When a hydrocarbon is burned in a limited amount of air, the principal products are water and the compound . . . .

44. The number of atoms represented by the formula $(NH_4)_2HPO_4$ is . . . .

45. The nitrogen compound which reacts with glycerin to form glycerol trinitrate is . . . .

46. If limestone is present as an impurity in some iron ores, it may be removed by using . . . as a flux.

47. When potassium nitrate is heated vigorously, potassium nitrite and the element . . . are formed.

48. The *formula* of the compound formed when ammonia reacts with hydrochloric acid is . . . .

49. Organic compounds having the same percentage composition by weight but different structural formulas are called . . . .

50. The solubility of a gas at constant pressure may be increased by decreasing the . . . .

Directions (51-60): Write on the line at the right of *each* statement the term (*decreases, increases, remains the same*) that, when inserted in the blank, will correctly complete the statement. [10]

51. As the acidity of hydrochloric acid solution increases, its pH . . . .

52. When the nucleus of an atom of a radioactive element emits a negative beta particle, the atomic number of the element . . . .

53. As bromine atoms form molecules, the atomic weight of the bromine . . . .

54. At standard conditions, as gases become heavier, the number of molecules in one gram-molecular volume . . . .

55. Ammonia water in a beaker is heated. As the temperature increases, the concentration of the solution . . . .

56. As the state of a substance changes from a solid to a gas, the average speed of the molecules . . . .

57. As the mass of a sample of a radioactive element is increased, the rate of radioactive decay . . . .

58. As the process for the electrolytic refining of copper progresses, the weight of the anode . . . .

59. As water is added to a solution of sodium chloride, the total number of sodium ions and chloride ions present . . . .

60. In general, as the atomic radius of atoms of nonmetallic elements increases, the oxidizing ability of the atom . . . .

Part II

Answer four questions from this part. Be sure that you answer all parts of each question selected. [Show all numerical work when computation is required.]

1. *a.* The diagrams lettered *A* through *H* represent various arrangements of apparatus and materials which are used in the laboratory.

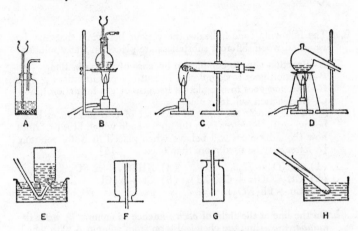

On the line at the right of *each* substance listed below, write the *letters* of the *two* diagrams which indicate the proper combination of apparatus and materials *generally* used to *prepare* and *collect* that substance. If a proper combination is *not* shown, write the letter *N* on the line at the right.　　[5]

(1) Chlorine　　　　　(4) Nitric acid
(2) Ammonia　　　　　(5) Iodine
(3) Hydrogen

b. Column *A* lists eight groups in the *Periodic Table*. Column *B* contains descriptions associated with some of these groups. Using the *Periodic Table* as a reference, write on the line at the right of *each* description in column *B* the *number* preceding the group from column *A* that is most closely related to the description.　　[5]

Column A	Column B
(1) IA	a. Shows valences of 3 and 5
(2) IIA	b. Forms the strongest bases
(3) IIIA	c. Contains the most active nonmetal
(4) IVA	d. Usually forms oxides of type XO_2
(5) VA	e. Cannot form compounds ordinarily
(6) VIA	
(7) VIIA	
(8) 0	

2. a. The following code indicates the various behaviors that may be expected when different substances are placed in water solution:

N—Reaction goes to completion because of neutralization.
P—Reaction goes to completion because of precipitation.
G—Reaction goes to completion because of gas formation.
O—No reaction will take place.

On the line at the right of *each* set of two substances listed below, write the *letter* from the above code which best describes how the substances will behave when placed in water solution. [A letter may be used more than once.]   [5]

(1) $AgNO_3 + H_2S$ (4) $KHSO_3 + H_2SO_4$
(2) $CH_3COOH + Ca(OH)_2$ (5) $Cr + NaCl$
(3) $Cu + Pb(NO_3)_2$

b. On the line at the right of *each* sentence in column B, write the *number* preceding the chemical term from column A with which that sentence is *most closely* related.   [5]

Column A	Column B
(1) esterification	a. Coke is prepared commercially by this method.
(2) polymerization	b. Solid CO_2 exhibits this property.
(3) destructive distillation	c. Sulfuric acid is used as a dehydrating agent in this process.
(4) electrolysis	d. Glycerin is a byproduct of this process.
(5) saponification	e. Active metals are separated from their compounds by this method.
(6) hydrogenation	
(7) sublimation	

3. *a.* Sulfur dioxide and carbon dioxide are two common gases in chemistry.

(1) For *each* gas, name a salt from which the gas may be prepared in the laboratory. [1, 1]

(2) For *each* gas, describe a chemical test for identifying the gas. [1, 1]

b. For *each* substance listed below, name an acid formed when the substance is dissolved in water: [3]
(1) hydrogen sulfide
(2) chlorine
(3) sulfur dioxide

c. According to modern theory, an acid is a proton (hydrogen ion) donor, and a base is a proton acceptor. When sodium acetate dissolves in water, the following reversible ionic reaction occurs:

$$CH_3COO^- + H_2O \rightleftarrows CH_3COOH + OH^-$$

(1) Write the *formulas* of the *two* acids in this equation. [1, 1]
(2) Which substance in the above reaction directly causes red litmus to turn blue? [1]

4. *a.* Write a correctly balanced equation for each of *three* of the following reactions: [2, 2, 2]

(1) Reaction of ammonium sulfate and potassium hydroxide
(2) Complete combustion of C_2H_5OH (ethyl alcohol)
(3) Reaction of silver nitrate and aluminum chloride
(4) Reaction of hydrochloric acid and manganese dioxide

b. Answer *two* of the following:

(1) Write a balanced *ionic* equation for the neutralization of sodium hydroxide by sulfuric acid. [2]
(2) Write an *electronic* equation for the oxidation of the ferrous ion to the ferric ion. [2]
(3) Copy the following nuclear equation *on your answer paper* and insert the *two missing numbers* in the proper places near element X: [2]

$$_4Be^9 + X \rightarrow _6C^{12} + _0n^1$$

5. Answer ALL parts of the following question: [The atomic weights from the *Reference Tables* may bo used to the *nearest whole numbers*; e.g., Cl = 35.46 becomes 35.]

a. Zinc may be oxidized by dilute nitric acid according to the following equation:

$$4Zn + 10HNO_3 \rightarrow 4Zn(NO_3)_2 + 3H_2O + NH_4NO_3$$

What weight of zinc nitrate will be produced when 16.0 grams of ammonium nitrate are also produced in the reaction?   [3]

b. Propane gas burns in chlorine according to the following equation:

$$C_3H_8 + 4Cl_2 \rightarrow 8HCl + 3C$$

What volume of chlorine will be consumed when 32 liters of hydrogen chloride gas are produced in the reaction?   [3]

c. At standard conditions, 500 milliliters of a certain gas weighs 0.600 gram. What is the molecular weight of the gas?   [2]

d. How many grams of $NaNO_3$ are needed to make one liter of a 0.500 molar (formal) solution of $NaNO_3$?   [2]

6. *a.* A neutral atom of an element has two electrons in its k-shell, eight electrons in its l-shell, and six electrons in its m-shell.
   (1) What is the atomic number of the element?   [1]
   (2) Describe the electron transfer which occurs when an atom of this element combines with calcium.   [1]

b. Draw a labeled diagram of the probable structure of *each* of the following: [Include all parts.]   [1, 1]
   (1) $_1H^2$ (2) O^{-2}

c. In terms of *neutrons,* state the specific function of *each* of the following in a nuclear reactor:
   (1) the graphite moderator   [1]
   (2) the boron steel control rods   [1]

d. Write the structural (graphic) formula for each of *two* of the following: [2]
   (1) ethylene
   (2) trichloromethane (chloroform)
   (3) normal butane

e. Catalytic cracking and polymerization are two processes used in increasing the yield of gasoline. Show the essential difference between the two processes by *briefly* indicating the purpose of each process.   [1, 1]

CHEMISTRY—JUNE 1962 (1)

Part 1

Answer all questions in this part.

Directions (1-40): Write on the line at the right of *each* statement or question the *number* preceding the term that, of those given, best completes the statement or answers the question.   [40]

1. When a bunsen flame was held under a cold, dry surface, droplets of water collecting on that surface indicated that the fuel contained   (1) carbon   (2) hydrogen   (3) carbon dioxide   (4) carbon monoxide

2. The flotation process is used in metallurgy to   (1) concentrate the ores   (2) oxidize sulfides   (3) reduce oxides   (4) decrease the density of electrolytes

3. Which two liquids are immiscible?   (1) water and methyl alcohol   (2) water and carbon tetrachloride   (3) water and glycerol   (4) kerosine and gasoline

4. Which particle weighs *least*?   (1) electron   (2) proton   (3) neutron   (4) alpha particle

5. Iodine is *least* soluble in   (1) ethyl alcohol   (2) carbon disulfide   (3) carbon tetrachloride   (4) water

6. Boiling temporary hard water may produce   (1) calcium bicarbonate   (2) calcium carbonate   (3) calcium hydroxide   (4) calcium sulfate

7. The *least* stable halogen acid is   (1) H_2F_2 (2) HCl   (3) HI   (4) HBr

8. A hydronium ion is a water molecule   (1) minus an electron   (2) plus a proton   (3) plus a neutron   (4) minus the oxygen

9. A chemical property common to oxygen and chlorine is that both   (1) are colorless   (2) reduce metals   (3) have the same oxidation number   (4) support combustion of hydrogen

10. The new international standard of atomic weights is based upon the mass of   (1) $_6C^{12}$ (2) $_{79}Au^{197}$ (3) $_{102}No^{253}$ (4) $_{85}At^{211}$

11. In the molecule of H_2S, the type of bonding is   (1) electrovalent   (2) polar covalent   (3) nonpolar covalent   (4) coordinate covalent

12. Which is an example of a strong electrolyte?   (1) potassium bromide   (2) ammonium hydroxide   (3) acetic acid   (4) ethyl alcohol

13. In the laboratory preparation of oxygen, manganese dioxide is used as   (1) a catalyst   (2) an oxidizing agent   (3) a reducing agent   (4) a dehydrating agent

14. In equal concentrations, which is the weakest acid?   (1) HI   (2) H_3PO_4 (3) H_2CO_3 (4) H_2SO_3

15. Which atomic particle would *not* be deflected by an electric field?   (1) proton   (2) neutron   (3) alpha particle   (4) beta particle

16. Nitric acid can *not* react with   (1) silver   (2) gold   (3) copper   (4) mercury

17. The number of ions represented by the formula $Fe_2(SO_4)_3$ is   (1) 5   (2) 6   (3) 14   (4) 17

18. In chemical changes, metals generally   (1) gain electrons   (2) lose electrons   (3) neither gain nor lose electrons   (4) share electrons

19. Large quantities of oxygen for commercial use are prepared by the   (1) heating of mercuric oxide   (2) heating of potassium chlorate   (3) action of chlorine on water producing hydrochloric acid and oxygen   (4) fractional distillation of liquid air

20. The reaction between a proton donor and a proton acceptor is called   (1) electrolysis   (2) oxidation   (3) neutralization   (4) reduction

21. Which metal will liberate hydrogen from cold water?   (1) zinc   (2) iron   (3) aluminum   (4) calcium

22. Which form of carbon is most suitable for adsorbing impurities?   (1) soot   (2) graphite   (3) lampblack   (4) activated charcoal

23. Radioactive changes differ from ordinary chemical changes in that radioactive changes   (1) are explosive   (2) absorb energy   (3) involve changes in the nucleus   (4) release energy

24. When an atom of cobalt loses two electrons, it becomes an ion with a charge of   (1) $+2$ (2) -2 (3) $+6$ (4) -6

25. When a substance changes from a solid directly into a gas, it is said to   (1) evaporate   (2) melt   (3) sublime   (4) condense

26. Chlorine may be prepared in the laboratory by the action of hydrochloric acid on   (1) $NaCl$ (2) $MnSO_4$ (3) MnO_2 (4) Na_2SO_4

27. In which pair are the rays most similar?   (1) alpha rays and beta rays   (2) gamma rays and X-rays   (3) alpha rays and gamma rays   (4) beta rays and X-rays

28. The number of protons in the nucleus of O^{17} is   (1) 7   (2) 8   (3) 9   (4) 17

29. Hydrogenation is a process used to prepare   (1) heavy water   (2) hydrogen from natural gas   (3) radioactive isotopes   (4) solid fats from vegetable oils

30. The number of atoms represented by $K_3Fe(CN)_6$ is   (1) 9   (2) 10   (3) 16   (4) 21

31. When an atom of an active metal combines with an atom of an active non-metal, the resulting compound is said to be   (1) coordinate covalent   (2) polar covalent   (3) nonpolar covalent   (4) ionic

32. A radioisotope has a 5-year half-life. After a given amount decays for 15 years, what fraction of the original isotope remains?

(1) $\frac{1}{2}$ (2) $\frac{1}{5}$ (3) $\frac{1}{8}$ (4) $\frac{1}{15}$

33. Which metal is *not* reduced from its ore by a commercial form of carbon?   (1) aluminum   (2) iron   (3) zinc   (4) lead

34. Nitrogen has the largest oxidation number in the compound   (1) KNO_3 (2) $(NH_4)_3PO_4$ (3) N_2O (4) NO_2

35. If a brown ring forms after ferrous sulfate solution and concentrated sulfuric acid are added to a solution of an unknown salt, the solution contained   (1) NH_4^+ (2) $S^=$ (3) Br^- (4) NO_3^-

36. K_2S is the salt of a   (1) weak acid and a weak base   (2) strong acid and a strong base   (3) strong acid and a weak base   (4) weak acid and a strong base

37. Which pair of elements is most commonly extracted by electrolysis?   (1) fluorine and zinc   (2) magnesium and aluminum   (3) iron and chlorine   (4) sodium and lead

38. Two grams of H_2 contain approximately the same number of molecules as (1) 36 grams of H_2O (2) 16 grams of O_2 (3) 8 grams of He   (4) 28 grams of N_2

39. When silver nitrate solution was added to an unknown salt solution, a white precipitate was formed which was insoluble in nitric acid and soluble in ammonium hydroxide. The unknown salt solution   (1) may have been a chloride   (2) must have been a chloride   (3) may have been a bromide   (4) must have been a bromide

40. In the reaction $2SO_2 + O_2 \rightleftharpoons 2SO_3$, the reaction will   (1) go to completion if O_2 is removed   (2) go to completion if the concentration of O_2 increases   (3) shift toward the formation of more SO_3 if the SO_3 concentration is decreased   (4) shift toward the formation of more SO_3 if the SO_2 concentration is decreased

Directions (41-50): Write on the line at the right of *each* statement the term that will correctly complete the statement.   [10]

41. The compound present in vinegar which is chiefly responsible for its sour taste is . . . .

42. The formula of the acid formed when H_2S is dissolved in water is . . . .

43. As more experimental evidence which tends to confirm a theory accumulates, the theory may be reclassified as a(an) . . . .

44. When a solution of magnesium chloride is mixed with a solution of Na_2CO_3, the insoluble substance has the formula . . . .

45. The gram molecular weight of bromide is . . . grams.

46. When nonmetallic oxides dissolve in water, they form a class of compounds known as . . . .

47. Electrovalent compounds tend to have . . . melting points.

48. In $K_2Cr_2O_7$, the oxidation number of the Cr_2O_7 radical is . . . .

49. The formula for dichlorodifluoromethane (Freon) is . . . .

50. When a mole (22.4 liters) of hydrogen gas burns in oxygen, the amount of steam formed is . . . mole(s).

Directions (51-60): Write on the line at the right of *each* statement the term (*decreases, increases, remains the same*) that, when inserted in the blank, will correctly complete the statement.   [10]

51. As the size of the particles of a solute decreases, the rate at which the solid goes into solution . . . .

52. As the temperature decreases, the rate of most chemical reactions . . . .

53. As the atomic number of the nitrogen family (Group V A) elements increases, the metallic property . . . .

54. As the sulfur atom is oxidized, the number of its electrons . . . .

55. As the number of neutrons in the nucleus of an atom increases, the atomic number of the element . . . .

56. As hydrochloric acid is added to a solution of silver nitrate, the number of metallic ions in solution . . . .

57. As concentrated sulfuric acid remains exposed to the air, its concentration . . . .

58. As the ferric ion gains an electron, its electrical charge . . . .

59. As one reads from left to right in Period 3 of the *Periodic Table,* the number of electrons in the second (L) shell . . . .

60. In general, as the number of bonds between adjacent carbon atoms decreases, the reactivity of the compound . . . .

Part II

Answer four questions from this part. Be sure that you answer all parts of each question selected. [Show all numerical work when computation is required.]

1. *a.* The following are diagrams of apparatus used in the chemical laboratory:

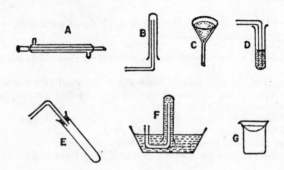

Write on the line at the right the *letter* of the apparatus which should be used for *each* of the following procedures: [5]

(1) To collect a soluble gas which is lighter than air

(2) To precipitate metallic sulfides out of solution

(3) To separate the solid component of a suspension

(4) To prepare and collect iodine

(5) To prepare oxygen by the decomposition of an oxide

b. Use the *Reference Tables* to answer the following questions:

Following is a list of elements: Al, Be, Ca, Mg, Ag, K

From this list select the element that best fits *each* statement below and write the *name* of this element in the space at the right. [An element may be used more than once.]   [5]

(1) Its hydroxide may act as either an acid or a base.

(2) It is the most powerful reducing agent.

(3) It reacts with a solution of hydriodic acid to form an insoluble salt.

(4) It forms a black compound when combined with sulfur.

(5) It has the smallest atomic diameter.

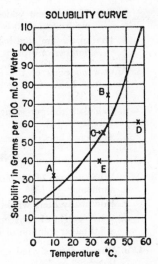

SOLUBILITY CURVE

2. *a.* The questions below refer to the accompanying chart. The curve represents saturation for a certain salt dissolved in 100 milliliters of water. Points A, B, C, D and E represent five solutions of the same salt with different concentrations and at different temperatures.

On the line at the right of *each* of the following, write the *number* preceding the word or expression that, of those given, best completes the statement or answers the question.   [5]

(1) The most dilute solution is solution   (1) *A*   (2) *B*   (3) *C*
(4) *D*

(2) A small crystal of this salt is added to each of the five solutions. Crystallization takes place in   (1) solution *E* only   (2) solutions *A* and *E*   (3) solutions *A* and *B*   (4) solutions *D* and *E*

(3) One hundred milliliters of solution *D* could be made saturated by (1) adding one gram of solute   (2) adding 10 grams of solute (3) increasing the temperature to approximately 60° C.   (4) lowering the temperature to approximately 40° C.

(4) How many grams of this salt should be added to one *liter* of water to prepare a saturated solution at 40° C.?   (1) 40   (2) 60   (3) 400   (4) 600

(5) If the temperature of 100 ml. of solution *C* were increased to 50° C., how many grams of this salt would have to be added to saturate the solution at the new temperature?   (1) 14   (2) 30   (3) 55 (4) 85

b. The following questions refer to the *Periodic Table of the Elements.* On the line at the right of *each* of the following, write the word or expression that best completes the statement.   [5]

(1) The *ion* of calcium has the same electronic structure as the atom of . . . .

(2) The element in the fifth period that is a more active metal than strontium (Sr) has the symbol . . . .

(3) Selenium has an atomic number of 34. The probable formula for hydrogen selenide is . . . .

(4) The element which has the greatest attraction for electrons (is most electronegative) is . . . .

(5) In the ion of a halogen element, the number of electrons exceeds the number of protons by . . . .

3. Answer *all* parts of the following question: [The atomic weights from the *Reference Tables* may be used to the *nearest whole numbers;* e.g., Cl = 35.46 becomes 35.]

   a. Calculate the percentage by weight of water of crystallization in $Na_2CO_3 \cdot 10H_2O$ [3]

   b. Ammonia burns in air according to the following equation:

   $$4NH_3 + 3O_2 \rightarrow 2N_2 + 6H_2O$$

   What volume of *air* is required for the complete combustion of 8 liters of ammonia?   [3]

   c. How many liters would 76 grams of fluorine gas occupy at S.T.P.?   [2]

   d. What weight of anhydrous hydrogen chloride is necessary to make 1 liter of a 3.0 molar solution of hydrochloric acid?   [2]

4. *a.* Write a correctly balanced equation for each of *three* of the following reactions: [2,2,2]
   (1) Reaction of bromine water and a solution of sodium iodide
   (2) Complete combustion of propane in oxygen
   (3) Laboratory preparation of nitric acid
   (4) Reaction of aluminum powder and manganese dioxide

   b. Answer *two* of the following: [2, 2]
   (1) Write a balanced ionic equation for the reaction between solutions of barium chloride and sodium sulfate.
   (2) Write the balanced electronic equation for the reaction occurring at the cathode during copperplating with copper (II) sulfate.
   (3) Write the nuclear equation for the transmutation of U^{239} to Np^{239}.

5. Explain each of *five* of the following true statements on the basis of scientific principles: [10]

   a. Of the metals in Group IA, cesium (Cs) is more chemically active than sodium (Na).

   b. A clear colloidal suspension may be distinguished from a clear solution by passing a beam of light through each of them.

   c. A water solution of aluminum sulfate turns litmus red.

   d. Although a water solution of NaOH turns litmus blue, a water solution of C_2H_5OH has no effect on litmus.

   e. When carbon dioxide is passed into limewater, a precipitate is formed. Upon further addition of carbon dioxide, the precipitate disappears.

   f. A one-molar solution of sodium chloride freezes at a lower temperature than a one-molar solution of sucrose.

   g. Ammonia is prepared according to the following reaction: $N_2 + 3H_2 \rightleftarrows 2NH_3$. As the pressure is increased from 200 atmospheres to 1,000 atmospheres, the yield of ammonia gas increases.

6. *a.* Draw structural formulas for *two* of the following: (1) pentane, (2) acetylene, (3) isopropyl alcohol.   [2]

  b. Four organic substances are sodium stearate, ethylene, ethyl acetate and ethanol. From these substances select (1) *one* which is usually prepared by esterification, (2) *one* which is usually prepared by saponification. [1, 1]

  c. Draw a labeled diagram of the probable structure of an atom of C^{14}. [1, 1]

  d. From the isotopes $_1H^3$, $_{26}Fe^{56}$, $_{27}Co^{60}$, $_{94}Pu^{239}$, select (1) *one* which often is used as a "fuel" in a fission reaction, (2) *one* which is often used as a "fuel" in a fusion reaction.   [1, 1]

  e. Two substances found in radioactive fallout are $_{38}Sr^{90}$ and $_{53}I^{131}$. Which of these substances is most likely to be a greater health hazard one year after the substances are formed? Explain.   [1, 1]

Part I

Answer all questions in this part.

Directions (1-36): Write on the line at the right of *each* statement or question the *number* preceding the term that, of those given, best completes the statement or answers the question. [36]

1. In the *Periodic Table*, most of the nonmetals are found on the (1) upper right-hand side (2) upper left-hand side (3) lower right-hand side (4) lower left-hand side

2. There is usually no oxidation-reduction in a reaction involving (1) single replacement (2) double replacement (3) simple decomposition (4) direct combination of elements

3. The smallest amount of radioactive material that will support a self-sustained reaction is called the (1) moderator (2) gram-molecular weight (3) critical mass (4) mole

4. A metal may have an atomic number of (1) 9 (2) 18 (3) 35 (4) 37

5. When a base combines with hydrochloric acid, one of the products is a (1) perchlorate (2) chloride (3) chlorite (4) chlorate

6. When Fe^{+2} is changed to Fe^{+3}, there is a (1) gain of one electron (2) gain of two electrons (3) loss of one electron (4) loss of three electrons

7. A solution may be tested for ionization by measuring its (1) temperature (2) density (3) viscosity (4) electrical conductivity

8. Which substance is formed during the test for a sulfate? (1) $BaCl_2$ (2) HNO_3 (3) $BaSO_4$ (4) H_2S

9. Tincture of iodine is (1) a suspension (2) a mixture (3) a compound (4) an emulsion

10. When concentrated sulfuric acid is heated with copper, the oxidation number of the sulfur in the gas which is produced is (1) $+1$ (2) $+2$ (3) $+3$ (4) $+4$

11. Which is the correct name for the compound having the formula $CuCl_2$? (1) copper(I)chloride (2) copper(II)chloride (3) cupric hypochlorite (4) cuprous hypochlorite

12. In the organic compound ethylene, the element bromine can best be introduced by the process of (1) addition (2) substitution (3) isomerism (4) allotropism

13. A colorless gas burns at the mouth of an open test tube, leaving a slight film of moisture and a yellowish powder. The gas might be (1) chlorine (2) sulfur dioxide (3) hydrogen (4) hydrogen sulfide

14. Sulfur is considered to be a reducing agent when it combines with (1) hydrogen (2) oxygen (3) sodium (4) zinc

15. The most dangerous method of preparing hydrogen is by the action of hydrochloric acid and (1) zinc (2) iron (3) potassium (4) aluminum

16. The nitride ion N^{-3} has the same number of orbital electrons as an atom of (1) helium (2) neon (3) beryllium (4) boron

17. Washing and flotation are methods of (1) concentrating ores (2) extracting metals from ores (3) polishing metals (4) galvanizing metals

18. Which is the best dehydrating agent? (1) H_2SO_4 (2) KCl (3) $Ca(ClO_3)_2$ (4) Na_2SO_4

19. When temporary hard water is boiled, which gas is given off? (1) hydrogen (2) oxygen (3) carbon monoxide (4) carbon dioxide

20. Under standard conditions of temperature and pressure, given equal volumes, the ratio of the number of atoms in CO to the number of atoms in CO_2 is (1) 1:1 (2) 1:2 (3) 2:3 (4) 3:2

21. A substance which has a large ratio of surface to mass will usually show the property of (1) amphoterism (2) adsorption (3) allotropism (4) isomerism

22. The formula weight for hydrated sodium carbonate ($Na_2CO_3 \cdot 10H_2O$) is (1) 106 (2) 142 (3) 266 (4) 286

23. Bromide ions can reduce (1) iodine atoms (2) iodide ions (3) chlorine atoms (4) chloride ions

24. When lime is exposed to air for a considerable length of time, it is converted into a material that is mainly (1) $CaCO_3$ (2) Na_2CO_3 (3) $CaOCl_2$ (4) NaOH

25. Dilute hydrochloric acid is added to a mixture of iron, sulfur and sodium chloride. The gas which comes off (1) turns moist red litmus blue (2) burns readily (3) is greenish-yellow (4) has a rotten-egg odor

26. Which solid will *not* dissociate when dissolved in water? (1) sodium sulfate (2) magnesium chloride (3) silver nitrate (4) sucrose

27. Au-198 has a half-life of 2.7 days. A one-gram sample of gold will have decreased to one-eighth gram in (1) 2.7 days (2) 5.4 days (3) 8.1 days (4) 10.8 days

28. Carbon dioxide is used as a (1) supporter of combustion (2) reducing agent (3) leavening agent (4) catalyst in burning hydrocarbons

29. Evidence that electrons are located in energy levels around the nucleus is indicated by the (1) atomic number of the elements (2) atomic mass of the elements (3) lines in the spectra of the elements (4) density of the elements

30. A water solution of a nonmetallic oxide may have a pH number of (1) 5 (2) 7 (3) 9 (4) 13

31. The number of atoms represented by the formula for plaster of Paris, $(CaSO_4)_2 \cdot H_2O$, is (1) 13 (2) 15 (3) 17 (4) 18

32. Nitrogen and oxygen are similar in that they both (1) form diatomic molecules (2) react vigorously at room temperature (3) are colored gases (4) are very soluble in water

33. In the *Reference Table*, the pH of alum is given as 3.2. For the concentrations given in the *Reference Table*, which statement is correct? (1) Alum is more acid than acetic acid. (2) Alum is more basic than borax. (3) Alum is more basic than citric acid. (4) Alum is less acid than boric acid.

34. Silicones are described as compounds that are (1) carbides of silicon (2) organic derivatives of silicon (3) mixtures of quartz and carbon (4) salts of silicic acid

35. An insoluble compound is formed when ferric bromide combines with (1) sodium chloride (2) sodium nitrate (3) sodium hydroxide (4) sodium bromide

36. Element X has an atomic number of 48 while Y has an atomic number of 7. The formula of a possible compound containing these elements is (1) XY (2) XY_2 (3) XY_3 (4) X_3Y_2

Directions (37-50): Write on the line at the right of *each* statement the term that, when inserted in the blank, will correctly complete the statement.   [14]

37. A chemical reaction in which the products may reform the original reactants is called a(an) . . . reaction.
38. When carbon burns in a limited supply of oxygen, the formula for the principal compound formed is . . . .
39. The smallest particle of an element that can undergo chemical change is called the . . . .
40. In order to obtain a metal from its compound, the . . . lost when it became a compound must be restored.
41. When two nonmetals combine to form a compound, they are usually held together by . . . bonding.
42. Decimal atomic weight values are the result of mixtures of . . . .
43. The number of electrons in the outermost shell of a fluoride ion is . . . .
44. The solubility of a gas at constant temperature may be increased by increasing the . . . .
45. When sodium chloride solution is electrolyzed, the name of the gaseous product formed at the negative electrode is . . . .
46. The anhydride of sulfuric acid has the formula . . . .
47. An acid in which chlorine has an oxidation number of $+5$ has the formula . . . .
48. A statement in chemical symbols which represents the composition of a substance is called a(an) . . . .
49. In electrolysis, oxidation always occurs at the . . . electrode.
50. An international group of scientists has agreed that the system of relative atomic weights be based on a value of . . . for carbon-12. As a result, the values of all other atomic weights have decreased.

Directions (51-60): Write on the line at the right of *each* statement the term (*decreases, increases, remains the same*) that, when inserted in the blank, will correctly complete the statement.   [10]

51. As the atomic number in VI *A* increases, the amount of "empty space" within the atom . . . .
52. If hydrogen ions are added to a solution of sodium hydroxide, the pH of the solution . . . .
53. When a metallic atom becomes an ion, the number of protons . . . .
54. If more sodium chlorate is added to a saturated solution of sodium chlorate at 50° C., the number of sodium ions . . . .
55. As the number of carbon atoms in an organic compound increases, the number of possible isomers . . . .
56. If the temperature of an unstable compound is decreased, its tendency to decompose generally . . . .
57. As chemical activity increases, the tendency of a metal to occur in the native state . . . .
58. As a solution of silver nitrate is added to a solution of sodium chloride, the total number of chloride ions in the solution . . . .
59. As radioactive sodium disintegrates, its half-life . . . .
60. As we proceed from top to bottom of the elements in Group *O* of the *Periodic Table*, the volume occupied by a mole (gram-molecular weight) of the gas at S.T.P. . . . .

CHEMISTRY—AUGUST 1962 (4)

Part II

Answer four questions from this part. Be sure that you answer all parts of each question selected. [Show all numerical work when computation is required.]

1. *a.* A study of the electron structure of six different elements yielded the following results. Use these data to answer *each* of the following questions:

Element	Electron Structure
A	2-8-8-1
B	2-6
C	2-8-5
D	2-8-18-18-7
E	2-8-18-32-18-1
F	2-8

On the line at the right of *each* question write the *letter* of the element, chosen from the list above, which best answers that question. [5]

(1) Which metallic element is found free in nature?
(2) Which element is the most active nonmetal?
(3) Which element is found in Group I *A*?
(4) Which element is chemically similar to nitrogen?
(5) Which element has an ion that would have the same electron structure as an atom of xenon?

b. Column *A* contains the chemical formulas for substances prepared in the laboratory. Column *B* lists common laboratory tests. Write on the line at the right of *each* test in column *B* the *number* preceding the formula in column *A* which is most closely associated with that test. [5]

Column A	Column B
(1) O_2	(a) Dissolve in water. Solution turns litmus blue.
(2) Br_2	(b) Bubble through limewater. White precipitate forms.
(3) NO	
(4) NH_3	(c) Insert glowing splint. Splint bursts into flame.
(5) H_2	(d) Dissolve in carbon tetrachloride. Solution turns red-orange.
(6) CO_2	
(7) I_2	(e) Mix with air. Reddish-brown gas forms.

2. In *some* of the following statements the term in italics makes the statement incorrect. For each *incorrect* statement, write on the line at the right the term that must be substituted for the italicized term to make the statement correct. For each *correct* statement, write the word *true* on the line at the right. [10]

a. A 0.1 N solution of sulfuric acid is *less* strongly acid than a 0.1 N solution of phosphoric acid.
b. The reaction between a water solution of bismuth nitrate and hydrosulfuric acid will produce a *yellow* precipitate.
c. *Nickel* is chemically more active than lead but less active than chromium.
d. When the active metal, calcium, reacts with water, the resulting compound is *calcium oxide*.
e. The most stable of the binary halogen acids is *hydriodic* acid.

f. When a crystal of solute is dropped into a solution, the crystal rapidly increases in size. The original solution was *saturated*.

g. The *molality* of a solution is the number of moles of solute per liter of solution.

h. In the electrolysis of fused sodium chloride, reduction occurs at the *negative* electrode.

i. At 25° C. it is possible to dissolve 40 grams of KNO₃ in 100 ml. of water. If the temperature is increased to 60°, it is possible to dissolve *seventy* additional grams of salt.

j. One mole of sodium chloride will lower the freezing point of a liter of water more than one mole of sugar because the atoms present in sodium chloride are held together by *coordinate-covalent* bonding.

3. *a.* (1) Write a balanced equation for the laboratory preparation of chlorine. [2]

   (2) By means of an electronic equation represent the oxidation which takes place in the laboratory preparation of chlorine. [2]

   b. Write a correctly balanced *ionic* equation for the reaction between water solutions of ammonium sulfate and barium nitrate. [2]

   c. Potassium dichromate reacts with sulfuric acid according to the following equation:

   $$4H_2SO_4 + K_2Cr_2O_7 \rightarrow Cr_2(SO_4)_3 + K_2SO_4 + 4H_2O + \frac{3}{2}O_2$$

   What weight of $K_2Cr_2O_7$ must be used to produce 87.0 grams of K_2SO_4? [3]

   d. What is the volume in liters occupied by 2 moles of phosgene gas at S.T.P.? [1]

4. Give a chemical explanation for each of *five* of the following: [10]

   a. During thunderstorms (accompanied by lightning and rain) it literally "rains nitric acid."

   b. A water solution of potassium carbonate will turn litmus paper blue, while a water solution of potassium sulfate will have no effect on the color of the paper.

   c. Neutrons may be preferred to alpha particles or beta particles in disintegrating atomic nuclei.

   d. It is possible to make a saturated but *not* a concentrated solution of calcium hydroxide.

   e. Sulfuric acid is frequently used in the esterification process.

   f. In the laboratory, sodium is stored under kerosine while white phosphorus is stored under water.

   g. Aluminum hydroxide will react with hydrochloric acid; it will also react with sodium hydroxide.

5. *a.* Using only electrons found in the valence shells, draw a diagram which represents the probable bonding in a molecule of ammonia. [2]

   b. Write a word equation to illustrate *each* of the following: [1, 1]
      (1) saponification
      (2) esterification

c. The formula weight of phosphoric acid is 98. What weight of phosphoric acid would be required to make 500 ml. of a 0.50 N solution?   [2]

d. Use the equation below to answer *each* of the following questions:

$$_{16}S^{32} + _{0}n^1 \rightarrow X + _1H^1$$

(1) What is the name of element X?   [1]
(2) What is its mass number?   [1]

e. In *each* case give the formula of the gas formed when dilute sulfuric acid is added to
(1) sodium sulfide   [1]
(2) sodium bisulfite   [1]

6. a. By means of diagrams represent the probable structure of the nuclei of *two* natural isotopes of silicon.   [2]

b. Write the structural (graphic) formula for each of *two* of the following: [2]
(1) dichlorodifluoromethane
(2) n-pentane
(3) methyl acetate

c. Propyl alcohol burns according to the following equation:

$$2C_3H_7OH + 9O_2 \rightarrow 6CO_2 + 8H_2O$$

What volume of carbon dioxide will be produced when 50 liters of oxygen combine with propyl alcohol?   [2]

d. The dipole water exerts an attractive force on a molecule of hydrogen sulfide, which also is polar. Name *two* particles produced as a result of this interaction. [1, 1]

e. Some metals are obtained from their compounds by reduction with carbon; others are obtained by reduction with electricity. Name a metal that, in large quantities, can be obtained
(1) only by electrolysis   [1]
(2) easily by reduction with carbon   [1]

CHEMISTRY—JUNE 1963 (1)

Part I

Answer all questions in this part.

Directions (1-40): Write on the line at the right of *each* statement or question the *number* preceding the term that, of those given, best completes the statement or answers the question. [40]

1. At standard conditions, which halogen sublimes?   (1) fluorine   (2) chlorine   (3) bromine   (4) iodine

2. If oil and water are made to mix by adding soap, the resultant mixture is called (1) a solution   (2) a suspension   (3) an emulsion   (4) a tincture

3. Which procedure is most likely to increase the solubility of nearly all solids? (1) stirring   (2) pulverizing the solid   (3) heating the solution (4) increasing the pressure

4. Polyunsaturates include hydrogenated oils which   (1) still have some double bonds   (2) have been fully hydrogenated   (3) are inedible   (4) are made by polymerization

5. The number of atoms in $(NH_4)_2CrO_4$ is   (1) 10   (2) 15   (3) 3   (4) 7

6. The most active metals are extracted from their ores by the process of reduction (1) with aluminum   (2) with carbon   (3) with hydrogen   (4) by electrolysis

7. Which kind of radioactive emission is *not* affected by an electric field? (1) alpha   (2) beta   (3) gamma   (4) proton

8. A saturated solution of a salt is an illustration of   (1) the Law of Definite Composition   (2) a mixture   (3) a compound   (4) a nonhomogeneous solution

9. The number of neutrons in a tritium nucleus is   (1) 1   (2) 2   (3) 3 (4) 0

10. A water solution of copper (II) sulfate has   (1) more hydronium ions than hydroxide ions   (2) more hydroxide ions than hydronium ions   (3) an equal concentration of hydronium and hydroxide ions   (4) neither hydronium nor hydroxide ions

11. The Law of Multiple Proportions is illustrated by   (1) KCl and $KClO_3$ (2) $MnSO_4$ and $MgSO_4$ (3) H_2O and H_2O_2 (4) NaBr and NaCl

12. One significant difference between true solutions and colloidal suspensions is that colloidal suspensions   (1) are clear   (2) will not separate out on standing (3) show the Tyndall effect   (4) will pass through a filter

13. The number of liters occupied by 17.0 grams of hydrogen sulfide at S.T.P. is (1) 1.54   (2) 11.2   (3) 22.4   (4) 44.0

14. An example of a carbohydrate is   (1) HCOOH   (2) $(C_6H_{10}O_5)_x$ (3) C_2H_5OH (4) CH_4

15. Given equal volumes, at S.T.P. the ratio of the number of atoms in ammonia to the number of atoms in sulfur dioxide is   (1) 1:1   (2) 1:2   (3) 3:2 (4) 4:3

16. A physical property of a gas which determines whether or not it can be collected by the displacement of water is its   (1) density compared with water (2) color   (3) boiling point   (4) solubility in water

17. When an atom loses two electrons, it becomes an ion with a charge of   (1) −2 (2) +2   (3) −6   (4) +6

18. Reaction rates involving organic compounds are usually much slower than those involving inorganic compounds because organic compounds (1) are usually ionized (2) are generally nonionic (3) have lower boiling points (4) have lower molecular weights

19. A reducing agent frequently used in metallurgy is (1) boneblack (2) carbon dioxide (3) manganese dioxide (4) coke

20. When FeS reacts with dilute HCl, the final solution weighs less than the sum of the original reactants because (1) some of the products escaped as a gas (2) the chloride ion is heavier than the sulfide ion (3) ferrous ions became ferric ions (4) this is an exception to the Law of the Conservation of Matter

21. In the preparation of the ester methyl salicylate, the substance used to obtain a greater yield from a given quantity of reactants is (1) water (2) salicylic acid (3) methanol (4) concentrated sulfuric acid

22. The number of *ions* formed when $(NH_4)_3PO_4$ dissociates in water is (1) 20 (2) 18 (3) 7 (4) 4

23. Of the following, the element whose atoms are larger than magnesium atoms is the element of atomic number (1) 10 (2) 11 (3) 3 (4) 17

24. Which physical property is most useful in identifying hydrogen gas? (1) color (2) odor (3) density (4) ability to burn

25. Which metal may be obtained readily from its ore by reduction with aluminum? (1) magnesium (2) chromium (3) sodium (4) calcium

26. A compound formed by uniting the element having atomic number 55 with the element having atomic number 16 will probably involve bonds that are (1) polar covalent (2) nonpolar covalent (3) coordinate covalent (4) electrovalent

27. The usual method of preparing carbon dioxide in the laboratory is to (1) decompose chalk by heat (2) decompose lime by an acid (3) warm dry ice (4) treat marble with HCl

28. Under ordinary conditions, which formula properly represents one molecular weight? (1) Cl_2 (2) NaCl (3) H (4) N

29. In KIO_4, the oxidation number of iodine is (1) −1 (2) +1 (3) −7 (4) +7

30. When zinc carbonate is roasted, one of the substances formed is (1) Zn (2) ZnO (3) ZnS (4) $Zn(HCO_3)_2$

31. One characteristic of an oxidizing agent is that it always (1) gains electrons (2) contains oxygen (3) is oxidized in a redox reaction (4) is a nonmetal

32. The weakest electrolyte is a solution of hydrogen (1) fluoride (2) chloride (3) bromide (4) iodide

33. At room temperature, the gas which will diffuse most readily through a porous container is (1) HCl (2) F_2 (3) H_2 (4) Ne

34. Which reaction involves *neither* oxidation nor reduction? (1) burning tin in chlorine gas (2) chemical union of iron and sulfur (3) decomposition of potassium chlorate (4) neutralization of sodium hydroxide with sulfuric acid

35. In the reaction $HCl + H_2O \rightarrow H_3O^+ + Cl^-$, the water molecule serves as (1) a proton acceptor (2) a proton donor (3) a weak acid (4) an electrovalent compound

36. The most electronegative element is (1) sodium (2) fluorine (3) carbon (4) iodine

37. As compared to a magnesium ion, the aluminum ion is (1) larger (2) chemically more active (3) more easily reduced (4) more easily oxidized

38. How many atoms are there in 18.0 grams of water? (1) 6.02×10^{23}
(2) 12.04×10^{23} (3) 18.06×10^{23} (4) 22.4
39. The pH of a water solution of sodium carbonate may be (1) 1.5 (2) 3.5
(3) 5.5 (4) 8.5
40. When a pupil introduced some barium chloride into the flame of his bunsen
burner, the flame became green in color. This result is best explained by the fact
that (1) chlorine is a green-colored gas (2) chlorine is an oxidizing agent
(3) an atom of barium has more electrons than an atom of chlorine (4) when
electrons return to a lower energy level, radiant energy may be emitted

Directions (41-50): Write on the line at the right of *each* statement the term that,
when inserted in the blank, will correctly complete the statement. [10]

41. An isotope of the element . . . is now used as the standard for atomic weights.
42. Uranium isotopes are usually separated by using compounds of the halogen . . . .
43. Inhibitors or accelerators of chemical reactions are generally called . . . .
44. The chemical formula for the sodium salt of hypochlorous acid is written . . . .
45. A bond formed by the *equal* sharing of electrons is known as a . . . bond.
46. An acid anhydride will react with a basic anhydride to form a type of compound
called a (an) . . . .
47. The maximum number of electrons that can be accommodated in the third shell
from the nucleus is . . . .
48. The formula of the second member of the acetylene (alkyne) series (C_nH_{2n-2})
is . . . .
49. The compound formed by the reaction of metallic calcium with water is
named . . . .
50. The mass of the nucleus of an atom, when compared to the total mass of the
individual particles comprising it, is . . . .

Directions (51-60): Write on the line at the right of *each* statement the term
(*decreases, increases, remains the same*) that, when inserted in the blank, will correctly
complete the statement. [10]

51. As crystals of sodium chloride are added to a saturated solution of sodium
chloride at constant temperature, the concentration of the solution . . . .
52. As metals in the electromotive series increase in activity, the stability of their
compounds generally . . . .
53. As more ethylene glycol is added to water, the freezing point of the solution . . . .
54. As the temperature and pressure on any radioactive substance is increased, the
time required for one-half of a given number of its atoms to decay . . . .
55. As the atomic weight of the *isotopes* of an element increases, the atomic
number . . . .
56. As electrons are removed from a sodium atom, the energy required to remove
each succeeding electron . . . .
57. In general, as one goes from left to right in any period of the *Periodic Table*, the
tendency for an element to be oxidized . . . .
58. In Period 2 of the *Periodic Table*, as the *atomic number* increases, the electrical
conductivity of the element . . . .

59. As hydronium ions are added to a solution of sodium hydroxide, the pH . . . .
60. In the equilibrium represented by the equation $N_2 + O_2 \rightleftarrows 2NO$, as the pressure increases, the amount of NO formed . . . .

Part II

Answer four questions from this part. Be sure that you answer all parts of each question selected. [Show all numerical work when computation is required.]

1. *a.* On the line at the right of *each* term in column *B*, write the *number* preceding the compound in column *A* which is most closely associated with that term. [5]

Column A	Column B
(1) K_2SO_4	(a) Strong base
(2) $Al(OH)_3$	(b) Proton donor
(3) NO_2	(c) Amphoteric compound
(4) HCl	(d) Acid anhydride
(5) KOH	(e) Nonelectrolyte
(6) $NaNO_3$	
(7) CH_3OH	

b. Use the *Reference Tables* to answer the following questions.
On the line at the right of *each* of the following, write the n umber or term which best answers that question. [5]

(1) In degrees centigrade, at what temperature do sodium nitrate and potassium nitrate have the same solubility?

(2) If 100 ml. of water saturated with potassium chlorate at 50°C. is cooled to 30° C., how many grams of the solid crystallize from the solution?

(3) How many grams of sodium chlorate are needed to saturate *50 ml.* of water at 35° C.?

(4) What is the average rate of increase in solubility in grams per 100 ml. per centigrade degree for potassium nitrate in the temperature range 60° C. to 70° C.?

(5) Assume that a solubility curve for a gas such as ammonia at one atmosphere pressure were plotted on the *Solubility Curve* graph. Reading from left to right, would this curve (1) slope upward, (2) slope downward or (3) go straight across? [Write the *number* preceding the correct answer.]

2. Atoms *Q*, *R* and *T* occur in the same period of the *Periodic Table*. In their outermost shells they have one, three and seven electrons, respectively. Answer *a*, *b* and *c* in the spaces provided at the right.

a. Using the symbols *Q*, *R* and *T*, write the most probable formulas for the compounds formed between

(1) *Q* and *T*   [1]

(2) *R* and *T*   [1]

b. Of the elements Q, R and T,

   (1) which two will probably form an ionic compound?   [1]

   (2) which one may form a diatomic molecule?   [1]

   (3) which one can be most easily reduced?   [1]

c. On the line at the right of *each* phrase in column B, write the *number* preceding the chemical term in column A which is most closely related to that phrase. [5]

Column A

   (1) addition
   (2) allotropism
   (3) esterification
   (4) isomerism
   (5) polymerization
   (6) saponification
   (7) substitution

Column B

   (a) Illustrated by the behavior of unsaturated hydrocarbons with a halogen such as bromine

   (b) Illustrated by the formation of compounds with the same molecular formula but with different structures

   (c) Illustrated by the difference in the physical properties of the various forms of carbon

   (d) The process by which "giant" organic molecules may be produced from smaller molecular units

   (e) The most probable type of reaction when saturated hydrocarbons react with a halogen such as bromine

3. a. Write a balanced equation for each of *three* of the following reactions: [2, 2, 2]

   (1) complete combustion of butane in oxygen

   (2) laboratory preparation of iodine

   (3) complete reduction of Fe_3O_4 by carbon monoxide

   (4) electrolysis of brine

  b. Answer *two* of the following: [2, 2]

   (1) Write a balanced ionic equation for the reaction between solutions of barium hydroxide and hydrochloric acid.

   (2) Write the nuclear equation for the emission of an alpha particle by $_{94}Pu^{239}$.

   (3) Write a balanced ion-electron equation for the reaction occurring at the cathode in the electrolysis of a solution of aluminum oxide in melted cryolite.

4. Answer all parts of the following question: [The atomic weights from the *Reference Tables* may be used to the nearest whole numbers; e.g., $Cl = 35.46$ becomes 35.]

  a. At S.T.P., a certain gas has a density of 1.78 grams per liter. Calculate its molecular weight. [2]

  b. Sodium chlorate is decomposed according to the following equation:

$$2NaClO_3 \rightarrow 2NaCl + 3O_2$$

What weight of oxygen gas will be produced when 120 grams of sodium chlorate are decomposed? [3]

  c. Calculate the percentage by weight of nitrogen in NH_4NO_3. [2]

d. How many grams of sodium iodide are present in 250 ml. of a 2.0 molar solution of this salt?   [3]

5. a. (1) Draw a labeled diagram of the apparatus used to prepare *and* collect nitric acid in the laboratory.   [2, 1]

   (2) Write a balanced equation for the laboratory preparation of nitric acid.   [2]

   b. When a solution of an unknown compound was heated, the products formed were water, carbon dioxide and calcium carbonate. Name the original unknown compound.   [1]

   c. A solution of an unknown compound produced a white precipitate when H_2S gas was bubbled through it. When silver nitrate was added to another portion of the unknown solution, a white precipitate resulted which was insoluble in dilute nitric acid and soluble in ammonia water. Name the unknown compound.   [1, 1]

   d. A student inserted a deflagrating spoon with burning sulfur into a flask containing a small amount of water and a strip of blue litmus paper. After the burning sulfur was removed, the flask was stoppered and shaken. The litmus paper turned pink. Name *two* compounds that may have been produced inside the flask.   [1, 1]

6. a. Draw structural diagrams for each of *three* of the following: [Electron-dot diagrams may be used where appropriate.]   [2, 2, 2]

   (1) the electron shell structure of *both* the atom and the ion of calcium

   (2) the nucleus and electron shell structure of $_7N^{13}$

   (3) the water molecule

   (4) a molecule of ethanol

   b. Explain each of *two* of the following statements on the basis of scientific principles: [2, 2]

   (1) Gold is generally found in the native state, while magnesium is usually found combined.

   (2) Concentrated sulfuric acid is a poor conductor of electricity, but dilute sulfuric acid is a good conductor of electricity.

   (3) The pH of carbonated water changes as the solution is heated in an open container.

Part I

Answer all questions in this part.

Directions (1-40): Write on the line at the right of *each* statement or question the *number* preceding the term that, of those given, best completes the statement or answers the question. [40]

1. All water-soluble acids   (1) produce hydrogen with zinc   (2) are equally strong   (3) produce salts that are very soluble in water   (4) react with water to produce hydronium ions

2. Compared with potassium, calcium   (1) has larger atoms   (2) has a lower density   (3) is more easily oxidized   (4) is less active chemically

3. The total number of atoms that have combined to form one molecule of $C_3H_5(NO_3)_3$ is   (1) 11   (2) 18   (3) 20   (4) 4

4. In the preparation of an ester, the yield of the ester is increased by the addition of   (1) water   (2) sodium chloride   (3) sulfuric acid   (4) sodium hydroxide

5. For reversible reactions at equilibrium, a rise in temperature will   (1) favor the endothermic reaction   (2) decrease the rates of the reactions   (3) cause the evolution of more heat   (4) have no effect upon the equilibrium

6. In the reaction $NH_3 + H_2O \rightarrow NH_4^+ + OH^-$, the water molecule serves as   (1) a proton donor   (2) a proton acceptor   (3) a weak base   (4) an electrovalent compound

7. A true property of *all* colloidal suspensions is their   (1) color   (2) ability to scatter a light beam   (3) cloudy appearance   (4) tendency to settle upon standing

8. When one mole of $Al_2(SO_4)_3$ dissociates in water, the number of moles of ions produced is   (1) 17   (2) 2   (3) 10   (4) 5

9. Increasing the pressure increases the solubility in water of   (1) solids and gases   (2) liquids only   (3) gases only   (4) both liquids and gases

10. Note the ionization constant for acetic acid in Table *M* of the *Reference Tables*. This value indicates that   (1) its pH is 1.8   (2) it is a weak acid   (3) it is a stronger acid than hydrochloric acid   (4) it is very soluble in water

11. Which hydrocarbon does *not* belong to the alkane (paraffin) series?   (1) C_5H_{12} (2) C_2H_4 (3) C_3H_8 (4) C_8H_{18}

12. Radiant energy is emitted from an atom when electrons fall back to lower energy levels. The electron change that would release the most energy is when an electron jumps from   (1) L to K shell   (2) M to L shell   (3) M to K shell   (4) M to N shell

13. Hydrocarbons having the same empirical formula but different structural formulas are called   (1) isotopes   (2) isomers   (3) polymers   (4) isobars

14. Under similar conditions, which of these gases diffuses most rapidly through a small opening?   (1) H_2 (2) CO_2 (3) CO (4) Cl_2

15. A bottle that had been filled almost to the top with concentrated sulfuric acid was left unstoppered. Over the weekend it overflowed. Which statement best explains this phenomenon?   (1) Unstable compounds often release gases during decomposition.   (2) Most acids increase in volume if exposed to the air.   (3) Some chemical compounds absorb moisture from the air.   (4) Evaporation takes place at the surface of the liquid.

16. A particle accelerator can *not* be used to accelerate   (1) electrons   (2) neutrons   (3) protons   (4) deuterons

17. When hydrogen is mixed with oxygen at ordinary temperatures, what happens? (1) An explosion occurs.   (2) A hydride is formed.   (3) Water is formed. (4) There is no apparent reaction.

18. An example of an acid is   (1) C_2H_5OH (2) CH_3CH_2COOH (3) CH_3OCH_3 (4) CH_3COCH_3

19. The most acidic of the following is a 0.1 N solution of   (1) sodium carbonate (2) borax   (3) alum   (4) trisodium phosphate

20. Transition metals are   (1) alkali metals   (2) Group A metals   (3) Group B metals   (4) base metals

21. Which of the following is a *nonelectrolyte?*   (1) CH_3OH (2) $Ba(OH)_2$ (3) CH_3COOH (4) NH_4OH

22. Which metal is most difficult to extract from its oxide?   (1) Cs   (2) Mg (3) Ag   (4) Ca

23. Which compound was previously thought impossible to form but has recently been produced in the laboratory?   (1) CuHe   (2) XeF_4 (3) $Ba(Na)_2$ (4) H_2O_2

24. During the formation of an ionic bond, the atom which transfers its valence electron is the atom with the   (1) higher electronegativity value   (2) lower electronegativity value   (3) higher ionization energy   (4) lower oxidation number

25. What weight of oxygen will combine with 3.0 grams of hydrogen to produce water?   (1) 1.5 g.   (2) .37 g.   (3) 6.0 g.   (4) 24 g.

26. A transmutation reaction must involve   (1) a transfer of electrons from a metallic atom to a nonmetallic atom   (2) a sharing of electrons by nonmetallic atoms of the same element   (3) an increase in the number of neutrons in the nucleus of an atom   (4) a change in the number of protons in a nucleus of an atom

27. Which element will *not* dissolve in dilute HCl?   (1) Na   (2) Zn   (3) Co (4) Cu

28. The *least* stable compounds are usually   (1) combinations of the most active elements   (2) combinations of the least active elements   (3) the products of exothermic reactions   (4) the ones most abundant in the earth's crust

29. At S.T.P., one liter of hydrogen gas contains approximately the same number of molecules as   (1) 1.0 liter of sulfur dioxide   (2) 2.0 liters of helium (3) 1.5 liters of ozone   (4) 0.5 liter of oxygen

30. In chemical reactions, metals generally   (1) act as oxidizing agents   (2) share electrons   (3) donate protons   (4) acquire positive oxidation numbers

31. On which of the following is the procedure of preparing hydrochloric acid by gently heating a mixture of NaCl and H_2SO_4 and dissolving the resulting gas in water based primarily?   (1) All chemical reactions are speeded up by heat. (2) Acids are produced only by double decomposition reactions.   (3) An acid with a low boiling point may be prepared by using an acid with a high boiling point.   (4) Compounds possessing different boiling points may be separated by destructive distillation.

32. A mixture of solutions of $NaNO_3$ and KCl was evaporated to dryness. The number of different salts in the residue was   (1) 1   (2) 2   (3) 3   (4) 4

33. The hydride ion has the same electron configuration as an atom of   (1) helium (2) lithium   (3) beryllium   (4) hydrogen

34. The addition of a single crystal of $NaClO_3$ to a solution of the salt causes additional crystals to precipitate. If there is no change of temperature, the resulting solution is   (1) unsaturated   (2) dilute   (3) saturated   (4) supersaturated

35. Selenium forms two acids, H_2SeO_3 and H_2SeO_4. The name of H_2SeO_3 is probably   (1) hydroselenic acid   (2) selenic acid   (3) hydrogen selenide   (4) selenious acid

36. The high electrical conductivity of metals is due chiefly to   (1) their high ionization potential   (2) the presence of mobile electrons in metal crystals   (3) the presence of filled electron shells   (4) the chemical activity of metal ions

37. The element chlorine consists of two natural isotopes, $_{17}Cl^{35}$ and $_{17}Cl^{37}$. These isotopes occur in the ratio of approximately 75% to 25%, respectively. Which should one use in order to calculate the correct average atomic mass?

(1) $\dfrac{35 + 37}{2} =$ (2) $(35 \times .75) + (37 \times .25) =$

(3) $\dfrac{(35 \times 3) + 37}{3} =$ (4) $\dfrac{(35 \times 3) + 37}{2} =$

38. A saturated solution of silver sulfate is   (1) neutral to litmus   (2) basic to litmus   (3) concentrated   (4) dilute

39. Decomposition is to synthesis as hydrolysis is to   (1) neutralization   (2) sublimation   (3) distillation   (4) analyzation

40. Which solution has the lowest freezing point?   (1) 1 M sugar   (2) 1 M barium chloride   (3) 1 M nitric acid   (4) 1 M sodium hydroxide

Directions (41-50): Write on the line at the right of *each* statement the term that, when inserted in the blank, will correctly complete the statement.   [10]

41. Copper oxide is heated and hydrogen gas is passed over it. Metallic copper results. The name of the compound formed is ....

42. The number of grams contained in 1.50 moles of CO_2 gas is ....

43. If a metallic oxide is reacted with a nonmetallic oxide, the compound produced is a (an) ....

44. The chemical symbol for the particle X in the equation

$$_{13}Al^{27} + _2He^4 \rightarrow X + _0n^1 \text{ is } ....$$

45. The *name* of the saturated hydrocarbon with the same number of carbon atoms as in $C_3H_5(OH)_3$ is ....

46. The reaction of methanol with acetic acid produces an organic compound called ....

47. The reduction of the most active metals (for example, Na and K) is usually accomplished by a process called ....

48. The oxidation number of the dichromate *ion* in $K_2Cr_2O_7$ is ....

49. In the laboratory preparation of chlorine gas, manganese dioxide acts as a (an) ....

50. The sodium salt of hydrosulfuric acid that is formed by completely replacing the hydrogen in the acid has the formula ....

Directions (51-60): Write on the line at the right of *each* statement the term (*decreases, increases, remains the same*) that, when inserted in the blank, will correctly complete the statement.   [10]

51. As 50 grams of $Na_2CO_3 \cdot 10H_2O$ are heated in an open evaporating dish, the weight of the contents of the dish ....

52. As the temperature of water increases, the rate at which most solids dissolve in the water ....

53. As the surface area of reactants increases, the reaction rate generally ....

54. As a solution of the ionic salt KBr is diluted, the total number of bromide ions ....

55. As the electronegativity difference between elements decreases, their tendency to form ionic compounds ....

56. As the concentration of a solution of sodium chloride increases, the numerical value of the pH ....

57. As the covalent atomic radii of the alkali metals increase, the oxidation number of these metals ....

58. As an element is reduced, its oxidation number algebraically ....

59. As dilute potassium hydroxide is added to a container of dilute sulfuric acid, the pH number of the resulting solution in the container initially ....

60. As the number of bonds between two adjacent carbon atoms in a compound increases, the chemical reactivity of the compound generally ....

Part II

Answer four questions from this part. Be sure that you answer all parts of each question selected. [Show all numerical work when computation is required.]

1. The *Periodic Table of the Elements* and/or Table *J* should be used as an aid in answering this question.
   a. On the line at the right of *each* of the following, write the *name* of the member of the halogen family—fluorine, chlorine, bromine, iodine, astatine—which best completes the statement: [3]
   (1) ... has the least tendency to gain electrons.
   (2) ... is the best oxidizing agent.
   (3) ... has the most metallic properties.

   b. The following graphs show the relationship between a particular physical or chemical property as the *Y*-axis and an increasing atomic number as the *X*-axis.

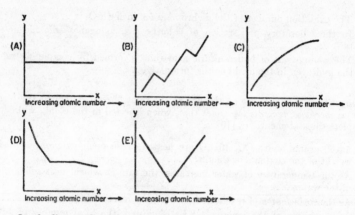

On the line at the right of *each* of the following, write the *letter* of the graph which best shows the relationship between

(1) ionization energy and increasing atomic number of Period 2   [1]
(2) atomic radii with increasing atomic number in Group VII *A*   [1]
(3) electronegativity with increasing atomic number in Group II *A*   [1]
(4) oxidation state with increasing atomic number in Group 1 *A*   [1]

c. Considering only the elements in Period 3 of the *Periodic Table*, state which element

(1) is the strongest reducing agent   [1]
(2) forms oxides that are most basic   [1]
(3) is most likely to form only covalent compounds   [1]

2. *a.* On the line at the right of *each* of statements (*a*)-(*e*), write the *number* of the chemical reaction, *chosen from the list below*, which that statement best describes.   [5]

Chemical Reactions

(1) $AgNO_3 + NaCl \rightarrow AgCl + NaNO_3$
(2) $2HgO \rightarrow 2Hg + O_2$
(3) $N_2 + O_2 \rightleftarrows 2NO$
(4) $2K + F_2 \rightarrow 2KF$
(5) $N_2 + 3H_2 \rightleftarrows 2NH_3$
(6) $Cl_2 + 2NaBr \rightarrow 2NaCl + Br_2$

(*a*) It produces the most stable compound.
(*b*) It does not involve oxidation-reduction.
(*c*) It goes to completion because a gas is formed.
(*d*) It goes to completion because an insoluble substance is formed.
(*e*) It involves an equilibrium which can be shifted to the right by the application of high pressure.

b. Refer to the Solubility Curves in the *Reference Tables for Chemistry* to answer *each* of the following questions: Write your answers on the lines at the right. [5]

(1) If 50 ml. of water saturated with potassium chlorate at 23° C. are slowly evaporated to dryness, how many grams of the dry salt will be recovered?

(2) What is the smallest volume of water in ml. required to dissolve completely 40 grams of $NaClO_3$ at 19° C.?

(3) A saturated solution of $NaNO_3$ in 100 ml. of water at 40° C. is heated to 50° C. Calculate the rate of increase in solubility in grams per degree.

(4) Which salt has a solubility which is relatively unaffected by changes in temperature?

(5) Thirty grams of KCl are dissolved in 100 ml. of water at 45° C. How many *additional* grams of KCl would be needed to make the solution saturated at 80° C.?

3. *a.* Write a balanced equation for each of *three* of the following reactions: [2, 2, 2]
   (1) the combustion of hydrogen sulfide in a limited supply of oxygen
   (2) laboratory preparation of ammonia
   (3) the reduction of chromium (III) oxide by magnesium
   (4) the reaction between solutions of aluminum sulfate and barium nitrate

   b. Answer *two* of the following: [2, 2]
   (1) Write a balanced ion-electron equation for the reaction occurring at the positive electrode during the electrolysis of melted magnesium chloride.

   (2) Write a nuclear equation for the emission of a beta particle from $^{234}_{90}$ Th.

   (3) Write a balanced ionic equation for the reaction between solutions of nitric acid and calcium hydroxide.

4. Answer *all* parts of the following question: [The atomic weights from the *Reference Tables* may be used to the nearest whole numbers; e.g., Cl = 35.453 becomes 35.]
   a. How many moles (gram molecular weights) of acetic acid are present in 2.0 liters of 0.25 molar solution?   [2]
   b. Calculate the weight in grams of one liter of the gas H_2F_2 at S.T.P.   [2]
   c. Copper oxide is reduced by ammonia according to the following equation:

   $$3CuO + 2NH_3 \rightarrow 3Cu + N_2 + 3H_2O$$

   What weight of nitrogen in grams is obtained by reduction of 120.0 grams of copper oxide?   [3]
   d. Octane vapor is burned according to the following equation:

   $$2C_8H_{18} + 25O_2 \rightarrow 16CO_2 + 18H_2O$$

   For the complete combustion of 8 liters of octane vapor, how many liters of
   (1) oxygen are required?   [2]
   (2) air are required?   [1]

5. *a.* (1) Draw a labeled diagram of the laboratory apparatus used to prepare *and* collect sulfur dioxide.   [2, 1]
   (2) Explain how one may convert sulfur dioxide to sulfuric acid.   [2]

   b. Explain *each* of the following statements on the basis of scientific principles.
   (1) Bromine reacts more readily with ethene (ethylene) than with ethane. [2]
   (2) Organic reactions generally proceed more slowly than do inorganic reactions.   [2]
   (3) The color of red litmus remains unchanged when it is put into an alcohol. [1]

6. *a.* The diagram shows the apparatus for silverplating a spoon.
    (1) What metal should be used at the anode?   [1]
    (2) What positive ion must be present in solution?   [1]
    (3) Write an ion-electron equation for the reaction occurring at the spoon.   [2]

  b. (1) Draw *either* electron-dot or electron-shell diagrams for each of *two* of the following compounds: [2, 2]
    (*a*) chlorine molecule
    (*b*) sodium fluoride
    (*c*) carbon tetrachloride
    (*d*) hydrogen chloride
    (2) For *each* compound selected in answer to (1), name the type of bond present.   [1, 1]

Part I

Answer all questions in this part.

Directions (1-54): For *each* statement or question, write on the separate answer sheet the *number* preceding the word or expression that, of those given, best completes the statement or answers the question. [54]

1. A change of pressure would have the greatest effect on the solubility of a   (1) solid in a solid   (2) gas in a liquid   (3) liquid in a liquid   (4) liquid in a solid

2. A true solution can *not* be   (1) colored   (2) dilute   (3) cloudy   (4) neutral

3. Which pair of substances is miscible?   (1) water and oil   (2) water and methyl alcohol   (3) water and carbon tetrachloride   (4) water and gasoline

4. Ethyl alcohol (ethanol) can dissolve both polar and nonpolar solutes because it   (1) is a symmetrical covalent molecule   (2) is a nonsymmetrical ionic compound   (3) contains hydrogen bonds   (4) contains a hydrocarbon radical and a functional hydroxyl group

5. If 2,000 milliliters of an aqueous solution contained 1 mole of $CaBr_2$, the solution would be classified as   (1) 1 molar   (2) 1 molal   (3) 0.5 molar   (4) 0.5 normal

6. A product obtained by strongly heating a crystal of blue copper sulfate is   (1) oxygen gas   (2) a hydrate   (3) an anhydrous salt   (4) an acid anhydride

7. Which halogen atom has the smallest atomic radius?   (1) fluorine   (2) chlorine   (3) bromine   (4) iodine

8. On the *Periodic Table*, where are nonmetals located?   (1) between Groups II A and III A (2) on the lower left-hand side   (3) on the upper left-hand side   (4) on the upper right-hand side

9. Which is characteristic of hydrogen?   (1) odorless, and a reducing agent   (2) very soluble in water, and combustible   (3) insoluble in water, and pale blue   (4) less dense than air, and inert

10. Which compound is the most unstable?   (1) H_2O (2) $Ca(OH)_2$ (3) SO_2 (4) NO

11. Which element is the best oxidizing agent?   (1) I_2 (2) Br_2 (3) Cl_2 (4) F_2

12. Which is the oxidation number of chlorine in the chlorate radical (ClO_3^{-1})?   (1) -1 (2) $+5$ (3) $+7$ (4) $+8$

13. Isotopes of hydrogen atoms *differ* in the number of   (1) electrons   (2) protons   (3) neutrons   (4) energy levels

14. The test for the nitrate ion is primarily concerned with the production of a   (1) liquid   (2) color   (3) precipitate   (4) sharp odor

15. When copper reacts with dilute nitric acid, which is the principal gas formed?   (1) N_2O (2) NO (3) N_2O_4 (4) N_2O_5

16. Which element has the greatest tendency to gain electrons?   (1) Sn   (2) I   (3) Cl   (4) Cs

17. Which organic solvent is *not* used in the laboratory test for bromine or iodine?   (1) C_2H_5OH (2) $CHCl_3$ (3) CS_2 (4) CCl_4

18. During the electrolysis of a sodium iodide solution, which substance is formed at the positive terminal? (1) I^- (2) I^0 (3) Na^+ (4) Na^0

19. Carbonic acid would probably be classified as (1) a very strong acid (2) an insoluble acid (3) a strong acid (4) a weak acid

20. When sulfur dioxide decolorizes a $KMnO_4$ solution, one product formed is $MnSO_4$. In this reaction the oxidation number of the manganese changes from (1) $+7$ to $+2$ (2) $+6$ to $+4$ (3) $+5$ to $+2$ (4) $+4$ to $+2$

21. By which of the following processes is a precipitate most commonly removed from water? (1) filtration (2) distillation (3) boiling (4) evaporation

22. In Period 2 of the *Periodic Table*, the element which forms oxides of the type X_2O belongs to (1) Group I A (2) Group II A (3) Group II B (4) Group VII A

23. At $0°$ C. and 760 mm., carbon monoxide is more soluble in water than is (1) ammonia (2) sulfur dioxide (3) nitrogen monoxide (4) nitrogen

24. Which atom contains the greatest number of neutrons? (1) ^{57}Fe (2) ^{58}Ni (3) ^{57}Mn (4) ^{58}Co

25. Decimal atomic masses are primarily due to mixtures of (1) isomers (2) impurities (3) allotropes (4) isotopes

26. Neutral atoms *must* contain (1) completed subshells (2) two electrons in their outermost energy level (3) an equal number of protons and electrons (4) an equal number of protons and neutrons

27. Atoms X and Y have the following electronic structures: X: 2-8-18-7; Y: 2-8-14-2. Which statement is *false*? (1) X and Y may form more than one compound. (2) X is lustrous and metallic. (3) Y is malleable and ductile. (4) Y is a conductor of electricity.

28. As compared to a Cl^- ion, a Mg^{+2} ion is (1) larger (2) chemically inactive (3) more easily oxidized (4) more easily reduced

29. Which is the strongest conjugate base listed on the *Reference Tables*? (1) NO_3^- (2) NH_2^- (3) NH_3 (4) Cl^-

30. When aluminum reacts with hydrogen, which is the formula for the resulting compound? (1) AlH_5 (2) AlH_4 (3) AlH_3 (4) Al_3H

31. In the neutralization of sulfuric acid with sodium hydroxide,
$$H_2SO_4 + XNaOH \rightarrow XH_2O + Na_2SO_4$$
the term "X" is equal to (1) 1 (2) 2 (3) 3 (4) 4

32. Which equation represents an addition reaction?
(1) $CH_4 + O_2 \rightarrow CO_2 + 2H_2O$
(2) $CH_4 + Br_2 \rightarrow CH_3Br + HBr$
(3) $C_2H_4 + Br_2 \rightarrow C_2H_4Br_2$
(4) $C_2H_4 + 3O_2 \rightarrow 2CO_2 + 2H_2O$

33. At S.T.P., the volume occupied by 32 grams of a gas is 22.4 liters. The gram-molecular weight of this gas is closest to (1) 1.43 gm. (2) 8 gm. (3) 32 gm. (4) 716.8 gm.

34. Which is the correct ratio by mass of iron to sulfur in the compound FeS? (1) 2:3 (2) 2:1 (3) 4:7 (4) 7:4

35. Deuterium oxide has a gram-molecular mass of (1) 20 (2) 2 (3) 22.4 (4) 44.8

36. Which substance is *not* classified as a base? (1) NaOH (2) LiOH (3) C_2H_5OH (4) $Ba(OH)_2$

37. In the neutralization of an acid and a base, the reaction goes to completion because of the formation of (1) water (2) a basic anhydride (3) an acid anhydride (4) a metal

38. Which is the poorest conductor of electricity? (1) crystalline NaCl (2) melted KCl (3) saturated NaCl solution (4) dilute HCl solution

39. In the reaction $HCl + H_2O \rightarrow H_3O^+ + Cl^-$, which substance causes litmus to turn red? (1) H_3O^+ (2) H_2O (3) HCl (4) Cl^-

40. A solution of hydrochloric acid contains (1) fewer hydronium ions than chloride ions (2) an equal number of hydronium and chloride ions (3) only hydronium ions (4) more hydroxide ions than hydronium ions

41. Alpha disintegration first results in the formation of a new element with the atomic number (1) increased by two (2) increased by four (3) decreased by two (4) decreased by four

42. Which is the characteristic functional group of organic acids? (1) —COOH (2) —OH (3) R— (4) CH_3—

43. A reason why carbon forms so many different compounds is that carbon atoms (1) gain electrons easily (2) form ionic bonds easily (3) form covalent bonds easily (4) lose their valence electrons easily

44. The reaction $C_5H_{12} + Br_2 \rightarrow C_5H_{11}Br + HBr$ illustrates (1) substitution (2) cracking (3) addition (4) polymerization

45. In ethyne (acetylene), the number of bonds between the carbon atoms is (1) 1 (2) 2 (3) 3 (4) 4

46. Certain valence electrons, when subjected to light of visible wavelength, become excited and reemit the light virtually unchanged. This illustrates the characteristic of (1) softness (2) ductility (3) luster (4) malleability

47. Metallic cesium has a lower boiling point than metallic lithium because metallic cesium (1) has a smaller atomic radius (2) has a lower atomic weight (3) has weaker bonding forces (4) is more active

48. Elements T, X, Y and Z have 1, 2, 5 and 6 electrons, respectively, in their outer shells. According to Arrhenius' theory, which elements will tend to form bases? (1) T and Z (2) Y and Z (3) X and Y (4) T and X

49. The greater the chemical activity of a metal, the greater is the tendency of its atoms to (1) form ionic bonds (2) form covalent bonds (3) gain protons (4) gain neutrons

50. Which property do all metals have in common? (1) action as catalysts (2) action as reducing agents (3) ability to form acids (4) ability to form covalent bonds

51. The reaction between hydrochloric acid and potassium hydroxide always results in the (1) formation of a precipitate (2) liberation of oxygen (3) liberation of hydrogen (4) liberation of heat

52. When a nonmetal reacts chemically with a metal, the nonmetal **(1)** is oxidized **(2)** is reduced **(3)** is neither oxidized nor reduced **(4)** forms a metallic bond

53. In general, inorganic chemical reactions in solution take place between **(1)** atoms **(2)** ions **(3)** molecules **(4)** elements

54. When one mole of NaOH is added to one mole of $HC_2H_3O_2$, the pH of the solution will be closest to **(1)** 9 **(2)** 6 **(3)** 5 **(4)** 4

Directions (55-60): Write in the space provided on the separate answer sheet the term (*decreases, increases, remains the same*) that, when inserted in the blank, will correctly complete the statement. [6]

55. The half-life of ^{24}Na is 15 hours. If it is placed in water, its half-life . . . .

56. As the chemical activity of a metal increases, the ease with which it can be extracted from its ore . . . .

57. As moist air is bubbled through concentrated sulfuric acid, the amount of water vapor in the air . . . .

58. As concentrated sulfuric acid is diluted by water, the ionization of the acid . . . .

59. Generally, as the difference in electronegativity between metallic and nonmetallic elements decreases, the tendency for these atoms to form covalent bonds . . . .

60. In the reaction H_2 (gas) + I_2 (gas) $\rightleftarrows$ 2HI (gas), as the pressure increases, the *rate* of reaction . . . .

Part II

This part consists of six groups. Choose four of these six groups. Show all numerical work; give units with all answers where the unit is not specified in the question.

Group 1

Directions (61-65): Refer to the Solubility Curves in the *Reference Tables for Chemistry* to answer *each* of the following. In the space provided on the separate answer sheet, write the term that, when inserted in the blank, will correctly complete *each* statement. [5]

61. The compound which is most soluble at 20° C. is . . . .

62. The number of grams of KNO_3 needed to saturate 100 ml. of H_2O at 70° C. is . . . .

63. The formula of the compound whose solubility varies inversely with the temperature is . . . .

64. One hundred ml. of a saturated solution of KCl at 80° C. will precipitate out 10 grams of the salt when cooled to a temperature of . . . ° C.

65. One hundred ml. of $NaNO_3$ solution is saturated at 10° C. The number of additional grams of $NaNO_3$ required to saturate this solution at 50° C. is . . . .

Directions (66-67): In the space provided on the separate answer sheet, write the term that, when inserted in the blank, will correctly complete *each* statement. [2]

66. The symbol for the element formed when a beta particle is emitted as a ^{234}Th nucleus decays is . . . .
67. The atomic mass number of the element produced by beta emission from a ^{234}Th nucleus is . . . .

Directions (68-70): In the space provided on the separate answer sheet, write the *number* of the organic compound, *chosen from the list below,* which is best described by *each* statement.   [3]

Organic Compounds

```
       H                    H  O                     H
       |                    |  ||                     |
(1) H—C—O—H        (2) H—C—C—O—H       (3) H—C≡C—C—H
       |                    |                          |
       H                    H                          H


       H     H                    H  H
       |     |                    |  |
(4) H—C—C—O—C—H         (5) H—C—C—H
       |     ||     |              |  |
       H     O     H              H  H
```

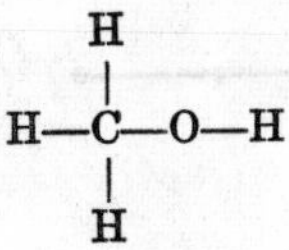

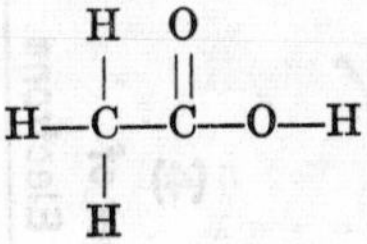

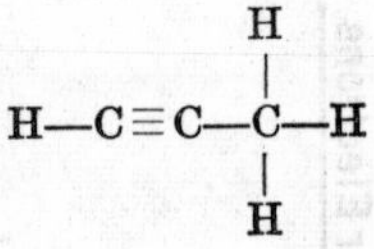

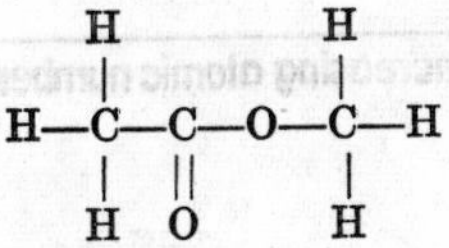

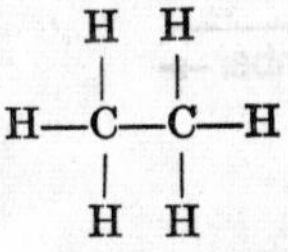

68. This compound is formed from the reaction of methyl alcohol and acetic acid.
69. This compound is an unsaturated hydrocarbon.
70. This compound is one whose water solution turns litmus red.

Group 2

Directions (71-74): The following graphs show the relationship between the outer shell electrons of atoms as the *y*-axis and increasing atomic number as the *x*-axis. In the space provided on the separate answer sheet, write the *number* of the graph that best shows the relationship between outer shell electrons and increasing atomic number of the group or period listed. [4]

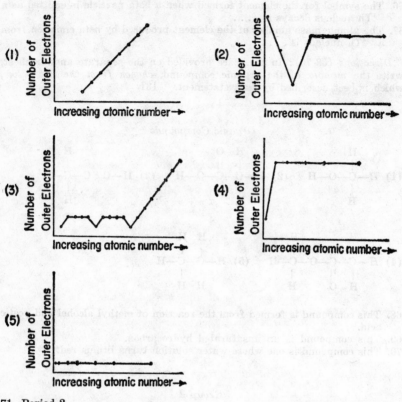

(1) Number of Outer Electrons — Increasing atomic number →

(2) Number of Outer Electrons — Increasing atomic number →

(3) Number of Outer Electrons — Increasing atomic number →

(4) Number of Outer Electrons — Increasing atomic number →

(5) Number of Outer Electrons — Increasing atomic number →

71. Period 2
72. Group O
73. Period 4
74. Group I A

Directions (75-76): The electronegativity for three elements is given below.

Element 1: 3.0
Element 2: 2.0
Element 3: 0.8

In the space provided on the separate answer sheet, write the *number(s)* which indicates the elements which, when inserted in the blank, will correctly complete the statement. [A number may be used more than once.] [2]

75. The most ionic compound would probably be a combination of elements . . . .

76. The element *most* likely to form diatomic molecules at room temperature is element . . . .

Directions (77-80): In the space provided on the separate answer sheet, write the *number* of the pair of substances, *chosen from the list below*, which is most closely associated with *each* statement.   [4]

Substances

(1) $NH_4OH + H_2SO_4$
(2) $Zn(OH)_2 + NaOH$
(3) $CaCO_3 + HCl$
(4) $AgNO_3 + CuCl_2$
(5) $K + H_2O$
(6) $Cu + NaCl$

77. A precipitate forms which darkens on exposure to light.
78. A reaction occurs which involves an amphoteric substance.
79. A reaction occurs involving oxidation and reduction.
80. A gas forms which turns limewater milky.

Group 3

Directions (81-85): The atomic masses from the *Reference Tables* may be used to the *nearest whole numbers;* e.g., $Cl = 35.453$ becomes 35.

81. Zinc reacts with hot, concentrated sulfuric acid according to the following equation:
$$4Zn + 5H_2SO_4 \rightarrow 4ZnSO_4 + H_2S + 4H_2O$$
Calculate the mass in grams of zinc needed to react completely with 49.0 grams of sulfuric acid.   [3]
82. Carbon disulfide reacts with oxygen according to the following equation:
$$CS_2 + 3O_2 \rightarrow CO_2 + 2SO_2$$
How many liters of oxygen are required to produce 90 liters of sulfur dioxide?   [2]
83. How many grams of sodium nitrate are required to produce 500 ml. of a 3.0 molar solution?   [2]
84. What is the percentage of nitrogen in the compound NH_4Cl?   [2]
85. Calculate the mass of 5 liters of carbon dioxide at 0° C. and 760 mm. of pressure.   [1]

Group 4

86. Write a balanced equation for each of *four* of the following reactions: [2, 2, 2, 2]
   a. Complete combustion of propene (C_3H_6)
   b. Reduction of iron (III) oxide by aluminum
   c. Laboratory preparation of nitric acid
   d. Reaction between solutions of lead (II) nitrate and hydrogen sulfide
   e. Synthesis of iron (III) chloride from its elements
87. Answer *either a* or *b*:   [2]
   a. Write a balanced ionic equation for the reaction between solutions of mercury (II) nitrate and potassium iodide.
   b. Given the equation $Zn + CuSO_4 \rightarrow ZnSO_4 + Cu$, write the ion electron equation for the oxidation reaction that takes place.

Group 5

88. Draw a labeled diagram of the apparatus used to prepare and collect ammonia in the laboratory.   [2, 1]
89. Describe a test that indicates that the gas is ammonia.   [1]
90. The equation for the Haber process is:

$$N_2 + 3H_2 \rightleftarrows 2NH_3 + \text{heat}$$

What is the effect on the equilibrium point if the pressure is increased? Explain.   [1, 1]

91. Explain *two* of the following on the basis of scientific principles: [2, 2]
    a. Bromide ions are more easily oxidized than fluoride ions.
    b. The pH of 0.1 N hydrochloric acid is different from the pH of 0.1 N acetic acid.
    c. A solution of potassium acetate turns red litmus blue.

Group 6

92. The structural formula for ammonia may be represented by the following diagram:

    a. Is the molecule polar or nonpolar? Explain.   [1, 1]
    b. Draw the electron-dot diagram for the ammonium ion and indicate the charge.   [1, 1]
    c. State *one* similarity and *one* difference between nuclei of ^{235}U and ^{238}U.   [1, 1]

93. Draw either electron-dot or electron-shell diagrams for each of *two* of the following substances: [2, 2]
    a. A water molecule
    b. Methane
    c. A molecule of fluorine
    d. Potassium chloride

REGENTS REFERENCE TABLES

SOLUBILITY CURVES

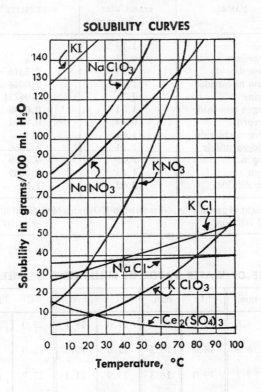

ACID-BASE CHART

CONJUGATE ACID	CONJUGATE BASE
HCl	Cl⁻
HNO₃	NO₃⁻
H₂SO₄	HSO₄⁻
H₃O⁺	H₂O
HSO₄⁻	SO₄⁼
Al(H₂O)₆⁺⁺⁺	Al(H₂O)₅(OH)⁺⁺
NH₄⁺	NH₃
H₂O	OH⁻
NH₃	NH₂⁻

acid strength decreases →

base strength decreases →

1

DENSITY AND SOLUBILITY OF SOME COMMON GASES

NAME	DENSITY grams/liter 0° C 760 mm.	SOLUBILITY*
Air	1.29	—
Ammonia	0.77	89.5
Carbon dioxide	1.98	0.3346
Carbon monoxide	1.25	0.0044
Chlorine	3.21	0.9972†
Nitrogen monoxide	1.34	0.0098
Hydrogen	0.09	0.0002
Hydrogen chloride	1.64	82.3
Hydrogen sulfide	1.54	0.7066
Nitrogen	1.25	0.0029
Oxygen	1.43	0.0069
Sulfur dioxide	2.93	22.83

* Weight of gas in grams dissolved in 100 grams of water at 0° C and 760 mm.   † at 10° C

PRESSURE OF WATER VAPOR IN MILLIMETERS OF MERCURY

° C	mm.	° C	mm.	° C	mm.	° C	mm.
0.0	4.6	17.0	14.5	21.0	18.7	25.0	23.8
5.0	6.5	18.0	15.5	22.0	19.8	26.0	25.2
10.0	9.2	19.0	16.5	23.0	21.1	27.0	26.7
15.0	12.8	20.0	17.5	24.0	22.4	28.0	28.3

PHYSICAL CONSTANTS

NAME	SYMBOL	VALUE
Speed of light	c	3.00×10^{10} cm/sec.
Avogadro's number	N_0	6.02×10^{23}
Universal gas constant	R	0.0821 liter-atm/mole-°K
Planck's constant	h	6.63×10^{-34} joule-sec.
Charge of electron	e	1.60×10^{-19} coulomb
Mass of an electron	m_e	9.11×10^{-28} gm.
Mass of a proton	m_p	1.67×10^{-24} gm.
Mass of a neutron	m_n	1.67×10^{-24} gm.

TABLE OF SOLUBILITIES IN WATER

i—nearly insoluble ss—slightly soluble s—soluble d—decomposes n—not isolated	acetate	bromide	carbonate	chloride	hydroxide	iodide	nitrate	oxide	phosphate	sulfate	sulfide
Aluminum	s	s	n	s	i	s	s	i	i	s	d
Ammonium	s	s	s	s	s	s	s	n	s	s	s
Barium	s	s	i	s	s	s	s	s	i	i	d
Calcium	s	s	i	s	ss	s	s	ss	i	ss	d
Copper II	s	s	i	s	i	d	s	i	i	s	i
Iron II	s	s	i	s	i	s	s	i	i	s	i
Iron III	s	s	n	s	i	s	s	i	i	ss	d
Lead	s	ss	i	ss	i	ss	s	i	i	i	i
Magnesium	s	s	i	s	i	s	s	i	i	s	d
Mercury I	ss	i	i	i	n	i	s	i	i	ss	i
Mercury II	s	ss	i	s	i	i	s	i	i	d	i
Potassium	s	s	s	s	s	s	s	s	s	s	s
Silver	ss	i	i	i	n	i	s	i	i	ss	i
Sodium	s	s	s	s	s	s	s	d	s	s	s
Zinc	s	s	i	s	i	s	s	i	i	s	i

IONIZATION CONSTANTS OF ACIDS AND BASES AT 25° C

Acetic acid	1.8×10^{-5}
Boric acid	5.8×10^{-10}
Carbonic acid	4.3×10^{-7}
Hypochlorous acid	3.5×10^{-8}
Phosphoric acid	7.5×10^{-3}
Ammonium hydroxide	1.8×10^{-5}
Lead hydroxide	9.6×10^{-4}

Some acids and bases which are completely or nearly completely ionized in dilute solutions at 25° C are:

ACIDS	BASES
Hydrochloric	Potassium hydroxide
Nitric	Sodium hydroxide
Sulfuric	

3

HEAT AND FREE ENERGY OF FORMATION
OF COMPOUNDS AT 25° C

COMPOUND	HEAT OF FORMATION kcal/mole (ΔH)*	FREE ENERGY OF FORMATION kcal/mole (ΔF)*
Aluminum oxide (s)	−399.09	−376.77
Ammonia (g)	−11.04	−3.98
Barium sulfate (s)	−350.2	−323.4
Calcium hydroxide (s)	−235.80	−214.33
Carbon dioxide (g)	−94.39	−94.26
Copper (II) sulfate (s)	−184.00	−158.2
Dinitrogen monoxide (g)	19.49	24.76
Ethyne (acetylene) (g)	54.19	50.00
Hydrogen fluoride (g)	−63.99	—
Hydrogen iodide (g)	5.93	—
Hydrogen oxide (ℓ)	−68.32	−56.69
Iron (II, III) oxide (s)	−267.0	−242.4
Lead monoxide (s)	−52.40	−45.25
Magnesium oxide (s)	−143.84	−136.13
Mercury (II) oxide (s)	−21.68	−13.99
Nitrogen monoxide (g)	21.60	20.72
Potassium chloride (s)	−104.18	−97.59
Sodium chloride (s)	−98.23	−91.79
Sulfur dioxide (g)	−70.96	−71.79
Zinc oxide (s)	−83.17	−76.05

(s) = solid   (ℓ) = liquid   (g) = gas
* Minus sign indicates an exothermic reaction.

pH VALUES FOR EQUIVALENT (0.1 N) SOLUTIONS

Hydrochloric acid	1.1	Alum	3.2
Sulfuric acid	1.2˙	Boric acid	5.2
Phosphoric acid	1.5	Pure water	7.0
Citric acid	2.2	Sodium bicarbonate	8.4
Acetic acid	2.9	Borax	9.2

Ammonium hydroxide	11.1
Sodium carbonate	11.6
Trisodium phosphate	12.0
Sodium hydroxide	13.0
Potassium hydroxide	13.0

4

STANDARD OXIDATION POTENTIALS

IONIC CONCENTRATIONS 1 MOLAL IN WATER AT 25° C	
HALF-CELL REACTION	E^0 (volts)
$Li = Li^+ + e^-$	3.05
$Rb = Rb^+ + e^-$	2.93
$K = K^+ + e^-$	2.93
$Cs = Cs^+ + e^-$	2.92
$Ba = Ba^{++} + 2 e^-$	2.90
$Sr = Sr^{++} + 2 e^-$	2.89
$Ca = Ca^{++} + 2 e^-$	2.87
$Na = Na^+ + e^-$	2.71
$Mg = Mg^{++} + 2 e^-$	2.37
$Be = Be^{++} + 2 e^-$	1.85
$Al = Al^{+++} + 3 e^-$	1.66
$Mn = Mn^{++} + 2 e^-$	1.18
$Zn = Zn^{++} + 2 e^-$	0.76
$Cr = Cr^{+++} + 3 e^-$	0.74
$Fe = Fe^{++} + 2 e^-$	0.44
$Cd = Cd^{++} + 2 e^-$	0.40
$Co = Co^{++} + 2 e^-$	0.28
$Ni = Ni^{++} + 2 e^-$	0.25
$Sn = Sn^{++} + 2 e^-$	0.14
$Pb = Pb^{++} + 2 e^-$	0.13
$H_2 = 2 H^+ + 2 e^-$	0.00
$Sn^{++} = Sn^{++++} + 2 e^-$	−0.15
$Cu^+ = Cu^{++} + e^-$	−0.15
$Cu = Cu^{++} + 2 e^-$	−0.34
$2 I^- = I_2 + 2 e^-$	−0.53
$Fe^{++} = Fe^{+++} + e^-$	−0.77
$2 Hg = Hg_2^{++} + 2 e^-$	−0.79
$Ag = Ag^+ + e^-$	−0.80
$Hg_2^{++} = 2 Hg^{++} + 2 e^-$	−0.92
$NO + 2 H_2O = NO_3^- + 4 H^+ + 3 e^-$	−0.96
$2 Br^- = Br_2 (\ell) + 2 e^-$	−1.07
$2 H_2O = O_2 + 4 H^+ + 4 e^-$	−1.23
$2 Cr^{+++} + 7 H_2O = Cr_2O_7^{--} + 14 H^+ + 6 e^-$	−1.33
$2 Cl^- = Cl_2 + 2 e^-$	−1.36
$Au = Au^{+++} + 3 e^-$	−1.50
$Mn^{++} + 4 H_2O = MnO_4^- + 8 H^+ + 5 e^-$	−1.51
$2 F^- = F_2 + 2 e^-$	−2.87

"REPRESENTATIVE" ELEMENTS

I A

H 13.5 / 2.1	II A	III A	IV A	V A	VI A	VII A
Li 5.4 / 1.0	Be 9.3 / 1.5	B 8.3 / 2.0	C 11.2 / 2.5	N 14.5 / 3.0	O 13.6 / 3.5	F 17.3 / 4.0
Na 5.1 / 0.9	Mg 7.6 / 1.2	Al 6.0 / 1.5	Si 8.1 / 1.8	P 10.9 / 2.1	S 10.3 / 2.5	Cl 13.0 / 3.0
K 4.3 / 0.8	Ca 6.1 / 1.0	Ga 6.0 / 1.6	Ge 8.1 / 1.8	As 10.5 / 2.0	Se 9.7 / 2.4	Br 11.8 / 2.8
Rb 4.2 / 0.8	Sr 5.7 / 1.0	In 5.8 / 1.7	Sn 7.3 / 1.8	Sb 8.5 / 1.9	Te 9.0 / 2.1	I 10.6 / 2.5
Cs 3.9 / 0.7	Ba 5.2 / 0.9	Tl 6.1 / 1.8	Pb 7.4 / 1.8	Bi 8.0 / 1.9	Po 2.0	At 2.2
Fr 0.7	Ra 5.3					

13.5 ← Ionization Energy*

↓ Electronegativity**

* 1st ionization energy in e.v.

** Arbitrary scale

HEATS OF REACTION

t = 25° C p = 1 atm.	kcal/mole*
H_2 (g) + $\frac{1}{2}$ O_2 (g) = H_2O (g)	−57.8
H_2 (g) + $\frac{1}{2}$ O_2 (g) = H_2O (ℓ)	−68.3
S (s) + O_2 (g) = SO_2 (g)	−71.0
H_2 (g) + S (s) + 2 O_2 (g) = H_2SO_4 (ℓ)	−194.0
$\frac{1}{2}$ N_2 (g) + $\frac{1}{2}$ O_2 (g) = NO (g)	21.6
$\frac{1}{2}$ N_2 (g) + O_2 (g) = NO_2 (g)	8.1
$\frac{1}{2}$ N_2 (g) + $\frac{3}{2}$ H_2 (g) = NH_3 (g)	−11.0
C (s) + $\frac{1}{2}$ O_2 (g) = CO (g)	−26.4
C (s) + O_2 (g) = CO_2 (g)	−94.0
2 C (s) + 3 H_2 (g) = C_2H_6 (g)	−20.2
* of the product formed	
(Minus sign indicates an exothermic reaction.)	

SOME EQUILIBRIUM CONSTANTS AT 25° C

$$Cu\ (s) + 2\ Ag^+\ (aq) = Cu^{+2}\ (aq) + 2\ Ag\ (s) \qquad 2 \times 10^{15}$$
$$CH_3COOH\ (aq) = H^+\ (aq) + CH_3COO^-\ (aq) \quad 1.8 \times 10^{-5}$$
$$AgCl\ (s) = Ag^+\ (aq) + Cl^-\ (aq) \qquad\qquad 1.7 \times 10^{-10}$$

OXIDATION STATES OF SOME RADICALS

CH_3COO^-	ClO_4^-	$H_2PO_4^-$	NO_3^-
$CO_3^=$	$Cr_2O_7^=$	H_3O^+	OH^-
$C_2O_4^=$	HCO_3^-	Hg_2^{++}	$PO_3^\equiv$
ClO^-	$HPO_4^=$	MnO_4^-	$PO_4^\equiv$
ClO_2^-	HSO_3^-	NH_4^+	$SO_3^=$
ClO_3^-	HSO_4^-	NO_2^-	$SO_4^=$

HALF-LIVES OF SOME RADIOISOTOPES

^{14}C	5,700 years
^{45}Ca	152 days
^{36}Cl	4×10^5 years
^{60}Co	5.3 years
^{137}Cs	33 years
^{131}I	8 days
^{42}K	12.4 hours
^{32}P	14.3 days
^{90}Sr	20 years

PARTICLES

electron	$_{-1}e^0$
neutron	$_0n^1$
proton	$_1H^1$
deuteron	$_1H^2$
triton	$_1H^3$
alpha particle	$_2He^4$

Periodic Table

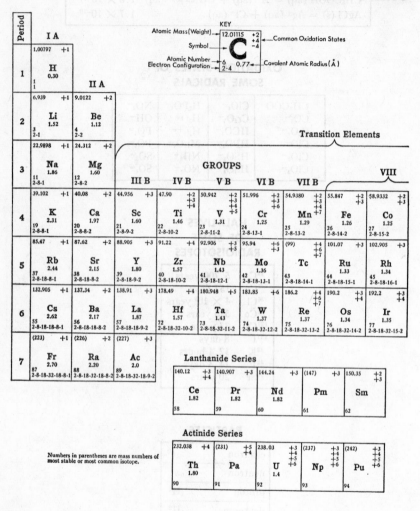

KEY

Atomic Mass (Weight) → 12.01115 +2 +4 -4 ← Common Oxidation States
Symbol → **C**
Atomic Number → 6
Electron Configuration → 2-4   0.77 ← Covalent Atomic Radius (Å)

Period										

I A
1.00797 +1
H 0.30
1
1

II A

1

6.939 +1
Li 1.52
3
2-1

9.0122 +2
Be 1.12
4
2-2

Transition Elements

2

22.9898 +1
Na 1.86
11
2-8-1

24.312 +2
Mg 1.60
12
2-8-2

GROUPS

III B **IV B** **V B** **VI B** **VII B** **VIII**

3

39.102 +1
K 2.31
19
2-8-8-1

40.08 +2
Ca 1.97
20
2-8-8-2

44.956 +3
Sc 1.60
21
2-8-9-2

47.90 +2 +3 +4
Ti 1.46
22
2-8-10-2

50.942 +2 +3 +4 +5
V 1.31
23
2-8-11-2

51.996 +2 +3 +6
Cr 1.25
24
2-8-13-1

54.9380 +2 +3 +4 +7
Mn 1.29
25
2-8-13-2

55.847 +2 +3
Fe 1.26
26
2-8-14-2

58.9332 +2 +3
Co 1.25
27
2-8-15-2

4

85.47 +1
Rb 2.44
37
2-8-18-8-1

87.62 +2
Sr 2.15
38
2-8-18-8-2

88.905 +3
Y 1.80
39
2-8-18-9-2

91.22 +4
Zr 1.57
40
2-8-18-10-2

92.906 +3 +5
Nb 1.43
41
2-8-18-12-1

95.94 +6 +3
Mo 1.36
42
2-8-18-13-1

(99) +4 +6 +7
Tc
43
2-8-18-14-1

101.07 +3
Ru 1.33
44
2-8-18-15-1

102.905 +3
Rh 1.34
45
2-8-18-16-1

5

132.905 +1
Cs 2.62
55
2-8-18-18-8-1

137.34 +2
Ba 2.17
56
2-8-18-18-8-2

138.91 +3
La 1.87
57
2-8-18-18-9-2

178.49 +4
Hf 1.57
72
2-8-18-32-10-2

180.948 +4
Ta 1.43
73
2-8-18-32-11-2

183.85 +6
W 1.37
74
2-8-18-32-12-2

186.2 +4 +6 +7
Re 1.37
75
2-8-18-32-13-2

190.2 +3 +4
Os 1.34
76
2-8-18-32-14-2

192.2 +3 +4
Ir 1.35
77
2-8-18-32-15-2

6

(223) +1
Fr 2.70
87
2-8-18-32-18-8-1

(226) +2
Ra 2.20
88
2-8-18-32-18-8-2

(227) +3
Ac 2.0
89
2-8-18-32-18-9-2

7

Lanthanide Series

140.12 +3 +4
Ce 1.82
58

140.907 +3
Pr 1.82
59

144.24 +3
Nd 1.82
60

(147) +3
Pm
61

150.35 +2 +3
Sm
62

Actinide Series

232.038 +4
Th 1.80
90

(231) +5 +4
Pa
91

238.03 +3 +4 +5 +6
U 1.4
92

(237) +3 +4 +5 +6
Np
93

(242) +3 +4 +5 +6
Pu
94

Numbers in parentheses are mass numbers of most stable or most common isotope.

8

of the Elements

Atomic weights conform to the 1961 values of the Commission on Atomic Weights.

	VII A	0
	1.00797 −1	4.0026 0
GROUPS	**H** 0.30	**He** 0.93
	1 1	2 2

III A	IV A	V A	VI A	VII A	0
10.811 +3	12.01115 +2 +4 −4	14.0067 +1 +2 +3 +4 +5 −1 −2 −3	15.9994 −2	18.9984 −1	20.183 0
B 0.88	**C** 0.77	**N** 0.70	**O** 0.66	**F** 0.64	**Ne** 1.12
5 2-3	6 2-4	7 2-5	8 2-6	9 2-7	10 2-8
26.9815 +3	28.086 +2 +4 −4	30.9738 +3 +5 −3	32.064 +4 +6 −2	35.453 +1 +5 +7 −1	39.948 0
Al 1.43	**Si** 1.17	**P** 1.10	**S** 1.04	**Cl** 0.99	**Ar** 1.54
13 2-8-3	14 2-8-4	15 2-8-5	16 2-8-6	17 2-8-7	18 2-8-8

Transition Elements

VIII

58.71 +2 +3	63.54 +1 +2	65.37 +2	69.72 +3	72.59 +2 +4	74.9216 +3 +5 −3	78.96 +4 +6 −2	79.909 +1 +5 −1	83.80 0
Ni 1.24	**Cu** 1.28	**Zn** 1.33	**Ga** 1.22	**Ge** 1.22	**As** 1.21	**Se** 1.17	**Br** 1.14	**Kr** 1.69
28 2-8-16-2	29 2-8-18-1	30 2-8-18-2	31 2-8-18-3	32 2-8-18-4	33 2-8-18-5	34 2-8-18-6	35 2-8-18-7	36 2-8-18-8
106.4 +2 +4	107.870 +1	112.40 +2	114.82 +3	118.69 +2 +4	121.75 +3 +5 −3	127.60 +4 +6 −2	126.9044 +1 +5 +7 −1	131.30 0
Pd 1.3	**Ag** 1.44	**Cd** 1.49	**In** 1.62	**Sn** 1.40	**Sb** 1.41	**Te** 1.37	**I** 1.33	**Xe** 1.90
46 2-8-18-18	47 2-8-18-18-1	48 2-8-18-18-2	49 2-8-18-18-3	50 2-8-18-18-4	51 2-8-18-18-5	52 2-8-18-18-6	53 2-8-18-18-7	54 2-8-18-18-8
195.09 +2 +4	196.967 +1 +3	200.59 +1 +2	204.37 +1 +3	207.19 +2 +4	208.980 +3 +5	(210) +2 +4	(210) −1	(222) 0
Pt 1.38	**Au** 1.44	**Hg** 1.55	**Tl** 1.71	**Pb** 1.75	**Bi** 1.46	**Po** 1.65	**At** 1.40	**Rn** 2.2
78 2-8-18-32-17-1	79 2-8-18-32-18-1	80 2-8-18-32-18-2	81 2-8-18-32-18-3	82 2-8-18-32-18-4	83 2-8-18-32-18-5	84 2-8-18-32-18-6	85 2-8-18-32-18-7	86 2-8-18-32-18-8

I B   **II B**

151.96 +2 +3	157.25 +3	158.924 +3	162.50 +3	164.930 +3	167.26 +3	168.934 +3	173.04 +2 +3	174.97 +3
Eu 2.04	**Gd** 1.79	**Tb** 1.77	**Dy** 1.77	**Ho** 1.76	**Er** 1.75	**Tm** 1.74	**Yb** 1.93	**Lu** 1.74
63	64	65	66	67	68	69	70	71

(243) +3 +4 +5 +6	(247) +3	(249) +3 +4	(251) +3	(254)	(253)	(256)	(254)	(257)
Am	**Cm**	**Bk**	**Cf**	**Es**	**Fm**	**Md**	**No**	**Lw**
95	96	97	98	99	100	101	102	103

INDEX

INDEX

INDEX

Charles' law, 432, 434-435, 438
Chemical bond, 66
Chemical calculations involving, gas laws, 432-436; molecular weight of a gas, 436; molecular weights from formulas, 87-88; percentage composition, 89-91; simplest formula of a compound, 431-432; volume-volume, 97-98; weight of a liter of gas, 88-89; weight-volume, 94-97; weight-weight, 91-93
Chemical combination, laws of, 52-53
Chemical equations. See Equations.
Chemical principles, summary, 408-413
Chemical properties, 5
Chemical reactions. See Reactions.
Chemist, work of, 7
Chemistry, definition, 1
Chemotherapy, 340
Chile saltpeter, 138, 202, 240
Chloride ion, test, 141
Chlorination, 36
Chlorine, chemical properties, 133-135; commercial preparation, 132; laboratory preparation, 131-132; occurrence, 130; physical properties, 133; uses, 135-136
Chloroform, 315
Chloromycetin, 340
Chlorophyll, 225
Chrome steel, 280
Cinnabar, 296
Citric acid, 323
Clorox, 135
Cloud chamber, 352
Coagulation, 35
Coal, 215-216
Coal furnace, reactions, 227
Coal gas, 230
Coal tar, 312
Cobalt nitrate tests, 291, 294
Coke, 216
College Board Achievement Test in Chemistry, questions and answers, 442-455
Colloids, applications, 43; definition, 41; properties, 41-42; tests, 43
Combustion, 12-13, 15
Common ion effect, 172, 237
Common substances, table, 440-441
Compounds, definition, 4; naming, 76-77
Concrete, 248-249
Conductivity of solutions, 108-109
Conductors, 258
Cones, 17
Confirmatory test, 141
Conservation of metals, 263-265
Contact process, 185-186
Coordinate covalence, 65
Co-polymerization, 337-338
Copper, compounds, 288; extraction, 285; occurrence, 285; properties, 287; refining, 285-286; uses, 287

Corrosion, 264-265
Corrosive sublimate, 297
Cosmotron, 355
Cotton, 335
Cottonseed oil, 325
Cottrell precipitator, 43
Covalence, 63-65, 302-303
Cracking, 309
Critical mass, 361
Cryolite, 129
Crystal lattice, 63
Crystallization, water of, 44
Crystals, definition, 43; preparation, 43
Curie, Marie and Pierre, 348, 438
Curium, 350
Cyanamid process, 199-200
Cyclotron, 354-355

Dacron, 337
Dakin's solution, 135
Dalton, John, 438; Atomic Theory, 50; Law of Multiple Proportions, 46, 53
Davy, Sir Humphry, 438; safety lamp, 14-15
DDT, 339
Decay, 14
Decomposition, 81, 83, 166-167
Decrepitation, 44
Dees, 355
Deficiency diseases, 343
Definite Proportions, Law of, 33-34
Degree of ionization, 110, 155, 402-404
Dehydrating action, 188
Deliquescence, 44, 237
Democritus, 50
Denatured alcohol, 319
Denitrification, 210
Density, 2
Destructive distillation, soft coal, 199, 216; wood, 216-217
Detergents, 327
Deuterium, 67
Deuteron, 353
Diamond, 218
Diatomic, 51
Diethyl ether, 322
Diluting concentrated sulfuric acid, 187
Dipoles, 65
Direct combination, 83, 166
Direct dyes, 341
Disinfectants, 135, 184
Disintegration, radioactive, 350-351
Dissociation of electrovalent compounds, 112-113
Distillation of water, 36-37
Döbereiner, Johann, 102
Dolomite, 245
Double replacement, 82, 168
Double salts, 124

INDEX

INDEX

14

INDEX

INDEX